B

1500d

SOLIDS UNDER PRESSURE

McGRAW-HILL SERIES IN MATERIALS SCIENCE AND ENGINEERING

PAUL AND WARSCHAUER *Solids under Pressure*
SHEWMON *Diffusion in Solids*

SOLIDS UNDER PRESSURE

edited by

William Paul
Division of Engineering and Applied Physics
Harvard University, Cambridge, Massachusetts

Douglas M. Warschauer
Research Division, Raytheon Company
Waltham, Massachusetts

McGraw-Hill Book Company, Inc.

New York   San Francisco   Toronto   London

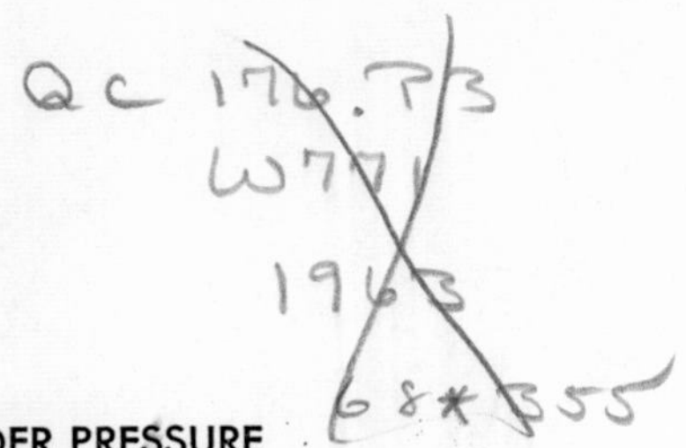

SOLIDS UNDER PRESSURE

 Library of Congress Catalog Card Number 62-20728

48930

To

P. W. Bridgman

Preface

During the last ten years high-pressure physics has been changing rapidly. The maximum attainable pressures, using both static and dynamic techniques, have increased five- or tenfold, and, notwithstanding a clear derivation from the early apparatus of Bridgman, a considerable diversity of pressure-containing vessels and related components has been developed. In the lower, hydrostatic, pressure range especially, much of the basic apparatus is now available commercially. Because of the arrival of new workers in the field, this seems to us to be a convenient time to pause in order to assess critically the value and significance of the past work and to try to extrapolate the probable most fruitful line of progress in the next few years, particularly in the higher pressure ranges.

In this volume, therefore, we have collected together thirteen articles on different aspects of research on the physics of crystalline solids at high pressures. We have deliberately excluded matter in other forms, and we have sought to reduce discussion of technique to the minimum required for full understanding of the measurements. These papers will, we believe, be a useful critical assessment, for the pressure expert and layman alike, of whether and where high pressures may be a useful tool for investigation.

It was originally conceived that this book would be a tribute to P. W. Bridgman on the occasion of his eightieth birthday in 1962. Prof. Bridgman, unaware of this, contributed the opening article, which we wanted to be a general outlook on the whole field as it was developing in 1960 and 1961, coupled with a statement of what would interest him were he still active. It is a matter of great regret to all of us who have contributed that he died before he could be told of this planned *Festschrift*. This book is one memorial to him, and as such bears his trace, implicitly throughout the work of all the contributors, and explicitly in the objective and enthusiastic survey in Chap. 1 of an area of research so long dominated by his genius.

We have taken the liberty of adding chapter subheadings, minor footnotes, and some references to Prof. Bridgman's article.

The fourteenth chapter was written by Harvey Brooks after he had read the original thirteen articles. We wanted a physicist of broad interests and experience to assess the progress made in these rather diverse topics and to present his own, necessarily personal, opinion of the way to future progress. We are grateful to Prof. Brooks for his authoritative review, in which he makes it abundantly clear that, although our present understanding of solids under pressure is fragmentary indeed, progress is certainly possible with the theory and experimental techniques now available.

The pressure unit of preference throughout the volume is the bar and its multiples: kilobar and megabar. It was not possible to use these units consistently throughout the book in view of certain problems of calibration in past literature (see Sec. 15-6d). The conversion between the bar and the other units used is: 1 bar = 1.0000×10^6 dynes/cm^2 = 1.0197 kg/cm^2 = 0.98692 normal atm = 14.504 psi. When pressure data from different laboratories are compared, the basis for calibration of the pressure scale should be carefully examined.

Although the exposition of technique was excluded from the articles, we were concerned with the absence of a convenient exhaustive monograph in English on the rapidly changing practices. The bibliography presented in Chap. 15 will, we hope, be a convenient starting point for newcomers to the field.

It is, in a sense, inappropriate for the editors to thank the contributors, for this is their book, and whatever value it has derives directly from their work, not ours. Let us therefore simply express our pleasure in collaborating with them. We do thank sincerely the various friends who have helped us with suggestions regarding the conception and contents of the book, particularly Harvey Brooks, who helped us to choose topics and suggested authors, and Thomas Deutsch, who suggested the addition of the bibliography of Chap. 15. Elizabeth Weeks and Madaleine Bennett helped greatly on reference problems and library research, and Dean Forbes was of much help in filling in incomplete references. The outstanding secretarial work of Norma Brouillet accelerated completion of the volume considerably, and the patient proofreading and completion of faulty references by Sue Warschauer were indispensable.

William Paul
Douglas Warschauer

Contents

DAVID LAZARUS

DEPARTMENT OF PHYSICS, UNIVERSITY OF ILLINOIS, URBANA, ILLINOIS

NORMAN H. NACHTRIEB

INSTITUTE FOR THE STUDY OF METALS, UNIVERSITY OF CHICAGO, CHICAGO, ILLINOIS

DOUGLAS M. WARSCHAUER

RESEARCH DIVISION, RAYTHEON COMPANY,
WALTHAM, MASSACHUSETTS

GEORGE BENEDEK

DEPARTMENT OF PHYSICS, MASSACHUSETTS INSTITUTE OF TECHNOLOGY,
CAMBRIDGE, MASSACHUSETTS

1

General Outlook on the Field of High-pressure Research

P. W. BRIDGMAN

Harvard University
Cambridge, Massachusetts

At the present time interest and activity in the field of high-pressure research are increasing with notable acceleration. No doubt a large part of this is due to the spectacular success of the General Electric Company in synthesizing industrial diamonds on an economically successful scale. A rapidly increasing number of laboratories are becoming equipped to deal with pressures in the low hundred-kilobar range and temperatures in the low thousands of degrees Centigrade. These pressures and temperatures can be sustained for times long enough to reach equilibrium conditions for many classes of phenomena. In addition to the new field of high static conditions thus recently opened, and of almost equal importance, is the somewhat prior discovery of methods of reaching much higher pressures and temperatures transiently by various detonation techniques.[1] De-

[1] See Chap. 13.

velopments here are the more or less direct outgrowth of the discovery of the effectiveness of shaped charges for military use during the last war.

As in any rapidly growing field there is danger in this new field of high pressure that not all the activity will be directed to the best advantage, and that short-range considerations, arising perhaps from competitive conditions and the understandable desire to achieve tangible results quickly, will play too large a role, to the detriment of longer-range and less personal considerations. It would seem therefore that it may be well to stop for a preliminary breather and take a look at the whole field in order that the attack may be directed as intelligently as possible. In thus attempting to look over the entire field, I shall be mostly concerned with the purely experimental aspect of the subject, and I shall draw to a very large extent on my own personal experience. This experience for the most part has been confined to pressures considerably below those now accessible, although it has at times reached into the lower edge of the new pressure range.

1-1 The New Field of High Generalized Mechanical Stress

It is in the first place to be emphasized that the new field is in reality much more complicated than would be indicated by the words "high pressure." Technically, "pressure" means hydrostatic pressure, which of course is only a special case of generalized stress with its six independent stress components. "High-pressure" physics is only a special case of "high-stress" physics, and the ultimate task of the physicist here is to find the effects of varying all six components of stress through the widest possible range. Hydrostatic stresses par excellence occur in and are transmitted by fluids, and, in the lower stress ranges formerly exploited, the overwhelmingly preponderate part of scientific activity was confined to the study of various effects of the pressures produced in fluids, acting either on other fluids or on solids immersed in them. Thus in the lower range of earlier experimenting, the condition that the stress should be a hydrostatic pressure could be automatically realized. But in the new range this is no longer the case, for at ordinary temperatures fluids cease to exist as such in the ten-kilobar range, and they turn into solids. Because of this, it becomes a matter of great technical difficulty to attain a state of true hydrostatic pressure in a highly stressed system whose members are of necessity solids. Still more is it a matter of great technical difficulty to apply and control a generalized stress system with its six arbitrary components.

Although the new field now open to us is the field of high generalized mechanical stress, I believe that most physicists would agree that the first, and perhaps most important, stage in conquering this field is mastering the effects of high hydrostatic pressure. It might be argued as to what extent this attitude is justified. It doubtless has partly a theoretical background and partly a practical background. It would appear plausible that it is only the hydrostatic component of stress that is capable of being raised to indefinitely high magnitude, for the other components of stress are limited by such phenomena as plastic flow and rupture. This could mean that in the ultimate domain of truly astronomical stresses the nonhydrostatic components degenerate to more or less irrelevant perturbations. Nevertheless, in the stress range below the astronomical, nonhydrostatic components can, in general, by no means be regarded as small perturbations; they are of the same order of magnitude as the hydrostatic components themselves. The presumptive importance of the nonhydrostatic components is enhanced when it is considered that the plastic-flow point and rupture strength may be enormously increased beyond their normal values by the action of the hydrostatic component.[2] I think it must not be too easily assumed that the only stress systems physically realizable at astronomical magnitudes are approximately hydrostatic.

1-1a Hydrostaticity. In most conventional forms of apparatus in use hitherto in this field the frictional effects contributed by the nonhydrostatic shearing components may be integrated by the design of the apparatus in such a way that they give a total force of the same order of magnitude as or even greater than the pure pressure itself. In fact this frictional force is usually deliberately exploited to make the seal. An extreme example is the optical window of Drickamer,[3] which is retained against the thrust of the internal pressure by friction on the sides. It is nevertheless, I believe, the present consensus that the most important immediate problem of technique in this field is to find methods of producing stress systems which are truly hydrostatic. The technical problems are particularly challenging in the important field of combined high pressure and low temperature, a field which has no counterpart in nature.

The importance of realizing a true hydrostatic pressure depends to a large extent on the sort of phenomenon concerned. If we are concerned merely with producing a qualitative effect, as in diamond synthesis, it is a matter of no importance at all. But the situation is different if it becomes a matter of measuring the physical parameters which control the phenomenon. Ideally, such a transformation as that of graphite into diamond is controlled by all six components of stress, not merely by the hydrostatic components, and the subject will not be mastered until the efforts of all six are determined. Such a high degree of mastery of the stress pattern

[2] P. W. Bridgman, "Studies in Large Plastic Flow and Fracture," McGraw-Hill Book Company, Inc., New York, 1952.

[3] See Chap. 12.

as is implied in this ideal is evidently a long way in the future. In the meantime we console ourselves as best we can with the hope that the nonhydrostatic components are comparatively unimportant and that such transformation phenomena are essentially controlled by the mean pressure (average of three principal stress components). Even so, it is at the present time difficult enough, particularly in the apparatus used by the General Electric Company and others of similar type, to know even what the mean hydrostatic stress is.[4] Our present experimental sights might well be set at determining acceptable values for this mean stress. It would then be for experiment to decide whether the mean stress enters into the thermodynamic equations for the transformation (for example, Clapeyron's equation) in the same way that the true hydrostatic pressure does. I think it should not be assumed too easily that in all cases the nonhydrostatic components will prove to be unimportant. In fact there is experimental evidence of the existence of at least one transition which occurs only in the presence of shearing stress.‡

1-1b Measurement of transitions. Up to now most of the extensive work which has been done on transformations or transitions under pressure has been directed toward finding the temperature at which a transition runs as a function of pressure. In this work, increasingly effective means are being found for making the stress system truly hydrostatic (by minimizing the effects of friction) and for obtaining good values for the mean stress. Much remains to be done, however, in finding methods capable of general application, instead of particular methods devised for particular situations. Perhaps the principal desideratum here is control of larger volumes. Full command of transitions will not be attained at high pressures, however, until we have methods for measuring the other independent thermodynamic parameters (in addition to temperature and pressure). This has been done in comparatively few cases; in these cases the parameter measured has been almost always the discontinuity of volume accompanying the transition. Latent heats are much more difficult to measure than volume discontinuities, because the latent heat of the reacting material is in general swamped by that of the massive containing apparatus. However, the use or investigation of all thermal phenomena is not thereby ruled out, as in the determination of temperature-arrest points on heating or cooling.

[4] See F. P. Bundy, W. R. Hibbard, Jr., and H. M. Strong (eds.), "Progress in Very High Pressure Research," John Wiley & Sons, Inc., New York, 1961. For a discussion of calibration techniques, see F. P. Bundy, Calibration Techniques in Ultrahigh Pressure Apparatus, *J. Eng. Ind.*, vol. 83, series 13, no. 2, pp. 207–214, 1961.

‡ Professor Bridgman may here be referring to his observation of a sudden drop in shear stress at high pressure in his work on three copper alloys about 1955. He had privately speculated that the discontinuities might be explained by formation of a new modification stable only under shear stress. [Ed.]

In general, change of volume is one of the most significant parameters to determine in the high-stress domain, not only in connection with transitions, but also for cubic compressibilities, which are generally regarded as of great theoretical importance. Change of volume is in general insensitive to nonhydrostatic components of stress, which means in particular that it is not sensitive to geometrical distortions in the specimen under measurement. Such geometrical distortions are exceedingly difficult to avoid. The result should be that measurements of the change of volume under pressure are comparatively easy to make. Nevertheless, relatively few have been made up to now.

Because geometrical distortions are so hard to avoid, a type of measurement which instrumentally is much easier to make than a volume measurement (namely, a measurement of electrical resistance) has, up to the present, a more doubtful physical significance than volume measurements. Changes of resistance as measured under high stress involve at least two effects, one due to the intrinsic effect of pressure on specific resistance, and one due to the changes of configuration of the specimen. The latter is controlled by adventitious features in the design of the apparatus and the method of applying stress. Unfortunately up to the present the adventitious component is, even under the best of circumstances, of the same order of magnitude as the intrinsic effect.

1-1c Challenges to technique. Here we have two immediate challenges to technique: first, to devise better methods of measuring volume changes, including both discontinuities and changes over a range, and second, to devise methods of applying pressure without distortion to specimens for resistivity or other sorts of measurement, or failing this, to devise satisfactory methods for correcting for the effects of distortion.

In addition to the two immediate challenges to technique just mentioned, it is possible to visualize an almost limitless number of other challenges. It is not easy to imagine methods capable of giving good values for the effect of pressure on dielectric constant or magnetic permeability or such obscure electrical effects as the four transverse effects or the full complement of twenty-one elastic constants of the general crystal.[5] Imagination of a high order will be required, the same sort of imagination as shown by Drickamer with his optical windows.

There is thus plenty to be done in the field of presently attainable pressures. When it comes to extending the pressure range, the most obvious problem is to find some way of extending the cascading method of supporting an inner vessel by nesting it in an outer vessel, beyond the single stage of cascading support to which we are at present limited. Present methods of exploiting frictional support so as to permit high stress concentrations in small regions are merely special and partial applications

[5] See Bibliography. [Ed.]

of the cascading principle. Whatever the ultimately successful method, it would seem that we must reconcile ourselves to the use of increasingly larger and more complex apparatus, with the increasing expense thereby implied, with perhaps, presently, instruments the size of cyclotrons, and all the unwelcome features of government support.

1-2 New Physical Phenomena

In speculating as to what sort of phenomena to anticipate when the pressure range is indefinitely increased, we may perhaps recognize two different ranges. In the first and lower range, to which we are at present almost exclusively confined, the atoms themselves are inviolate, and phenomena are determined in largest part by the interaction of atoms or molecules. The second, higher, range is one in which the atoms are subject to increasing deterioration, resulting ultimately in a "pressure squash" of protons and electrons. The first steps in atomic deterioration might be expected to be the rearrangement of electron orbits within the individual atoms and the sharing of orbits between atoms. Because there are many electrons in the majority of elements, and because there are a great many possible electron orbits, it would seem that we have the potentiality for an enormously richer variety of phenomena in the high-pressure range of atomic deterioration than in the conventional lower range of atomic inviolability. One may anticipate discontinuous rearrangements of electron orbits, in which case there will be discontinuous effects on various physical parameters such as we find in a conventional transition, or the rearrangement averaged over a pressure range, in which case there will be points of inflection and ranges in which the change of the parameters is in an "abnormal" direction. It is most unfortunate, and it offers another challenge to technique, that this region of increasing "fine structure" in the properties of matter should be precisely the region in which physical measurement becomes increasingly blurred because of technical difficulties.

1-2a Phase transitions in solids. It is not to be expected that the domain of electronic rearrangement within the atom is sharply separated from the domain of atomic inviolability. In fact a few instances are already known in which it would appear that electronic rearrangements provide the mechanism for observed effects. The most definite of these are the transitions of cesium and cerium, in which there are large volume discontinuities with no change in the type of lattice, which is the same type of close-packed structure on both sides of the transition. In these two cases theoretical calculations have indicated rather definitely what the precise electronic rearrangement must be. In general, the electronic rearrangement need not be as abrupt as in these two cases. There are in fact anomalies in the behavior of all the rare-earth metals, most of them spread over a pressure range which one might plausibly anticipate to be due to electronic rearrangements. These invite further experimental and theoretical study. The rare-earth metals are particularly favorable candidates for this sort of thing because of the frequent occurrence of unoccupied inner electron shells. The probable existence of an indefinite number of abnormal ranges at high pressures due to interior electronic rearrangements makes any smooth extrapolation of results obtained at lower pressures increasingly hazardous. We can less and less be confident of the reality of any extrapolated phenomenon at high pressure; actual production and exhibition of the phenomenon becomes increasingly essential. The same remark applies, but much less forcibly, to interpolation.

1-2b Anomalous behavior of liquids. Qualitatively the general behavior to be anticipated at very high pressures, that is, the occurrence of smooth normal behavior interspersed with ranges of the abnormal behavior which accompanies electronic rearrangement, is very much like the behavior which I have already found in almost all liquids at lower pressures. At pressures in the thousands or low tens of thousands of atmospheres it appears, as the accuracy of measurement is increased, that all liquids exhibit regions of "abnormal" behavior characteristic of the individual liquid, superposed on a rough generalized behavior which may be taken to characterize liquids as such. I have explained these effects as perhaps arising from the details of the interlocking to which the molecules of a liquid are forced by sufficiently high pressures, the details being different for each different sort of molecule. I had only started on the exploration of these effects when I abandoned work on them to take up the (to me) more enticing possibilities of extending the pressure range. But I am convinced that a great deal more remains to be done in finding how the fine structure of the temperature-pressure behavior of liquids depends on the individual molecule. Theoretically there is a wide field here for further exploitation, and experimentally there is the challenge of the high accuracy of measurement demanded and the difficulty of defining the conditions necessary to obtain reproducible results.[6]

1-2c Behavior of alloys. Another area of investigation at comparatively low pressures not yet exhausted is that of the properties of alloys. There is an enormous amount of potential complexity here, and the few studies I have made indicate the field has barely been entered. There are a number of examples of new phases produced under pressure; in some cases the new high-pressure phase may be brought down to atmospheric pressure, where it is capable of permanent existence as a new alloy form. Here again there is a challenge to the theoretical physicist,

[6] For a good review, see P. W. Bridgman, Recent Work in the Field of High Pressures, *Revs. Mod. Phys.*, vol. 18, no. 1, 1946. [Ed.]

namely, to find how to anticipate the possible stable existence at atmospheric pressure of hitherto unknown forms. This, of course, is merely a special case of the problem of predicting all possible transitions and the conditions of stable or metastable existence of the various forms. It is probable that the limitations set by the necessity for a suitable spontaneous nucleation preceding the appearance of a new phase will prove to be vitally important here, as has already proved the case in diamond synthesis.

1-2d New permanently stable forms. It is intriguing to speculate that there may be a number of new hitherto unsuspected forms permanently stable under atmospheric pressure, which can be produced if only some critical stress can be exceeded. We already have a couple of examples in black phosphorus‡ and solid black carbon bisulfide. One may claim with some justification that diamond itself is almost an example, because considering the extreme rarity of diamond in nature, it would seem to have been to a large extent a matter of luck that diamond was known before General Electric synthesized it. A number of possible candidates present themselves for such new irreversibly created forms. I have unsuccessfully tried permanently to transform sulfur, perhaps the most plausible candidate. One could imagine possibilities of fantastic physical properties if one could only produce a close-packed carbon lattice, of density severalfold greater than that of diamond. (The possibilities would be exciting enough if one could produce a sintered diamond aggregate, analogous to the cemented carbides.) Or even if a new form could not be permanently retained at atmospheric pressure, it might be possible to produce such forms with greatly enhanced physical properties within the interior of a cascaded nest of pressure vessels, thus permitting otherwise impossible extensions of the present pressure range. In principle, predicting the occurrence of such new forms is straightforward enough and involves the calculation of the stability of all conceivable lattices. But up to now it would have involved unsurmounted computational difficulties to carry out any such program. Now, perhaps, the accessibility of calculating machines offers some prospect of success. In default of this, if I were again active in reaching new high pressures, I could not resist the temptation of subjecting plausible substances to the action of hitherto unreached pressures to see whether some permanent change had been produced.

‡ It is of interest that black phosphorus can be produced at essentially atmospheric pressure, using mercury as catalyst. (See H. Krebs, H. Weitz, and K. H. Worms, Die katalytische Darstellung des schwarzen phosphors, *Z. anorg. u. allgem. Chem.*, vol. 280, p. 119, 1955.) This presents the intriguing possibility that other metastable forms produced at high pressure may be obtained at atmospheric pressure. [Ed.]

1-2e Effect of pressure on electrical resistance. We pass now from this discussion of the possible effects of pressure on transitions of various sorts to consider the effects of pressure on electrical resistance. It is in the first place to be remarked that there is at present no adequate theory of the effect of pressure on resistance, and in fact little has been done with this topic in the last thirty years. Experimentally there is a great wealth of undigested material waiting theoretical discussion and understanding.[7] This applies particularly to the range below 30 kilobars, where unambiguous results can be obtained. In the range above 30 kilobars it is at least now evident that the phenomena exhibit a greater qualitative richness and diversity than was at one time suspected. It would seem that there is no simple type of behavior which can be called "normal" here. In the range of lower pressures it would have been plausible to anticipate that "normal" behavior of resistance under pressure would be a smooth decrease with decreasing curvature, perhaps asymptotically to zero or some finite resistance at infinite pressure. The broadest generalization that now appears justified is that the change of resistance with pressure is in general not smooth, but that there are more or less extended episodes of "abnormal" behavior. Whether these are usually associated with internal electronic rearrangements does not at present appear. There are a number of cases of minimum resistance at high pressure, one or two of maximum resistance, many cases of reversals of curvature with points of inflection, and several highly spectacular instances of an enormous cusplike increase of resistance with recovery to the initial order of magnitude at still higher pressures. In the semiconductors there are sometimes dramatically large effects. There is no obvious correlation between changes of resistance and changes of volume. There is no rule which connects the direction of resistance change at a transition with the direction of volume change, and instances are known of volume discontinuities with no detectable resistance change and, conversely, of resistance discontinuities with no detectable volume change.

1-2f Pressure calibration using resistance discontinuities. It has already been remarked that the technique problem of straightforwardly determining resistance as a function of hydrostatic pressure has not yet been satisfactorily solved. The great difficulty is to eliminate

[7] For critical discussion of the present status of agreement between theory and experiment see, for example, A. W. Lawson, The Effect of Hydrostatic Pressure on the Electrical Resistivity of Metals, in Bruce Chalmers and R. King (eds.), "Progress in Metal Physics," vol. 6, chap. 1, Pergamon Press, New York, 1956; F. P. Bundy and H. M. Strong, Behavior of Metals at High Temperatures and Pressures, in F. Seitz and P. Turnbull (eds.), "Solid State Physics," vol. 13, Academic Press, Inc., New York, 1962; and Chap. 8 of this volume. [Ed.]

the effect of irreversible plastic distortion. In my own work I had to make complicated adjustments for this (the details varying with each special case), leaning heavily on measurements in the truly hydrostatic range up to 30 kilobars. My ultimate objective was to get an idea of the most probable shape of the pressure-resistance curve as a whole, not to get best values for the resistance at any specified pressure. In the various adjustments, in particular in adjusting the slope at 30 kilobars to agree with the previously determined slope, some distortion of the pressure scale was inevitable. As a result of this distortion there was usually some displacement of the pressures of the discontinuities indicating polymorphic transitions. These displaced pressures of transition were allowed to stand without further correction in my final tabulation of the results, and I contented myself with as concise an account of the particular adjustment procedure as I could accomplish without going to the extreme of reproducing all the experimental data. The pressures of tabulated discontinuity thus obtained did not in general agree with the pressures of transition which I had previously obtained by the much more reliable method of change of volume. It is to be remarked that in general it is not known to what extent agreement is to be expected because of the unknown effect of the large component of shearing stress known to be present in the resistance measurements. It is in any event much to be regretted that some recent work in this field, particularly that at General Electric, has utilized the tabulated pressures of resistance discontinuities as calibration-fixed points, rather than the much more reliable pressures of volume discontinuities. However, the situation is in the process of being straightened out, and recent measurements, particularly by Kennedy and by Drickamer, are on the way to establishing the pressures of transition under true hydrostatic pressure in terms of resistance measurements. The solution of the more difficult problem of finding the true shape of the pressure-resistance curve in its entirety would appear, however, not to be so far advanced.

1-2g The melting curve. Another fruitful topic for investigation in the ranges now available is the character of the melting curve. So far, the probability seems to be that a "normal" melting curve will rise indefinitely with continually decreasing curvature. My own experimental examination of this question has been confined to comparatively low temperatures, but there is recent work by Clark at the Geophysical Laboratory[8] in which the same state of affairs has been found to hold up to 1200°C for a number of alkali halides. Up to date there appears to be only one possible exception to the rule: the melting curve of rubidium

[8] S. P. Clark, Jr., Effect of Pressure on the Melting Points of Eight Alkali Halides, *J. Chem. Phys.*, vol. 31, pp. 1526–1531, 1959.

investigated by Bundy[9] of the General Electric Company. Bundy, using the method of change of resistance, followed the melting with increasing pressure, and presently found a maximum temperature, followed by decreasing temperatures at higher pressures. But Bundy himself stated that it was not certain that he was following the melting curve at higher pressures, and it seems to me by no means impossible that it was actually a transition between two solid forms, and that the melting curve had been lost in a triple point.

There are several cases known of "abnormal" falling melting curves, which occur when the crystalline phase exceptionally has a greater volume than the liquid. It is to be expected that such exceptional solid phases will presently become unstable and give way to a normal solid with smaller volume than the liquid (and in consequence a rising melting curve). This actually occurs for water, bismuth, and gallium, but apparently pressures have not yet been pushed high enough to produce this effect in antimony, although a transition is known in antimony near 80 kilobars at room temperature which might do the trick. Nor has the effect been found in germanium, which shows a falling melting curve that has been followed for hundreds of degrees into the hundred-kilobar range.

The important question arises as to what is "normal" in a melting curve at astronomically high pressures. How would shifting electronic orbits be expected to affect it? It would seem that very few substances have been investigated hitherto for which the pressure has been carried high enough to force electronic rearrangements, and it is quite conceivable that our generalization with regard to the melting curve would have to be abandoned under drastically altered conditions, if indeed what one would be willing to call "melting" occurs at all under these conditions.

1-3 Problems in the Lower Pressure Range

Let us now return to a consideration of the domain of less than astronomical pressures. The experimental physicist will hardly be able to exhaust this lower domain in the foreseeable future. This is the domain in which, in the first instance, all six stress components are the experimental variables (in addition to temperature) or, ultimately, in the case of transient and dynamic nonequilibrium phenomena, there are nine stress components. The ultimate problem is a complete mapping out of the behavior of matter under nine arbitrary stress components. In the more usual range of six arbitrary components, large deviations from linearity in the relation between stress and strain are to be expected at

[9] F. P. Bundy, Phase Diagram of Rubidium to 150,000 kg/cm² and 400°C, *Phys. Rev.*, vol. 115, pp. 274–277, 1959.

high stresses. Under conventional conditions, not only is the relation between stress and strain linear, but it is also reversible. As the range of stress increases, there are increasing departures from this simple behavior; there are departures from linearity, the stress-strain relation is no longer reversible but there is hysteresis, and finally there are permanent alterations of configuration when stress returns to zero. These phenomena gradually extend themselves, first into the range dominated by fracturing and other phenomena of discontinuity, to be followed presently by the phenomena of indefinitely large plastic flow and the disappearance, over most of the range, of the phenomena of fracturing. Time effects become increasingly important, and parameters associated with the rate of flow obtrude themselves. The two domains of normally sharply distinguishable phenomena, that is, the domain of ordinary static phenomena and the domain of times (measured in microseconds) of the phenomena of detonation, become increasingly blurred and eventually merge together.

Only the beginning of an attack has been made on this enormous field. Initial explorations have been presented in my book[2] and in my studies of the behavior of a large number of substances under combined shearing and normal stress,[6] but the conditions in all this work were highly specialized. It is clear that a great wealth of qualitative behavior, to say nothing of quantitative behavior, awaits more detailed study. In particular, the possibility of transitions which occur only with the cooperation of shearing stress demands further study.

I should have liked to investigate further a phenomenon of rather unconventional character in this region. On a number of occasions, when studying the behavior of glass in a stress range in which there were still discontinuous fracturing effects, I found large and capricious electrical effects, manifested by spasmodic deflections in a ballistic galvanometer connected across the two platens of the shearing apparatus. It is natural to associate these with polarization effects arising from the fracturing of molecular dipoles.

1-4 Shock-wave Techniques

The very highest pressures will doubtless continue to be reached by some sort of shock-wave technique.[10] It is conceivable that a way will be found of superposing shock-wave pressures on static pressures, although there are indications that the ordinary chemical type of detonation may be increasingly difficult to produce at higher pressures. Perhaps some fortunate experimenters may ultimately be able to command the use of atomic explosives in studying this field. It appears that there are still pressing questions in the ordinary range of detonation which must be solved before this powerful tool becomes capable of yielding results of

[10] See Chap. 13.

pressure standard. The object of this work is to establish experimental equations of state which may be compared with theoretical models. Bridgman often carried out the measurements at several temperatures, thus obtaining data sufficient to check Grüneisen's law. This law is the subject of another chapter, and we shall not dwell on it here. In general, Bridgman fitted his data with a quadratic equation,

$$\frac{\Delta V}{V_0} = -aP + bP^2 \tag{2-1}$$

where V_0 = initial volume
ΔV = incremental volume change induced by hydrostatic pressure P
a,b = temperature-dependent coefficients

$\Delta V/V_0$ is the initial compressibility but should not be used as the compressibility at any finite pressure. In general, the values of a and b depend on the range of pressure used in the experiments. Murnaghan has suggested the use of a more elaborate equation which fits Bridgman's data better over a more extended pressure range. This equation, which is based on finite-strain theory, is of the form

$$P = \frac{3}{2} K_0 \left[\left(\frac{V_0}{V}\right)^{7/3} - \left(\frac{V_0}{V}\right)^{5/3} \right] \left\{ 1 - \xi \left[\left(\frac{V_0}{V}\right)^{2/3} - 1 \right] \right\} \tag{2-2}$$

where K_0^{-1} is the initial compressibility and ξ is an adjustable parameter of the order of unity. This equation is widely used by geophysicists for purposes of extrapolating the behavior of materials to pressures exceeding those now available in the laboratory. Equation (2-2) is similar in form to theoretical expressions for the compressibility derived from the Thomas-Fermi-Dirac theory. All such equations must be applied with caution in view of the existence of pressure-induced phase transformations arising from either changes in atomic packing or breakdown of electronic structure.

One difficulty with Bridgman's data is that, for the most part, the measurements are confined to a few temperatures in the neighborhood of 300°K. Extrapolation of these values to 0°K is difficult, and hence comparison with theories which neglect the effects of thermal vibrations is correspondingly uncertain. Some amelioration of this problem has been provided by recent experiments at helium temperatures on soft materials such as the rare gases and the alkali metals using quasi-hydrostatic techniques. This work has recently been reviewed by Swenson.[4]

The first measurements of other elastic constants under pressure were those of Birch, who studied the torsional oscillations of metal bars sub-

[4] C. A. Swenson, Compression of the Alkali Metals to 10,000 Atmospheres at Low Temperature, *Phys. Rev.*, vol. 99, no. 2, pp. 423–430, 1955. (See also Chap. 5.)

jected to pressure in a gaseous medium. In zero-order approximation, the viscosity of a gas is independent of pressure. Hence, it was possible to keep the Q of the resonators sufficiently high so that precise measurements could be made of the change in frequency of the oscillations with pressure, thus determining the shear modulus. Accurate data on Young's modulus are very difficult to obtain by this method, owing to the high radiation damping caused by the dense gas atmosphere. Birch's[5] early measurements were confined to polycrystalline samples. The first complete determinations of all the elastic constants of cubic crystals were carried out by Lazarus[6] who studied NaCl, KCl, aluminum, copper, and β-brass. Lazarus used the pulse-echo technique, which does not suffer the disadvantages involved in the resonance approach. More recently, his work has been considerably extended, both experimentally and theoretically, by a number of investigators, foremost among whom are C. S. Smith and his collaborators.[7]

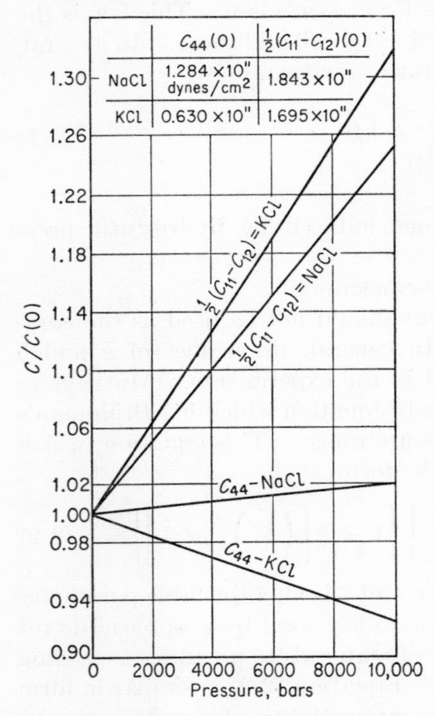

Fig. 2-1 The pressure dependence of $(C_{11} - C_{12})/2$ and C_{44} in NaCl and KCl. The decrease in C_{44} in KCl is presumably associated with its ultimate transformation to the CsCl structure. (*After Lazarus.*)

The work by Lazarus brought out several interesting features, one of which is illustrated in Fig. 2-1. This graph depicts the behavior of the elastic constants C_{12} and C_{44} as a function of pressure in NaCl and KCl. Both constants increase with increasing pressure in NaCl, but although in KCl C_{12} behaves in a normal way, C_{44} decreases as P increases. It is possible that this phenomenon

[5] F. Birch, The Effect of Pressure on the Modulus of Rigidity of Several Metals and Glasses, *J. Appl. Phys.*, vol. 8, no. 2, pp. 129–133, 1937.

[6] D. Lazarus, The Variation of the Adiabatic Elastic Constants of KCl, NaCl, CuZn, Cu, and Al with Pressure to 10,000 Bars, *Phys. Rev.*, vol. 76, no. 4, pp. 545–553, 1949.

[7] W. B. Daniels and C. S. Smith, Pressure Derivatives of the Elastic Constants of Copper, Silver, and Gold to 10,000 Bars, *Phys. Rev.*, vol. 111, no. 3, pp. 713–721, 1958; W. B. Daniels, in F. P. Bundy, W. R. Hibbard, Jr., and H. M. Strong (eds.), "Progress in Very High Pressure Research," John Wiley & Sons, Inc., New York, 1961.

is associated with the fact that KCl undergoes a phase transformation from the fcc to the bcc form at higher pressures. It would be of some interest to repeat this experiment on RbCl. Lazarus initiated such an experiment before leaving my laboratory, but unfortunately it was never completed.

Another interesting aspect of his work is that the relation

$$C_{12} - C_{44} = 2P \tag{2-3}$$

which is a generalized form of the Cauchy relation valid for crystals in which the forces are radially symmetric was not confirmed. This relation is a special case of finite-strain theory which has been practically uninvestigated except for the exploratory experiments of Hughes et al. on glass and certain plastics.

Both the foregoing features are examples of the breakdown of the Grüneisen relation and indicate that its widespread application, although frequently successful, is dramatically wrong on occasion. In these experimental results, we find one of many justifications for carrying out experiments on solids not only as a function of temperature, but also as a function of pressure. It is not sufficient to assume that the effects of temperature may be described in terms of a unique thermodynamic function of volume alone. The explicit as well as the implicit effects of temperature must be taken into account.

2-2b Anelastic effects. We turn now to another area of mechanical experiments, namely, the study of anelastic effects, of the type discussed by Zener,[8] which arise from the presence of dislocations, impurity atoms, and other disordering phenomena in crystals. The data available at the present time are relatively sparse. Of the various related possibilities for studying such phenomena as internal friction and creep, stress relaxation is the most readily adaptable to the limited confines of a high-pressure vessel. Experiments of this sort were initiated by Lazarus over ten years ago[9] at Chicago. These proved unsatisfactory, owing to superimposed permanent effects. The field lay fallow until recently, when Lazarus[10] and others resumed this type of work. Their investigations provide data on the activation volume of a variety of diffusion processes which control the relaxation mechanism. In this sense, they supplement the experiments on other such diffusion-controlled mechanisms as ionic conductivity and radioactive tracers discussed elsewhere in this book at some length (see Chap. 3). Suffice it to say at this

[8] C. Zener, "Elasticity and Anelasticity of Metals," University of Chicago Press, Chicago, 1948.

[9] D. Lazarus, Private Communication.

[10] D. Lazarus, in F. P. Bundy, W. R. Hibbard, Jr., and H. M. Strong (eds.), "Progress in Very High Pressure Research," John Wiley & Sons, Inc., New York, 1961.

juncture that pressure is a powerful tool in the study of such activated processes and, combined with relatively simple models such as the strain-energy model developed by the author and others, provides a method for deciding on the type of relaxation mechanism prevailing in various instances. For example, the activation volume for the formation of the defects responsible for the ionic conductivity in AgBr is 16 cm^3/mole. This result is consistent only with a Frenkel mechanism of disorder, as a Schottky mechanism would imply an activation volume in excess of the molal volume, which is 29 cm^3.

2-2c Plastic deformation. The foregoing brief discussion of elastic and anelastic properties of solids under pressure leads naturally into the more complex phenomena associated with plastic deformation. A concern with the latter is the sine qua non of high-pressure technicians. It is therefore not surprising to learn that Bridgman[11] also led the way in this area, and his investigations are reported in a fascinating but relatively little-known book based on extensive investigations at the Watertown Arsenal during World War II. Bridgman was not a voluble man. The potentially tragic consequences of high-pressure experiments were impressed on the author by a rather bizarre physical pantomime in which Bridgman surmounted an imaginary stile to avoid a possible trajectory of a pinched-off electrical lead ejected by his apparatus.

The principal results of Bridgman's experiments on plasticity relate to the differences in behavior between three-dimensional and two-dimensional stress systems and the anthropomorphic misconceptions about those situations derived from more elementary one-dimensional experiments.

Apart from the more spectacular type of fractures studied by Bridgman, one change in material properties induced by pressure appears to be fairly basic: materials become more plastic, i.e., the reduction in area is greater before tensile failure under a significant hydrostatic pressure than under normal conditions. Thus, sapphire (Al_2O_3) single crystals which fail normally in a completely brittle manner at atmospheric pressure can tolerate a 30 percent elongation before tensile failure at 10 kilobars. In a gross sense, this behavior may be understood in terms of the physical explanation for the enhanced strength of tempered glass. The superposition of a one-dimensional tensile stress to a preexisting hydrostatic pressure can only promote crack propagation which leads to brittle failure when the absolute magnitude of the tensile stress exceeds the pressure by a quantity of the order of magnitude of the yield stress. Thus, the yield stress is apparently higher at higher pressures. Under these circumstances, the competing flow processes arising from dislocation arrays may not be cut off by a disastrous crack, and appreciable flow may

[11] P. W. Bridgman, "Studies in Large Plastic Flow and Fracture," McGraw-Hill Book Company, Inc., New York, 1952.

occur before ultimate partition of the sample. Because of the pressure existing at the time of his experiments, Bridgman was perforce concerned primarily with polycrystalline samples in most of these experiments. Bridgman, however, obtained a patent for practical enhancement of the hardness of ordinary cold-rolled steel, and this practical application is being pursued here, as well as in Russia by Vereshchagin[12] and his collaborators in the Moscow Institute for High Pressures.

Only isolated efforts have been made to pursue the scientific aspects of these phenomena. Peter Haasen and the author[13] have carried out some experiments on the behavior of single crystals to ascertain whether there is

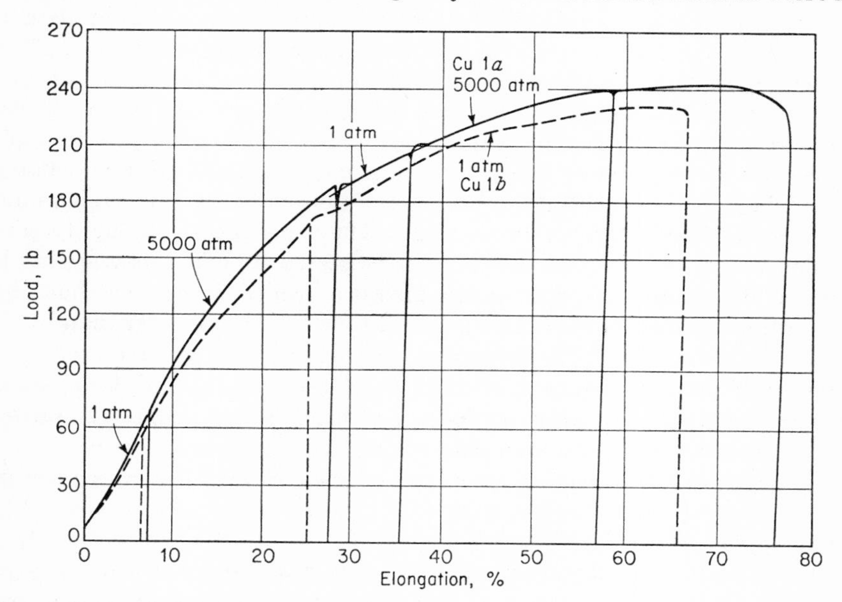

Fig. 2-2 Load-elongation curves for single-crystal copper. (*After Haasen and Lawson.*)

an essential difference between these and polycrystalline samples, owing to the presence of grain boundaries. Typical stress-strain curves of various crystals of copper are shown in Fig. 2-2. They illustrate the enhanced work necessary to produce the same deformation and the enhanced ultimate elongation before fracture. Nickel, for inexplicable reasons, appears to be an exception. The authors made an effort to correlate their data with existing dislocation theory, but it is clear that in

[12] L. F. Vereshchagin, in F. P. Bundy, W. R. Hibbard, Jr., and H. M. Strong (eds.), "Progress in Very High Pressure Research," John Wiley & Sons, Inc., New York, 1961.

[13] P. Haasen and A. W. Lawson, Der Einfluss hydrostatischen Druckes auf die Zugverformung von Einkristallen, *Z. Metallk.*, vol. 49, pp. 280–291, 1958.

a field in which the theory is chameleonic in aspect and the data is sparse, much work remains to be done.

Another type of mechanical experiment directed toward studying the effects of hydrostatic pressure on plastic properties of solids is the study of creep. The first studies of this nature are those of Robert Christy[14] on steady-state high-temperature creep in AgBr. The backdrop for Christy's approach was laid by a variety of previous experiments on the effect of pressure on transport in this material, carried out in my laboratory. These experiments have been summarized elsewhere. In essence, the prior experiments indicated that AgBr is an ionic conductor in which the transport was dominated by Frenkel pairs of Ag^+ interstitials and the associated vacancies on normal Ag^+ sites in the lattice. Earlier, however, Nabarro[15] had suggested that in simple monatomic metals the steady-state creep was a diffusion-controlled process. At ordinary temperatures, AgBr has plastic properties reminiscent of those of lead. However, in a diatomic lattice both ions must move to preserve charge neutrality, which suggests that the activation enthalpy for creep would be much higher in AgBr than in lead. The experiments of Christy confirmed this suspicion and were further bolstered by experiments (simple before-and-after) on creep under pressure, which indicated that the activation volume for creep was too high to be explained other than by an activated process controlled by the very large bromine ion. The subsequent experiments of Tannhauser[16] on the diffusion of radioactive bromine in AgBr give strong support for Christy's viewpoint. The theoretical analysis of Weertman,[17] developed independently by Christy,[18] however, raises certain new questions to be resolved by future experiments.

2-3 Phase Transformations

A concomitant to the study of compressibility is the discovery of various types of phase transformations induced by pressure. Again, Bridgman is the principal source of our information on these effects. The extension of such studies into higher and higher pressure ranges has revealed an ever-increasing number of new phases.

[14] R. W. Christy, Creep of Silver Bromide at High Temperature, *Acta Met.*, vol. 2, pp. 284–295, 1954.

[15] F. Nabarro, "Report of a Conference on the Strength of Solids," London Physical Society, London, 1948, p. 75.

[16] D. S. Tannhauser, Self-diffusion of Bromine in Silver Bromide, *J. Phys. Chem. Solids*, vol. 5, pp. 224–235, 1958.

[17] J. Weertman, Theory of Steady-state Creep Based on Dislocation Climb, *J. Appl. Phys.*, vol. 26, no. 10, pp. 1213–1217, 1955; Steady-state Creep through Dislocation Climb, *J. Appl. Phys.*, vol. 28, no. 3, pp. 362–364, 1957.

[18] R. W. Christy, Theory of Creep Limited by Self-diffusion, *J. Appl. Phys.*, vol. 30, no. 5, pp. 760–764, 1959.

The experiments involved range from simple tracking of a freezing curve to the denumeration of seven and more phases in the *P-T* plane of more complex substances such as ice, urea, camphor, or bismuth. The investigation of such phenomena hardly holds much appeal for the contemporary solid-state physicist unless some hope of new understanding looms on the horizon. The phenomena appear on first sight to be either hopelessly complex or utterly trivial. More mature reflection now indicates that neither is the case. The relatively sparse data now available from X-ray diffraction studies at high pressures show that expected phase changes may not materialize; complicated changes in packing may occur leading to changes from high to low symmetry. Further study along these lines offers considerable promise of settling some major questions about phase changes.

What are these questions? We mention only a few here: Is there a critical point between the gaseous and solid states? Because, as thermodynamically required, every transformation under pressure must be to a phase of greater density, must all high-pressure phases be those which are crystallographically closer packed, i.e., have a larger number of nearest neighbors? Do the theoretically derived fusion curves agree with experiment? Are the rules for the relative stability of ionic crystals obeyed? Is there a law of corresponding states for phase diagrams of related solids?

The answers to these questions now available are at best fragmentary. One of the major handicaps with which the experimentalist has to contend is the lack of an adequate X-ray technique for unraveling the structures of high-pressure phases. In recent years, some progress has been made, and a few high-pressure phases have been identified. The techniques involved are exasperating, and the data crude. Because only powder patterns have been obtained, it is possible to resolve only simple structures. In many cases, only a few lines are available, and it is necessary to couple the X-ray data with volume changes to distinguish between various possibilities. Intensities are distorted by the presence of shear because most of the techniques are quasi-hydrostatic; this also results in large uncertainties in the determination of the pressure. Nevertheless, some rather surprising effects have been uncovered. Cerium undergoes a phase transformation without change in symmetry, being face-centered cubic both above and below the transformation.[19] Swenson[20] has traced the transformation in the *P-T* plane to its culmination in a critical point. This unusual phenomenon has been explained as arising from a rearrangement in the electronic shell structure, a $4f$ electron being "squeezed"

[19] A. W. Lawson and T. Y. Tang, Concerning the High Pressure Allotropic Modification of Cerium, *Phys. Rev.*, vol. 76, no. 2, pp. 301–302, 1949.

[20] R. Herman and C. A. Swenson, Temperature Dependence of the Phase Transition in Cerium, *J. Chem. Phys.*, vol. 29, no. 2, pp. 398–400, 1958.

into a 5*d* state. This change effectively increases the valence of the cerium from Ce^{3+} to Ce^{4+}, thereby inducing a large collapse in volume. A similar explanation has been suggested for the large change in volume of cesium, but as yet no X-ray data are available, owing partly to its high absorption coefficient and partly to its great chemical reactivity.

Lacking any evidence to the contrary, we often assume that transformations under pressure always produce a closer-packed structure. It seems reasonable to assume that the phase change in KCl in the neighborhood of 20 kilobars is from the NaCl structure to the CsCl structure. This assumption is bolstered by theoretical studies and, moreover, has been clearly established by direct experimentation.[21] It appears to be dangerous to extrapolate from the behavior of KCl, however. Thus AgCl, which has a transformation near 100 kilobars, does not appear to condense to the CsCl form.[22] The evidence on this seems reasonably good, for it is a lot easier to make negative statements about structures than positive ones. Indeed, it is possible to index the five observed lines of the high-pressure modification of AgCl in a manner consistent with the observed volume change using a Hg_2Cl_2 layer structure. Assuming this rather unexpected form is the correct diagnosis, we can justify the difference in behavior between KCl and AgCl on the basis of a relatively large contribution of van der Waals forces to the binding energy of the latter, increasing more rapidly with pressure than the Coulomb contribution.

The work of Grilly et al.[23] at Los Alamos on the fusion curves of He^3 and He^4 tends to lend support to the Simon theoretical fusion curve. The experimental error is rather large, but the pressure range on a corresponding-state argument, although absolutely small, is relatively large. Unfortunately, the recent work of Bundy[24] on melting curves of rubidium seems to cast some doubt on the general validity of this equation. This fusion curve (see Fig. 2-3) exhibits an apparent maximum of the fusion temperature as a function of pressure. In view of the uncertainty connected with the quasi-hydrostatic techniques, it would be desirable to have further work of this nature before reaching a firm conclusion on this point.

[21] J. Jamieson, Introductory Studies of High-pressure Polymorphism to 24,000 Bars by X-Ray Diffraction with Some Comments on Calcite II, *J. Geol.*, vol. 65, p. 334, 1957.

[22] J. Jamieson and A. W. Lawson, X-ray Diffraction Studies in the 100 Kilobar Range, *J. Appl. Phys.*, vol. 33, p. 766, 1962.

[23] R. L. Mills and E. R. Grilly, Melting Curves of He^3, He^4, H_2, D_2, Ne, N_2, and O_2 up to 3500 kg/cm^2, *Phys. Rev.*, vol. 99, no. 2, pp. 480–486, 1955; Melting Curves of H_2, D_2, and T_2 up to 3500 kg/cm^2, *Phys. Rev.*, vol. 101, no. 4, pp. 1246–1247, 1956.

[24] H. M. Strong, in F. P. Bundy, W. R. Hibbard, Jr., and H. M. Strong (eds.), "Progress in Very High Pressure Research," John Wiley & Sons, Inc., New York, 1961.

A number of years ago Guggenheim[25] carried out some theoretical analyses of the form which a law of corresponding states for solids should take. This work suggests that materials chemically similar in nature should have similar phase diagrams in the P-T plane. Relatively little work has been carried out in this area, but Trappeniers[26] has investigated the phase diagram of CBr_4 and compared it to that of CCl_4. More recently, Stevenson[27] has compared the phase diagrams of NH_4Cl with those of NH_4Br and NH_4I. They are illustrated in Fig. 2-4. The

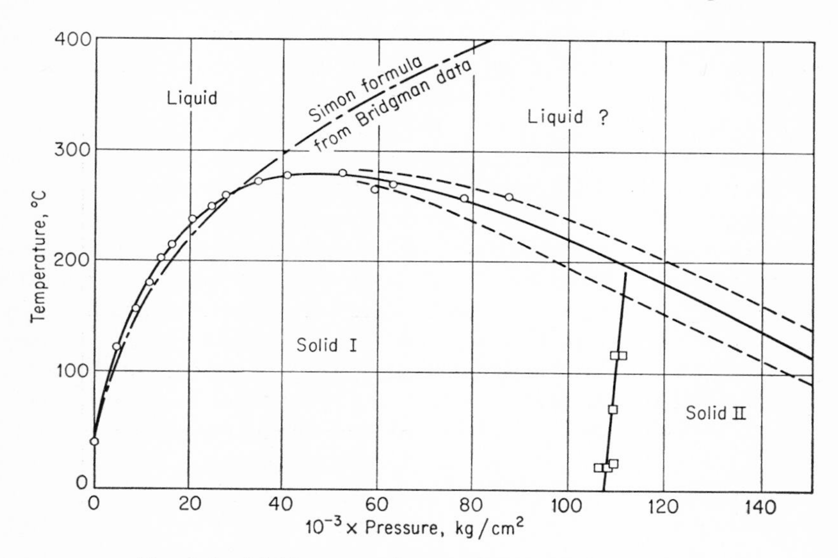

Fig. 2-3 Melting curve for rubidium. (*After Bundy.*)

various phases involve different positions and/or orientations of the ammonium tetrahedra on a cubic array of halogens. The tetrahedra are on the faces of the cube formed by the halogen ions in the α phase and are presumably rotating freely. In the β, γ, and δ phases, the tetrahedra are at the center of the cube, being oriented parallel, antiparallel, and at random, respectively. Nagamiya has explained the β-δ transition on the basis of octupole-octupole interactions, and Stevenson's experiments seem to bear out this contention.

A somewhat more trivial case, but not without interest, is that of Bridg-

[25] E. A. Guggenheim, The Principle of Corresponding States, *J. Chem. Phys.*, vol. 13, no. 7, pp. 253–261, 1945.

[26] N. Trappeniers, Polyatomic Molecules and the Law of Corresponding States, *Physica*, vol. 17, no. 5, pp. 501–510, 1951.

[27] R. Stevenson, Phase Transitions in the Ammonium Halides, *J. Chem. Phys.*, vol. 34, no. 5, pp. 1757–1762, 1961.

man concerning the phase diagrams of H_2O and D_2O, revealing the effects of thermal agitation. In general, it seems safe to conclude that chemically similar substances may have similar phase diagrams. This does not necessarily apply universally, e.g., NaCl does not transform in the same way as KCl, antimony is not similar to bismuth, etc., at least in the experimentally available pressure range.

The crying need in this general area is for more extensive as well as intensive work, coupled with adequate, or at least supportive, X-ray evidence. It is unfortunate that crystallographers have progressed to such difficult problems (which can be attacked with high-speed computers) that it is difficult to interest them in the crude data now obtained

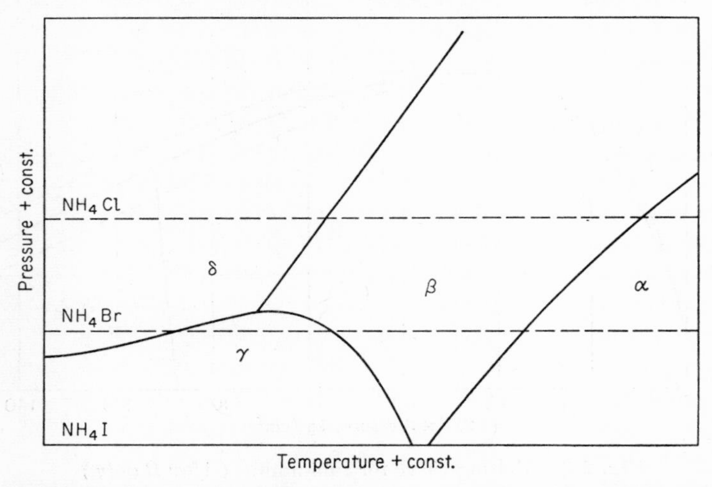

Fig. 2-4 Schematic generalized phase diagram for ammonium halides showing in outline the general type of correlation among the various phases. (*After Stevenson.*)

at high pressures in which a better guestimate is sometimes the only result.

Phase changes are usually detected by observing discontinuities in volume or electrical conductivity as a function of pressure. Techniques for this type of observation have been developed for the highest pressures yet achieved and for a wide range of temperatures. A combination of both methods is often useful in clarifying obscure situations, as some phase changes associated with minor volume changes may produce large changes in electrical conductivity, and vice versa. In the case of reconstructive transformations involving diffusive atomic movements, large regions of indifference to pressure may becloud the situation. Indeed, it is sometimes impossible to effect a thermodynamically expected change in phase by pressure alone. A case in point is the calcite-aragonite equilibrium curve. In such cases, it is often necessary to study the equilibrium through an intermediary labile phase. One scheme, used by Jamieson[28] to study the $CaCO_3$ system, was to study the electrical conductance of saturated aqueous solution of aragonite and calcite. The pressure producing equal conductance of the two solutions at a given temperature is the equilibrium point. Jamieson developed a polytetrafluorethylene cell for these studies to avoid contamination of the solutions by foreign ions. The technique has been used in studying a variety of other systems.

2-4 Transport Phenomena

2-4a Electrical conductivity. The data to be discussed in this section include electrical and thermal conductivity and diffusion. It will not be necessary to dwell at length here on the electrical conductivity. The extensive work by Bridgman on metals has been reviewed elsewhere.[29] In brief, the decreases in resistance of "good" metals with increasing pressures may be qualitatively understood in terms of a decrease in the amplitude of vibration of the atoms about their normal lattice sites with a concomitant decrease in their scattering cross sections.

However, more complicated behavior patterns, which may in fact dominate, are superimposed on this general trend. These phenomena arise from changes in the Fermi energy, which is also changed by the pressure, leading to rapidly varying changes of overlap into higher Brillouin zones. A case in point is the minimum in resistance in the alkali metals at high pressures. This behavior is illustrated in Fig. 2-5. Recently, Dugdale[30] has suggested that simultaneous studies of resistivity and thermoelectric power may help to unravel band-structure effects from thermal effects. He has pointed out that the absolute thermoelectric powers at temperatures high compared with the Debye temperature should be given by

$$S = \frac{-\pi^2 k^2 T}{3eE_F}\left[\frac{\partial \ln \rho(E)}{\partial \ln E}\right]_{E=E_F} \tag{2-4}$$

where E_F = Fermi energy
$\rho(E)$ = resistivity
k = Boltzmann's constant
e = electronic charge

[28] J. Jamieson, Phase Equilibrium in the System Calcite-Aragonite, *J. Chem. Phys.*, vol. 21, no. 8, pp. 1385–1390, 1953.

[29] A. W. Lawson, in B. Chalmers and R. King (eds.), "Progress in Metal Physics," vol. 6, Pergamon Press, New York, 1956.

[30] J. S. Dugdale, Electrical Resistivity at Low Temperatures, *Science,* vol. 134, no. 3472, pp. 77–86, 1961.

Dugdale suggests that the minimum in resistance in cesium and other alkali metals is associated with a large distortion of the Fermi surface, which results in an increase in Umklapp processes and hence the scattering cross section. Recent measurements by Dugdale and Mundy[31] on the thermoelectric power of cesium appear to confirm this point of view, the sign of the thermoelectric power changing in the neighborhood of the resistance minimum.

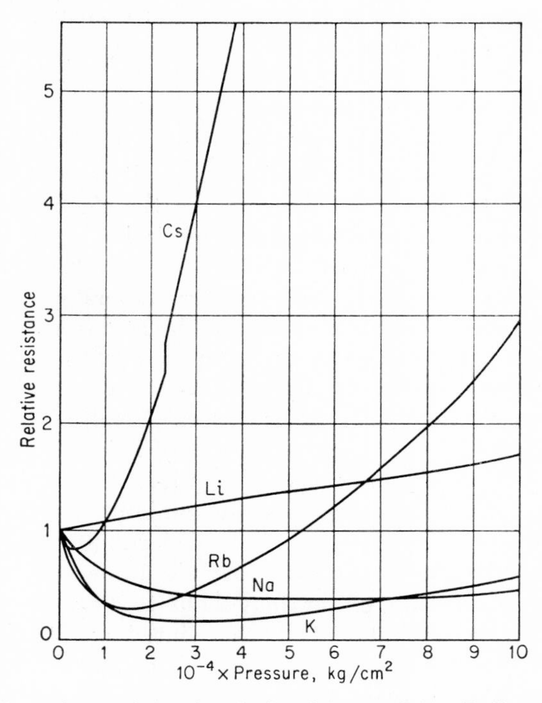

Fig. 2-5 The dependence of the electrical resistance of the alkali metals on pressure, showing the existence of a minimum. (*After Bridgman.*)

A similar situation appears to exist in LiPb in the β phase. This phenomenon was first studied under pressure by Wilson,[32] who interpreted a kink in the conductivity-pressure curve as evidence of order-disorder phenomena. Unpublished work by Lazarus[33] revealed that in this case also, the thermoelectric power reversed sign in the neighborhood of the

[31] J. S. Dugdale and J. N. Mundy, The Pressure Dependence of the Thermoelectric Power of the Alkali Metals at Room Temperature, *Phil. Mag.*, vol. 6, pp. 1463–1473, 1961.

[32] T. C. Wilson, The Effect of High Pressure on the Order-Disorder Transformation in Alloys, *Phys. Rev.*, vol. 56, pp. 598–611, 1939.

[33] D. Lazarus, Private Communication.

kink, suggesting the occurrence of a critical overlap. Lacking definitive information on the crystal structure, Lazarus did not carry out any further experimental work.

Distortions of Fermi surfaces by pressure indicate the desirability of obtaining direct evidence about the effect of pressure on their shapes. Unfortunately, the study of Fermi surfaces in general requires either very low temperatures to produce long relaxation times in the Fermi distribution, or very high frequencies. As yet very few experiments have been carried out, owing to the difficulty of combining the various techniques

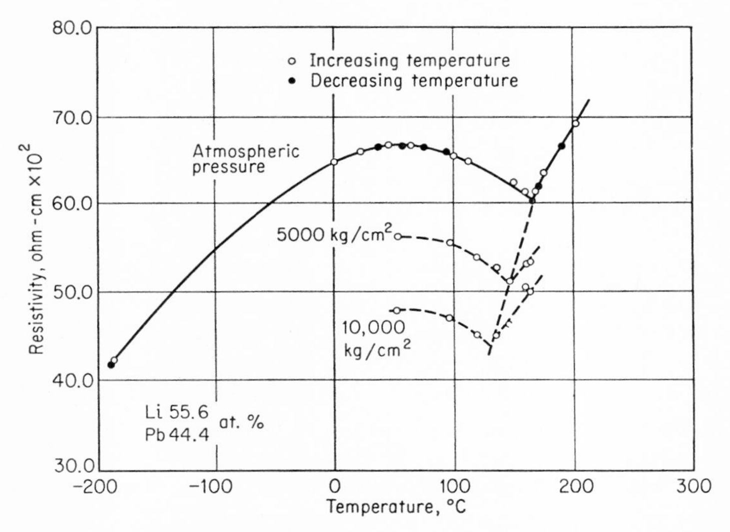

Fig. 2-6 The cusplike dependence of the resistance of β-LiPb on temperature and pressure, presumably due to the sensitive behavior of a Fermi surface near a Brillouin-zone boundary. (*After Wilson.*)

required, i.e., low temperatures, high magnetic fields, high pressures, and often either electromagnetic or acoustic radiation. Nevertheless, a few starts in this direction have been made. Brandt et al.[34] have studied the De Haas–Van Alphen effect in bismuth by freezing water around the sample in a closed container. A pressure of about 2 kilobars is achieved in this way and produces a shift in E_F which is beyond experimental error. The observed shift is of the order of magnitude predicted by band theory. Transport studies of this sort are in their infancy, and considerable work is required to establish more versatile techniques for this purpose.

[34] N. V. Brandt and V. A. Venttsel, Effect of Uniform Compression on the Oscillation of the Magnetic Susceptibility of Bismuth at Low Temperatures, *Soviet Phys. JETP,* vol. 35, no. 5, pp. 757–760, 1959.

Presumably, the complicated behavior of pressure thermocouples is intimately connected with the detailed effects of pressure on band structure. The extensive investigations of Bridgman on these phenomena have never been subjected to theoretical analysis. As our understanding of Fermi surfaces increases, it would be of interest to ascertain if these phenomena can be explained even qualitatively.

In recent years, the effect of pressure on the electrical conductivity of semiconductors has been the subject of fairly intensive investigation. My older review of the literature is quite out of date. Happily, this situation is being remedied by another contribution to this book (see Chap. 8) and no more need be said at this juncture. The same is true of ionic conductivity, a phenomenon closely related to solid-state diffusion; both are covered in Chap. 3.

We should remark here, however, on the interesting properties to be expected in the pressure dependence of the conductivity of the transition-metal oxides. These materials have been the subject of a theoretical study by Mott,[35] who suggests that they afford suitable possibilities for studying the transition from nonmetallic to metallic conductivity. The sort of behavior Mott anticipates is illustrated in Fig. 2-7. This behavior is reminiscent of the change in conductivity as one traverses the critical temperature of mercury.[29] In any case, our understanding of how electrical transport depends on atomic separation would be materially enhanced by experimental studies which would establish the validity of Mott's point of view. Such investigations have already been initiated at this laboratory.

2-4b Thermal conductivity. A topic which deserves some discussion here is heat transport, or thermal conductivity. Bridgman[1] has studied a variety of solids, both metallic and nonmetallic. In the case of "good" metals, Bridgman's results seemed difficult to understand in terms of what might be expected from the Wiedemann-Franz ratio. Starr's[36] later experiments, however, revealed that the early results were suspect, and his data are more compatible with those on electrical conductivity. In the case of insulators,[37] Bridgman's observations are more reliable and appear to be in agreement with a crude theory consistent with the Grüneisen approximation. According to this model, the heat conductivity K should vary as

$$K = A_0/3\gamma^2 T x_T^{3/2} \rho^{1/2} \tag{2-5}$$

[35] N. F. Mott, The Transition to the Metallic State, *Phil. Mag.*, vol. 6, pp. 287–309, 1961.

[36] C. Starr, The Pressure Coefficient of Thermal Conductivity of Metals, *Phys. Rev.*, vol. 54, pp. 210–216, 1938.

[37] A. W. Lawson, On the High Temperature Heat Conductivity of Insulators, *J. Phys. Chem. Solids*, vol. 3, p. 155, 1957.

where T = absolute temperature
ρ = density
γ = Grüneisen's constant
x_T = bulk modulus
A_0 = lattice parameter

Equation (2-5) is of course valid only in the range of temperatures which are large compared to the Debye temperature.

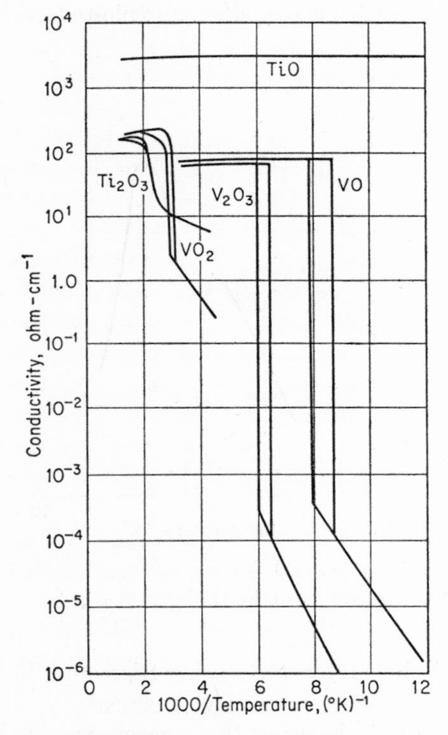

Fig. 2-7 The temperature dependence of the conductivity of titanium and vanadium oxides. According to Mott, the effect of 100 kilobars pressure should be to shift the transition by a factor of 2. (*After Morin.*)

An interesting contrast to studies on the thermal conductivity of NaCl at room temperature is afforded by an experiment carried out by Wilks et al.[38] on solid helium along its melting curve. The Debye temperature

[38] J. Wilks et al., The Thermal Conductivity of Solid Helium, *Proc. Roy. Soc. London*, vol. A214, pp. 546–563, 1952; The Thermal Conductivity of Solid Helium, *Proc. Phys. Soc. London*, vol. A64, pp. 89–90, 1951; The Thermal Conductivity of Solid Helium at High Densities, *Phil. Mag.*, vol. 44, pp. 664–674, 1953.

is altered appreciably by the pressure because of the very high compressibility of solid helium, and it is possible to study the effect of Debye temperature on heat transport. The effects are large, as may be seen from Fig. 2-8, which exhibits Wilks's data. These effects comprise an interesting example of how studies in a relatively low pressure range, coupled with other techniques and an *appropriately chosen* solid, may portray a class of behavior as yet not accessible to detailed study in other materials even at the highest pressures now attainable. In general, the rare gases have not yet been sufficiently exploited with respect to other

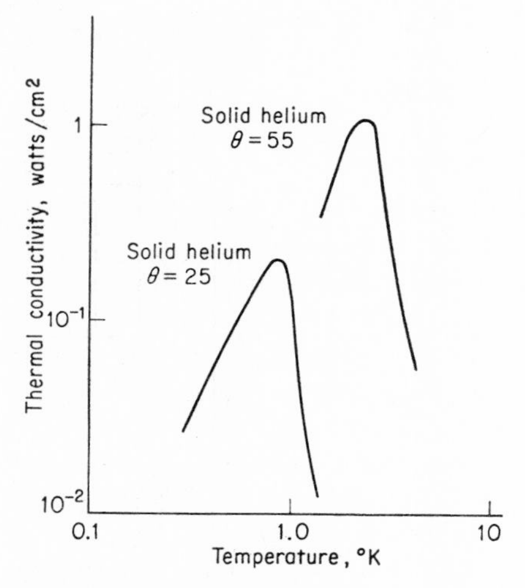

Fig. 2-8 Heat conductivity in solid helium, showing the dependence of heat conductivity on Debye temperature. (*After Wilks, et al.*)

physical changes induced by pressure. Rice and his students at the University of Chicago are currently engaged in studying transport phenomena in the liquid phases of these gases, but similar studies in the solid state offer a virgin territory.

Another area relating to heat conductivity which has not been explored as a function of pressure is the contribution to transport by excitation processes. Here we have in mind the studies of Jaffé[39] and Busch[40] relative to the exponential increase of thermal conductance of semiconductors at high temperatures. This phenomenon is apparently associated with

[39] A. Jaffé, Heat Transfer in Semiconductors, *Can. J. Phys.*, vol. 34, pp. 1342–1355, 1956.

[40] G. Busch and M. Schneider, Heat Conduction in Semiconductors, *Physica*, vol. 20, no. 11, pp. 1084–1086, 1954.

the heat of excitation of carriers in the conduction band, which becomes dominant in intrinsic semiconductors as the temperature is raised. The effect of pressure on this contribution is of prime importance to geophysicists concerned with the flow of heat in the interior of the earth and the estimated temperature at great depths below its crust.[41] A variety of phenomena could play a role. These have been discussed elsewhere. Transport by radiation[42] and the contribution of excitation processes[43] apparently could be significant factors in determining the temperature distribution in the earth. More experiments are needed, however, to support these speculative conclusions. Pressure affords a tool for such work because it is not likely that radiation transport at high temperatures would be materially affected by pressure, while large effects on excitation processes are to be expected.

2-5 Dielectric Phenomena

Experimental information relating to the effect of hydrostatic pressure on electrical susceptibility is sparse. The literature contains a few scattered references to the pressure dependence of the Curie temperature in various ferroelectrics such as rochelle salt[44] and $BaTiO_3$.[45] As an example of this type of work we refer to Fig. 2-9, where Bancroft's data on the rochelle-salt phase diagram are presented. This work is useful in helping the theoretician to construct models explaining ferroelectricity. A number of such models have been constructed, but it seems dubious that they will remain the final word after more progress has been made in explaining the properties of normal dielectrics.

2-5a The alkali halides. The effect of pressure on the dielectric constant of simple cubic materials such as NaCl, KCl, and MgO was investigated by Mayburg[46] a number of years ago in my laboratory at Chicago. Coupling his low-frequency data with Burstein and Smith's[47] optical determinations of the index of refraction in the same materials,

[41] S. P. Clark, Effect of Radiative Transfer on Temperatures in the Earth, *Bull. Geol. Soc. Am.*, vol. 67, pp. 1123–1124, 1956.

[42] A. W. Lawson and J. Jamieson, Energy Transfer in the Earth's Mantle, *J. Geol.*, vol. 66, pp. 540–551, 1958.

[43] J. Jamieson and A. W. Lawson, High Temperature Heat Conductivity of Some Metal Oxides, *J. Appl. Phys.*, vol. 29, no. 9, pp. 1313–1314, 1958.

[44] D. Bancroft, The Effect of Hydrostatic Pressure on the Susceptibility of Rochelle Salt, *Phys. Rev.*, vol. 53, pp. 587–590, 1938.

[45] W. J. Merz, The Effect of Hydrostatic Pressure on the Curie Point of Barium Titanate Single Crystals, *Phys. Rev.*, vol. 78, no. 7, pp. 52–54, 1950.

[46] S. Mayburg, Effect of Pressure on the Low Frequency Dielectric Constant of Ionic Crystals, *Phys. Rev.*, vol. 79, no. 2, pp. 375–382, 1950.

[47] E. Burstein and P. L. Smith, Photoelastic Properties of Cubic Crystals, *Phys. Rev.*, vol. 74, no. 2, pp. 229–236, 1948.

he was able to show that the pressure variation of the lattice polarizability was not in accord with the older theories of Born,[48] Mott,[49] and Højendahl.[50]

This result is not altogether surprising in view of the fact that at the time of Mayburg's experiments, Szigetti's[51] sweeping analysis of dielectric phenomena and its relation to reststrahlung and compressibility had

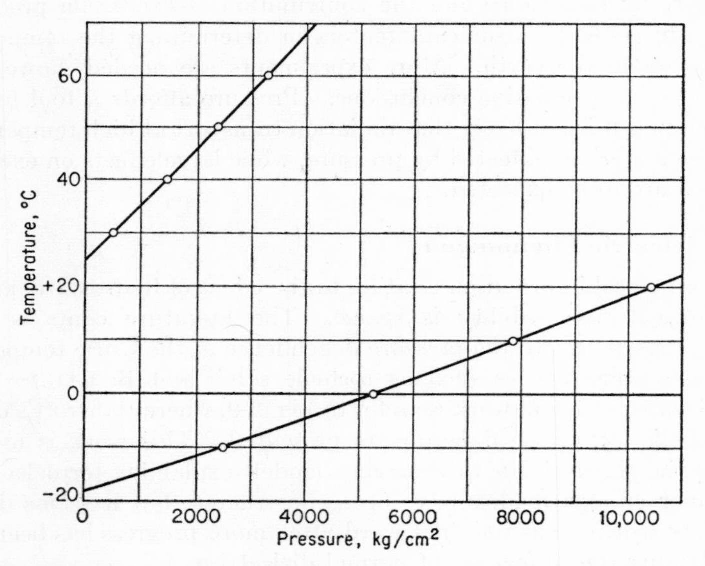

Fig. 2-9 Pressure dependence of the upper and lower Curie temperatures in rochelle salt. (*After Bancroft.*)

not yet been published. According to this theory, the dielectric constant ϵ is given by

$$\epsilon - n^2 = \frac{4\pi}{v}\left(\frac{n^2+2}{3}\right)^2 \frac{e^{*2}}{\mu\Omega_t^2} \tag{2-6}$$

$$\mu\Omega_t^2 = 6a\beta\left(\frac{n^2+2}{\epsilon+2}\right) \tag{2-7}$$

[48] M. Born and M. Goeppert Mayer, p. 759 in A. Smekal (ed.), "Handbuch der Physik," vol. 24, part 2, Springer-Verlag, Berlin, 1933.

[49] N. F. Mott and M. J. Littleton, Conduction in Polar Crystals, *Proc. Faraday Soc.*, vol. 34, pp. 485–499, 1938.

[50] K. Højendahl, Studies in the Properties of Ionic Crystals, *Kgl. Danske Videnskab. Selskab*, vol. 16, no. 2, 1938.

[51] B. Szigetti, Polarisability and Dielectric Constant of Ionic Crystals, *Trans. Faraday Soc.*, vol. 45, pp. 155–166, 1949; Compressibility and Absorption Frequency of Ionic Crystals, *Proc. Roy. Soc. London*, vol. A204, pp. 51–62, 1950.

where n = index of refraction
β = compressibility
e^* = effective ionic charge
v = volume of unit cell
μ = reduced mass of neutral ion pair

When these equations are applied to the alkali halides, it is found that they are satisfied only if e^* is appreciably less than e, the electronic charge. This result is in apparent conflict with the choice of $e^* = e$ required to explain the cohesive energy in these crystals, in which covalency may be expected to be negligible. This discrepancy was explained by Dick and Overhauser[52] and others[53] by a model in which displacement of the electronic shells with respect to the nucleus, owing to interionic repulsive forces, is taken into account. This point of view has been exploited by Cochran and his collaborators,[54] who have used it to predict dispersion effects in a variety of substances. Recently, Havinga[55] has suggested that the equations of the shell model in the more extended form are competent to explain the temperature and pressure dependence of the dielectric constants of these simple cubic lattices. We view this conclusion as misleading. Apparently, Havinga was unaware of Mayburg's extensive data. A more complete numerical comparison[56] of these data with Havinga's equations reveals a systematic error of about a factor of two. We believe this difference arises from a decrease in the electronic polarizability α of the shells, resulting from the decreased interatomic distance. In Havinga's model, α is assumed independent of pressure, the variation of the index of refraction n with pressure being ascribed solely to the change in internal field as prescribed by the Lorentz field. Further work is apparently needed to clarify the situation. It should be remarked that the assumptions of central forces (Cauchy condition) and nearest-neighbor interactions are also involved, and it is by no means clear which assumption constitutes the weak link in the argument.

In this connection, we should mention that a good deal of our understanding of alkali halides is based on the orthogonalized atomic orbitals of

[52] B. J. Dick and A. W. Overhauser, Theory of the Dielectric Constants of Alkali Halide Crystals, *Phys. Rev.*, vol. 112, no. 1, pp. 90–103, 1958.

[53] J. E. Hanlon and A. W. Lawson, Effective Ionic Charge in Alkali Halides, *Phys. Rev.*, vol. 113, no. 2, pp. 472–478, 1959.

[54] W. Cochran et al., Theory of the Lattice Vibrations of Germanium, *Phys. Rev. Letters*, vol. 2, pp. 495–497, 1959; Theory of the Lattice Vibrations of Germanium, *Proc. Roy. Soc. London*, vol. A253, pp. 260–276, 1959; Lattice Dynamics of Alkali Halide Crystals, *Phys. Rev.*, vol. 119, no. 3, pp. 980–999, 1960.

[55] E. E. Havinga, Contribution to the Theory of the Dielectric Properties of the Alkali Halides, *Phys. Rev.*, vol. 119, no. 4, pp. 1193–1198, 1960.

[56] R. Payne and A. W. Lawson, unpublished calculations.

Löwdin.[57] Whether this approach is adequate, or whether a more sophisticated approach based on molecular orbitals is necessary, is unsettled at this time. According to the latter point of view, a real transfer of charge corresponding to the degree of covalency is required. It is not known whether or not the latter point of view is consistent with the severe distortions of electronic shell structure required by Witte's[58] X-ray data. An appreciable transfer of charge seems unreasonable on energetic grounds. Yet we have already used the increase in covalency as a justification for the observed diffraction pattern of the high-pressure modification of AgCl. The schizophrenia between the spectroscopic, or chemical, approach and the band-theoretical approach, which takes into account all the Kubic harmonics necessary to satisfy the periodic crystal potentials, is sorely in need of clarification.

2-6 Optical Phenomena

We shall not concern ourselves in this section with the extensive and exciting experiments of Drickamer and his collaborators, to which Chap. 12 of this book is devoted. The experiments of Burstein and Smith[47] on the variation of index of refraction with pressure have been mentioned in passing in the previous section. We add no more except to remark that it would be desirable to check that the data available for piezo-optical coefficients are tensorially consistent with his data. So far as we know, such a numerical check has not been made.

2-6a *F* centers. Some reference should be made to the work of Jacobs[59] in the range below 10 kilobars on the absorption by *F* centers in the alkali halides. Although Drickamer has extended this work into a pressure range more than an order of magnitude greater, the uncertainties in compressibility make theoretical comparisons difficult. In any case, to the extent that the two sets of data overlap, the agreement is well within the combined experimental errors. We exhibit typical data from Jacobs's thesis in Fig. 2-10.

The point of interest in this work is the detailed comparison of the data with the theoretical predictions of Lax[60] and O'Rourke[61] concerning the

[57] P. Löwdin, "A Theoretical Investigation of Some Properties of Ionic Crystals," Almquist and Wiksells, Uppsala, 1948.

[58] H. Witte and E. Wolfel, Electron Distributions in NaCl, LiF, CaF_2, and N, *Rev. Mod. Phys.*, vol. 30, no. 1, pp. 51–55, 1958.

[59] I. S. Jacobs, Effect of Pressure on *F* Center Absorption in Alkali Halides, *Phys. Rev.*, vol. 93, no. 5, pp. 993–1004, 1954.

[60] M. Lax, The Franck-Condon Principle and Its Application to Crystals, *J. Chem. Phys.*, vol. 20, no. 11, pp. 1752–1760, 1952.

[61] R. C. O'Rourke, Absorption of Light by Trapped Electrons, *Phys. Rev.*, vol. 91, no. 2, pp. 265–270, 1953.

dependence of line width and frequency of the characteristic absorption on temperature and pressure. These predictions are based on a model which takes into account the complexities involved in multiphonon interactions.

The principal conclusion derived from Jacobs's work is the fact that the shift in absorption energy of the F centers towards the blue can be

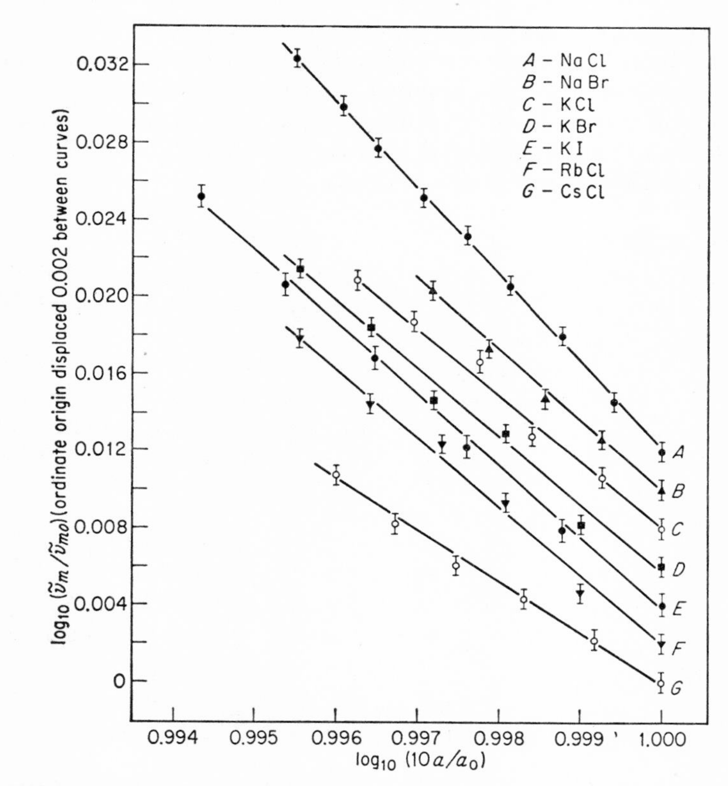

Fig. 2-10 Experimental curves of peak wave number as a function of lattice parameter, referred to value at atmospheric pressure. (*After Jacobs.*)

explained almost entirely by the dependence of the energy levels on the interatomic distance a. In contrast, to describe the temperature dependence of this quantity one must take into account not only the effect of thermal expansion on a, but also the effect of anharmonic forces in producing a change in lattice frequency spectrum when an electron is ejected from an F center. To explain the relatively insensitive dependence of the width of the absorption band on pressure, Jacobs found it necessary to consider two mechanisms. The first mechanism arises from the variation in the energy contributed by the phonons partaking in the transition. The second arises from the fluctuations in the diameter of the well trapping the electron. This latter effect is responsible for the finite width of F-band absorption at absolute zero. By combining these two effects, Jacobs was able to describe the relatively slight dependence of bandwidth on pressure rather well. However, he did find it necessary to take into account the enhanced compressibility of the lattice in the neighborhood of a vacancy in computing the mean square fluctuation of well diameter. The average number of phonons participating in the absorption process may be computed from the combined effects of temperature and pressure. This number turns out to be about 5.4, in reasonable agreement with the theoretical estimate of 4 made by Huang and Rhys on the basis of Simpson's wave functions for NaCl.

2-7 Magnetic Effects

The amount of systematic work on the effect of pressure is appallingly small. Early work in this field[62,63] involved rather cumbersome techniques which in general were thermodynamically inconsistent[64–66] and at variance with the relatively sparse data collected more recently.

The lack of data on magnetic phenomena under pressure is rather surprising in view of the rather direct information which is obtainable on both the interatomic and intra-atomic exchange interactions, as well as the indirect evidence on the coupling of these interactions through the magnetocrystalline anisotropy.

The measurements of interest in this field fall into three categories: (1) change of saturation magnetization with pressure, (2) change in Curie temperature with pressure, and (3) ferromagnetic resonance as a function of pressure. The first category of experiments is related basically to the intra-atomic effects, the second is related to the interatomic effects, while the third gives information about their interaction.

The most recent results on the effect of pressure on saturation magnet-

[62] A. Ebert and A. Kussman, Änderung der Sättigungsmagnetisierung durch allseitigen Druck, *Physik Z.*, vol. 38, pp. 437–445, 1937.

[63] A. Michels et al., Influence of Pressure on the Curie Point of a 70–30% Ni-Cu Alloy, *Physica*, vol. 4, no. 10, pp. 1007–1016, 1937; The Effect of Pressure on the Curie Point of a Monel Alloy, *Physica*, vol. 8, no. 1, pp. 53–57, 1941.

[64] J. C. Slater, Note on the Effect of Pressure on the Curie Point of Iron-Nickel Alloys, *Phys. Rev.*, vol. 58, pp. 54–56, 1940.

[65] M. Kornetzki, Über die Verschiebung der Curietemperatur durch allseitigen Druck, *Physik Z.*, vol. 44, pp. 296–302, 1943.

[66] M. Kornetzki, Über die Abhangigkeit der Volumenmagnetostriktion und des Weiss'schen Factors von der Temperatur und der Gitterkonstante, *Z. Physik*, vol. 98, pp. 289–313, 1935.

ization are those of Kouvel and Wilson,[67] who have summarized the prior literature and discussed the reliability of the various measurements. The most extensive data on the effect of pressure on Curie temperatures are those obtained by Patrick[68] in the author's laboratory; they are shown in

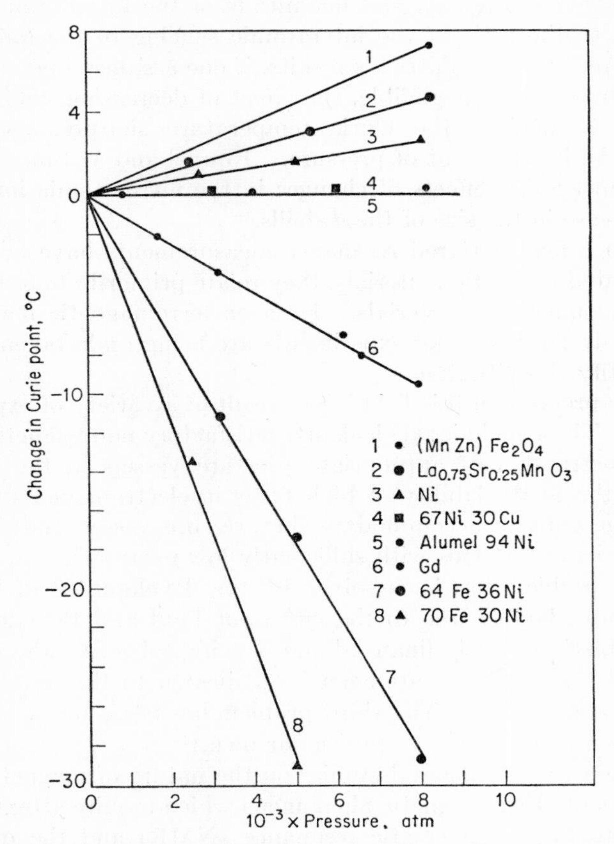

Fig. 2-11 Shift in Curie temperature with pressure in a variety of magnetic materials. (*After Patrick.*)

Fig. 2-11. Kouvel and Wilson conclude that their data in conjunction with Patrick's force the conclusion that σ_0, the magnetic moment at

[67] J. S. Kouvel and R. H. Wilson, Effects of Pressure on Magnetic Interactions in Metals, in F. P. Bundy, W. R. Hibbard, Jr., and H. M. Strong (eds.), "Progress in Very High Pressure Research," John Wiley & Sons, Inc., New York, 1961.

[68] L. Patrick, The Change of Ferromagnetic Curie Points with Hydrostatic Pressure, *Phys. Rev.*, vol. 93, no. 3, pp. 384–392, 1954.

absolute zero temperature, is pressure dependent. This fact is **not** included in previous theoretical analyses.[69]

A major contribution of Patrick's work is the conclusion that the famous interaction curve of Bethe and Slater[69] is qualitatively violated. This curve relates the sign and magnitude of the interatomic-exchange interaction to the ratio of the interatomic spacing to the radius of the *d* shells. According to Patrick's results, if one assumes that interatomic effects of pressure are negligible, the effect of decreasing volume in iron should be to depress the Curie temperature sharply. Actually, it appears to be independent of pressure. Kouvel and Wilson ascribe this to the compensating effects of changes in the intra-atomic interactions, e.g., a decrease in the size of the *d* shells.

Although a few scattered resonance measurements have been carried out on isolated magnetic materials, they relate primarily to ferrimagnetic and antiferromagnetic materials. Data on ferromagnetic materials are conspicuously lacking[70] and experiments are being undertaken at Riverside to rectify this situation.

The slow progress in this field is the result of a variety of experimental problems. These include: (1) lack of a satisfactory nonmagnetic material for the construction of appropriate pressure vessels in the 10-kilobar range, (2) the unavailability of high fields in electromagnets with sufficiently large gaps to accommodate the pressure vessel, and (3) lack of adequate microwave seals with sufficiently low mismatch.

The first problem has been solved by the development of beryllium-copper bombs, largely due to the efforts of Paul and Benedek.[71] The second problem is largely financial and is being solved by the support of enlightened Federal and state agencies dedicated to the development of our scientific resources. The third problem has been solved in a variety of schemes, among which we prefer our own.[72]

In addition to fundamental studies on the nature of magnetism, there are a variety of other magnetic phenomena which require attention. We refer here to nuclear magnetic resonance (NMR) and the quadrupole resonance phenomena. A summary of this work is presented in Chap. 9,

[69] J. C. Slater, Atomic Shielding Constants, *Phys. Rev.*, vol. 36, pp. 57–64, 1930; A. Sommerfeld and H. Bethe, Elektronentheorie der Metalle, p. 595 in A. Smekal (ed.), "Handbuch der Physik," vol. 24, part 2, Springer-Verlag, Berlin, 1933.

[70] D. Gugan and G. Rowland, The Pressure Dependence of the Ferromagnetic Anisotropy Energy, *Proc. Phys. Soc. London*, vol. 72, pp. 207–213, 1958.

[71] G. B. Benedek, W. Paul, and H. Brooks, Conductivity, Hall Effect, and Magnetoresistance in *n*-type Germanium and Their Dependence on Pressure, *Phys. Rev.*, vol. 100, no. 4, pp. 1129–1139, 1955.

[72] A. W. Lawson and G. E. Smith, High-pressure Microwave Window, *Rev. Sci. Instr.*, vol. 30, no. 11, pp. 989–991, 1959.

but we should like to refer here to the as yet unpublished work of Baron[73] on the NMR spectra of alkali halides carried out at the University of Chicago. Baron's work centers around the study of the chemical shift of the NMR of the positive and negative ions in a variety of alkali halides which transform at moderate pressures from the fcc structure (NaCl type) to the bcc structure (CsCl type). A typical set of such data is shown in Fig. 2-12. This work is important in testing recent theories

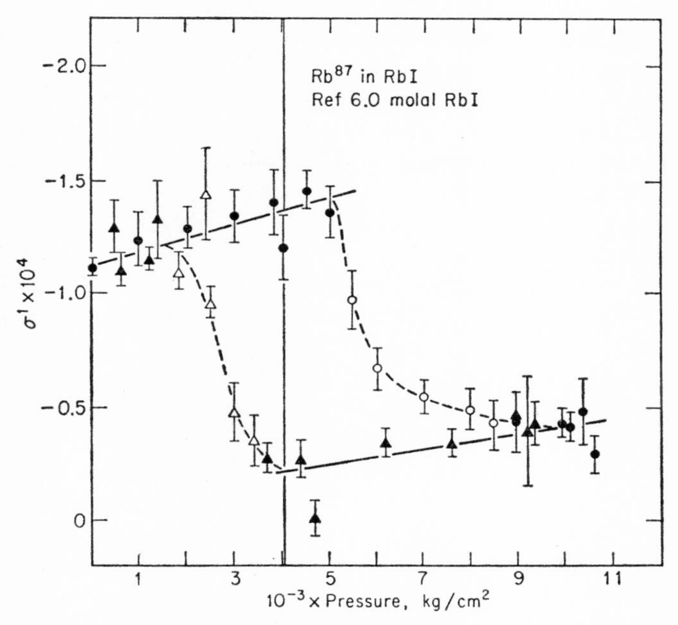

Fig. 2-12 The chemical shift of Rb^{87} in RbI versus pressure. σ' is the difference between the nuclear-magnetic-resonance frequencies in the salt and in the reference solution divided by the frequency in the reference solution. (*After Baron.*)

of the chemical shift. Despite the relatively poor signal-to-noise ratio in Baron's experiments and his difficulties with hysteresis and residual strains, the preponderance of his evidence indicates that the existing theories are deficient in their present form. Baron has suggested that the introduction of next-nearest-neighbor interactions tends to reduce the discrepancy between theory and experiment. Whether this point of view is correct, or whether basic alterations in the existing models are necessary, can be decided only by further experiments.

[73] R. Baron, in a paper submitted to *Phys. Rev.*

2-8 Summary

In this chapter, we have discussed various roles of high pressures in the study of the solid state. These examples are selective in nature, a preponderance of emphasis having been given to experiments with which the author is personally acquainted. This rather human distortion does not detract from the major contributions of other authors whose work has been slighted here. Many of them are contributors to this book.

All of us are indebted to the Office of Naval Research, the Office of Aerospace Research, the Bureau of Ordnance, the Advanced Research Project Agency, the Atomic Energy Commission, and the National Science Foundation for their support. This help we gratefully acknowledge. But most of all we are indebted to Bridgman, who unlocked the doors to the many mysteries we now explore.

3

Effect of High Pressure on Diffusion

DAVID LAZARUS
Department of Physics
University of Illinois
Urbana, Illinois

NORMAN H. NACHTRIEB
Institute for the Study of Metals
University of Chicago
Chicago, Illinois

3-1 Introduction

In a large number of solid-state reactions, a critical role is played by the rate at which atoms can migrate through the lattice. Diffusion limits the hardness of solids as well as their ductility under load, their corrosion resistance, and their phase stability. It enters into ionic conduction, the photographic process, sintering, and devitrification. It may produce effects which enormously enhance or completely negate the use of certain materials under some environmental conditions.

Because of its extraordinary practical importance, solid-state diffusion has been actively investigated for the better part of a century by workers in many fields. This effort has produced an enormous body of experimental data which support the fact that, contrary to popular belief, solids are not impermeable, rigid arrays of atoms. In a typical solid, and at temperatures well below the melting point, each atom may move between adjacent lattice sites once per microsecond or more frequently. The major scientific interest in solid-state diffusion has centered about detailed elucidation of mechanisms which can permit such enormous rates of atomic motion while simultaneously preserving the "solidity" of a solid, as demonstrated by its elastic rigidity and by the geological and X-ray evidence for long-range and short-range order.

Considerable progress has been made in the past two decades, spurred in part by the ready availability of radioisotopes for use as tracers in precise measurements. The most serious attention has focused on the following mechanisms:

1. Direct interchange of pairs of atoms or higher-order multiplets (ring mechanisms)
2. Diffusion by virtue of vacant lattice sites in the crystalline solid (vacancy mechanisms)
3. Diffusion by virtue of extra lattice sites (interstitial mechanisms)
4. Diffusion by virtue of naturally occurring large regions of misorientation in the crystal (boundary mechanisms)
5. Diffusion by virtue of local melting in the lattice (relaxion mechanism)
6. Diffusion by quantum-mechanical tunneling

It seems well established that at temperatures far below the melting point, in well-equilibrated solids, atom motion is largely confined to internal regions of misorientation such as grain boundaries and dislocations. At high temperatures, and even at low temperatures in solids which have been damaged by plastic deformation and irradiation, diffusion apparently is largely due to vacancy and interstitial mechanisms. Tunneling appears to be of importance only for hydrogen and possibly helium diffusion. No direct evidence has been found to support the exchange or relaxion mechanisms, and these are somewhat contraindicated by phenomena such as the Kirkendall effect which show that lattice sites are not conserved during diffusion, and that the major part of the kinetic energy is carried by a single atom in a diffusive jump.

Interstitial mechanisms dominate for high-temperature diffusion of small atoms in open lattices, e.g., carbon or nitrogen in iron, and also in some ionic solids, particularly the silver halides. The vacancy mechanism for diffusion appears to be dominant at high temperatures in most close-packed solids—salts and oxides, as well as metals. Combinations of these two mechanisms occur in some special cases, particularly in semiconductors (e.g., copper in germanium) and in irradiated and plastically deformed solids.

The validity of the mechanisms involving the point imperfections, interstitials and vacancies, is largely based on direct experimental results. This is supported by detailed theoretical calculations which are noteworthy, not only for their complexity, but also for the unfortunately large number of approximations which are seemingly indigenous to solid-state theory. Because of such difficulties, it has not been possible to calculate with any precision a number of parameters of interest, such as the energy and volume changes associated with the production and motion of the point defects and the interactions between defects and other defects, impurities, and dislocations. Such detailed information can at present be derived only from precise experiments, and is scanty or entirely lacking for many materials.

All experimental methods involve study of direct or indirect diffusion-limited processes as a function of temperature and pressure. The interpretation of experimental results is conditioned to a great extent by the basic reaction-rate model used to represent the diffusion process.

Experimentally, the temperature dependence of the diffusivity D, in single-phase systems, is invariably found to obey a simple Arrhenius relation,

$$D = D_0 \exp \frac{-Q}{RT} \tag{3-1}$$

in which the "frequency factor" D_0 and "activation energy" Q are temperature-independent; R is the gas constant, and T the absolute temperature. The most successful theoretical models, from the viewpoint of their consistency with Eq. (3-1), have been based on the well-known theory of absolute reaction rates.[1] The elementary diffusive jump is considered in terms of transitions, in thermal equilibrium, between a "ground-state" representative of atoms at equilibrium lattice sites and an "excited-state" characteristic of atoms in a high-energy configuration between adjacent lattice sites. The probability per unit time that a diffusional jump will occur, Γ_m, is then given by

$$\Gamma_m = \frac{nkT}{h} \exp \frac{-(G_2^* - G_1)}{kT} \tag{3-2}$$

where the exponential term is defined as the ratio of the partition functions of the excited and ground states, excluding the degree of freedom associated with the direction of motion through the barrier in the excited

[1] See F. Seitz, p. 77 in R. Smoluchowski (ed.), "Phase Transformation in Solids," John Wiley & Sons, Inc., New York, 1951.

state; n is the number of independent ways in which the system may go from the ground to the excited state, and h is Planck's constant.

Zener[2] has shown that, under conditions in which the vibrations of the atom are restricted to a plane normal to the jump direction and the diffusional jump occurs in equilibrium, the barrier to motion is simply the isothermal isobaric work required to move the atom between adjacent sites. Under these conditions, the diffusivity is given, in a form analogous to Eq. (3-1), by

$$D = \gamma a^2 \bar{\nu} \exp \frac{\Delta S}{R} \exp \frac{-\Delta H}{RT} \tag{3-3}$$

where γ = numerical constant of order unity depending on geometry of lattice
a = lattice parameter
$\bar{\nu}$ = vibration frequency usually taken equal to Debye frequency (without much justification)
ΔS, ΔH = entropy, enthalpy changes associated with jump

If the jump process requires the presence of a thermally produced defect, as in the vacancy and interstitial mechanisms, ΔS and ΔH contain terms related to the creation as well as the motion of the defect:

$$\begin{aligned} \Delta S &= \Delta S_f + \Delta S_m \\ \Delta H &= \Delta H_f + \Delta H_m \end{aligned} \tag{3-4}$$

From comparison of Eqs. (3-3) and (3-1), it is evident that, according to this model, the frequency factor and activation energy may be defined by

$$\begin{aligned} D_0 &= \gamma a^2 \bar{\nu} \exp \frac{\Delta S}{R} \\ Q &= \Delta H \end{aligned} \tag{3-5}$$

Vineyard[3] has considered the many-body aspects of the diffusional problem and has shown that a solution similar to Eq. (3-3) can be derived on rather less restrictive assumptions. In addition, the frequency term $\bar{\nu}$ can be explicitly defined in terms of the normal modes of the ground and excited states.

A priori calculations of the important terms in Eq. (3-3), particularly ΔS and ΔH, have invariably proven extremely difficult. In no case are theoretical values sufficiently precise to permit detailed comparison with experiment. Instead, Eq. (3-3) has proven most useful in establishing

[2] C. Zener, Theory of D_0 for Atomic Diffusion in Metals, p. 289 in W. Shockley (ed.), "Imperfections in Nearly Perfect Crystals," John Wiley & Sons, Inc., New York, 1952.

[3] G. A. Vineyard, Frequency Factors and Isotope Effects in Solid State Rate Processes, *J. Phys. Chem. Solids*, vol. 3, p. 121, 1957.

direct relationships between values of D_0 and Q measured for different systems.

Objections raised to the reaction-rate model have been based on several considerations:

1. Quantum effects are ignored.
2. The diffusional jump is considered as basically reversible; irreversibility enters, if at all, purely a posteriori.
3. It is implicitly assumed that the diffusional jump takes place in a time long compared with the thermal-relaxation time of an extensive portion of the lattice, so that it is meaningful to ascribe thermodynamic properties to the excited state. This assumption has not been tested by direct experiment.
4. The use of an ensemble average in the statistical-mechanical treatment tends to obscure the physical aspects of the diffusional process.

Attempts to construct a model which takes account of these points have to date proven to be largely unsuccessful. Quantum effects have been treated by a perturbation-theoretic method[4] and, except for hydrogen, appear to result only in slight changes in the pre-exponential term. However, a complete quantum-mechanical treatment has never been attempted. The one serious attempt to consider the process as a priori irreversible[5] has met with poor success and has grossly overestimated the mass dependence of the diffusivity.[6] Two dynamical models have been proposed[7,8] which provide some insight into the details of the diffusion process. However, these involve a number of additional parameters which are, if possible, more difficult to calculate than the original entropy and enthalpy terms in Eq. (3-3), and these models are not as yet sufficiently refined to permit detailed comparison with experiment.

Due to the considerable success of the reaction-rate model in analyzing the temperature dependence of the diffusivity, Eq. (3-3) may with some justification be used to correlate the pressure dependence of D, despite the possible validity of the objections noted. Using the familiar thermodynamic relation

$$dG = V\,dP - S\,dT \tag{3-6}$$

one may consider pressure effects in terms of the "activation volume"

[4] E. P. Wigner, On the Quantum Correction for Thermodynamic Equilibrium, *Phys. Rev.*, vol. 40, p. 749, 1932.

[5] I. Prigogine and T. A. Bak, Diffusion and Chemical Reaction in a One Dimensional Condensed System, *J. Chem. Phys.*, vol. 31, p. 1360, 1959.

[6] J. G. Mullen, Isotope Effect in Intermetallic Diffusion, *Phys. Rev.*, vol. 121, p. 1649, 1961.

[7] S. A. Rice, Dynamical Theory of Diffusion in Crystals, *Phys. Rev.*, vol. 112, p. 804, 1958.

[8] R. Kikuchi, Dynamics of Crystalline Diffusion, *Ann. Phys.*, vol. 11, p. 306, 1960.

$\Delta V = (\partial \Delta G/\partial P)_T$. From Eq. (3-3), ΔV is evidently given by

$$\Delta V = RT \left(\frac{\partial \ln D}{\partial P} \right)_T - RT \left(\frac{\partial \ln \gamma a^2 \bar{\nu}}{\partial P} \right)_T \tag{3-7}$$

The first term on the right may be evaluated directly by measurement, at constant temperature, of the variation with pressure of the rate of some established diffusion-limited process. Direct determination of the second term is more difficult, since the pre-exponential term in Eq. (3-3) can seldom be evaluated precisely, but only by measurement of diffusion over a large temperature range, which is frequently impractical in high-pressure measurements because of the long times involved. However, the magnitude of the second term can readily be evaluated from the known pressure dependence of the lattice constant and elastic moduli if the frequency term $\bar{\nu}$ is assumed to be derivable classically. In general, this second term is small and contributes less than 10 percent to ΔV.

If the diffusion-limited process under consideration involves both creation and motion of defects, then, since the free energy ΔG will be a sum of terms $\Delta G_f + \Delta G_m$, the activation volume will be a sum of terms ΔV_f, the change in volume of the crystal on formation of the defect, and ΔV_m, the lattice dilatation attending the elementary diffusion jump.

If further simplifying assumptions are made about the nature of the diffusion process, the activation volume can be interpreted entirely in terms of macroscopic parameters of the solid and the measured enthalpy term in Eq. (3-3). Keyes discusses the general thermodynamic basis for such a treatment in Chap. 4 of this volume.

3-2 Experimental Methods

In principle, all the techniques used to study diffusion at atmospheric pressure may be adapted to high pressures.[9] In this section are discussed the main experimental approaches which have been used to study diffusion and related phenomena with this additional parameter. Chief among these are radioactive-tracer methods, ionic conductivity, anelastic relaxation, quench-resistivity measurements, magnetic relaxation, nuclear magnetic resonance, and plastic flow under uniaxial stress (creep).

The essential requirements common to all these methods are a high-pressure system and adequate temperature control within its working volume. Particularly for the conventional type of diffusion measurement involving the use of radioactive tracers to follow the diffusive penetration, long-time stability of both pressure and temperature is essential. Ultrahigh pressures are generally not necessary, since large effects are usually encountered within the range 1 to 10,000 bars for solid-

[9] For a review of techniques used for ordinary diffusion studies, see C. T. Tomizuka, "Methods in Experimental Physics," vol. 5, Academic Press, Inc., New York, 1960.

state diffusion. Purely hydrostatic pressures are required, as a rule, to avoid introduction of excess defects by plastic deformation.

3-2a High-pressure generating apparatus. Two essentially different methods have been used for generating high pressures: the Bridgman method and the Hall "belt" or "tetrahedral-anvil" method (see Chap. 15 for references). In the former a hydraulic fluid (liquid or gas) is confined to a vessel that contains the diffusion specimen, and pressure is generated by the displacement of a piston. The vessel is usually made of hardened heat-treated steel, although for NMR and magnetic-relaxation methods a nonmagnetic material such as beryllium-copper alloy must be used. Commonly the working cylinder is about 6 in. in diameter by 8 in. in length and has a useful interior volume of about 50 cm^3. It is connected to the intensifier system or generating cylinder by means of capillary tubing or connecting pipe with the aid of Bridgman ring seals. The pressure fluid (pentane, hexane, Dow-Corning 200 silicone fluid, argon, helium, or nitrogen) is injected into the generating cylinder through high-pressure steel capillary tubing from a priming reservoir by means of an oil hydraulic pump. A piston with O-ring or Bridgman copper and neoprene washer seals intensifies the pressure in the generating cylinder through the force applied by a hydraulic ram. Pressures are usually measured by means of a coil of manganin wire in the high-pressure fluid; its resistance is measured with a Wheatstone bridge, and a continuous record of pressure may be obtained by feeding the unbalance current of the bridge through a standard resistance into a strip-recording potentiometer. Calibration of the manganin gauge is accomplished at the freezing pressure (7,640 kg/cm^2) of mercury at 0.00°C. Since control of the pressure to within 1 percent over long periods of time (up to 10 days) is sometimes required in tracer-diffusion measurements, it is necessary to provide for intermittent pumping to offset minor leaks in the system. This can be conveniently done by using a simple microswitch and relay in the recording-potentiometer circuit to operate a motor-driven hydraulic pump. An apparatus of the type described, using silicone fluid (3 centistokes viscosity), can be used for temperatures up to about 400°C over a range of pressures to 10 kilobars. Higher temperatures are not feasible because of decomposition of the pressure fluid. Either external heating of the vessel with an oil or salt bath or internal heating is feasible. For temperatures above 400°C a furnace must be provided within the vessel, and a gas must be used as the pressure fluid. Difficulties with temperature control are more serious with internal heating because of convection currents, but may be minimized by filling the vessel cavity with inert space-filling material. In the use of gases, an oil-gas pressure intensifier is used to boost the pressure from 2,000 psi (cylinder pressure) to about 30,000 psi prior to the final stage of compression by the Bridgman generating cylinder. Here it is important to prevent traces of oil used in the intensifier from contaminating the gas.

The Hall apparatus uses a fundamentally different method of generating and transmitting hydrostatic pressure to the test specimen. Tungsten carbide anvils, driven by hydraulic rams, confine a pyrophyllite cylinder or tetrahedron that serves as the specimen-confining and pressure-transmitting medium. The actual sample container is a tube of metal which runs through the pyrophyllite and serves simultaneously as the internal furnace. Electrical contacts are made to the sample tube through metal angle tabs across opposite edges of the insulating pyrophyllite, and the heating current is supplied through the contacting carbide anvils. A platinum–10 percent rhodium or chromel-alumel thermocouple is spot-welded to the sample tube and its leads are brought out through the pyrophyllite that is extruded along the edges of the carbide anvils. The specimen tube may be filled with a silicone fluid to ensure quasi-hydrostatic pressure if the temperature is not above 540°C. Pressure calibration is carried out by noting the change in electrical resistance as a function of press load for such phase transitions as Bi I–liquid or Bi I–Bi II at known temperatures. Temperature calibration of thermocouples is accomplished by measurement of the melting point of such standard substances as lead as a function of pressure.

3-2b Tracer-diffusion methods. The measurement of diffusion coefficients with the aid of radioactive tracers, while often tedious and time-consuming, is an absolute method against which less direct methods must be checked. Its use at high hydrostatic pressures has much in common with corresponding measurements at atmospheric pressure. In general, however, diffusivities are lower at high pressure, sometimes by more than three orders of magnitude, and special problems are thereby introduced. As with all radioactive-tracer methods applied to diffusion studies, it is important to ensure freedom from activities of foreign contaminating elements which may be present in the source material or which may be produced as daughter elements through radioactive decay. Half-life determinations combined with range-energy measurements with absorber foils may be sufficient to disclose foreign activities, but the surest criterion of isotopic purity is provided by beta- or gamma-ray spectrometers. Often it is possible to absorb undesirable low-energy radiation with absorber foils or to discriminate against their detection with a pulse-height analyzer in the proportional counting range. When such methods fail, some scheme of chemical separation of the contaminant is necessary, either prior to or subsequent to the diffusion anneal. To this end, separations based upon controlled electrodeposition, solvent extraction, or carrier precipitation are often used.

It is also important in high-pressure diffusion studies that the pressure fluid itself not introduce any impurities into the diffusion specimen, since extremely small amounts of dissolved impurity may cause large changes in diffusion rates. Pressure fluids, liquid or gas, should be chemically stable at the pressures and temperatures employed and must be of high purity, particularly with respect to oxygen.

The method of applying the radioactive tracer presents no difficulties. Ordinarily one of two diffusion geometries is employed: (1) the doubly infinite cylinder or (2) the semi-infinite cylinder. In the former, which is applicable to readily deformable substances such as soft metals and molecular crystals, a cylinder of the material containing a homogeneous distribution of the tracer element is pressure welded across its basal surface to a similar cylinder which lacks the tracer. The distribution of tracer throughout the double cylinder is given by the complementary error function

$$\frac{C}{C_0} = 1 - \frac{2}{\pi^{1/2}} \int_0^{(x_0 - x)/2(Dt)^{1/2}} \exp(-y^2)\, dy \tag{3-8}$$

where C_0 is the tracer concentration at the weld interface, and C is the concentration at a distance $x_0 - x$ from the interface. Determination of the diffusion coefficient involves sectioning the cylinder after the diffusion anneal, measuring the tracer activity in each section by counting methods, and evaluating the limit of the integral from tables of the error-function integral. This method recommends itself to substances which (like the alkali metals or phosphorus) are so chemically reactive that the deposition and preservation of a thin film of tracer is virtually impossible.[10,11]

Far more convenient to employ experimentally, and simpler in the evaluation of its results, is the semi-infinite-cylinder geometry for diffusion specimens. The tracer may be vapor-deposited on the basal surface of the diffusion cylinder or, alternatively, electrodeposited. The distribution of tracer after the diffusion anneal follows the exponential function

$$\frac{C}{C_s} = \frac{1}{(\pi Dt)^{1/2}} \exp \frac{-x^2}{4Dt} \tag{3-9}$$

where C_s is the initial surface concentration of the tracer and C is the tracer concentration at a depth x at time t. The diffusion coefficient is readily evaluated from plots of $\ln C$ versus x^2, whose slopes are $-1/4Dt$.

(a) Sectioning Methods. Inasmuch as the rates of atom movement are diminished by hydrostatic pressure, the sectioning of a diffusion specimen for construction of the penetration profile demands more care than at

[10] N. H. Nachtrieb, J. A. Weil, E. Catalano, and A. W. Lawson, Self-diffusion in Sodium. II. The Effect of Pressure, *J. Chem. Phys.*, vol. 20, p. 1189, 1952.

[11] N. H. Nachtrieb and A. W. Lawson, Effect of Pressure on Self-diffusion in White Phosphorus, *J. Chem. Phys.*, vol. 23, p. 1193, 1955.

ambient pressure. As may be seen from Eq. (3-9), the mean penetration distance varies as $(Dt)^{1/2}$. Since it is generally not feasible to increase the diffusion time beyond a few days, it becomes important to section with higher precision and on a smaller scale than in ordinary zero-pressure diffusion studies. Four sectioning methods have been used that lend themselves to diffusion measurement: precision lathe turning, microtoming, precision grinding (lapping), and anodic electrochemical dissolution. Regardless of which of these methods is used, it is preferable to determine the activity in the section removed rather than to resort to autoradiography or surface counting.

The lathe technique has been developed to a high degree of precision by use of a special chuck to permit orientation of the diffusion-specimen cylinder face parallel to the lathe axis.[9] A sensitive dial indicator facilitates the alignment of the specimen, and a microbalance is used for determining the section thickness (usually from 0.0010 to 0.0050 cm).

The sledge-base microtome has been used for sectioning soft metals such as lead and tin down to thicknesses of 0.0002 cm. As in the preceding method, alignment of the specimen such that sections are taken parallel to the reference surface is most important. This is readily accomplished to an angular precision of better than 1′ of arc (about 2 microns/cm) by use of an optical method. There appears to be no difficulty in adapting the microtome to the sectioning of metals as hard as silver and copper. Thicknesses of sections are best determined by calculation from their weights and the density.

For hard or brittle substances which are not conveniently sectioned by either of these methods, the principle of precision lapping or grinding is well suited. Several precision-grinding instruments have been described[12,13] which are especially useful for the removal of thin layers from germanium and other brittle substances. The abrasive action is achieved by automatic motion of the specimen on a rotating flat plate on which abrasive papers are mounted. Substitution of optically flat quartz or aluminum oxide plates bearing a film of an abrasive compound in a lubricating vehicle makes possible the removal of submicron-thick layers of material from the diffusion specimen. Techniques using such instruments are useful in preparing suitably flat (less than one-half wavelength) surfaces on diffusion specimens prior to tracer deposition and facilitate radiochemical analysis of the diffused sample. Either the residual activity of the crystal may be measured as lapping progresses or, preferably, the thin layer of removed material may be counted with end window counters.

[12] H. Letaw, Jr., L. M. Slifkin, and W. M. Portnoy, A Precision Grinding Machine for Diffusion Studies, *Rev. Sci. Instr.*, vol. 25, p. 865, 1954.

[13] B. Goldstein, Precision Lapping Device, *Rev. Sci. Instr.*, vol. 28, p. 289, 1957.

For the sectioning of metals such as lead and many of the less noble metals, electrolytic-dissolution procedures are sometimes convenient. In their study of the effect of very high pressures on self-diffusion in lead using the "belt" apparatus, for example, Hudson and Hoffman[14] developed a technique in which 2-micron-thick layers of lead were removed from cylindrical diffusion specimens. The anodic specimens were rotated in an electrolytic cell, and the activity was recovered from the electrolyte. Attention must be given to the elimination of strain from the crystals to ensure uniform layer removal. Either specimen weight loss or (for anodic processes whose current efficiency is 100 percent) measurement of the total electric charge passed through the cell may be used to calculate section thicknesses.

3-2c Measurement of ionic conductivity at high pressure. A powerful method for investigating the mechanism of atom movements in solids is available when the electrical conductance is purely ionic in origin. In crystalline salts such as the alkali halides, silver bromide, and the lead halides, the transport of charge arises entirely from the migration of cations or anions in an electric field. In such substances both diffusion and conductance involve the jumping of the same ionic species, and the two phenomena are related through the Nernst-Einstein relation

$$D_i = \frac{\mu_i kT}{z_i e} \tag{3-10}$$

where D_i, μ_i, and $z_i e$ are the diffusion coefficient, electrical mobility, and charge for the ith ionic species, respectively. A great advantage of the conductance method over tracer-diffusion methods is that sample sectioning is not involved. In principle, the measurement is made in an instant of time and may be repeated indefinitely. The requirements of long-time pressure and temperature stability are therefore much less demanding than in tracer-diffusion procedures. A drawback of the conductance method is that it measures the total conductance due to all mobile ionic species and does not take account of the motion of electrically neutral complexes. In common with diffusion measurements, it permits the study of pure as well as "doped" salts by growing crystals with small but definite concentrations of another salt whose cation or anion is of different valence. For example, cadmium bromide in solid solution in silver bromide introduces a vacancy in the cation sublattice for each added Cd^{++}. In the range of dilute solutions the law of mass action is assumed to govern the concentration of cation vacancies and cation interstitials at each temperature: $X_v X_i = K$, where X_v and X_i represent the vacancy and interstitial concentrations and K is the equilib-

[14] J. B. Hudson and R. E. Hoffman, The Effect of Hydrostatic Pressure on Self-diffusion in Lead, *Trans. AIME*, vol. 221, p. 761, 1961.

rium constant. It is thus possible to distinguish between lattice vacancies and interstitial ions as the dominant mobile species from the increase or decrease in electrical conductance caused by doping.

Kurnick[15] studied the effect of hydrostatic pressure on the electrical conductance of pure silver bromide and silver bromide doped with cadmium bromide. His measurements were made at pressures up to 8 kilobars in the Bridgman-type apparatus previously described at temperatures of 202, 251, and 289°C. In such measurements 1,000-cycle alternating current is used to avoid electrode-polarization effects, and the specimen conductance is determined with an impedance bridge. The experiment is carried out by measuring the ratio of the conductance of pure and doped AgBr at each temperature and pressure for cadmium concentrations ranging from 0.005 to 0.10 atomic percent. This is accomplished by mounting the two cylindrical crystals between silver electrodes, with a third silver-electrode spacer between them. Electrical leads from the electrodes, as well as thermocouple leads, are taken through pipestone insulating cones in the plug of the working vessel; the latter serves as well as the support for the jig-mounted crystals. Either the pure or the doped crystal may be placed in the bridge circuit by a switch whose common terminal is connected to the center silver electrode. The data obtained consist of conductivity isobars and isotherms as a function of cadmium-ion concentration. Their analysis yields the activation energy for both Frenkel and Schottky defects, together with the mobility energy for silver vacancies and interstitial silver ions. In addition, the corresponding activation and mobility volumes are deduced (see Table 3-1) for the particles involved in both types of lattice disorder. Pierce[16] has carried out similar studies for impure alkali halides up to temperatures of 500°C.

A major difficulty with ionic-conductivity measurements arises from the finite parallel electrical resistance of the electrical leads to the high-pressure system. For pipestone-insulated leads, the parallel resistance is frequently within an order of magnitude of that of the specimen crystal. Proper account of these effects can be made by use of a sufficient number of leads to permit separate determination of the parallel lead resistance at each temperature and pressure.

3-2d Anelastic-relaxation methods. The phenomenon of anelastic relaxation, or internal friction, permits study of diffusion at very low temperatures in a number of substitutional and interstitial metal systems, since the relaxation times involved are those characteristic of a single

[15] S. W. Kurnick, The Effects of Hydrostatic Pressure on the Ionic Conductivity of AgBr, *J. Chem. Phys.*, vol. 20, p. 218, 1952.

[16] C. B. Pierce, Effect of Pressure on the Ionic Conductivity in Doped Single Crystals of Sodium Chloride, Potassium Chloride, and Rubidium Chloride, *Phys. Rev.*, vol. 123, p. 744, 1961.

atomic jump time. Such techniques are therefore well suited to high-pressure studies, in which the attainment of high temperatures poses considerable difficulties. However, the torsional-pendulum technique used by Wert and Zener[17] does not lend itself to high-pressure systems. A suitable modification has been devised by Tichelaar and Lazarus.[18] The basis of the method is to measure the time-dependent relaxation of the stress required to maintain a coiled helix of the specimen at a constant strain. One end of the specimen, formed into 20-mil wire and wound as a helical spring, is attached to the bottom of the vessel cavity. Its upper end is attached to a soft iron armature, which is drawn upward into a solenoid until it contacts a stop. The extension of the helix when the armature contacts the stop determines the constant strain of the specimen. The stress needed to maintain this strain is determined from the solenoid current, which is just sufficient to draw the armature to the contact stop. Distortion from cubic symmetry caused by the stress is relieved by a redistribution in the short-range order. The stress diminishes exponentially with time according to

$$\sigma = \sigma_\infty \left(1 + \delta \exp \frac{-t}{T_R}\right) \tag{3-11}$$

A characteristic time for the relaxation process is obtained by locating the maximum in the function $t\sigma$ against t. The characteristic time T_m is found to be a unique property of the system for a given temperature and pressure. Its temperature dependence yields the activation energy for the diffusional relaxation of atoms in the stress field,

$$T_m = T_0 \exp \frac{-\Delta H}{RT} \tag{3-12}$$

and the value of ΔH agrees well with Nowick's[19] result by the internal-friction torsional-pendulum method, and with standard tracer sectioning results.[20]

This method is adaptable to all systems which show a typical Zener relaxation and has been used for studies of α-silver-zinc[18] and for interstitial vanadium alloys.[21]

[17] C. A. Wert and C. Zener, Interstitial Atomic Diffusion Coefficients, *Phys. Rev.*, vol. 76, p. 1169, 1949.

[18] G. W. Tichelaar and D. Lazarus, Effect of Pressure on Anelastic Relaxation in Silver-Zinc, *Phys. Rev.*, vol. 113, p. 438, 1959.

[19] A. S. Nowick, Anelastic Measurements of Atomic Mobility in Substitutional Solid Solutions, *Phys. Rev.*, vol. 88, p. 925, 1952.

[20] D. Lazarus and C. T. Tomizuka, Self Diffusion in Silver-Zinc, *Phys. Rev.*, vol. 103, p. 1182, 1956.

[21] G. W. Tichelaar, R. V. Coleman, and D. Lazarus, Effect of Pressure on the Mobility of Interstitial Oxygen and Nitrogen in Vanadium, *Phys. Rev.*, vol. 121, p. 748, 1961.

3-2e Quench-resistivity measurements. Koehler[22] and his colleagues introduced methods by which the energy of formation and the energy of motion of vacancies may be separately measured. High-purity wires are heated to various temperatures and rapidly quenched to trap vacancies at concentrations characteristic of the high temperature. Resistivity measurements made at low temperatures on wires quenched from a series of high temperatures lead to the energy of vacancy formation. Study of the isothermal decay of the excess resistivity at various intermediate temperatures leads to the energy of vacancy motion. Ideally, the annihilation of vacancies present at concentrations in excess of equilibrium values occurs by their migration to randomly distributed sinks and should be a first-order kinetic process, but higher-order kinetics are frequently observed.

In principle, the techniques are adaptable to high pressures and to the direct determination of the volume of formation and the volume of motion of vacancies separately. The techniques are difficult, but enough has been accomplished to indicate that they provide a unique tool which deserves extensive study and development. Tomizuka[23] has attempted the quenching of platinum wires, heated in situ in a gas high-pressure system and has shown the general feasibility of the method for obtaining the volume of vacancy formation. One of the chief difficulties is to obtain a sufficiently rapid quench rate to ensure trapping all the vacancies. The thermal conductivity of the dense gas atmosphere is apparently high enough to accomplish this if the initial temperature is high and the wire diameter is small.

More progress has been made in determining the mobility volume of vacancies. Emrick[24] has succeeded in measuring ΔV_m for gold from studies of the excess resistivity decay at 70 to 80°C at pressures up to 10 kilobars. For such measurements, gold wires (0.016 in. in diameter) are quenched at atmospheric pressure from about 700°C. There is no necessity to ensure that all excess vacancies be retained, since it is sufficient merely to determine the rate constant for the process as a function of pressure at constant temperature. In measurements of this type a ratio method is employed, with a standard well-annealed gold wire for reference. Measurements are made in liquid hydraulic fluid with the high-pressure vessel externally thermostated to ± 0.02°C in an oil bath.

[22] J. W. Kauffman and J. S. Koehler, The Quenching-in of Lattice Vacancies in Pure Gold, *Phys. Rev.*, vol. 88, p. 149, 1952; J. E. Bauerle and J. S. Koehler, Quenched-in Lattice Defects in Gold, *Phys. Rev.*, vol. 107, p. 1493, 1957.

[23] C. T. Tomizuka, Feasibility of Quenching Lattice Defects in Noble Metals under Hydrostatic Pressure, *Bull. Am. Phys. Soc. II*, vol. 4, p. 181, 1960.

[24] R. M. Emrick, Pressure Effect on Vacancy Migration Rate in Gold, *Phys. Rev.*, vol. 122, p. 1720, 1961.

The quenched and reference specimens are mounted on the bottom plug of the working vessel. Unlike the atmospheric-pressure measurements of Koehler et al., in which the resistance ratio is measured at very low temperatures to minimize thermal contributions to the resistivity, the high-pressure electrical-resistivity measurements must be made at the annealing temperature because of the large thermal inertia of the high-pressure vessel. This imposes the severest limitation on the experiment and requires extremely close control of differences in temperature of the specimen and reference.

3-2f Relaxation of magnetic permeability. A method which bears a faint resemblance to the mechanical relaxation method earlier described was developed by Bosman, Brommer, and Rathenau[25] to study the rate of movement of nitrogen and carbon atoms in iron. It depends upon the measurement of the rate of decrease of the initial magnetic permeability of iron containing interstitial impurities following its demagnetization in an alternating magnetic field of diminishing intensity. The effect is assumed to arise from a redistribution of the randomly situated interstitial atoms following demagnetization. In their redistribution to stabler interstitial sites, the atoms pin the magnetic domain walls, whose mobility therefore decreases with time. The permeability measurements, made with a very small measuring field of 5×10^{-4} oersted, detect the resistance to motion of the domain walls.

The specimen, situated in a gas pressure vessel at 3 kilobars, consisted of a torus of 36 stacked iron rings, each 0.1 mm thick and with outer and inner diameters of 1.8 cm and 0.8 cm, respectively. Demagnetization was carried out by repeated application of a 50-cycle alternating-current field of decreasing amplitude immediately prior to the permeability measurements, alternately at 1 bar and 3 kilobars, with the feeble measuring field. Several relaxation times were observed, the principal ones being characteristic of the motion of interstitial atoms in iron. Pressure up to 3 kilobars was found to alter the relaxation time only very slightly and to lead to extremely small activation volumes for the motion of the interstitial atoms.

3-2g Nuclear-magnetic-resonance method. The temperature-dependent narrowing of the nuclear-magnetic-resonance line width has yielded results for the activation energy for self-diffusion which are in generally good agreement with those from tracer-diffusion methods.[26]

[25] A. J. Bosman, P. E. Brommer, and G. W. Rathenau, The Influence of Pressure on the Mean Time of Stay of Interstitial Nitrogen in Iron, *Physica*, vol. 23, p. 1001, 1957.

[26] D. F. Holcomb and R. E. Norberg, Nuclear Spin Relaxation in Alkali Metals, *Phys. Rev.*, vol. 98, p. 1074, 1955.

Either the spin-lattice relaxation time T_1 or the spin-spin phase memory relaxation time T_2' may be employed to measure the frequency of diffusive jumps. The method is limited to nuclear spin systems which are free from complicating nuclear quadrupole interactions and has been useful to study self-diffusion in the alkali metals. The technique requires the use of the sample metal in the form of colloidally dispersed particles in order that sufficient sensitivity be obtained, a consequence of the small penetration depth of high-frequency fields. This is conveniently done by preparing emulsions of the metal in a paraffinic dispersing medium.

Adaptation of nuclear-magnetic-resonance methods to high-pressure self-diffusion measurements has been made by Barnes, Engardt, and Hultsch.[27] Using the spin-echo technique, they found log T_2' for lithium metal to be proportional to pressure to 7 kilobars. The resonance line width ν is proportional to $T_2'^{-1}$, and the total activation volume is given by

$$\Delta V_{\text{act}} = -RT\left(\frac{\partial \ln T_2'}{\partial P} - \frac{\partial \ln \nu_0}{\partial P} - 6\frac{\partial \ln a}{\partial P}\right) \qquad (3\text{-}13)$$

where ν_0 is a characteristic lattice frequency and a is the lattice parameter. The principal contribution to ΔV_{act} comes from the first term.

3-2h Creep measurements at high pressure. The plastic flow of metals under uniaxial stress is a thermally activated process whose rate-determining step appears to be governed by the diffusive jumps of atoms. Ordinarily the phenomenon is studied at atmospheric pressure by noting the rate of elongation of metal wire or rods under various loads as a function of temperature. Activation energies for the process appear to be comparable with, and sometimes a little greater than, activation energies for self-diffusion.[28]

Butcher and Ruoff[29] have adapted a high-pressure technique to the study of creep in pure lead by use of a specimen-holding jig and slide-wire potentiometer to measure the rate of elongation of the specimen within a high-pressure cylinder. Their specimen was a 1-mm-diameter polycrystalline lead wire, whose lower end was attached to a dead-load mass that made contact with a vertical potentiometer slide-wire. The voltage drop across the two halves of the slide-wire was measured as a function of time at various pressures to follow the elongation rate. A sensitivity of at least 5×10^{-5} in. in elongation was achieved, and the measurements

[27] R. G. Barnes, R. D. Engardt, and R. A. Hultsch, Nuclear Magnetic Resonance Determination of Activation Volume for Diffusion in Lithium, *Phys. Rev. Letters*, vol. 2, p. 202, 1959.

[28] J. Weertman, Creep of Indium, Lead, and Some of Their Alloys with Various Metals, *Trans. AIME*, vol. 218, p. 207, 1960.

[29] B. M. Butcher and A. L. Ruoff, Pressure and Temperature Dependence of High-temperature Creep in Lead, *Bull. Am. Phys. Soc. II*, vol. 6, p. 243, 1961.

were made in the region of secondary creep, which is linear in time for strains between 3.5 and 16 percent. The activation volume for creep is obtained from the relation

$$\frac{\dot{\varepsilon}_1}{\dot{\varepsilon}_2} = \exp \frac{V_c(P_2 - P_1)}{RT} \tag{3-14}$$

where $\dot{\varepsilon}_1$ and $\dot{\varepsilon}_2$ are creep rates at pressures P_1 and P_2.

3-2i Boundary-marker-shift experiments at high pressure. The diffusion-controlled motion of inert marker wires at the boundaries which define steep concentration gradients in dissimilar metal-diffusion couples (the Kirkendall effect) has proved a useful tool for the study of diffusion mechanisms in alloys. Marker displacements are found to vary with the square root of time and to depend upon the difference in the self-diffusion coefficients of the component species. The existence of a Kirkendall effect is usually taken to indicate the operation of a vacancy mechanism, particularly when, as is often observed, porosity is found to have developed in the metal in the wake of the moving markers. The voids appear to be precipitated lattice vacancies whose concentration at the site of pore formation has exceeded the equilibrium density. There is no a priori reason for excluding other diffusion mechanisms (e.g., interstitial diffusion) when the Kirkendall effect is observed, but the occurrence of voids is strong presumptive evidence for vacancy diffusion.

Boundary-marker shifts should be altered by hydrostatic pressure, and the technique promises to be a valuable adjunct to tracer methods for the study of atom movements in solids in which there are gradients in the chemical potential. Heitkamp[30] observed the motion of marker wires in alloy couples made of 95 percent indium, 5 percent thallium and 75 percent indium, 25 percent thallium (weight percent). Copper and molybdenum wires were embedded in the interfaces of sandwiches made from discs of the alloys, and their displacements were measured with a comparison microscope following diffusion anneals at 1, 3500, and 5400 bars in a pentane high-pressure system. The displacement appeared to vary in inverse proportion to the pressure, decreasing about 9.7 percent per kilobar at 150°C for the alloy pair studied. Indium was found to be the more rapidly diffusing species in the Kirkendall experiment, in agreement with expectations based upon the relative self-diffusion coefficients of indium and thallium in their pure state. No voids were apparent on the specimen surface, but it is interesting to note that the average scatter in the markers' positions was decreased at high pressures (compared with atmospheric pressure).

[30] D. Heitkamp, Die Druckabhängiskeit des Kirkendall-Effektes, *Z. physik. Chem.*, vol. 21, p. 82, 1959.

3-3 Experimental Results

Partly because of the technical difficulties previously noted, and partly because of the very novelty of the field, there is only an extremely small body of experimental data relevant to the effect of hydrostatic pressure on diffusion. All the pertinent data published to date are listed in Table 3-1.

All experiments measure the actual volume change in a finite specimen. As Eshelby[31] has shown, the local relaxation about a center of dilatation or compression will result in a somewhat greater relaxation in the volume of the entire solid because of the image term arising from the free surface. For an isotropic solid, he has shown that the measured volume relaxation is greater than the local relaxation by a factor of $3(1 - \sigma)/(1 + \sigma)$, where σ is Poisson's ratio. For the various materials listed in the table, this factor varies from 1.25 to 1.81. For comparison with atomic models which treat only local relaxations, the effect of the image term has been deleted in the defect volumes given in the last two columns, using the values of Poisson's ratio listed. These values have been derived from single-crystal elastic constants[32] using the averaging methods of Voight[33] to deduce equivalent polycrystalline moduli.

In general, measured values of the activation volume are accurate to about ± 10 percent. In the several measurements in which the measured activation volume must be associated with the sum of volumes for formation and motion of defects (presumably vacancies), it is not possible, a priori, to ascertain the relative fraction of the volume to be associated with ΔV_f and ΔV_m. Thus, in these cases, one can only set upper limits to each of the unrelaxed defect-volume terms, on the assumption that the other term vanishes. In actuality, because of the image correction, the measured activation volume for formation could be negative if there were very large inward relaxation of neighboring atoms about a vacancy. Under such somewhat unlikely circumstances, the values for $V'_{m_{\max}}$ could be slightly larger. Under no circumstances would the atomic jump itself be associated with an inward relaxation; thus the measured activation volume for motion should always be positive. The listed values of $V'_{f_{\max}}$ are therefore probably realistic upper limits for defect volumes.

Within the accuracy of current techniques, there seems to be no definite evidence that the activation volume for diffusion is temperature-dependent. In a few cases, some evidence of a temperature dependence was

[31] J. D. Eshelby, Distortion of a Crystal by Point Imperfections, *J. Appl. Phys.*, vol. 25, p. 255, 1954.

[32] See H. B. Huntington, in F. Seitz and D. Turnbull (eds.), "Advances in Solid State Physics," vol. 7, Academic Press, Inc., New York, 1958.

[33] W. Voight, "Lehrbuch der Krystalphysik," pp. 716–761, B. G. Teubner Verlagsgesellschaft, mbH, Stuttgart, 1928.

noted; however these do not seem to represent any true systematic behavior and are probably simply reflections of uncertainties in the data.

There is some evidence, particularly for sodium and phosphorus, that the activation volume is a function of pressure, decreasing by as much as 20 percent as the pressure varies from 1 bar to 10 kilobars. Because of uncertainties in the pressure dependence of the second term in Eq. (3-7), this effect cannot be established unambiguously. Where such a pressure dependence has been found, the values of activation volume given in Table 3-1 are those which apply at 1 bar.

All the experimental results listed, with the exception of carbon and nitrogen in iron, were obtained with high-pressure systems operating over a range of about 10 kilobars or higher. For the interstitial-iron cases, the pressure range available was only 3 kilobars. This fact is possibly significant in assessing the null result obtained for iron, since all other systems studied show a definite, if small, effect of pressure on the diffusion rate.

3-4 Discussion

3-4a General features. As is evident from Table 3-1, all the solid systems studied, except for iron, show a qualitatively similar dependence of the diffusion rate on pressure. The activation volumes are uniformly positive, corresponding to an exponential decrease in diffusion rate with increasing pressure, and all are of the same order of magnitude as the molar volume of the diffusing constituent. The relative activation volume is not noticeably dependent on the crystal structure or compressibility of the material, being indeed somewhat larger for silver than for the much more compressible sodium. The ionic compounds show systematically larger activation volumes than the metals, except for the motional volume for interstitial silver in AgBr, which is quite small, similar to that for self-diffusion in gold.

It is interesting to compare these results with similar measurements made of the pressure dependence of the diffusion rate in liquids. Very few liquid systems have been studied, but these show strikingly smaller activation volumes than do solids. For liquid mercury, the activation volume for self-diffusion is 0.57 cm^3, only about 4 percent of the atomic volume.[34] Similarly, for liquid gallium, the activation volume of 0.55 cm^3 corresponds to about 5 percent of the atomic volume.[35] This general tendency closely parallels that of the relative temperature dependence of the diffusion rate in liquids and solids. Despite the fact that the

[34] N. H. Nachtrieb and J. Petit, Self-diffusion in Liquid Mercury, *J. Chem. Phys.*, vol. 24, p. 746, 1956.

[35] J. Petit and N. H. Nachtrieb, Self-diffusion in Liquid Gallium, *J. Chem. Phys.*, vol. 24, p. 1027, 1956.

Table 3-1 Activation Volumes for Diffusion

System	Structure	Technique	Quantity measured	$\Delta V_{\text{measured}}$, cm³/mole	"Molar" volume,[o] cm³/mole	Poisson's ratio	Relative "unrelaxed"[p] defect volume	
							$V'_{f_{\max}}$	$V'_{m_{\max}}$
Li[a]	bcc	NMR	$\Delta V_f + \Delta V_m$	3.4	13.1 (vol. Li)	0.245	0.59	0.14
Na[b]	bcc	tracer D	$\Delta V_f + \Delta V_m$	12.4	24 (vol. Na)	0.292	0.71	0.32
P[c]	ortho	tracer D	$\Delta V_f + \Delta V_m$	30	68 (vol. P)	0.33 ?	0.73	0.30
Sn[d]	bct	creep	$(\Delta V_f + \Delta V_m)$?	5	27 (vol. Sn)	0.350	0.44	0.13
Ag[e]	fcc	tracer D	$\Delta V_f + \Delta V_m$	9.2	10.3 (vol. Ag)	0.353	0.94	0.63
Au[f]	fcc	quench R	ΔV_m	1.5	10.2 (vol. Ag)	0.412	....	0.12
Pb[g]	fcc	tracer D	$\Delta V_f + \Delta V_m$	13.0	18.2 (vol. Pb)	0.392	0.79	0.55
Pb[h]	fcc	creep	$(\Delta V_f + \Delta V_m)$?	15.5	18.2 (vol. Pb)	0.392	0.88	0.59
AgZn[i]	fcc	anel. relax.	$\Delta V_f + \Delta V_m$	5.4	10.0 (vol. Ag)	0.353?	0.68	0.38
V-O[j]	bcc	anel. relax.	ΔV_m − int.	1.7	2 ? (vol. O)	0.28 ?	....	0.50
V-N[j]	bcc	anel. relax.	ΔV_m − int.	1.1	2 ? (vol. N)	0.28 ?	....	0.33
Fe-C[k]	bcc	mag. relax.	ΔV_m − int.	0.0	2 ? (vol. C)	0.275	....	0
Fe-N[k]	bcc	mag. relax.	ΔV_m − int.	0.0	2 ? (vol. N)	0.275	....	0
AgBr[l]	NaCl	ion. cond.	ΔV_f − Frenkel	16	9 (vol. Ag)	0.397	1.4	
		ion. cond.	ΔV_f − Schottky	~44	29 (vol. AgBr)	0.397	1.2	
		ion. cond.	ΔV_m − Ag int.	2.7	9 (vol. Ag)	0.397	....	0.24
		ion. cond.	ΔV_m − Ag vac.	7.4	9 (vol. Ag)	0.397	....	0.63
AgBr[m]	NaCl	tracer D	$\Delta V_f + \Delta V_m$ − Br	~44	20 (vol. Br)	0.397	1.7	1.7
NaCl(Ca^{++})[n]	NaCl	ion. cond.	ΔV_m − Na vac.	7.7	5.4 (vol. Na)	0.249	....	0.79
KCl(Sr^{++})[n]	NaCl	ion. cond.	ΔV_m − K vac.	7.0	10.8 (vol. K)	0.250	....	0.36

[a] R. A. Hultsch, R. D. Engardt, and R. G. Barnes, Activation Volume for Self-diffusion in Lithium, *Bull. Am. Phys. Soc. II*, vol. 5, p. 420, 1960.

[b] N. H. Nachtrieb, J. A. Weil, E. Catalano, and A. W. Lawson, Self-diffusion in Sodium. II. The Effect of Pressure, *J. Chem. Phys.*, vol. 20, p. 1189, 1952.

[c] N. H. Nachtrieb and A. W. Lawson, Effect of Pressure on Self-diffusion in White Phosphorus, *J. Chem. Phys.*, vol. 23, p. 1193, 1955.

[d] K. L. DeVries, G. S. Baker, and P. Gibbs, Pressure Dependence of Creep, *Bull. Am. Phys. Soc. II*, vol. 6, p. 164. 1961.

[e] C. T. Tomizuka, R. C. Lowell, and A. W. Lawson, Self Diffusion in Silver under Hydrostatic Pressure up to 8,000 Atm., *Bull. Am. Phys. Soc. II*, vol. 5, p. 181, 1960.

[f] R. M. Emrick, Pressure Effect on Vacancy Migration Rate in Gold, *Phys. Rev.*, vol. 122, p. 1720, 1961.

[g] N. H. Nachtrieb, H. A. Resing, and S. A. Rice, Effect of Pressure on Self-diffusion in Lead, *J. Chem. Phys.*, vol. 31, p. 135, 1959.

[h] B. M. Butcher and A. L. Ruoff, Pressure and Temperature Dependence of High-temperature Creep in Lead, *Bull. Am. Phys. Soc. II*, vol. 6, p. 243, 1961.

[i] G. W. Tichelaar and D. Lazarus, Effect of Pressure on Anelastic Relaxation in Silver-Zinc, *Phys. Rev.*, vol. 113, p. 438, 1959a.

[j] G. W. Tichelaar, R. V. Coleman, and D. Lazarus, Effect of Pressure on the Mobility of Interstitial Oxygen and Nitrogen in Vanadium, *Phys. Rev.*, vol. 121, p. 748, 1961.

[k] A. J. Bosman, P. E. Brommer, and G. W. Rathenau, The Influence of Pressure on the Mean Time of Stay of Interstitial Nitrogen in Iron, *Physica*, vol. 23, p. 1001, 1957; The Influence of Pressure on the Mean Time of Stay of Interstitial Carbon in Iron, *Physica*, vol. 26, p. 533, 1960.

[l] S. W. Kurnick, The Effects of Hydrostatic Pressure on the Ionic Conductivity of AgBr, *J. Chem. Phys.*, vol. 20, p. 219, 1952.

[m] D. S. Tannhauser, Self Diffusion of Bromine in Silver Bromide, *J. Phys. Chem. Solids*, vol. 5, p. 224, 1958.

[n] C. B. Pierce, Effect of Pressure on the Ionic Conductivity in Doped Single Crystals of Sodium Chloride, Potassium Chloride, and Rubidium Chloride, *Phys. Rev.*, vol. 123, p. 744, 1961.

[o] Approximate volume of the diffusing constituent.

[p] For measurements which relate $\Delta V_{\text{measured}}$ to the sum $\Delta V_f + \Delta V_m$, $V'_{f_{\max}}$ is calculated for $\Delta V_m = 0$ and $V'_{m_{\max}}$ is calculated for $\Delta V_f = 0$; all values are corrected to infinite lattice by deletion of "image" terms (see text) and are given in units of corresponding "molar" volume.

diffusivity in the liquid state may be several orders of magnitude larger than that in the solid state at equivalent temperatures, the activation energy for diffusion in the liquid is generally much smaller than that in the solid. Some of the possible implications of this parallelism will be discussed later.

3-4b Atomic models. The activation volume calculated from Eq. (3-7), while it assuredly has the proper units to be described as a volume, can be identified as a physically meaningful volume and be compared with atomic volumes for defects only if the underlying assumptions regarding the basic description of the diffusion process in terms of equilibrium statistical mechanics are correct. As noted earlier, the reaction-rate theory, despite its successes, contains a number of questionable, or at least uncertain, hypotheses. The quantitative comparison of the measured activation volumes tabulated in Table 3-1 with those derived from theoretical atomic models therefore becomes a check not only on the atomic models, but also on the fundamental validity of the reaction-rate description.

Unfortunately, no completely satisfactory atomic models have yet appeared to permit such a detailed comparison. Despite this fact, since the mechanisms for diffusion in most of the tabulated systems have been fairly well established by other experiments, it is possible to make a rough comparison and to assess the relative success of the current atomic models.

(*a*) *Hard-sphere Model.* The simplest description of a solid is that of an assembly of hard spheres with a lattice structure identical with that of the true solid, the diameter of the spheres being equal to the nearest-neighbor distance. The relative atomic volumes of lattice defects can then readily be estimated, with the following results:

1. fcc lattice: For a vacancy mechanism, ΔV_f should be equal to 1 atomic volume, since the vacancy is formed simply by removing an atom from the interior to the surface. No relaxation is possible about the vacancy. The motion volume ΔV_m should be about 0.8 atomic volume. The total activation volume for diffusion should then be about 1.8 atomic volumes. For an interstitial mechanism, ΔV_f should be large, about 3 atomic volumes, while ΔV_m should be small, about .01 atomic volume.

2. bcc lattice: For a vacancy mechanism, if there is no relaxation inward about the vacancy, ΔV_f would be 1 atomic volume and ΔV_m would be zero. If inward relaxation occurs, which is possible in this lattice, ΔV_f would be about 0.3 atomic volume, and ΔV_m about 0.7 atomic volume. In either case, the total activation volume should be about 1 atomic volume. For interstitial diffusion of small impurities, ΔV_m should be of the order of magnitude of the volume of the interstitial.

For lattices which are not cubic, such as that of tin, the activation volumes for formation and motion would be somewhat smaller than those of the corresponding cubic lattice.

Comparison of these estimates with the results listed in Table 3-1 shows, rather surprisingly, that even the simplest model gives results which agree with experiment to well within an order of magnitude. Indeed, agreement is generally satisfactory to within a factor of 2 or 3. The hard-sphere model apparently consistently overestimates the activation volumes, particularly for the metals.

(b) *Central-force Models.* Inevitably, there must be some relaxation of neighboring atoms inward about a vacancy and outward about an interstitial. A number of workers have attempted to calculate these effects for fcc and bcc lattices by minimizing the elastic energy of the resulting distorted crystal. Kanzaki[36] has calculated the relaxation about a vacancy in rare-gas solids, considering the discrete nature of the lattice, by expansion of the displacements in terms of the normal coordinates. He concluded that there was negligible relaxation about vacancies in these fcc lattices. A similar result was obtained by Hall[37] and by Nardelli and Repani,[38] who used an elastic model and a Lennard-Jones 6-12 potential for calculating the relaxation about a vacancy in solid argon. To date, there are no data available for comparison of activation volumes in rare-gas solids.

Girifalco and Weizer[39] have examined the relaxation about vacancies in a number of cubic metals. In their model the interatomic potential was described entirely in terms of a Morse potential with parameters suitably chosen to give correct elastic constants. No electronic interactions were considered. With this model, they found that only small inward relaxations, about 5 percent of an atomic volume, would be expected about vacancies in fcc metals, but that in bcc metals as much as 20 to 30 percent inward relaxation might occur.

Huntington[40] and Seeger and Bross[41] have calculated the relaxation around a vacancy in copper using a Born-Mayer potential to represent

[36] H. Kanzaki, Point Defects in Face-centered Cubic Lattice. I. Distortion around Defects, *J. Phys. Chem. Solids*, vol. 2, p. 24, 1957.

[37] G. L. Hall, Distortion around Point Imperfections in Simple Crystals, *J. Phys. Chem. Solids*, vol. 3, p. 210, 1957.

[38] G. Nardelli and A. Repani, Preliminary Results on the Creation Energy of a Vacancy in Solid Argon, *Physica*, vol. 24, p. S182, 1958.

[39] L. A. Girifalco and V. G. Weizer, Vacancy Relaxation in Cubic Crystals, *J. Phys. Chem. Solids*, vol. 12, p. 260, 1960; Application of the Morse Potential Function to Cubic Metals, *Phys. Rev.*, vol. 114, p. 687, 1959.

[40] H. B. Huntington, Self-consistent Treatment of the Vacancy Mechanism for Metallic Diffusion, *Phys. Rev.*, vol. 61, p. 325, 1942.

[41] A. Seeger and H. Bross, Elektronentheoretische Untersuchungen uber Fehlstellen in Metallen, *Z. Physik*, vol. 145, p. 161, 1956.

the closed-shell repulsion terms. Huntington also considered the repulsive electrostatic forces between the screened vacancy and its nearest neighbors and concluded that these would just balance the Born-Mayer forces, so that negligible relaxation should occur about the vacancy. Seeger and Bross also concluded that there would be negligible relaxation by considering the combined effects of the Born-Mayer term and the change in kinetic energy of the conduction electrons about a relaxed vacancy. Huntington used a similar approach to calculate the relaxation about an interstitial in copper[42] and concluded that the outward relaxation about an interstitial would correspond to a volume change of about three atomic volumes.

Probably the most complete treatment of the lattice distortion about a vacancy and an interstitial in copper is that of Tewordt.[43] He treated the atoms adjacent to the defect as discrete particles with interaction forces given by a Born-Mayer potential. The balance of the crystal was considered as a continuum joined to the outer atoms of the set surrounding the defect by proper elastic solutions. The equilibrium state of the lattice was determined by successive solutions of sets of linear algebraic equations. By this method Tewordt calculated that the inward relaxation about a vacancy in copper would be large, in the range of 45 to 53 percent of an atomic volume, while there would be an outward relaxation about an interstitial of 1.6 to 2 atomic volumes. Moreover, he concluded that changes in electronic energy due to the relaxation about the vacancy and interstitial would *not* negate these effects, since the effective screening charge of the defect would be appreciably altered by the relaxation. This treatment is still highly approximate, partially because of the use of elastic solutions for an isotropic continuum, and, possibly more important, because of the use of the Born approximation to calculate the phase shifts of the electron wave functions about the relaxed vacancy.

There are no adequate calculations of the activation volume for motion of vacancies in metals. Huntington and Seitz[44] estimate that the barrier atoms at the saddle configuration are displaced about 10 percent in the jump process, while Fumi[45] calculates a value only about one-half as large. In either case, ΔV_m should be considerably less than 1 atomic volume, consistent with the one value available for gold.

[42] H. B. Huntington, Elastic Strains Around an Interstitial Atom, *Acta Met.*, vol. 2, p. 554, 1954.

[43] L. Tewordt, Distortion of the Lattice around an Interstitial, a Crowdion, and a Vacancy in Copper, *Phys. Rev.*, vol. 109, p. 61, 1958.

[44] H. B. Huntington and F. Seitz, Mechanism for Self-diffusion in Metallic Copper, *Phys. Rev.*, vol. 61, p. 315, 1942.

[45] F. G. Fumi, Vacancies in Monovalent Metals, *Phil. Mag.*, vol. 46, p. 1007, 1955.

Guccione, Tosi, and Asdente,[46] using a model similar to that of Tosi and Fumi,[47] have calculated the displacements of ions adjacent to a diffusing cation or anion in NaCl and KCl. They considered two contributions to the interaction potential: a repulsive interaction either of the Born-Mayer type or a "soft" r^{-12} potential, and Coulomb interactions between point ions. This treatment shows that in salts, unlike metals, the electrostatic interactions should be dominant, and there should be an *outward* relaxation of neighboring atoms about a vacancy, the volume of formation of the vacancy being about 1.5 atomic volumes. The activation volume for motion can also be estimated,[16] assuming that the diffusion path is along a cube-face diagonal. With this model, ΔV_m is about 0.6 atomic volume.

Comparison of these theoretical predictions with the data in Table 3-1 shows a reasonable agreement between theory and experiment. The close-packed metals show somewhat larger activation volumes than those with more open structures, and the ionic crystals show activation volumes larger than those of the metals. There seems to be strong support for Tewordt's conclusion that there is considerable relaxation inward about vacancies in fcc metals, since the total activation volume is in all cases less than 1 atomic volume. A detailed comparison between theory and experiment is not justified at this time, largely because values of ΔV_f alone are not available for the fcc metals, and only crude theoretical estimates are available for ΔV_m.

3-4c Semiempirical models. Keyes has shown that the activation volume can be interpreted entirely in terms of macroscopic parameters and the activation enthalpy for diffusion, if the barriers to formation and motion of defects are exclusively elastic in nature. As shown in Chap. 4, such a model gives very satisfactory agreement with experiment. However, the success of Keyes's approach should not be used to justify the consideration only of elastic interactions in atomistic models.

Rice and Nachtrieb,[48] noting the parallelism between the effects of pressure on diffusion and on the solid-liquid transition, have proposed a law of corresponding states between diffusion and melting. According to this model, the activation volume for diffusion ΔV_D is related to the

[46] R. Guccione, M. P. Tosi, and M. Asdente, Migration Barriers for Cations and Anions in Alkali Halide Crystals, *J. Phys. Chem. Solids*, vol. 10, p. 162, 1959.

[47] M. P. Tosi and F. G. Fumi, The Interaction between Equilibrium Defects in the Alkali Halides; the ≪Ground State≫ Binding Energy of the Vacancy Pair, *Nuovo cimento*, vol. 7, p. 95, 1958.

[48] S. A. Rice and N. H. Nachtrieb, On the Dynamical Theory of Diffusion in Crystals. II. Pressure Dependence of the Self-diffusion Constant, *J. Chem. Phys.*, vol. 31, p. 139, 1959.

volume change on melting ΔV_M by

$$\Delta V_D = \frac{\Delta H_D}{\Delta H_M} \Delta V_M \tag{3-15}$$

where ΔH_D and ΔH_M are, respectively, the activation enthalpies for diffusion and melting. This relation gives excellent agreement with the measured activation volumes for the metals, particularly for sodium and lead, but rather grossly underestimates the activation volumes for the ionic solids.

3-5 Conclusions

The activation volumes derived from Eq. (3-7) are reasonable and in remarkably good agreement with admittedly inadequate atomic models. This result, particularly when combined with the success of the reaction-rate theory in explaining the mass dependence of the diffusion rate,[6] provides strong evidence for the general validity of the equilibrium statistical-mechanical treatment of the diffusion process.

In this light, the study of pressure effects on rate-limited processes becomes a powerful and unique method for directly determining the volume changes associated with transition states as well as the volumes of defects in the nearly perfect lattice. Further theoretical work on atomic models of defect configurations is sorely needed, and additional experimental results would form a sound basis for evaluation of the theories. Particularly with the present extremely limited body of available data, the following classes of experiments would be expected to be exceptionally useful:

1. High-pressure diffusion measurements using tracers for pure metals and alloys, covalent crystals, van der Waals crystals, and ionic crystals. Experiments could be performed on single-crystal and polycrystalline specimens of both pure and doped materials. Such experiments would form the basis for understanding the equilibrium defect structure in the important classes of solids.

2. Bulk conductivity and junction methods for interstitial diffusion of impurities in semiconductors as a function of pressure.

3. Effects of pressure on Kirkendall shifts accompanying chemical diffusion.

4. Studies of the effect of high pressure on creep and fatigue to correlate these important phenomena with defect motion.

5. Studies of the effect of pressure on ionic conductivity at high and low temperatures in pure and doped specimens, to permit separate determination of ΔV_f and ΔV_m.

6. High-pressure experiments on quenched resistivity and anelastic relaxation of metals to determine ΔV_f and ΔV_m.

7. Studies of the effect of pressure on the annealing of defects in plastically deformed and irradiated solids, to gain insight into the nature of more complicated defect configurations.

8. High-pressure experiments on the formation of color centers, to elucidate the mechanism for their production.

9. High-pressure studies of nuclear magnetic resonance and anelastic relaxation, to permit diffusion studies in systems not amenable to tracer methods and to extend the temperature range of diffusion measurements.

10. Studies of the effect of high pressure on recrystallization and grain growth.

11. Studies of the effect of high pressure on plastic flow in solids.

Fortunately, the successful completion of such important experiments need not wait for a completely adequate theory or for significant advances in high-pressure technology. All the listed experiments involve known techniques which should be adaptable to a high-pressure environment without excessive modification. With proper care, such experiments would all be expected to give results of good precision with apparatus operating in a hydrostatic pressure range to 10 kilobars. Accumulation of a body of precise data, as a result of such studies, should prove an enormous asset in constructing an adequate theory of the defect solid state.

4

Continuum Models of the Effect of Pressure on Activated Processes

ROBERT W. KEYES

IBM Research Laboratory
Yorktown Heights, New York

Many important phenomena in crystals, in particular, diffusion and ionic conductivity, result from the existence of imperfections in the crystal.[1–4] A crystal containing imperfections has a higher energy than a perfect crystal. Therefore, the equilibrium concentration of imperfections is controlled by a Boltzmann factor. For this reason processes which are sensitive to the thermal equilibrium concentration of defects are called activated processes. The description of activated processes in terms of thermodynamic parameters of activation will be given in Sec. 4-1.

[1] J. Frenkel, Thermal Agitation in Solids and Liquids, *Z. Physik*, vol. 35, p. 652, 1926.

[2] C. Wagner and W. Schottky, Theory of Arranged Mixed Phases, *Z. physik. Chem.*, vol. 11, p. 163, 1930.

[3] W. Jost, Diffusion and Electrolytic Conduction in Crystals, *J. Chem. Phys.*, vol. 1, p. 466, 1933.

[4] For a review of the development of modern concepts of atomic defects in crystals, see K. Hauffe, "Reaktionen in und an festen Stoffen," pp. 1–41, Springer-Verlag, Berlin, 1955.

The interpretation of these parameters by the application of thermodynamics to continuum models of lattice imperfections will be described in the succeeding sections.

4-1 Thermodynamics of Activated Processes

The thermodynamic potential which is most useful for describing an imperfect crystal is the Gibbs free energy G. A crystal containing imperfections can be regarded as a system whose state is defined by thermodynamic variables of the usual type (for example, pressure, temperature, and chemical composition) plus a variable N, which represents the number of imperfections in the crystal. Thus G has the form[1–7]

$$G = \sum_i N_i \mu_i + N\mu \tag{4-1}$$

where the N_i and μ_i are, respectively, the numbers and chemical potentials of atoms of type i, and μ is the chemical potential of the imperfection in question.

The concentration of crystal imperfections in most cases involving atomic defects is sufficiently small so that the imperfections can be treated as an ideal dilute solution,[8] and the interactions between them can be neglected. In this case Eq. (4-1) has the form

$$\mu = RT \ln \frac{N}{N_a} + \Delta G^* \tag{4-2}$$

Here the first term represents the entropy of mixing. N_a is the number of sites on which the atomic imperfection might be located, e.g., the number of atomic sites in the crystal in the case of vacancies in a monatomic lattice. The second term of Eq. (4-2) is called the "free energy of activation." It represents the increase in the free energy of the crystal caused by the introduction of an imperfection, not counting the entropy of mixing.

The extension of Eqs. (4-1) and (4-2) to cases in which there is more than one type of imperfection is straightforward. In some such cases the interactions between different types of defects are so strong that they must be taken into account. This can often be accomplished by regard-

[5] N. F. Mott and R. W. Gurney, "Electronic Processes in Ionic Crystals," p. 26, Oxford University Press, New York, 1940.

[6] J. Bardeen, Diffusion in Binary Alloys, *Phys. Rev.*, vol. 76, p. 1403, 1949.

[7] J. Bardeen and C. Herring, Diffusion in Alloys and the Kirkendall Effect, in "Atom Movements," American Society for Metals, Cleveland, 1951.

[8] E. A. Guggenheim, "Thermodynamics," pp. 277–284, Interscience Publishers, Inc., New York, 1957.

ing interacting defects as a separate species of defect which is formed by chemical reaction of individual atomic defects.[9]

The equilibrium concentration of defects in a simple case can be found by applying the condition $\mu = 0$ to Eq. (4-2):

$$N = N_a \exp \frac{-\Delta G^*}{RT} \tag{4-3}$$

This equation provides a link between theory and experiment. Physical models of lattice defects provide means for the calculation of ΔG^* in terms of various microscopic and macroscopic parameters of materials, whose values are known from evidence not related to the existence of the defects. On the other hand, the macroscopic physical properties which are sensitive to the existence of the defects give estimates of N.

The most commonly studied properties of solids which are sensitive to the existence of atomic defects are diffusion and ionic conductivity. These phenomena require not only that defects exist, but also that they move through the solid. The motion of defects is also an activated process, since a defect has positions of minimum energy in the crystal lattice, and work is required to remove the defect from a position of minimum energy to the top of the energy barrier which separates it from another position of minimum energy. In fact, there are important cases (in particular, the diffusion of interstitial solutes) in which the presence of the defect in question is not the result of an activated process, and the only activation energy involved in the transport of the defect is the activation energy of motion. The thermodynamic description of the motion of a lattice defect over a free-energy barrier was originally given by Wert and Zener,[10,11] who showed that the rate at which a defect traverses a barrier is

$$\frac{1}{\tau} = \nu \exp \frac{-\Delta G^*}{RT} \tag{4-4}$$

where ν is the vibration frequency of the defect in the direction which carries it over the barrier and ΔG^* is the free energy required to move the defect from a position of minimum energy to the top of the barrier.

The diffusion constant of an atomic species is given by[11]

$$D = \tfrac{1}{2}\Sigma\Gamma_i(\Delta X_i)^2 \tag{4-5}$$

[9] J. E. Hanlon, Diffusion of Cadmium in Pure and Cadmium-doped AgBr, *J. Chem. Phys.*, vol. 32, p. 1492, 1960.

[10] C. Wert and C. Zener, Interstitial Atomic Diffusion Coefficients, *Phys. Rev.*, vol. 76, p. 1169, 1949.

[11] C. Zener, Theory of D_0 for Atomic Diffusion in Metals, *J. Appl. Phys.*, vol. 22, p. 372, 1951; Theory of Diffusion, p. 289 in W. Shockley (ed.), "Imperfections in Nearly Perfect Crystals," John Wiley & Sons, Inc., New York, 1950.

where i = index of possible jumps which atom can make

Γ_i = rate at which it makes jump i

ΔX_i = change in coordinate X of the atom during jump i

Equation (4-5) refers specifically to cubic crystals, in which the diffusion-constant tensor is isotropic and D is independent of the choice of the direction of the coordinate X. Usually the most probable type of jump dominates the diffusion process, and i enumerates the different orientations of this type of jump. Then all the Γ_i are equal, and the remaining summation over $(\Delta X_i)^2$ in Eq. (4-5) reduces to a geometrical factor times the square of the lattice parameter. The expression for the diffusion constant for the case of an interstitial solute becomes

$$D = fa^2\tau^{-1} \tag{4-6}$$

where f is a dimensionless geometrical factor, a is the lattice parameter, and τ is given by Eq. (4-4). It is seen that ΔG^* can be derived from D by the relation

$$\Delta G^* = -RT \ln \frac{D}{fa^2\nu} \tag{4-7}$$

Equations (4-6) and (4-7) also hold for the diffusion constant of a vacancy. In the case of diffusion of a tracer atom by the vacancy mechanism, it is necessary to include in the jumping probabilities (the Γ_i's) the probability that the site to which the tracer atom jumps is vacant. This introduces a factor N/N_a into Eq. (4-6). However, it can be seen by taking N/N_a from Eq. (4-3) that Eq. (4-7) is still valid, provided that ΔG^* is interpreted as the sum of the ΔG^*'s for the creation of a vacancy and for its jumping probability. Similarly, analysis shows that Eq. (4-7) is valid for the interstitial mechanism of diffusion, for the ring mechanism, and for impurity diffusion when the lattice defect is bound to the impurity.[11,12] Thus Eq. (4-7) provides a useful starting point for the interpretation of diffusion data, even though the atomic mechanism involved in the elementary diffusive jump has not been identified. The error introduced by a lack of knowledge of the atomic mechanism involved consists of an uncertainty in the dimensionless constant f. This uncertainty is not large enough to seriously affect the usefulness of Eq. (4-7), however. In typical cases of self-diffusion a change of f by a factor of 2 will change ΔG^* by only 5 percent.

The use of Eq. (4-7) also requires some estimate of ν, the vibrational frequency of the jumping atom. A good value of ν can be obtained in principle by appropriate normal-mode analyses of the defective crystal.[13,14]

[12] A. D. LeClaire, The Theory of D_0 in the Arrhenius Equation for Self-diffusion in Cubic Metals, *Acta Met.*, vol. 1, p. 438, 1953.

[13] G. Vineyard, Frequency Factors and Isotope Effects in Solid State Rate Processes, *J. Phys. Chem. Solids*, vol. 3, p. 121, 1958.

[14] S. Rice, Dynamical Theory of Diffusion in Crystals, *Phys. Rev.*, vol. 112, p. 804, 1958.

A useful approximate method is to use the Debye frequency for ν if the jumping atom has about the same mass as the atoms of the host lattice, and to represent the potential well and barrier through which the atom moves by a sinusoid in other cases. The value calculated for ΔG^* is insensitive to the value chosen for ν in the same way that it is insensitive to the value of f.

The other thermodynamic functions of activation can be obtained from ΔG^* in the usual way:

$$\Delta S^* = -\left(\frac{\partial \Delta G^*}{\partial T}\right)_P \tag{4-8}$$

$$\Delta V^* = \left(\frac{\partial \Delta G^*}{\partial P}\right)_T \tag{4-9}$$

$$\Delta H^* = \left[\frac{\partial(\Delta G^*/T)}{\partial(1/T)}\right]_P \tag{4-10}$$

Ordinarily the temperature and pressure dependence of a and ν make only a very small contribution to the temperature and pressure dependence of D, and in the computation of ΔG^* it is adequate to regard $fa^2\nu$ as a constant. Then ΔV^* and ΔH^* can be obtained directly from the pressure and temperature dependence of D:

$$\Delta V^* = -RT\left(\frac{\partial \ln D}{\partial P}\right)_T \tag{4-11}$$

$$\Delta H^* = -R\left[\frac{\partial \ln D}{\partial(1/T)}\right]_P \tag{4-12}$$

Therefore, the uncertainty in the values of γ and ν does not affect the derived values of ΔV^* and ΔH^*.

4-2 The Strain-energy Model

The models which have been used to relate the thermodynamic parameters of atomic defects to other properties of the crystal lattice can be divided into two general types: (1) atomic models, in which the energy of the defect is calculated from assumed forms of the interatomic potentials, and (2) continuum models, in which the defect is regarded as a distortion of a continuum having the properties of the macroscopic crystal. The atomic models allow the energy of specific types of defects to be calculated in a direct way from assumed forms of the interatomic potentials; the forms can be derived from macroscopic properties of the crystal. It is quite difficult in practice to carry through this program for calculating the properties of a defect on the atomic model, since the number of interactions which must be taken into account to obtain accurate results is very large.

The continuum models, on the other hand, permit relations between the parameters of defects to be obtained by the application of thermodynamics to the continuum. Their fault, however, is that they provide no a priori means for determining the extent of the distortion of the continuum to be associated with the defect. Thus some measure of the magnitude of the distortion must be obtained either by regarding one of the experimentally determined parameters of the defect as the required measure or by reference to an atomic model. For the purposes of the present work, in which the most significant property of a defect is its activation volume, the continuum models are most useful.

The continuum model which has provided most insight into the thermodynamics of lattice imperfections is the strain-energy model. This model was originally conceived by Zener to account for the decrease in density of heavily cold-worked metals.[15] Subsequently, Wert and Zener used it to explain the entropy factors associated with the atomic processes responsible for diffusion in solids.[10,11] The fact that the strain-energy model also explains the activation volumes derived from studies of the effects of hydrostatic pressure on diffusion in solids was pointed out by the author.[16]

A dynamical formulation of the problem of the motion of a defect in a crystal lattice can also be given.[14] Manley has shown that the dynamical formulation is essentially equivalent to the thermodynamic formulation, and that the thermodynamic parameters can be interpreted in terms of the strain energy as described by Zener.[17]

We shall follow Zener;[18] the strain-energy model will be explained here by considering a system which consists of a cylindrical specimen of an elastically isotropic solid subjected to a torque L applied to the two end faces and immersed in a fluid which is maintained at a pressure P. The energy differential of the solid is

$$dE = -P\,dV + T\,dS + L\,d\phi \tag{4-13}$$

Equation (4-13) can be used to construct the differential of G:

$$dG = d(E + PV - TS) = V\,dP - S\,dT + L\,d\phi$$

Since dG is a perfect differential,

$$\left(\frac{\partial V}{\partial \phi}\right)_{P,T} = \left(\frac{\partial L}{\partial P}\right)_{\phi,T} \tag{4-14}$$

[15] C. Zener, Theory of Lattice Expansion Introduced by Cold Work, *Trans. Am. Inst. Mining Met. Engrs.*, vol. 147, p. 361, 1942.

[16] R. W. Keyes, Volumes of Activation for Diffusion in Solids, *J. Chem. Phys.*, vol. 29, p. 467, 1958; Volumes of Activation II, *J. Chem. Phys.*, vol. 32, p. 1066, 1960.

[17] O. P. Manley, A Method of Evaluating Diffusion Coefficients in Crystals, *J. Phys. Chem. Solids*, vol. 13, p. 244, 1960.

[18] C. Zener, Relation between Residual Strain Energy and Elastic Moduli, *Acta Cryst.*, vol. 2, p. 163, 1949.

and
$$\left(\frac{\partial S}{\partial \phi}\right)_{T,P} = -\left(\frac{\partial L}{\partial T}\right)_{\phi,P} \tag{4-15}$$

Multiplying both sides of Eq. (4-14) by $(1/L)$ and introducing W to denote the work done by the torque in twisting the specimen, it is found that

$$\left(\frac{\partial V}{\partial W}\right)_{P,T} = \left(\frac{\partial \ln L}{\partial P}\right)_{\phi,T}$$

The torque L is related to ϕ in an elastic solid by

$$L = \frac{\pi C R^4}{2} \phi$$

Then Eq. (4-14) becomes

$$\left(\frac{\partial V}{\partial W}\right)_{P,T} = \left(\frac{\partial \ln C}{\partial P}\right)_T - \chi \tag{4-16}$$

where C is the elastic shear modulus and χ is the isothermal compressibility.

Equation (4-16) is a result of macroscopic elastic theory. The use of a strain-energy model of a lattice imperfection means that the work performed in creating the imperfection is elastic work to which macroscopic elastic theory can be applied. Thus the isothermal isobaric work W is identified with ΔG^*, the free energy of the lattice imperfection. The change in volume associated with the performance of this elastic work is identified with the volume of activation ΔV^*. Equation (4-16) thus becomes

$$\frac{\Delta V^*}{\Delta G^*} = \left(\frac{\partial \ln C}{\partial P}\right)_T - \chi \tag{4-17}$$

$$\frac{\Delta V^*}{\Delta G^*} = \left[-\left(\frac{\partial \ln C}{\partial \ln V}\right)_T - 1\right]\chi \tag{4-18}$$

Eq. (4-18) allows a comparison to be made between a property of a lattice imperfection and a parameter determined by mechanical measurements.

The experiment which gives the value of the right-hand side of Eq. (4-18), namely, the measurement of the pressure derivative of the elastic shear moduli, has been carried out for only a few materials. An estimate of the values of the pressure derivatives is furnished by the Grüneisen approximation. If it is assumed that all the vibrational frequencies of the lattice depend on volume in the same way, then it can be shown[19] that

$$\left(\frac{\partial \ln C}{\partial \ln V}\right)_T = -(2\gamma + 1/3) \tag{4-19}$$

[19] J. C. Slater, "Introduction to Chemical Physics," p. 239, McGraw-Hill Book Company, Inc., New York, 1939.

and that

$$\gamma = \frac{\beta}{\chi C_v} \tag{4-20}$$

where γ is called the Grüneisen constant and C_v is the specific heat per unit volume. Substitution of Eq. (4-19) into Eq. (4-18) gives

$$\frac{\Delta V^*}{\Delta G^*} = 2(\gamma - 1/3)\chi \tag{4-21}$$

Equation (4-21) is a useful form for comparison with experiment, since the parameters on the right-hand side of Eq. (4-20) are known for a great many materials. Satisfactory values of C_v in this equation can be obtained from the law of Dulong and Petit. The pressure dependence of the elastic constants of some crystals has also been measured. Table 4-1 is presented as an aid in evaluating the accuracy of the

Table 4-1 A Comparison of Pressure Derivatives of Elastic Shear Moduli with Values Derived from the Grüneisen Approximation and with the Temperature Variation*

Material	Constant†	$-\left(\frac{\partial \ln C}{\partial \ln V}\right)_T$	$2\gamma + 1/3$‡	$-\left(\frac{\partial \ln C}{\partial \ln V}\right)_P$
Copper	C'	4.17	4.25	7.6
	C''	3.31	4.25	8.8
Silver	C'	5.09	4.69	8.8
	C''	4.24	4.69	9.6
Gold	C'	7.08	3.93	7.0
	C''	4.94	3.93	6.8
Aluminum	C'	5.93	4.54	6.4
	C''	5.08	4.51	7.8
Sodium	C'	2.44	2.83	10.3
	C''	2.42	2.83	7.6
KCl	C'	1.38	3.25	7.6
	C''	5.82	3.25	14.5
NaCl	C'	0.52	2.89	1.0
	C''	6.10	2.89	12.3

* The data are derived from many sources. The measurements of the effect of pressure on elastic constants are due to Lazarus (see reference 30) and various workers in the laboratory of C. S. Smith at the Case Institute of Technology.

† $C' \equiv C_{44}$, and $C'' \equiv 1/2(C_{11} - C_{12})$.

‡ γ is determined from Eq. (4-20).

Grüneisen approximation in the present context. In it measured values of $(\partial \ln C/\partial \ln V)_T$ for several cubic crystals are compared with the values predicted by Eqs. (4-20) and (4-21) from the coefficients of thermal expansion and compressibility. It is seen that for the metals the

Grüneisen approximation gives a useful though rough guide to the values of the pressure derivatives; in most cases the predicted value is within 25 percent of the measured. The data for the ionic crystals are much less encouraging. The values of $(\partial \ln C/\partial \ln V)_T$ are quite different for the two shear moduli, and neither is close to $2\gamma + \frac{1}{3}$. The most that can be said about ionic crystals is that the Grüneisen approximation gives

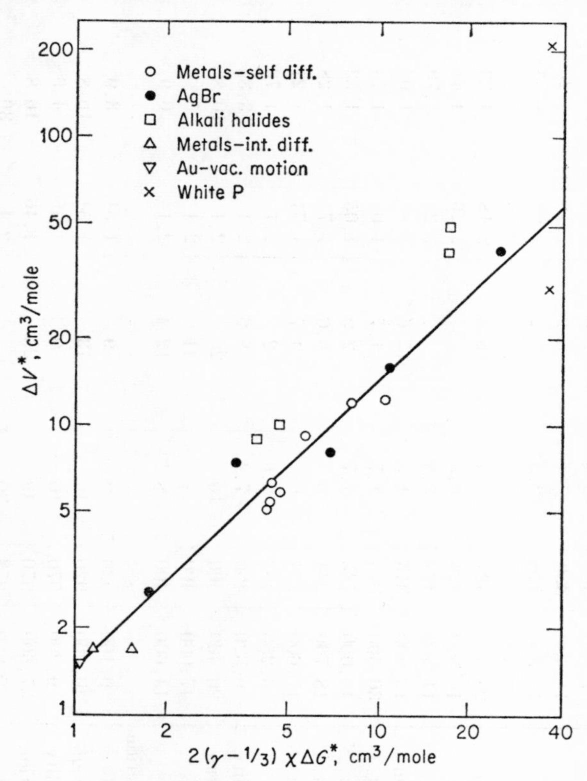

Fig. 4-1 A comparison of measured values of ΔV^* with those calculated from ΔG^* by means of Eqs. (4-20) and (4-21). The data are presented in Table 4-2.

a value for $(\partial \ln C/\partial \ln V)_T$ which is near the average for the two shear moduli, and that no more satisfactory treatment is available. Since most of the data available refer to metals, the treatment of ionic crystals is a relatively minor point.

Fortunately a large body of accurate experimental measurements is available for comparison with Eq. (4-21). A comparison of observed values of ΔV^* with those calculated from Eqs. (4-20) and (4-21) is given in Table 4-2. It is seen that the comparison is satisfactory in the sense that the observed ΔV^* are roughly proportional to $2(\gamma - \frac{1}{3})\chi\, \Delta G^*$.

Table 4-2 Comparison of Measured Activation Volumes with Eq. (4-21)†

Material	Process	ΔG^*, cal/mole	T, °K	ΔV^*, cm³/mole	ΔS^*, cal/mole-degree	γ	ΔV^*(calculated)‡, cm³/mole	$\frac{\Delta V^*}{\Delta V^*(\text{calculated})}$
Sodium	Self-diffusion	7,800	363	12.4	7.3	1.25	10.4	1.2
Lithium	Self-diffusion	11,400	300	5.1	6.2	1.16	4.25	1.2
Lead	Self-diffusion	19,900	526	12.0	8.2	1.99	8.05	1.5
Silver	Self-diffusion	26,600	940	9.2	10	2.18	5.64	1.6
0.7 Ag–0.3 Zn	Internal friction	28,000	424	5.4	9.5	2.18	4.33	1.2
0.8 In–0.2 Tl	Diffusion of In	10,600	424	6.3	.....	2.26	4.41	1.4
0.8 In–0.2 Tl	Diffusion of Tl	11,300	424	5.8	.....	2.26	4.70	1.2
Gold	Vacancy motion	13,900	313	1.5	15.6	1.80	1.02	1.5
Vanadium	Diffusion of int. O	30,500	363	1.7	1.7	1.05	1.14	1.5
Vanadium	Diffusion of int. N	41,000	433	1.7	2.9	1.05	1.53	1.1
Iron	Diffusion of int. C	18,700	234	0	6.0	1.71	1.28	0
Iron	Diffusion of int. N	17,600	234	0	4.7	1.71	1.21	0
AgBr	Int. mobility	3,250	400	2.6	2	2.1	1.73	1.5
AgBr	Vacancy mobility	6,320	400	7.4	8.6	2.1	3.35	2.2
AgBr	Frenkel formation	20,400	400	16	20	2.1	10.8	1.5
AgBr	Br diffusion	47,000	400	41	41	2.1	25	1.6
AgBr	Cd diffusion	14,600	400	8.1	12.4	2.1	6.9	1.2
AgI	Electric conduction	......	...	.....	.....	....	.....	negative
NaCl	Vacancy mobility	9,100	920	9	9	1.51	3.9	2.3
NaCl	Frenkel formation	40,000	920	40	13	1.51	16.8	2.4
KCl	Vacancy mobility	9,200	970	10	9	1.46	4.6	2.2
KCl	Frenkel formation	37,600	970	49	23	1.46	16.8	2.9
White phosphorus	Self-diffusion I	10,000	273	30	.....	2.4	36	0.9
White phosphorus	Self-diffusion II	10,000	313	210	225	2.4	36	5.8

† Data on the pressure dependence of diffusive processes in solids have been reported by many authors. However, most of the work is from three laboratories: that of A. W. Lawson and N. H. Nachtrieb in the Institute for the Study of Metals of the University of Chicago, that of D. Lazarus at the University of Illinois, and that of W. Jost at the University of Göttingen. (See also Chap. 3 of this book.)

‡ Calculated according to Eqs. (4-20) and (4-21).

The observed values are, however, on the average about 1.5 times the calculated ones. The extra factor is unusually large for the alkali halides. The existence of the proportionality is more clearly indicated by Fig. 4-1, in which the observed values of ΔV^* are plotted logarithmically against the calculated values.

The extra factor of 1.5 which appears in the relationship between ΔV^* and ΔG^* is puzzling. Lawson[20] has suggested that this factor may be a result of the temperature dependence of χ. The value of χ at the temperature of the diffusion experiment should be used in Eq. (4-21). However, in the calculations of Table 4-2, values of χ at about 300°K were used, since these are the only ones available for most substances. Most of the data of Table 4-2 are obtained at temperatures above 300°K. Since the compressibilities of solids increase with increasing temperature, the factor introduced by the temperature dependence of χ is in the right direction to explain the discrepancy between Eq. (4-21) and the data. The extra factor is also of about the right magnitude in many cases. There are two cases in Table 4-2 which are obviously in disagreement with the predictions of the model of this section. One of these is the case of interstitial carbon and nitrogen in iron.[21–23] The disagreement is especially difficult to understand in this case because it is just for interstitial carbon in iron that the strain-energy model was most successful in accounting for the entropy of diffusion.[10,11] In addition, the apparently quite similar cases of interstitial nitrogen and oxygen in vanadium are in good agreement with the strain-energy model. The disagreement cannot be attributed to a failure of the Grüneisen theory to give a satisfactory value of the pressure dependence of C. Measurements of the pressure dependence of the shear moduli of polycrystalline iron and steel show that dC/dP is roughly similar to that found for other metals.[24]

Further comment on this question would be untimely here, since we understand that additional experimental work on this question is being carried on by Lazarus and collaborators using a somewhat different method than that employed by Bosman et al.[21–23]

The other exceptional case in Table 4-2 is that of ionic conductivity in

[20] A. W. Lawson, in a private communication.

[21] A. J. Bosman, P. E. Brommer, and G. W. Rathenau, The Influence of Pressure on the Mean Time of Stay of Interstitial Nitrogen in Iron, *Physica*, vol. 23, p. 1001, 1957.

[22] A. J. Bosman, P. E. Brommer, L. C. H. Eijkelenboom, C. J. Schinkel, and G. W. Rathenau, The Influence of Pressure on the Mean Time of Stay of Interstitial Carbon in Iron, *Physica*, vol. 26, p. 533, 1960.

[23] A. J. Bosman, Magnetic After-effect of Interstitials, thesis, University of Amsterdam, Amsterdam, 1960.

[24] F. Birch, The Effect of Pressure on the Modulus of Rigidity of Several Metals and Glasses, *J. Appl. Phys.*, vol. 8, p. 129, 1937; D. S. Hughes and J. L. Kelly, Second-order Elastic Deformation of Solids, *Phys. Rev.*, vol. 92, p. 1145, 1953.

AgI, in which ΔV^* is negative.[25] Any attempt to analyze this situation must be very speculative because of the scarcity of information on the physical properties of AgI. A negative ΔV^* could, of course, be explained by assuming that $(\partial C/\partial V)_T$ is positive. This is not an impossible situation. It may even be a plausible one in view of the fact that AgI at the temperature of the experiment (110°C) is a relatively unstable crystal. It undergoes a phase transition at 145°C and undergoes a different transition at about 4,000 kg/cm².

4-3 Activation Entropy and Activation Volume

The entropy of activation can also be obtained from the strain-energy model. This is accomplished by developing Eq. (4-15) parallel to the development of Eq. (4-14), which resulted in Eq. (4-18). It is found that the analogue of Eq. (4-18) is

$$\frac{\Delta S^*}{\Delta G^*} = -\beta \left[\left(\frac{\partial \ln C}{\partial \ln V} \right)_P + 1 \right] \tag{4-22}$$

and thus that

$$\frac{\Delta V^*}{\Delta S^*} = \frac{\chi}{\beta} \frac{(\partial \ln C/\partial \ln V)_T + 1}{(\partial \ln C/\partial \ln V)_P + 1} \tag{4-23}$$

If it is assumed (as, for example, is the case in the simple Grüneisen model already referred to) that C depends on temperature and pressure only through the volume, then

$$\left(\frac{\partial \ln C}{\partial \ln V} \right)_P = \left(\frac{\partial \ln C}{\partial \ln V} \right)_T$$

Equation (4-23) reduces to

$$\frac{\Delta V^*}{\Delta S^*} = \frac{\chi}{\beta} \tag{4-24a}$$

In fact, writing Eq. (4-24a) in the form

$$\frac{(\partial \Delta G^*/\partial P)_T}{(\partial \Delta G^*/\partial T)_P} = \frac{(\partial V/\partial P)_T}{(\partial V/\partial T)_P} \tag{4-24b}$$

shows that it is just a statement that ΔG^* is a function only of V. It must be a consequence of any model which possesses this property. Conversely, any model for which Eqs. (4-24) are true must have the property that ΔG^* is a function only of V.

The interpretation of the pressure dependence of diffusive processes in terms of the idea expressed by Eqs. (4-24) was apparently originally

[25] K. Wagener, Pressure Dependence of Ionic Conductivity in AgBr and AgI, *Z. physik. Chem.*, vol. 23, p. 305, 1960.

formulated by Jost and collaborators.[26,27] It has also been exploited by Lawson.[28,29] For example, Lawson used ideas based on atomic models of defects to estimate ΔV^* and showed that Eq. (4-24) then gave useful estimates of ΔS^*.[29]

The validity of the approximation that the elastic constants are functions only of volume [Eqs. (4-24)] is checked by column 5 of Table 4-1. Comparison of columns 5 and 3 shows a definite correlation between the two volume derivatives. However, $(\partial \ln C/\partial \ln V)_P$ is generally somewhat larger than $(\partial \ln C/\partial \ln V)_T$ as noted by Lazarus.[30] The difference varies from a negligible amount to a factor of 2. Thus the strain-energy model predicts that values of $\Delta S^*/\Delta V^*$ will be close to, but usually slightly larger than, those predicted by Eqs. (4-24). Lawson found this to be the case.[28] The most extreme example is that of sodium. Table 4-1 shows that the temperature derivatives of the elastic shear moduli of sodium are much larger than is predicted from the volume effect. This fact is correlated with an anomalously large entropy of self-diffusion in sodium, as shown in Table 4-2.

Combining Eqs. (4-21) and (4-24), or simply introducing the Grüneisen approximation into Eq. (4-22), gives

$$\Delta S^* = 2(\gamma - \tfrac{1}{3})\beta\,\Delta G^* \tag{4-25}$$

For metals β is approximately related to the melting temperature by $\beta T_m = 0.06$. Introducing this approximation into Eq. (4-25) and substituting an average value of 2 for $(\gamma - \tfrac{1}{3})$ gives

$$\Delta S^* = 0.24\beta\,\Delta G^* \tag{4-26}$$

Since ΔG^* is approximately the same as ΔH^*, Eq. (4-26) has the same form as the correlation discovered by Dienes[31] and already explained on the basis of the strain-energy model by Zener.[11]

4-4 Other Models

It has been shown in an earlier work that many models of lattice defects lead to results which closely resemble those obtained from the

[26] W. Jost and G. Nehlep, Dependence of the Ionic Conductivity of Solids on Pressure, *Z. physik. Chem.*, vol. 34B, p. 348, 1936.

[27] W. Jost and S. Mennenoh, The Pressure Dependence of the Ionic Conductivity of Silver Halides, *Z. physik. Chem.*, vol. 196, p. 188, 1950.

[28] A. W. Lawson, Correlation of ΔS^* and ΔV^* in Simple Activated Processes in Solids, *J. Phys. Chem. Solids*, vol. 3, p. 250, 1957.

[29] A. W. Lawson, Diffusion of Impurities in Amorphous Polymers, *J. Chem. Phys.*, vol. 32, p. 131, 1960.

[30] D. Lazarus, The Variation of the Adiabatic Elastic Constants of KCl, NaCl, CuZn, Cu, and Al with Pressure to 10,000 Bars, *Phys. Rev.*, vol. 76, p. 545, 1949.

[31] G. J. Dienes, Frequency Factor and Activation Energy for Diffusion in Metals, *J. Appl. Phys.*, vol. 21, p. 1189, 1950.

strain-energy model.[16] One of these which may help account for the agreement obtained between Eqs. (4-21) and (4-24) and the data on ionic crystals is the dielectric-polarization model.[16] In this model the work expended in creating a lattice defect is regarded as polarizing the lattice. Briefly stated, the results corresponding to Eq. (4-21) can be obtained for this case as follows:

The work of creating a defect is performed by moving a charge q with the magnitude of an electronic charge from one location in the crystal to another, leaving a net charge of opposite sign at the original location. The work performed in this process is

$$\Delta G^* = \frac{q^2}{2KZ}$$

where Z is some parameter with the dimensions of length. The activation volume associated with this process is

$$\frac{\Delta V^*}{\Delta G^*} = \left(\frac{\partial \ln \Delta G^*}{\partial P}\right)_T = -\left(\frac{\partial \ln K}{\partial P}\right)_T + \frac{\chi}{3}$$
$$= \chi\left[\left(\frac{\partial \ln K}{\partial \ln V}\right)_T + \tfrac{1}{3}\right]$$

The formal resemblance of this equation to Eq. (4-18) is apparent. Table 4-3 shows that the similarity is almost quantitative.[32] The values of $(\partial \ln K/\partial \ln V)_T$ span about the same range as the values of $(\partial \ln C/\partial \ln V)_T$

Table (4-3) The Effect of Pressure on the Dielectric Constants of Ionic Crystals*

Crystal	$(\partial \ln K/\partial \ln V)_T$	$(\partial \ln K/\partial \ln V)_P$
MgO.........	5.3	
LiF...........	3.0	3.6
NaCl.........	2.3	2.8
KCl..........	1.9	3.2
KBr..........	1.7	

* S. Mayburg, Effect of Pressure on the Low-frequency Dielectric Constant of Ionic Crystals, *Phys. Rev.*, vol. 79, p. 375, 1950.

and are within a factor of 2 of $2\gamma + \frac{1}{3}$, the Grüneisen value for the latter quantity. In addition, $(\partial \ln K/\partial \ln V)_P$, the volume derivative as obtained from the temperature dependence of the dielectric constant, bears about the same relation to $(\partial \ln K/\partial \ln V)_P$ as was found for the corresponding derivatives of the elastic moduli. Therefore Eq. (4-21) is

[32] S. Mayburg, Effect of Pressure on the Low-frequency Dielectric Constant of Ionic Crystals, *Phys. Rev.*, vol. 79, p. 375, 1950.

applicable to the dielectric-polarization model to about the same extent that it is applicable to the strain-energy model.

The strain-energy model and the dielectric-polarization model are the only continuum models which appear to be relevant to the materials of Table 4-2. Results similar to Eq. (4-21) can also be obtained from various atomic models of defects.[16] In the special case of vacancy formation, if it is assumed that ΔV^* is about one-half an atomic volume, an equation similar to Eq. (4-21) seems to follow from practically any concept of a vacancy.[16,33,34]

A quite different model of solid-state diffusion has been used by Borelius to obtain results similar to those of the models used here.[35,36] According to Borelius the increase in volume of a solid during the elementary self-diffusion is equal to the volume of a hard atomic core.[35] Borelius's relation between this core volume, here denoted also by ΔV^*, and the activation energy for diffusion can be put in the form

$$\Delta V^* = \tfrac{1}{3}\chi \frac{d \ln \chi}{d \ln V} \Delta G^*$$

This relation is obviously closely analogous to that derived from the strain-energy model [Eq. (4-18)]. However, it contains the extra factor $\frac{1}{3}$ and gives values for ΔV^* which are only about one-third those of Eq. (4-18).

Thus it appears to be fairly generally true that an equation of the form of Eq. (4-21),

$$\frac{\Delta V^*}{\Delta G^*} = k\chi \tag{4-27}$$

holds for activated processes in solids.[16] Equations (4-24) appear to have a similar generality and applicability.[28] In the following sections some further aspects of the application of Eqs. (4-24) and (4-27) will be discussed.

4-5 Related Effects

The models employed above are also useful in connection with other phenomena not of a diffusive nature. These other applications will be described in this section.

[33] A. W. Lawson, Relation between the Eyring and Doolittle Diffusion Equations, *J. Chem. Phys.*, vol. 30, p. 1114, 1959.

[34] A. W. Lawson, S. Rice, R. D. Corneliusen, and N. H. Nachtrieb, Dynamical Theory of Diffusion in Crystals III, *J. Chem. Phys.*, vol. 32, p. 447, 1960.

[35] G. Borelius, On the Energy of Activation for Self-diffusion in Metals, *Arkiv Fysik*, vol. 11, p. 259, 1956.

[36] G. Borelius, On the Origin of the Internal Pressure in Metals, *Arkiv Fysik*, vol. 16, p. 437, 1960.

One obvious application is the one for which Zener originally introduced the strain-energy model, namely, the relation between the dilation and the stored energy of cold work.[15] The defects involved in this case are dislocations. The energy is determined by direct calorimetric measurements, and the dilation by volumetric measurements. The form in which Eq. (4-21) applies to the cold-work case is

$$\frac{\delta V}{V} = 2(\gamma - 1/3)\chi E_s \qquad (4\text{-}28)$$

Here $\delta V/V$ is the fractional increase in volume of the cold-worked material and E_s is the stored energy per unit volume. A reexamination of Eq. (4-28) is particularly appropriate, since careful measurements in which both $\delta V/V$ and E_s were determined from the same specimen were carried out by Clarebrough, Hargreaves, and West[37] subsequent to Zener's work.[38] The application of Eq. (4-28) to the data of Clarebrough, Hargreaves, and West is shown in Fig. 4-2. It is seen that the proportionality implied by Eq. (4-28) is indeed present. However, as in the case of the data illustrated by Fig. 4-1, the predicted volume increase is too large by a factor of about 1.4.

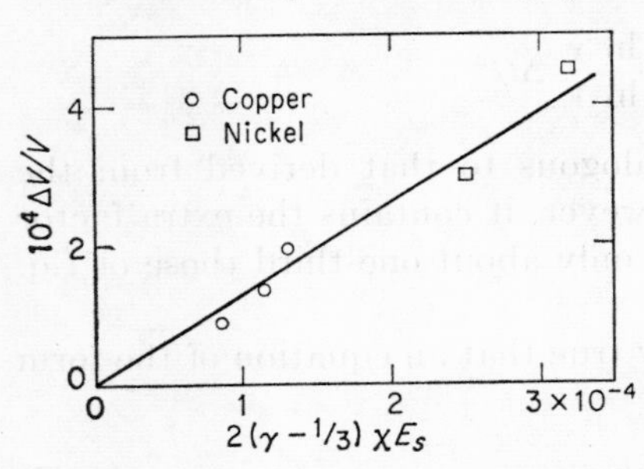

Fig. 4-2 A comparison of the data of Clarebrough, Hargreaves, and West[37] with the relationship described by Eq. (4-28).

Zener's theory has been extended to elastically anisotropic materials by Toupin and Rivlin.[39]

The principles developed for dislocations also apply to the relation between stored energy and lattice expansion of materials damaged by irradiation.[40]

Foreign atoms represent another source of lattice strain in solid solutions. The solubility has the form

$$x = \exp\frac{-\Delta G_s}{RT}$$

[37] L. M. Clarebrough, M. E. Hargreaves, and G. W. West, Release of Energy during Annealing of Deformed Metals, *Phil. Mag.*, vol. 1, p. 528, 1956; Density of Dislocations in Compressed Copper, *Acta Met.*, vol. 5, p. 738, 1957.

[38] A. Seeger and P. Haasen, Density Changes of Crystals Containing Dislocations, *Phil. Mag.*, vol. 3, p. 470, 1958.

[39] R. A. Toupin and R. S. Rivlin, Dimensional Changes in Crystals Caused by Dislocations, *J. Math. Phys.*, vol. 1, p. 8, 1960.

[40] R. W. Keyes, Relation between Stored Energy and Dilatation in Irradiated Graphite, *Bull. Am. Phys. Soc.*, vol. 6, p. 244, 1961.

The entropy of solution can be calculated from measurements of the solubility as a function of temperature. Zener has analyzed measurements of this type in aluminum and shown the existence of a correlation between ΔS_s and ΔG_s, as is to be expected on the basis of a strain-energy model.[41] The relationship should be given by Eq. (4-25). A comparison of the data discussed by Zener with Eq. (4-25) is given in Table 4-4. The value of $(\partial \ln C/\partial P)_T$ is about 5.5 for aluminum, and $\beta \approx 9 \times 10^{-5}\,°\text{K}^{-1}$. Therefore Eq. (4-22) becomes $\Delta S_s = 4 \times 10^{-4}\,\Delta G_s$. It is seen that the magnitude of the entropy is roughly correct. The tendency for high values of ΔG_s to be associated with high values of ΔS_s is reproduced, as pointed out by Zener.[39] Thus, although no measurements of the effect of pressure on solid solubilities are available, the success of the strain-energy model in interpreting the ΔS_s leads to the expectation that it could also be used to predict the corresponding ΔV_s according to Eq. (4-21).

Table 4-4 Entropy Factors of Solid Solutions in Aluminum*

Solute	ΔG_s (at 1000°K), kcal/mole	ΔS_s (calculated), cal/mole-degree	ΔS_s (observed), cal/mole-degree
Nickel	14.0	5.6	8.1
Zirconium	12.4	5.0	4.6
Chromium	9.2	3.7	6.4
Manganese	7.8	3.1	6.0
Silicon	5.8	2.3	5.6
Copper	4.7	1.9	5.4

* Suggested by the analysis of C. Zener (see reference 41).

It has been pointed out by Burris and Laidler[42] that the entropies and activation volumes of many liquid-phase chemical reactions are roughly proportional, as suggested by Eqs. (4-24). Some examples are shown in Fig. 4-3.

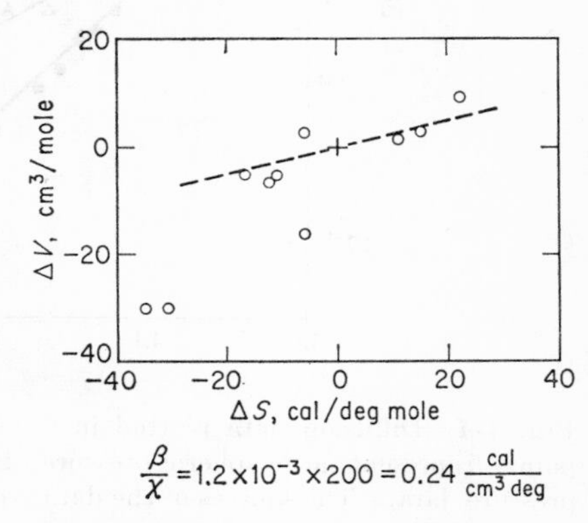

Fig. 4-3 The relationship between the volumes and entropies of activation for chemical reactions in the liquid phase. Most of the data represent the examples given by Burris and Laidler.[42] The dotted line is the relationship described by Eqs. (4-24) with typical values for liquids substituted for β and χ.

[41] C. Zener, The Role of Statistical Mechanics in Physical Metallurgy, in "Thermodynamics in Metallurgy," American Society for Metals, Cleveland, 1950.

[42] C. T. Burris and K. J. Laidler, The Influence of Hydrostatic Pressure on the Rates of Ionic Reactions, *Trans. Faraday Soc.*, vol. 51, p. 1497, 1955.

4-6 Activation Volumes and Melting

No discussion of activation volumes would be complete without a description of the interesting ideas of Nachtrieb and collaborators concerning the relation between diffusion and melting.[43–46] The important

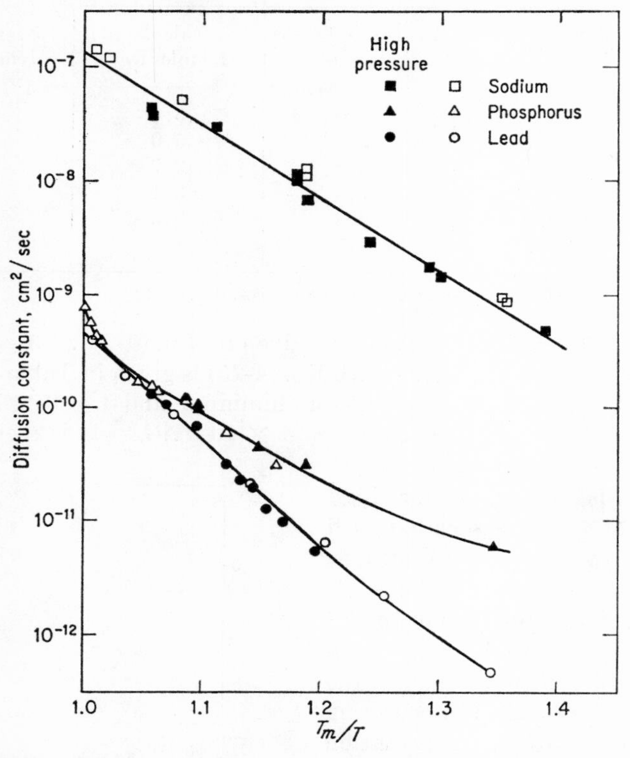

Fig. 4-4 Diffusion data plotted in the form suggested by Nachtrieb. The open points represent atmospheric-pressure data, and the full points represent high-pressure data. The sources of the data are references 43 to 45.

observation which they made is illustrated in Fig. 4-4. The point of this figure is that D, the self-diffusion coefficient as a function of temperature

[43] N. H. Nachtrieb, J. A. Weil, E. Catalano, and A. W. Lawson, Self-diffusion in Solid Sodium. II. The Effect of Pressure, *J. Chem. Phys.*, vol. 20, p. 1189, 1952.

[44] N. H. Nachtrieb and A. W. Lawson, Effect of Pressure on Self-diffusion in White Phosphorus, *J. Chem. Phys.*, vol. 23, p. 1193, 1955.

[45] N. H. Nachtrieb, H. A. Resing, and S. A. Rice, Effect of Pressure on Self-diffusion in Lead, *J. Chem. Phys.*, vol. 31, p. 135, 1959.

[46] S. A. Rice and N. H. Nachtrieb, Dynamical Theory of Diffusion in Crystals II, *J. Chem. Phys.*, vol. 31, p. 139, 1959.

and pressure, depends only on $T/T_m(P)$, where $T_m(P)$ is the melting temperature at pressure P. The pressure dependence of D comes about through the pressure dependence of $T_m(P)$.

In order to interpret Nachtrieb's result in terms of activation volumes, it is convenient to introduce a parameter θ defined by

$$\theta \equiv \frac{T_m(P)}{T} \tag{4-29}$$

Then Nachtrieb's result is

$$D(P, T) = D(\theta) \tag{4-30}$$

By Eqs. (4-29) and (4-30), the activation volume can be written in the form

$$\begin{aligned} \Delta V^* &= -RT\left(\frac{\partial \ln D}{\partial P}\right)_T \\ &= -RT\frac{d \ln D}{d\theta}\left(\frac{\partial\theta}{\partial P}\right)_T \\ &= -RT\frac{1}{T_m(P)}\left(\frac{\partial \ln D}{\partial(1/T)}\right)_P\frac{1}{T}\frac{dT_m(P)}{dP} \end{aligned} \tag{4-31}$$

introducing the Clapeyron equation,

$$\frac{1}{T_m}\frac{dT_m}{dP} = \frac{\Delta V_m}{\Delta H_m}$$

and ΔH^* from Eq. (4-12),

$$\Delta H^* = -R\frac{\partial \ln D}{\partial(1/T)}$$

into Eq. (4-31) gives

$$\Delta V^* = \frac{\Delta V_m}{\Delta H_m}\Delta H^* \tag{4-32}$$

Equation (4-32) was originally proposed by Nachtrieb, Resing, and Rice[45] and Rice and Nachtrieb.[46] These authors showed that it is in excellent agreement with the data on sodium and lead.

Nachtrieb has pointed out that an interesting test of the relationship expressed by Fig. 4-4 and Eq. (4-32) would be provided by a measurement of the effect of pressure on diffusion in some substance for which dT_m/dP is negative. The result of Fig. 4-4 predicts that ΔV^* should be negative for such a case. A negative ΔV^* would probably be in disagreement with the strain-energy model, since there is no reason to believe that the sign of $(\partial \ln C/\partial P)_T$ is related to that of dT_m/dP.

4-7 Metallurgical Implications

Many phenomena important in metallurgical processing are of the types discussed in this chapter. Generally, metallurgical structures are complex nonequilibrium structures which result from competition among various atomic processes. If the relative free energies involved in the competing atomic processes are changed by pressure, it can be expected that new types of metallurgical structures may be produced by processing under pressure. Specific examples are described in Chap. 11. In the present section it will be pointed out that the relative free energies of different atomic processes in a material are not changed by the application of pressure in cases in which the models used here apply. Thus, these models do not encourage the use of pressure as an aid in metallurgical processing.

According to Eq. (4-27) the application of pressure merely changes the temperature scale for activated processes in a material. That is, the exponent which controls a process can be written

$$\frac{\Delta G^*(P)}{RT} = \frac{\Delta G^*(0)}{RT^\dagger}$$

where $T^\dagger$ is an effective temperature at pressure P, given by

$$T^\dagger = \frac{T}{1 + k\chi P} \tag{4-33}$$

This factor is the same for all processes in a given material. Therefore, it is to be expected that metallurgical structures whose formation depends on competition among various diffusive processes will not be strongly affected by pressure. The effects produced by pressure will be similar to those which can be produced by a change of the temperature scale at atmospheric pressure.

The effect of pressure on the results of metallurgical heat treatments will, of course, also be sensitive to the pressure dependence of various driving forces or free-energy differences between different structures. However, these forces scale in the same way as the ΔG^*'s of diffusive processes in many cases. The examples of the free energies of substitutional solutes and the energy of dislocations were discussed in Sec. 4-5. It is likely that phenomena involving grain boundaries will be analogous to those involving dislocations, since the former can be resolved into arrays of the latter. Thus it is to be expected that the effect of pressure will frequently be equivalent to the change of temperature scale described by Eq. (4-33) for both the driving forces and the rate processes.

In other cases the rate at which structures can be produced is limited by the competition between diffusion and melting. For example, it has been suggested that homogenization of alloys might be accelerated by the application of pressure because the increase of the melting temperature produced by the pressure would allow the homogenization to be carried out at higher temperatures. The results of Nachtrieb, described in Sec. 4-6, suggest that this is not so.

These considerations do not mean that pressure is valueless as a tool in metallurgy. On the contrary, there are important metallurgical phenomena which are not even approximately encompassed by the models discussed here. An outstanding and very significant example is the α-γ transition in iron and its alloys. Another, concerning which available information is scanty, is nucleation barriers. Furthermore it is by no means universally true that free energies of solution are dominated by strain energy and that the pressure effects are expected to follow the description of Sec. 4-5. The point is that the profitable use of pressure as a tool in metallurgy requires the participation of some phenomenon other than ordinary diffusive processes and driving forces controlled by strain energy.

4-8 Liquids

Two frequently studied transport properties of liquids, diffusion and fluidity, are manifestations of the motion of atoms. They are connected by the Stokes-Einstein relation

$$D = \frac{k_0 T}{3\pi a \eta}$$

where D = diffusion coefficient with same phenomenological significance as D for solid
a = diameter of sphere having volume of molecule
η = viscosity

It is to be expected that the diffusive motion of atoms in a liquid will be to some extent similar to the atomic diffusive processes in crystals. In fact, activated-state concepts quite similar to those familiar in solids have been used to interpret the transport properties of liquids.[1,47]

The activated-state interpretation of diffusive motion in liquids assumes that a large concentration of vacancies is always present in a liquid. An atom can then move through the liquid by jumping into a vacant site. The jumping is an activated process entirely analogous to the jumping of an atom into a vacancy in a solid. The thermodynamic parameters of activation ΔG^*, ΔV^*, and ΔS^* can be calculated from measurements of η or D and their temperature and pressure dependence. Thus it is of interest to examine the extent to which Eqs. (4-24) and (4-27)

[47] J. Frenkel, "Kinetic Theory of Liquids," Oxford University Press, New York, 1940.

are applicable to liquids. The test of Eq. (4-27) is presented in Fig. 4-5. It is seen that the required proportionality is approximately verified. The constant k, however, turns out to be only about 2, in contrast to the value of 4 or 5 which applies to solids.

Furthermore, the values of ΔS^* for liquids are not in as good agreement with the predictions of the activated-state theory as they are in solids. The measured values of ΔS^* are considerably smaller than those calculated from the ΔV^*'s by Eq. (4-24a). In some cases ΔS^* even turns out to be negative.

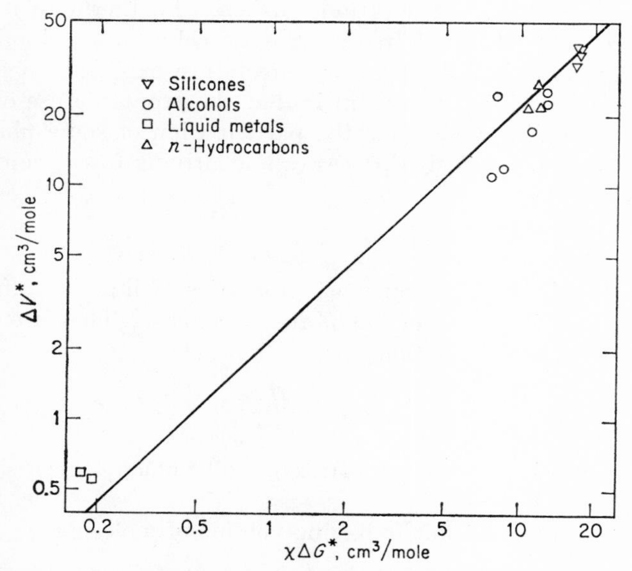

Fig. 4-5 The relation between ΔV^* and ΔG^* for liquids.

Very large effects on the properties of liquids occur in the experimental pressure range. It is therefore possible to see clearly the pressure dependence of the thermodynamic activation parameters, in contrast to the usual situation in solids. Such pressure dependences are illustrated in Fig. 4-6 for two typical cases, isopropyl alcohol and the trimer silicone liquid. Activated-state theory predicts that the pressure variation of ΔV^* should closely parallel that of $\chi\Delta G^*$, in accord with Eq. (4-27). It is seen that this prediction is verified at the low end of the pressure ranges, but very large departures from proportionality appear at higher pressures. The ratio of ΔV^* to $\chi\Delta G^*$ increases to 15 at 30 kilobars in isopropyl alcohol.

Thus it is seen that the activated-state theory which is found to be applicable to solids does not give a very good description of diffusive processes in liquids.

There is an alternative point of view which has been successfully used to interpret diffusive processes in liquids. This is based on an equation suggested by Doolittle,[48] who showed that the temperature dependence of the viscosity of liquids can be described by

$$\eta = \xi \exp \frac{Q}{V_f} \tag{4-34}$$

where ξ and Q are constants and V_f is the free volume per mole, that is, the molar volume of the liquid minus the volume of a mole of molecules

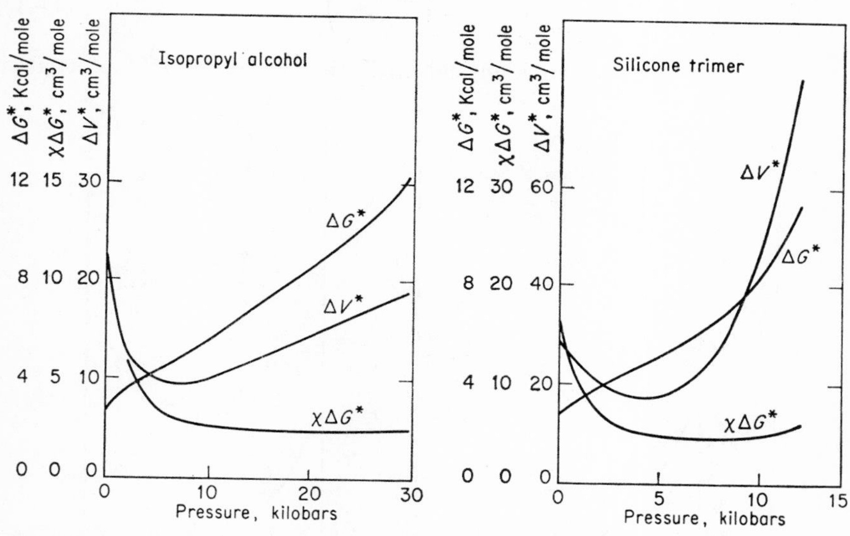

Fig. 4-6 Pressure dependence of the calculated activation parameters for liquids. (*P. W. Bridgman, Viscosities to 30,000 kg/cm², Proc. Am. Acad. Arts Sci., vol. 77, p.* 115, 1949.)

regarded as hard cores. A theoretical justification of Eq. (4-34) has been given by Cohen and Turnbull.[49] The theory of these authors shows the relation of ξ to atomic constants and also shows that Q has the same order of magnitude as the core volume. The value of ξ is about that which would be used in an activated-state theory if the viscosity were written in the form $\eta = \xi \exp(\Delta G^*/RT)$.

[48] A. K. Doolittle, Dependence of the Viscosity of Liquids on Free Space, *J. Appl. Phys.*, vol. 22, p. 1471, 1951.

[49] M. Cohen and D. Turnbull, Molecular Transport in Liquids and Glasses, *J. Chem. Phys.*, vol. 31, p. 1164, 1959.

The implications of Eq. (4-34) with respect to the pressure dependence of viscosity will now be examined.

The free volume V_f has the form

$$V_f = V - V_0 \tag{4-35}$$

where V_0 is the hard-core volume. It will be assumed that V_0 is independent of pressure. It is possible to describe the pressure variation in terms of the parameters which result from the activated-state assumption. That is,

$$\Delta G^{**} \equiv RT \ln \frac{\eta}{\xi} \tag{4-36}$$

$$\Delta V^{**} \equiv \left(\frac{\partial \Delta G^{**}}{\partial P}\right)_T \tag{4-37}$$

ΔG^{**} and ΔV^{**} are then identical with the ΔG^* and ΔV^* plotted in Fig. 4-5.

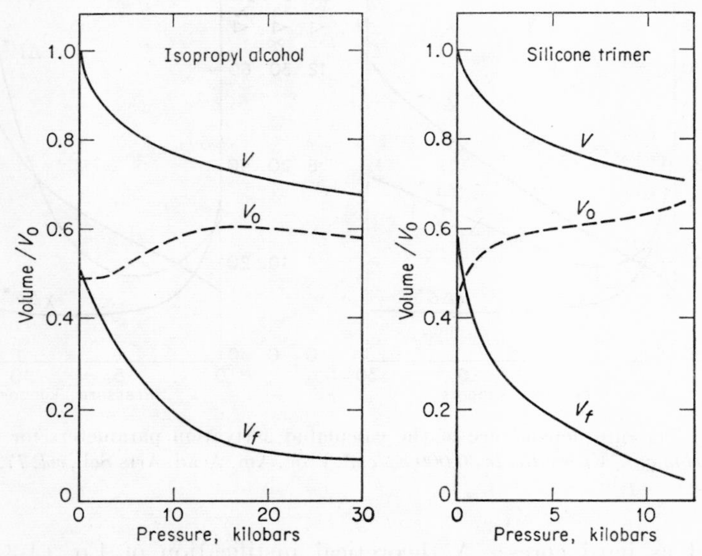

Fig. 4-7 Analysis of the pressure dependence of the free volume of liquids according to Eqs. (4-35) to (4-38) for the liquids of Fig. 4-6.

It is easy to verify from Eqs. (4-34) to (4-37) that

$$\Delta V^{**} = \left[\frac{V}{V - V_0}\right] \chi \, \Delta G^{**} \tag{4-38}$$

The core volume V_0 is about two-thirds of V in typical cases. Thus Eq. (4-38) is $\Delta V^{**} \approx 3\chi\Delta G^{**}$. This approximately accounts for the result shown by Fig. 4-5.

Equation (4-38) also accounts for the rise in $\Delta V^{**}/\chi\Delta G^{**}$ at high pressures, since the free volume, $V - V_0$, becomes very small at high pressure. In fact, Eq. (4-38) can be used to calculate V_0/V as a function of pressure. If the model is correct, V_0 should turn out to be independent of pressure. The values of V_0 and V_f determined from Eqs. (4-38) and (4-35) for the examples of Fig. 4-6 are shown in Fig. 4-7. It is seen that although V_0 is not exactly constant, most of the change of V with pressure is due to a change of V_f. Thus it appears that the free-volume theory gives a somewhat more satisfactory account of the pressure dependence of viscosity than the activated-state theory.

4-9 Electronic Activation

An entirely different class of activated processes has also been extensively studied at high pressures, namely, the activation of electrons into excited electronic states. Since these processes are treated in detail in other chapters of this book, only a few points bearing on the similarity and the differences between electronic activation and the atomic processes discussed in this chapter will be mentioned here.

One important type of electronic activation is the excitation of electrons from the valence band to the conduction band in a semiconductor. These processes can be studied by measuring the equilibrium number of excited electrons in a way analogous to that in which atomic imperfections can be studied by measuring the equilibrium concentration of atomic defects. The concentration of electrons excited across the intrinsic gap has the form

$$n_i = N_c \exp \frac{-\Delta G^*}{2RT} \tag{4-39}$$

where N_c is an appropriately defined effective density of electronic states. Brooks[50] and James[51] have shown that the energy gaps determined by optical methods are the same as ΔG^* in Eq. (4-39).

It turns out that the relations among ΔV^*, ΔS^*, and ΔG^* which were found to hold for atomic processes are not even roughly applicable to the intrinsic excitation of semiconductors. Figure 4-8*a* shows that the correlation between ΔV^* and ΔG^* described by Eq. (4-27) is completely absent. The reason is that the models which must be used to describe semiconductor energy levels are completely different from those used to

[50] H. Brooks, Theory of Electrical Properties of Germanium and Silicon, pp. 85–182 in L. Marton (ed.), "Advances in Electronics and Electron Physics," vol. 7, Academic Press, Inc., New York, 1955.

[51] H. M. James, Statistical Mechanics of Semiconductor Crystals with Electron-vibration Coupling, pp. 204–212 in R. G. Breckenridge, B. R. Russell, and E. E. Hahn (eds.), "Photoconductivity Conference," John Wiley & Sons, Inc., New York. 1956.

describe atomic processes. The semiconductor problem is very complicated, but certain general features have emerged.[52–54]

Figure 4-8b shows that the proportionality between ΔS^* and ΔV^* implied by Eqs. (4-24) also fails in the semiconductor case. The entropy of Eqs. (4-24), which results from the dependence of the vibrational frequencies on volume, is of course present in semiconductors. It is shown by the dashed line in Fig. 4-8b. There is, however, another contribution to the entropy which is always positive. In contrast to the case of atomic processes, this other contribution is usually much larger

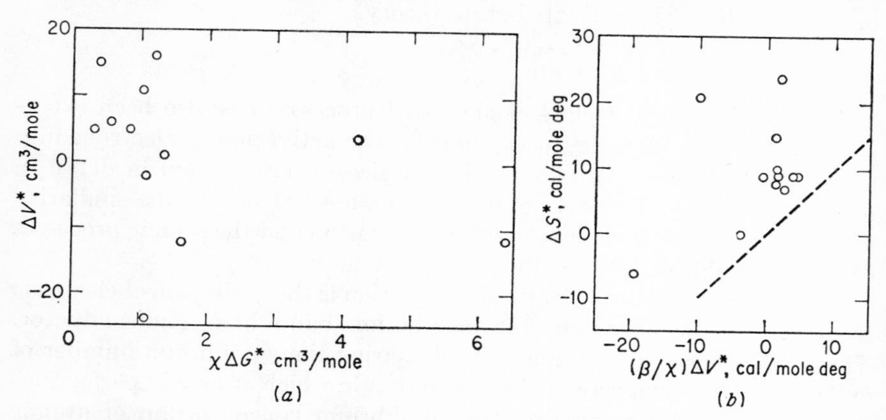

Fig. 4-8 Thermodynamic parameters of activation for the intrinsic excitation of semiconductors plotted in the forms suggested by Eqs. (4-27) and (4-24). (*R. W. Keyes, The Effects of Elastic Deformation on the Electrical Conductivity of Semiconductors, pp.* 149–221 *in F. Seitz and D. Turnbull (eds.), "Solid State Physics," vol.* 2, *Academic Press, Inc., New York,* 1960.)

than the $(\beta/\chi)\Delta V^*$ contribution. The theory of the extra positive contribution, which is due to direct electron-lattice interaction, has been given by Fan[55] and Brooks.[50]

The other type of electronic excitation in solids which has been studied at high pressures is the excitation of electrons between electronic states

[52] R. W. Keyes, The Effect of Elastic Strain on the Conductivity of Homopolar Semiconductors, in M. Schön and H. Welker (eds.), "Semiconductors and Phosphors," Interscience Publishers, Inc., New York, 1958.

[53] T. E. Slykhouse and H. G. Drickamer, Effect of Pressure on the Optical Absorption Edge of Germanium and Silicon, *J. Phys. Chem. Solids*, vol. 7, p. 210, 1958; A. L. Edwards, T. E. Slykhouse, and H. G. Drickamer, Effect of Pressure on Zincblende and Wurtzite Structures, *J. Phys. Chem. Solids*, vol. 11, p. 140, 1959.

[54] W. Paul, Effect of Pressure on the Properties of Germanium and Silicon, *J. Phys. Chem. Solids.* vol. 8, p. 196, 1959. (See also Chap. 8 of this volume.)

[55] H. Y. Fan, Temperature Dependence of the Energy Gap in Semiconductors, *Phys. Rev.*, vol. 82, p. 900, 1951.

localized at some atomic impurity or imperfection. The excitation energy is measured as an optical absorption line in these cases. The absorption energy is frequently quite different from the difference in free energy of the crystal between the two states of excitation. This discrepancy between the absorption energy and the free energy of activation is demonstrated by the very large relaxation of the electronic center which sometimes follows optical excitation.[56] Thus it is not to be expected that the thermodynamic interpretations developed above will be applicable. Nevertheless, it is interesting to note that the relations

$$\left(\frac{\partial\,\Delta E}{\partial P}\right)_T \approx 1.2\chi\,\Delta E$$

[which is reminiscent of Eq. (4-27)] and

$$\left(\frac{\partial\,\Delta E}{\partial T}\right)_P = \frac{\beta}{\chi}\,\Delta E$$

[the equivalent of Eqs. (4-24)] are as accurately satisfied for F centers as the corresponding equations are for the case of atomic defects. The interpretation of these facts in terms of models of an F center has been given by Jacobs.[57] It should also be noted, however, that the phenomena are entirely different for other types of electronic centers. Chapter 12 should be consulted for details.

4-10 General Comments

The purpose of this section is to discuss the relevance of the results described above to current and projected high-pressure research. This subject has already been touched on in some of the preceding sections.

The most prominent feature which emerges from the discussion of activated atomic processes in solids is that, to the extent that equations such as Eqs. (4-24) and (4-27) are valid, measurements of the temperature and pressure dependence of the rates of the diffusive process contain no new information. Thus the determination of ΔG^* by a single measurement of a diffusion constant completely characterizes an activated process. This statement, obviously, is not quantitatively accurate for several reasons: There are in fact appreciable deviations from the equations in question. The uncertainty in the factor ν, and in some cases in the factor f, in Eq. (4-7) leads to some uncertainty in ΔG^*. The limitations of the Grüneisen approximation as an estimate of the numerical coefficient in Eq. (4-27)

[56] See, for example, D. L. Dexter, Theory of the Optical Properties of Imperfections in Nonmetals, pp. 353–411 in F. Seitz and D. Turnbull (eds.), "Solid State Physics" vol. 6, Academic Press, Inc., New York, 1958.

[57] I. S. Jacobs, Effect of Pressure on F-center Absorption by Alkali Halides, *Phys. Rev.*, vol. 93, p. 993, 1954.

may be quite serious in some materials. Nevertheless, certain conclusions and general comments seem justifiable:

1. Measurements of ΔV^* do not provide a good basis for distinguishing between atomic models of defects. Whatever criteria can be applied to ΔV^* to make such a distinction can be applied with about the same significance to ΔG^*. It should be emphasized that this conclusion is not essentially theoretical in nature. It is simply an extrapolation from the considerable body of excellent experimental work which has accumulated in the field of effects of pressure on diffusive processes in solids. In fact, the contribution of theory in this area is minor as compared to the contribution of experiment. Theory merely serves to suggest the way in which the extrapolation from experiment should be performed.

2. The deviations from the prediction of the strain-energy model are beyond experimental error. Explanations of the deviations will undoubtedly be valuable in elucidating diffusive mechanisms. However, an accurate quantitative study of the deviations will probably require a higher experimental accuracy than that currently available.

3. There are apparently anomalous cases which may suggest fruitful areas for further exploration. The examples in Table 4-2 are ionic conductivity in the low-temperature, low-pressure phase of silver iodide and the diffusion of interstitial solutes in iron.

4. Very interesting work will probably be done in the future on atomic processes in types of materials not represented in Table 4-2. The data presented there are essentially restricted to ionic crystals and metals. The extent to which the relations suggested by results on these materials are applicable to molecular and covalently bonded crystals is a worthwhile question. It might be expected that similar relationships will emerge in the case of molecular crystals; long-range forces are involved, and models of lattice defects should be similar to those which are useful in ionic crystals and metals. However, work on the noble gases would be especially interesting, since these solids are particularly susceptible to theoretical treatment based on atomic models.

5. Current understanding of covalent semiconductors suggests that the picture may be quite different there. Models of many types of lattice imperfections interpret the defect energies in terms of the energies of electronic bonding states. The electronic densities are localized in regions with no more than 1 atomic volume, and it is difficult to see why any long-range strain patterns should exist. Furthermore, an unusually wide variety of defect types and of methods of investigation is available. It is, of course, conceivable that relationships similar to Eqs. (4-27) and (4-24) will follow from some of the appropriate models; it was found in Sec. 4-4 that these relationships have a generality not easily anticipated. However, as mentioned in Sec. 4-9, electronic phenomena in semiconduc-

tors have so far been found to be very different from the atomic processes discussed earlier.

6. The example of the electronic processes illustrates an important point. Because of the unanticipated generality of relations (4-24) and (4-27) it is tempting to inquire whether they have some foundation in the pure thermodynamics of one-component systems. The results for electronic processes show that they are actually valid only for a broad class of models of an activated process. Thus the derivation of Eqs. (4-24) and (4-27) without reference to physical features of a model which distinguishes the processes to which these equations apply from those to which they do not apply is not possible.

7. The study of the pressure dependence of atomic processes in covalent crystals is also relevant to Nachtrieb's ideas. The covalent crystals usually have a negative ΔV_m which, as discussed in Sec. 4-6, suggests that ΔV^* will be negative.

8. W. R. Heller has pointed out that the effect of pressure on diffusive processes in which the elementary atomic jump takes place by quantum-mechanical tunneling should be quite different from the effects on the activated-state models. This may also be a fruitful area for exploration.

5

The Equation of State of Solids at Low Temperature

N. Bernardes‡ C. A. Swenson

Institute for Atomic Research and Department of Physics
Iowa State University
Ames, Iowa

5-1 Introduction

The development of theories to describe the experimental properties and behavior of matter inevitably involves approximations which may be mathematical and/or physical in nature. In many cases it is very difficult to assess the error introduced by these approximations, since approximate methods usually become necessary just at the point at which the situation (either mathematical, or physical, or both) becomes rather intricate.

The total energy of a system (either cohesive at absolute zero or a thermodynamic average at finite temperatures) is the bulk property which is most amenable to theoretical treatment. The calculation of the

‡ Now at the University of Sao Paulo, Brazil.

cohesive energy of a system, for instance, either becomes a problem in statics (for a classical system) or involves only the stationary-state solutions of the Schrödinger equation. On the other hand, it would be considerably more difficult to calculate almost any other bulk property such as the electrical or thermal conductivity.

Thus it would be expected that a theoretical treatment of the cohesive properties will involve a minimum of approximations when compared with similar treatments of other properties of matter. The success of a theoretical calculation of an equation of state (that is, of the cohesive energy or, preferably, of the Helmholtz free energy as a function of volume V and temperature T) will give information about the various approximations which must be made. It must be pointed out, however, that the success of a calculation of the cohesive properties does not necessarily guarantee the validity of the assumptions which are involved. A simple example can be given for the case of metals, in which it is possible to account for the cohesive energy using the assumption that the "atoms" of the metal interact according to a convenient central law of force; however, this assumption proves to be completely unsatisfactory for the calculation of the elastic constants of the metal.

The preceding at least should provide justification for a certain amount of both theoretical and experimental interest in the equation of state of solids. The only real test of the basic theoretical assumptions involves a direct comparison of theoretical predictions with low-temperature experimental data. It is somewhat unfortunate that the experimental determinations of the low-temperature equation of state are not completely straightforward and free from approximations themselves, so it is useful to survey the present status of both the theoretical calculations and the experiments with which the calculations are compared.

5-2 Experimental Considerations

An ideal method for obtaining equation-of-state data at low temperatures would consist in immersing a single crystal of a substance in a fluid and of measuring the changes in length of the sample along the principal crystalline axes as the pressure of the fluid was varied. While this can be done with some precision at room temperature,[1] all fluids become solid at low temperatures and moderate pressures, and less ideal methods must be used under these conditions. In practice, three experimental methods are available, each of which can give to varying degrees of precision at least a portion of the data which could be obtained from the ideal experiment. These methods involve, in order of difficulty, the approximate measurement of the P-V-T relationship by a piston-

[1] P. W. Bridgman, Linear Compressions to 30,000 kg/cm², Including Relatively Incompressible Substances, *Proc. Am. Acad. Arts Sci.*, vol. 77, pp. 187–234, 1949.

displacement technique, the measurement of a heat capacity at constant volume as a function of molar volume and temperature, and the direct measurement of the pressure variation of the elastic constants using ultrasonic techniques. X-ray methods also might be applicable.[2]

5-2a Piston-displacement technique. The first of these methods uses a modification of the piston-displacement technique developed by

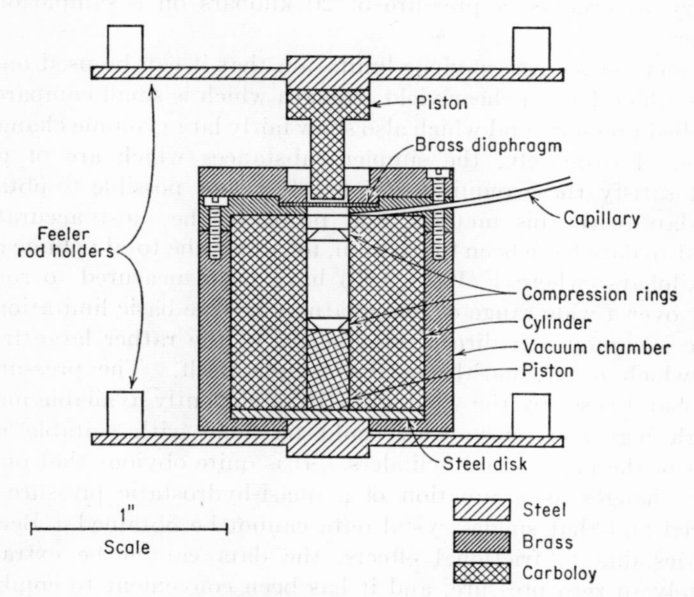

Fig. 5-1 A high-pressure sample holder which has been used to determine the equation of state of xenon.[5] The gas is condensed into the holder by means of the capillary and is frozen in the cylinder. The diaphragm then is broken by the piston, the sample is compacted, and after a "seasoning" cycle the changes in length of the sample are directly related to the volume changes. For a further discussion, see references 2 and 5.

Bridgman for obtaining P-V data near room temperature.[2-4] Here, the sample is placed in a cylinder (see Fig. 5-1), the ends of which are closed by pistons. If this combination is placed in a hydraulic press, the changes

[2] A fairly complete discussion of experimental high-pressure work to, roughly, January, 1960, with emphasis on the low-temperature aspects, has been given in C. A. Swenson, Physics at High Pressure, pp. 41–147 in F. Seitz and D. Turnbull (eds.), "Solid State Physics," vol. 11, Academic Press, Inc., New York, 1960. Also see Chap. 15.

[3] P. W. Bridgman, "The Physics of High Pressures," with supplement, G. Bell & Sons, Ltd., London, pp. 397–404, 1949.

[4] J. W. Stewart, Compressibilities of Some Solidified Gases at Low Temperature, *Phys. Rev.*, vol. 97, pp. 578–582, 1955.

in length with applied force will be proportional (with suitable corrections) to the changes in volume of the sample with pressure. In practice, it is desirable to vary the temperature of the sample, so the press is constructed with long force members that allow the force generated by the hydraulic ram at room temperature to be transmitted to the sample holder at low temperature.[2,4–6] Very roughly, a force of 8 tons is necessary to produce a pressure of 20 kilobars on a sample of ¼-in. diameter.

This method has the obvious limitation that it can be used only with samples which have a shear yield strength which is small compared with the applied pressure, and which also show fairly large volume changes with pressure. Fortunately, the simpler substances which are of primary interest satisfy these requirements.[2,4] It is not possible to obtain precision data with this method, and probably the most accurate data reported to date have been for sodium, for which the total volume changes in 20 kilobars (where $V/V_0 = 0.80$) have been measured to roughly 2 percent over a wide range of temperatures.[6] One basic limitation to the possible accuracy is a direct consequence of the rather large frictional forces which occur, mostly in the sample itself. The pressure limit (25 kilobars) is set by the yield strength of currently available materials, although higher-pressure work could be done with suitable external support of the pistons and cylinders. It is quite obvious that only total volume changes as a function of a quasi-hydrostatic pressure can be measured and that single-crystal data cannot be obtained. Because of difficulties due to frictional effects, the data cannot be extrapolated accurately to zero pressure, and it has been convenient to combine the P-V data at constant temperature with separate measurements of the thermal expansion at zero pressure.[6]

5-2b Calorimetric determinations. The calorimetric method is particularly adapted to the very compressible solidified gases and has been used, in practice, only for solidified helium. Here, the temperature dependence of the heat capacity at constant volume is determined for various molar volumes or densities of the solid. These data, when combined with a single P-V isotherm or the P-T relationship along the melting line, give the equation of state $V(P, T)$ as well as all the other thermodynamic functions.[7,7a]

[5] J. R. Packard, An Experimental Equation of State for Solidified Xenon, unpublished thesis, Iowa State University, 1962.

[6] R. I. Beecroft and C. A. Swenson, An Experimental Equation of State for Sodium, *J. Phys. Chem. Solids*, vol. 18, pp. 329–344, 1961. Subsequent work has shown that the pressure scale used in this paper is 3 percent low.

[7] J. S. Dugdale and F. E. Simon, Thermodynamic Properties and Melting of Solid Helium, *Proc. Roy. Soc. London*, vol. A218, pp. 291–310, 1953.

[7a] E. C. Heltemes and C. A. Swenson, Heat Capacity of Solid He3, to be published in *Phys. Rev.*

These experiments are difficult, however, because fairly massive high-pressure vessels are needed, and the heat capacity of the container can become larger than that of the sample. The method is practical only for the solidified gases, for which the low-temperature heat capacities are large relative to those of possible container materials. Dugdale and Simon used this method for solid helium to 2.5 kilobars.[7] Their samples were solidified at constant volume, and, because of the high compressibility of the solid, only a small pressure drop (20 percent) occurred at the solidification line. Helium at higher pressures, and most other solidified gases, are fairly incompressible, and the relaxation of the pressure upon solidification at constant volume would become appreciable. It is possible, however, to solidify the sample at constant pressure, and, hence, to begin constant-volume heat-capacity measurements at the temperature and pressure of the melting line. In this manner, heat-capacity measurements could be made at volumes corresponding to pressures of 20 kilobars at absolute zero using recently developed high-pressure gas techniques.[8] This has not been done, but measurements have been made of the effect of pressure on superconducting transitions in which pressures up to 3 kilobars were transmitted by helium which was solidified at constant pressure.[9,10]

5-2c Ultrasonic methods. The third method, which can yield, in principle, the most precise data and the greatest amount of information, involves the use of ultrasonic techniques to measure directly the pressure and temperature variation of the elastic constants of a single crystal. Ultrasonic measurements are being made routinely over a wide range of temperatures at zero pressure,[11] and isothermal measurements of the pressure dependence also have been made.[2] Work of this type, extending over a range of temperatures and pressures, faces the multiple problems of bringing electrical connections into a high-pressure cylinder at low temperature, bonding the transducer to the single-crystal sample, and, finally, transmitting the pressure to the sample in a temperature and pressure region in which fluids no longer exist. These problems undoubtedly can be solved for the alkali metals and other less compressible substances which are solid at room temperature, but the difficulties would seem almost insurmountable for the solidified rare gases. Anderson has used gaseous helium as a pressure transmitter to 40°K to measure ultrasonically

[8] D. Langer and D. M. Warschauer, Notes on a High Pressure Gas Apparatus, *Rev. Sci. Instr.*, vol. 32, pp. 32–34, 1961.

[9] C. H. Hinrichs and C. A. Swenson, Superconducting Critical Field of Tantalum as a Function of Temperature and Pressure, *Phys. Rev.*, vol. 123, p. 1106, 1961.

[10] J. E. Schirber and C. A. Swenson, The Superconductivity of α and β Mercury, *Phys. Rev.*, vol. 123, p. 1115, 1961.

[11] H. B. Huntington, The Elastic Constants of Single Crystals, pp. 213–351 in F. Seitz and D. Turnbull (eds.,) "Solid State Physics," vol. 7, Academic Press, Inc., New York, 1958.

the temperature and pressure dependence of the elastic constants of fused silica in what is perhaps the most comprehensive work along these lines to date.[12]

Even if the experimental problems are solved, there remain difficulties in the interpretation of the data. The longitudinal elastic constants which are measured as a function of pressure at constant temperature are adiabatic, not isothermal, quantities. In order to compare the results with static measurements, the compressibility, for instance, must be converted from k_s (adiabatic) to k_T (isothermal) using the relationship

$$k_T = k_s\left(1 + \frac{\beta^2 VT}{k_s C_p}\right) = k_s(1 + \beta\Gamma T) \tag{5-1}$$

where $\beta = V^{-1}(\partial V/\partial T)_p$ is the thermal expansion, C_p is the specific heat at constant pressure, and $\Gamma = \beta V/k_s C_p = \beta V/k_T C_v$ is a Grüneisen constant which will be discussed in Sec. 5-5 but which is a function, in general, of both temperature and volume. Measurements of k_s as a function of temperature and pressure can be converted to k_T only if the quantity in parentheses in Eq. (5-1) is known as a function of pressure and temperature. The correction term for sodium, which is a typical simple solid, is 0.07 at room temperature and atmospheric pressure and decreases by a factor of 2 at a pressure of 20 kilobars, where $V/V_0 = 0.80$.[6] Thus, a P-V-T surface can be constructed from k_s data as a function of temperature and pressure only by means of a self-consistent approach. In the limit as the temperature approaches zero, the two compressibilities become identical, and no ambiguity arises. Nevertheless, this would seem to be the only feasible approach for those substances which do not adapt themselves readily to the other two methods.

5-2d X-ray methods. The applications of X-ray techniques to high-pressure work have been devoted primarily to a study of crystal-structure changes at phase transformations.[13] Work at room temperature has been reported on the change with pressure of the lattice constants of cerium[14] and graphite.[15] The only low-temperature X-ray work at

[12] O. L. Anderson, An Accurate Determination of the Equation of State by Ultrasonic Measurements, pp. 225–255 in F. P. Bundy, W. R. Hibbard, Jr., and H. M. Strong (eds.), "Progress in Very High Pressure Research," John Wiley & Sons, Inc., New York, 1961.

[13] J. C. Jamieson, Diamond Cell for X-ray Diffraction Studies under High Pressure, pp. 10–15 in F. P. Bundy, W. R. Hibbard, Jr., and H. M. Strong (eds.), "Progress in Very High Pressure Research," John Wiley & Sons, Inc., New York, 1961.

[14] L. F. Vereschchagin, Investigations (in USSR) in the Area of the Physics of High Pressures, pp. 290–303 in F. P. Bundy, W. R. Hibbard, Jr., and H. M. Strong (eds.), "Progress in Very High Pressure Research," John Wiley & Sons, Inc., New York, 1961.

[15] S. S. Kabalkino and L. F. Vereschchagin, X-ray Investigation of the Linear Compressibility of Graphite at Pressures up to 16,000 kg/cm², *Doklady Akad. Nauk S. S. S. R.*, vol. 131, pp. 300–302, 1960.

high pressures that has been reported involves the determination of the crystal structure of the β phase of solid He4[16] and the γ phase of solid He3[17] in the liquid-hydrogen region at pressures of over 1 kilobar. As of the moment, it is difficult to assess the potentialities of this type of measurement.

5-3 General Theoretical Considerations

Two steps are involved in the development of an equation of state for a system. First, the Schrödinger equation which describes the system must be solved to give the ground-state energy (or cohesive energy at absolute zero) as a function of volume, as well as the spectrum of excited states which will be of importance at temperatures above absolute zero. Second, statistical mechanics must be used to calculate thermodynamic averages using the energy eigenvalues obtained in the first step.

If one is interested only in the equation of state for temperatures below a given temperature T_0, then it is sufficient to know only those excited states which lie within an energy range of the order of kT_0 above the first excited state. This is because most of the contribution to the constant-volume partition function comes from the low-lying states. It follows directly that the equation of state at absolute zero can be obtained completely from a knowledge of the ground-state energy as a function of volume $E_0(V)$, since

$$P = P_0(V) = \frac{-dE_0(V)}{dV} \tag{5-2}$$

The same model which gives the ground-state energy satisfactorily may not give good values for the excited states. As an example, the Einstein (independent-particle) model can provide good values for the ground-state energy of the lattice at all volumes (if correlation effects are not important) and, hence, an accurate equation of state at absolute zero. On the other hand, the excited states of a lattice as given by this model are not correct, and their use in evaluating the partition function (and the thermodynamic properties) gives an equation of state which is not correct. This is demonstrated by the difference between the exponential dependence of the specific heat predicted by this model for low temperatures and the observed T^3 dependence.

The converse is true also. That is, the temperature derivatives of the free energy F at constant volume can be evaluated from a knowledge of the excited states alone, since the temperature-dependent contributions to F and, hence, these derivatives are independent of the choice of the

[16] R. L. Mills and A. F. Schuch, Crystal Structure of the β Form of He4, *Phys. Rev. Letters*, vol. 6, p. 263, 1961.

[17] A. F. Schuch and R. L. Mills, New Allotropic Form of He3, *Phys. Rev. Letters*, vol. 6, p. 596, 1961.

origin from which the energies are measured (i.e., independent of any additive temperature-independent term in the free energy). This is, for instance, the situation which is encountered in the theory of specific heats. A similar situation exists in cases in which a magnetic field is one of the variables of state. In the remainder of this section, the theoretical problem will be outlined in a general form, while in Sec. 5-4 specific results will be discussed.

The Schrödinger equation which describes the stationary states of a system of N nuclei and $n = ZN$ electrons (Z = atomic number) involves the kinetic energy of the electrons K_e and of the nuclei K_n and the several Coulomb attractions V_{en} and repulsions V_{ee} and V_{nn} among them. This equation reads

$$\mathcal{H}\Psi = [K_e + K_n + V_{ee} + V_{en} + V_{nn} + \mathcal{H}'(x, X; \sigma, \Sigma)]\Psi_\nu(x, \sigma; X, \Sigma) = E_\nu \Psi_\nu \quad (5\text{-}3)$$

where Ψ_ν is the (total) wave function describing the quantum-mechanical state (eigenstate ν, eigenvalue E_ν) of the entire system. $\mathcal{H}'(x, \sigma; X, \Sigma)$ represents any additional interactions (such as an external pressure, a magnetic field, relativistic effects, and L-S coupling). Whenever possible, lower-case letters (x and σ) will refer to electronic variables, and capital letters to nuclear variables. In Eq. (5-3) x and σ, on one hand, and X and Σ, on the other, denote space and spin variables of the electrons and nuclei, respectively.

Since the nuclei are much heavier than the electrons, Eq. (5-3) can be separated into two equations,[18] one describing the motion of the electrons [Eq. (5-5) below] for a fixed configuration (X^0, Σ^0) of the nuclei, and the other [Eq. (5-6)] describing the motion of the nuclei in the average field of the electrons:

$$\Psi_\nu(x, \sigma; X, \Sigma) \cong \Phi_\alpha(X, \Sigma)\varphi_\beta[x, \sigma; X^0, \Sigma^0] \quad (5\text{-}4)$$

$$(K_e + V_{ee} + V_{en} + V_{nn})\varphi_\beta[x, \sigma; X^0 \Sigma^0] = \mathcal{E}_\beta(X^0, \Sigma^0)\varphi_\beta \quad (5\text{-}5)$$

$$[K_n + \mathcal{E}_\beta(X, \Sigma)]\Phi_\alpha(X, \Sigma) = E_{\alpha,\beta}\Phi_\alpha \quad (5\text{-}6)$$

In Eq. (5-5), the electronic energy eigenvalue $\mathcal{E}_\beta$ depends on the nuclear configuration (X^0, Σ^0) which was chosen, and this quantity plays the role of a potential energy of interaction between the nuclei in Eq. (5-6). Since the system of electrons in any practical case involving a solid is always highly degenerate (thermodynamically), the system of electrons as far as nuclear motion is concerned can be considered as being in its ground state φ_0, and the subscript can be omitted in Eq. (5-6). This will

[18] M. Born and K. Huang, "The Dynamical Theory of Crystal Lattices," Oxford University Press, New York, 1954.

introduce errors of the order of kT/E_F (E_F being the Fermi energy) which are negligible at any ordinary temperature.

In the case of a solid, the (quantum-mechanical) average positions $\langle X \rangle$ of the nuclei will form a regular lattice, $\mathbf{X}_i{}^0$, and the volume V will appear as a variable of state in Eqs. (5-4) to (5-6) through the nearest-neighbor locations $\mathbf{X}^0{}_{ij}$. Equations (5-5) and (5-6) must be solved for a solid only for configurations $\mathbf{X}_i$ close to the lattice configuration $\mathbf{X}_i{}^0$ (the nuclear spins Σ will have only a negligible effect on the electronic motion φ).

There are essentially two different approaches to the solution of Eq. (5-5), depending on the degree of approximation possible. Consider an element for which the free atoms have an ionization potential V_I and an average distance R_0 between nearest neighbors in the solid. The perturbation on any atom due to the presence of its z neighbors is at most of the order of $V_p = (z/2)(e^2/2R_0)$. Hence, if $V_I \gg V_p$, the presence of neighbors will not appreciably affect the electronic motion as compared with the motion in a free atom, and the electronic wave function φ_β in Eq. (5-6) will bear a definite resemblance to the free-atom electronic wave function. If a value of z of the order of 10 is chosen and the numerical value of the electronic charge is used, the condition $V_I \gg V_p$ can be written as

$$V_I R_0 \gg 30 \text{ ev-Å} \tag{5-7}$$

where V_I is in electron volts and R_0 is in angstrom units.

It is easy to verify that for all solids (in which R_0 is small) only the solidified inert gases (helium, neon, argon, etc., in which $V_I \approx 20$ ev) can satisfy the condition in Eq. (5-7) for all electrons. This relationship may be satisfied for other solidified elements by the inner-core electrons, but is certainly violated by the valence electrons. Hence, the state φ of these valence electrons will bear very little resemblance to their state in a free atom.

Since the equation of state at absolute zero will be obtained from $E_{\alpha,\beta}$ of Eq. (5-6) (and possibly just from $\mathcal{E}_\beta$), the two approaches possible for the calculation of a theoretical equation of state at absolute zero depend on whether or not Eq. (5-7) is satisfied. One of these approaches will be useful in determining the equation of state for solid helium, neon, argon, etc., or even metallic vapors (where a large R_0 exists), while the other will be necessary for all other solids, except for ionic crystals, which form a third category due to the presence of long-range Coulomb forces between the ions.[18]

Equations (5-5) and (5-6) can be further simplified by noting that the nuclear spins Σ have a negligible effect on the equation of state of any solid except He3 and possibly H_2. Thus, they may be disregarded in these equations, which then become

$$(K_e + V_{ee} + V_{en} + V_{nn})\varphi_\beta(x, \sigma; X^0) = \mathcal{E}_\beta(X^0)\varphi_\beta \tag{5-8}$$
$$[K_n + \mathcal{E}_\beta(X^0)]\Phi_\alpha(X^0) = E_{\alpha,\beta}\Phi_\alpha(X^0) \tag{5-9}$$

If Eq. (5-7) is satisfied, the electronic eigenvalue is given, to a good approximation, by

$$\mathcal{E}(X_1, X_2, \ldots, X_N) = \sum_{i>j=1}^{N} V_2(\mathbf{X}_i, \mathbf{X}_j) + \sum_{k>l>m=1}^{N} V_3(\mathbf{X}_k, \mathbf{X}_l, \mathbf{X}_m) + \cdots \tag{5-10}$$

where V_2 is a function of the coordinates of a pair of nuclei only, V_3 is a function of the coordinates of a triplet of nuclei, etc. V_2 usually is called the two-body potential, and V_3, V_4, . . . the many-body potentials. The separation in Eq. (5-10) is useful only if the contribution which arises from many-body forces is negligible. In practice, it is possible to obtain only a very rough estimate of the magnitude of V_3 from Eq. (5-8), and it is fortunate that in practice this quantity turns out to be sufficiently small so that many-body forces are customarily neglected in Eqs. (5-9) and (5-10). Then $V_2(x_i, x_j)$ is obtained from the solution of Eq. (5-8) for $N = 2$, and the problem is essentially that of two atoms (2 nuclei and $2Z$ electrons):

$$(K_e + V_{ee} + V_{en_1} + V_{en_2} + V_{n_1n_2})\varphi(x, \sigma; X_{ij}) = V_2(X_{ij})\varphi \tag{5-11}$$

Both φ and V_2 will be functions only of the distance between the nuclei ($X_{ij} = |\mathbf{X}_i - \mathbf{X}_j|$), since the quantity in parentheses on the left-hand side is spherically symmetric. Several attempts have been made[18–20] to solve Eq. (5-11) for a pair of inert gas atoms, with moderate success. V_2 in this equation is usually separated into two parts, the first being an attractive term, the so-called van der Waals force, which is predominant at large interatomic separations, and the second being a repulsive term, often called the overlap repulsion, which is very strong at short interatomic distances. It should be borne in mind, however, that this separation comes about only because two different methods of approximation are needed for these cases in dealing with Eq. (5-11), and that both forces are due to the several Coulomb repulsions and attractions between the $2Z$ electrons and 2 nuclei.

The two-body potential V_2 for a given Z would be expected to be

[19] H. Margenau, Van der Waals Forces, *Rev. Mod. Phys.*, vol. 11, pp. 1–36, 1939.

[20] J. de Boer, Quantum Effects and Exchange Effects on the Thermodynamic Properties of Liquid Helium, pp. 1–58 in C. J. Gorter (ed.), "Progress in Low Temperature Physics," vol. 2, Interscience Publishers, Inc., New York, 1957.

characterized by four constants involving the range and strength of both the repulsive and the attractive forces. Even before the advent of quantum mechanics, V_2 was represented by the so-called Mie-Lennard-Jones potential,

$$V_2(r) = Ar^{-m} - Br^{-n} \qquad m > n;\ A,\ B,\ m,\ n > 0 \tag{5-12}$$

London and Eisenschitz[21] were the first to estimate B and n using the quantum-mechanical Eq. (5-11), and while they were able to show that $n = 6$, only an estimate of B was possible. Slater and Kirkwood[22] solved Eq. (5-11) approximately and showed that the repulsive term should be represented by an exponential rather than an inverse power as in Eq. (5-12). By that time, sets of constants A, B, m, n had been chosen for the inert gases from the empirical fitting of experimental data, mainly through the work of Lennard-Jones and his co-workers,[23] and Eq. (5-12) had been used extensively. A comparison between the theoretical potentials[20] and the empirical potentials of this form [Eq. (5-12)] shows deviations of the order of 10 to 20 percent which must be ascribed either to the presence of many-body forces in a macroscopic system or to the approximations which are introduced in the solution of the two-atom problem or, more likely, to both of these.

The exhaustive pioneering work of Lennard-Jones and others has shown that the choice of $n = 6$ and m between 9 and 16 [together with corresponding values of $A(m)$ and $B(n)$] gives a good description of most of the bulk properties for the inert gases, as well as for the permanent diatomic gases such as nitrogen and hydrogen.[24,25] These same empirical potentials should provide a satisfactory basis for a calculation of the properties of the solidified inert gases, since Eq. (5-7) is satisfied in this case.

If Eq. (5-7) is not satisfied, the concept of two-body forces cannot be introduced, and Eq. (5-6) must be handled using different methods. It is no longer convenient to separate the electronic energy $\mathcal{E}(X_1, X_2, \ldots, X_N)$ into the form of Eq. (5-10), and solutions of Eq. (5-8) for the electronic motion are sought for a perfect, undistorted lattice and for a

[21] F. London and R. Eisenschitz, Über das Verhältness der van der Waalsschen Kräfte zu den homöopolaren Bindungskräften, *Z. Physik*, vol. 60, pp. 491–527, 1930.

[22] J. C. Slater and J. G. Kirkwood, The Van der Waals Forces in Gases, *Phys. Rev.*, vol. 37, pp. 682–697, 1931.

[23] J. E. Lennard-Jones, On the Determination of Molecular Fields. I. From the Variation of the Viscosity of a Gas with Temperature, *Proc. Roy. Soc. London*, vol. A106, pp. 441–462, 1924; On the Determination of Molecular Fields. II. From the Equation of State of a Gas, *Proc. Roy. Soc. London*, vol. A106, pp. 463–477, 1924.

[24] R. H. Fowler and E. A. Guggenheim, "Statistical Thermodynamics," Cambridge University Press, New York, 1952.

[25] A. H. Wilson, "Thermodynamics and Statistical Mechanics," Cambridge University Press, New York, 1957.

lattice which is slightly distorted in a simple and convenient manner (in order to calculate elastic coefficients).[26] Most of the work along these lines has been concerned with metals.

In the following, the discussion will be restricted primarily to the inert gases, on one hand, and to metals, on the other, as illustrations of the theoretical methods. In the next section, the equations of state at absolute zero will be discussed for the solidified inert gases and for the alkali metals. A discussion of the equation of state at higher temperatures will follow in Sec. 5-5.

5-4 Equation of State at Absolute Zero

5-4a The solidified inert gases. As was discussed in the preceding section, the bulk properties of these solids should be derivable from the solutions of a Schrödinger equation for N particles (atoms) which interact according to given two-body interatomic potentials:

$$\left[-\frac{\hbar^2}{2m}\sum_{i=1}^{N}\nabla_{x_i}{}^2 + \tfrac{1}{2}\sum_{i=1}^{N}\sum_{j=1}^{N} V(X_{ij})\right]\Phi_n(X, \Sigma) = E_n\Phi_n(X, \Sigma) \qquad (5\text{-}13)$$

The interatomic potential $V(X_{ij})$ in general will involve four constants which characterize the strength and range of both the attractive and the repulsive forces [A, B, m, and n in Eq. (5-12), for instance]. These in principle could be calculated directly as functions of the atomic number Z. $V(X_{ij})$ represents an energy which is a function of the interatomic separation and which, from dimensional considerations, will involve at least two constants. Hence, it has been customary to take two of the four constants as fixed and independent of Z [for instance, $n = 6$ and $m = 12$ in Eq. (5-12)], so that the dependence of $V(X_{ij})$ on the atomic number Z is contained in the other two constants which may be taken as a range σ (length) and a strength ϵ (energy). Hence, $V(X_{ij})$ may be written as

$$V(X_{ij}) = \epsilon v\left(\frac{X_{ij}}{\sigma}\right) \equiv \epsilon v(x_{ij}) \qquad (5\text{-}14)$$

where $\epsilon = \epsilon(Z)$, $\sigma = \sigma(Z)$, and $v(x)$ is a dimensionless universal function which is independent of the atomic number Z. With this choice, Eq. (5-13) can be written as

$$\left[-\lambda^2\sum_{i=1}^{N}\nabla^2_{x_i} + \tfrac{1}{2}\sum_{i=1}^{N}\sum_{j=1}^{N} v(X_{ij})\right]\Phi_n(X, \Sigma) = E'_n\Phi_n \qquad (5\text{-}15)$$

[26] F. Seitz, "The Modern Theory of Solids," chap. 10, McGraw-Hill Book Company, Inc., New York, 1940.

where $\lambda^2 \equiv \hbar^2/2M\epsilon\sigma^2$, $E'_n = E_n/\epsilon$, and $\nabla^2_{x_i}$ is the Laplacian with respect to the dimensionless variable $x = X/\sigma$.

The optimum values of the constants ϵ and σ vary slightly in the opinions of different authors.[27,27a] For the purpose of the present work, the values of the constants for a 6-12 Lennard-Jones potential as adopted by de Boer will be used.[20] These are given in Table 5-1.

Table 5-1 Values of the Parameters ϵ and σ in the 12-6 Potential,[20] together with Conversion Factors to Reduced Units

	ϵ, °K	σ, Å	ϵ/σ^3, bars	$N\sigma^3$, cm³/mole	λ
He3	10.2	2.56	83.9	10.11	0.347
He4	10.2	2.56	83.9	10.11	0.302
H_2^1	37	2.93	203.1	15.15	0.195
H_2^2	37	2.93	203.1	15.15	0.137
Neon	36.2	2.74	242.9	12.39	0.0658
Argon	121	3.40	425.0	23.67	0.0212
Krypton	166	3.66	467.3	29.50	0.0113
Xenon	232	3.98	508.0	37.97	0.0070

Since the primary interest of this section is in the equation of state of solids at absolute zero, this discussion will be restricted to ground-state solutions only. As was pointed out in Sec. 5-1, a knowledge of the ground-state energy of a system as a function of volume is sufficient to describe the equation of state at absolute zero, so Eq. (5-15) must be solved to give $E_0(V)$. It is convenient to measure the various quantities which are involved in terms of dimensionless units, and in the ensuing discussion, the energy per atom will be measured in units of ϵ ($E' = E_0/N\epsilon$), the volume per atom in units of σ^3 ($V' = V/N\sigma^3$), and the pressure in units of ϵ/σ^3 [$P' = P/(\epsilon/\sigma^3)$]. Hence, Eq. (5-2) can be written as

$$P' = \frac{-dE'}{dV'} \tag{5-2a}$$

The use of these units will be assumed unless otherwise stated; the primes will be omitted. The values of the appropriate conversion factors for various gases are given in Table 5-1.

Several authors have solved Eq. (5-15) using different methods of approximation, and from their solutions it is possible to obtain equations

[27] J. O. Hirschfelder, C. F. Curtis, and R. B. Bird, "Molecular Theory of Gases and Liquids," John Wiley & Sons, Inc., New York, 1954.

[27a] G. Boato and G. Casanova, A Self-consistent Set of Molecular Parameters for Neon, Argon, Krypton, and Xenon, *Physica*, vol. 27, pp. 571–589, 1961.

of state at absolute zero which are essentially consistent.[27–29] The subsequent discussion will be based on the approach used by one of the authors.[29]

An inspection of Table 5-1 will show that quantum-mechanical effects (i.e., $\lambda \neq 0$) can be expected to yield corrections which are small for the heavier elements, appreciable for argon and neon, and very large for helium. Nuclear spins will have a negligible effect in all cases except for He3. In the event that $\lambda \ll 1$, the kinetic-energy term in Eq. (5-15) can be dropped, and the problem reduces to a problem in statics or a summation over a lattice. This is the case which will be discussed in the remainder of this section.

In this approximation, the cohesive energy can be written as

$$E_0 = \tfrac{1}{2} \sum_{i \neq j} \sum v(x_{ij}) = \frac{N}{2} \sum_{i \neq 0} v(x_i) \tag{5-16}$$

where the x_i's describe a lattice. The lattice summation in this equation can be evaluated for a Mie-Lennard-Jones potential for different types of lattices, and the results are tabulated.[27] Equation (5-12) can be rewritten in the form of Eq. (5-14) as

$$V(r) = Ar^{-m} - Br^{-n} = \gamma_{m,n}\epsilon \left[\left(\frac{r}{\sigma} \right)^m - \left(\frac{r}{\sigma} \right)^n \right] \equiv \epsilon v(x) \tag{5-17}$$

where $\gamma_{m,n}$ is a number chosen such that $-\epsilon v$ represents the minimum value of $V(r)$. For this potential, Eq. (5-16) reduces to

$$E_0 = \frac{N}{2} \gamma_{m,n} (C_m x_o^{-m} - C_n x_0^{-n}) \tag{5-18}$$

where C_m and C_n are tabulated constants [27] which depend only on the type of lattice, and which to a first approximation can be taken equal to the number of nearest neighbors. x_0 is the nearest-neighbor distance in units of σ. Finally, in reduced units, the volume dependence of the ground-state energy can be expressed as

$$E_0(V) = \alpha V^{-m/3} - \beta V^{-n/3} \tag{5-19}$$

where α and β depend respectively on m and n and also on the type of lattice. The discussion may be restricted to a close-packed lattice since

[28] N. Bernardes, Theory of Solid Ne, A, Kr and Xe at 0°K, *Phys. Rev.*, vol. 112, pp. 1534–1539, 1958.

[29] N. Bernardes, Quantum Mechanical Law of Corresponding States for Van der Waals Solids at 0°K, *Phys. Rev.*, vol. 120, pp. 807–813, 1960. (There are several typographical errors in this paper. In Table II, $c_{12} = 12.13$. In Eq. 28 and following, $g_{00} = 2.83$. Figures 5 and 6 are incorrect in precise details, but correct in general behavior.)

all the inert gases (except helium at reduced pressures[30,31]) solidify in a close-packed lattice.‡

Successive differentiations of Eq. (5-19) with respect to pressure can be used to give the zero-pressure volume V_0, the cohesive energy E_0, and the P-V relationship, as well as the bulk modulus at zero pressure B_0. The respective values for $m = 12$ and $n = 6$ are (in reduced units)

$$V_0(0) = 0.916 \tag{5-20}$$
$$E_0(0) = -8.61 \tag{5-21}$$
$$B_0(0) = 75 \tag{5-22}$$
$$P_0(V) = 24.3V^{-5} - 28.9V^{-3} \tag{5-23}$$

Equation (5-23) represents a classical ($\lambda = 0$) equation of state which is the same for all inert gases, and demonstrates the existence of a law of corresponding states for them. That is to say, their physical properties satisfy the same set of equations when these properties are expressed in the proper units.

In order to compare these results with experiment, the experimental values of ϵ and σ (and the appropriate conversion factors) as given in Table 5-1 must be used. This comparison is given in some detail elsewhere.[29] The nonexistence of a law of corresponding states of this type for the solidified inert gases is demonstrated in Fig. 5-2, where the experimental low temperature (20°K) P-V data for neon,[32] argon,[33] and xenon[5] are plotted in reduced form (V/V_0 versus P/B_0). The pressure range is 20 kilobars in each case. Equations (5-22) and (5-23) imply that these curves should be identical, and the differences between them as shown by the progressive increase in "softness" with decreasing atomic mass (or increasing λ) are indicative of quantum-mechanical effects. It will be shown in a subsequent section that these differences can be understood quantitatively by the inclusion of zero-point energy effects. The corresponding curve for the alkali metals (see Sec. 5-4*b*) is shown for comparison.

5-4b The alkali metals. The assumption that Eq. (5-7) holds does not apply to most solids, particularly metals. Because of the

[30] A. F. Schuch, E. R. Grilly, and R. L. Mills, Structure of the α and β Forms of Solid He3, *Phys. Rev.*, vol. 110, p. 775, 1958.

[31] N. Bernardes, On the Different Crystallographic Phases of Solid Helium, USAEC Research and Development Report, Ames Laboratory, IS-285, 1960.

[32] J. W. Stewart, The Compression of Solidified Gases to 20,000 kg/cm^2 at Low Temperatures, *J. Phys. Chem. Solids*, vol. 1, pp. 146–158, 1956.

[33] J. W. Stewart, private communication, 1960. We are indebted to Prof. Stewart for communicating these results to us.

‡ The differences between cubic close-packed and hexagonal close-packed lattices represent one part in 10^4 and hence are not important except, apparently, for helium.[7,16,17,30,31]

complications introduced by the existence of free electrons, the concept of two-body forces [Eq. (5-10)] cannot be used when metals are discussed. The various approximations which must be used in a calculation of the cohesive energy and equation of state of metals make this an exceedingly complex problem, and the reader is referred to several review articles[34–38]

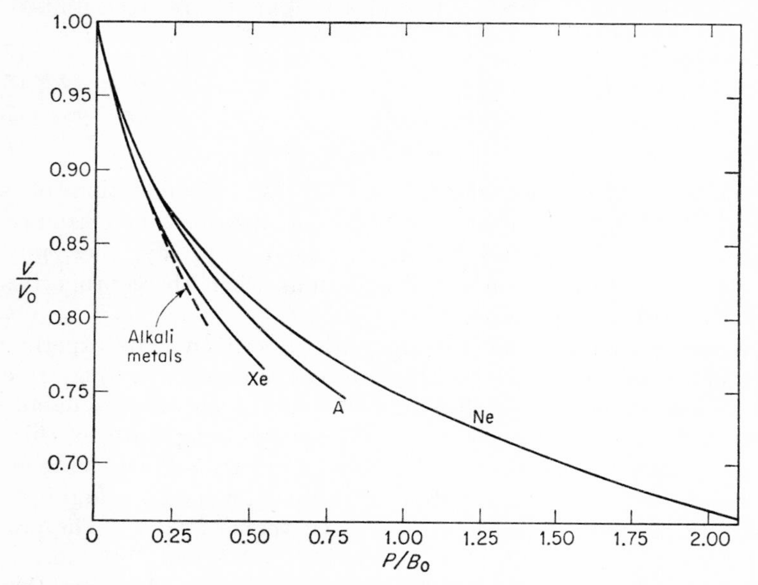

Fig. 5-2 A reduced plot of the low-temperature equation of state for the alkali metals (see Fig. 5-3 for more detail) xenon,[5] argon,[33] and neon.[32] V_0 and B_0 are the volume and bulk modulus at zero pressure in each case.

for a discussion of the theory and a general comparison with experiment. The most extensive low-temperature equation-of-state data exist for the alkali metals, and the following discussion will be restricted to them. Since these atoms, with a single electron outside a closed shell, form the simplest possible class of metals, it would be expected that any basic

[34] J. R. Reitz, Methods of the One-electron Theory of Solids, pp. 2–95 in F. Seitz and D. Turnbull (eds.), "Solid State Physics," vol. 1, Academic Press, Inc., New York, 1955.

[35] E. P. Wigner and F. Seitz, Qualitative Analysis of the Cohesion in Metals, pp. 97–126 in F. Seitz and D. Turnbull (eds.), "Solid State Physics," vol. 1, Academic Press, Inc., New York, 1955.

[36] F. S. Ham, The Quantum Defect Method, pp. 127–192 in F. Seitz and D. Turnbull (eds.), "Solid State Physics," vol. 1, Academic Press, Inc., New York, 1955.

[37] D. Pines, Electron Interaction in Metals, pp. 367–450 in F. Seitz and D. Turnbull (eds.), "Solid State Physics," vol. 1, Academic Press, Inc., New York, 1955.

[38] H. Brooks, Quantum Theory of Cohesion, *Nuovo cimento*, vol. 7, supplement, pp. 165–244, 1958.

calculations apply most correctly in this case. The basis of the comparison of experimental data with theory given below will be a simple theory first put forth by Bardeen,[39] which, although not correct, will illustrate the difficulties involved.

The cohesive energy of the alkali metals is discussed most commonly on the basis of the so-called Wigner-Seitz method. In this method, the crystal is subdivided into polyhedra, and in the case of the alkali metals each polyhedron contains only one electron. These polyhedra are replaced by spheres of radius r_s whose volumes are equal to the volume occupied by each atom of the metal. The pressure dependence of r_s gives the equation of state of the metal at absolute zero.

Bardeen suggested that for these metals (to a first approximation) the energy relationship should be of the form[39,26]

$$E(r_s) = ar_s^{-3} + br_s^{-2} + cr_s^{-1} \tag{5-24}$$

where the middle right-hand term represents the electronic kinetic, or Fermi, energy, and the other two right-hand terms represent the potential energy of the electrostatic interaction of each electron with the rest of the solid. Thus, the energy of the whole solid can be written as a function of volume,

$$\begin{aligned} E(V) &= A\,\frac{V_0}{V} + B\left(\frac{V_0}{V}\right)^{2/3} - C\left(\frac{V_0}{V}\right)^{1/3} \\ &= Ay^3 + By^2 - Cy \end{aligned} \tag{5-25}$$

where V_0 is the volume at zero pressure, and A, B, and C are constants which in principle can be calculated.

In the context of our discussion of the inert gases, two additional terms should be included in Eq. (5-25), which considers only the electrons in a cell and their interaction with the nucleus. These terms would describe the effects of nuclear zero-point motion and the interaction between all pairs of closed electronic shells. The latter is similar in nature to the interaction between two inert gas atoms, as was discussed in the preceding section, and can be shown to have only a small effect on the compressibility of the alkali metals, except at very high pressures.[38] The same is true for the influence of the nuclear zero-point motion, and this will be discussed in the next section. Nevertheless, it is very difficult to assess the exact effect of these small corrections, due to the uncertainties and approximations which are involved in any calculation of the electronic energy.[38]

One method for the comparison of the theoretical expression for the energy [Eq. (5-25)] with experimental data is to compare calculated and

[39] J. Bardeen, Compressibilities of the Alkali Metals, *J. Chem. Phys.*, vol. 6, pp. 372–378, 1938.

experimental P-V isotherms for very low temperatures. Equation (5-25) can be shown to give (with the requirement that E is a minimum at $y = 1$ and, hence, $C = 3A - 2B$)

$$PV_0 = y^4(y-1)\left[2A + \frac{2B}{3} + A(y-1)\right] \tag{5-26}$$

This may be rewritten (with $3V_0/k_0 = 2A + 2B/3$) as

$$Pk_0 = y^4(y-1)\left[3 + \frac{Ak_0}{V_0}(y-1)\right] \tag{5-27}$$

where V_0 and k_0 are the zero-pressure volume and compressibility, respectively. The second term in brackets is usually small and is the only contribution which should be characteristic of the individual alkali metal.

The experimental data for the alkali metals are given in Fig. 5-3, where V/V_0 is plotted versus $Pk_0 = P/B_0$. It can be seen that in this

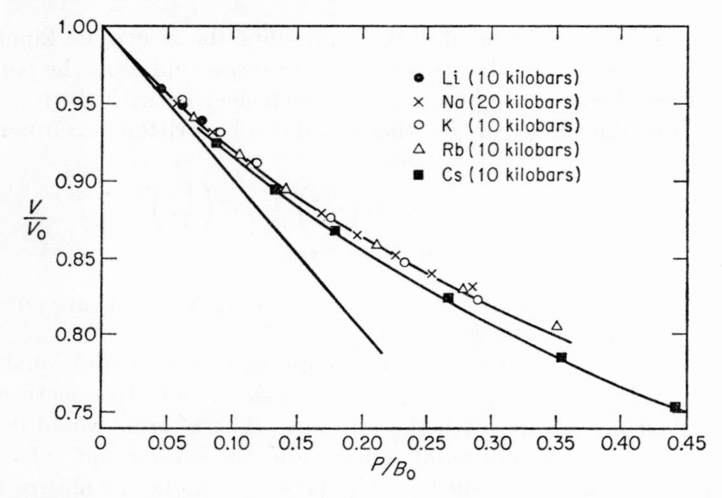

Fig. 5-3 The low-temperature equations of state for the alkali metals. The data for sodium are to 20 kilobars,[6] while those for lithium, potassium, rubidium, and cesium are to 10 kilobars.[40]

representation the data for sodium (to 20 kilobars),[6] potassium (to 10 kilobars),[40] and rubidium (to 8 kilobars)[40] are identical for volume decreases up to 18 per cent. The deviations for lithium (if any)[40] are in the direction which shows that this metal is "too hard," while cesium is definitely "too soft," when compared with the other alkali metals. The solid curve through the sodium, potassium, and rubidium data in Fig. 5-3 was drawn using Eq. (5-27) with $Ak_0/V_0 = 4.2$, while the curve

[40] C. A. Swenson, Compression of the Alkali Metals to 10,000 Atmospheres at Low Temperature, *Phys. Rev.*, vol. 99, pp. 423–430, 1955.

through the cesium data was drawn using $Ak_0/V_0 = 0$. The fit is well within experimental error in each case, while the difference between the two curves would appear to be outside experimental error.

In earlier comparisons, experimental values of the cohesive energy, initial compressibility, and molar volume at zero pressure were used to evaluate the constants B and C empirically for comparison with the theoretical values.[26,39,40] The agreement was considered satisfactory, although the predicted shape of the P-V isotherm was not correct, except possibly for sodium.[40] Ham[36] has given a comparison of experimental data with a theory which is based on the more rigorous quantum-defect method. Here, explicit energy calculations for three values of y were fitted to an equation of the form of Eq. (5-25), and pressures for a given value of V/V_0 as calculated from this fit [Eq. (5-26)] were compared with the actual experimental pressures for the same V/V_0. The agreement was not particularly good, except for potassium, for which only a 5 percent discrepancy was found.

An alternative procedure involves using the initial compressibility, the zero-pressure molar volume, and the value of Ak_0/V_0 which is needed to fit the experimental P-V data to evaluate the constants A, B, and C. The identity of the curves for sodium, potassium, and rubidium (Fig. 5-3) implies that the ratio A/B must be a constant for these three metals. There is no basis for this in the elementary theory,[26,39] and, indeed, the values of A, B, and C obtained in this manner give cohesive energies [Eq. (5-25) with $y = 1$] which bear no resemblance to experimental values.

The detailed considerations of the theory of the alkali metals[36,38,41] which take into account the explicit electronic structure of the individual elements give no suggestion that a common equation of state or law of corresponding states should exist for sodium, potassium, and rubidium.

It would appear from the complications of the problem that the calculation of the equation of state for each of the alkali metals is a problem in itself which must be solved explicitly, and that a generalized solution in proper reduced variables is not possible for this class of substances as it is for the solidified inert gases (see the next section). The qualitatively different behavior of the P-V curve for cesium (and possibly for lithium) from that of the curve for sodium, potassium, and rubidium is probably associated with the very different electronic structure which is possessed by the metals in these cases.[42] Cesium, in particular, shows considerable dependence of its electronic properties upon even moderate pressures at

[41] J. Bardeen, An Improved Calculation of the Energies of Metallic Li and Na, *J. Chem. Phys.*, vol. 6, pp. 367–371, 1938.

[42] F. S. Ham, Band Calculations of the Shape of the Fermi Surface in the Alkali Metals, in W. A. Harrison and M. B. Webb (eds.), "The Fermi Surface," John Wiley & Sons, Inc., New York, 1960.

room temperature,[43] and at high pressures (40 kilobars) and room temperature, a phase transition occurs in this metal with a very large volume change. This has been postulated as due to the movement of a $6s$ electron into a $5d$ orbital, with no change in the crystal structure.[44] It is possible that this transition is "smeared out" as the temperature is lowered, and that a gradual change in the electronic wave function with pressure at low temperature is responsible for the softness of this metal.[40]

From a purely empirical viewpoint, the similarity of the shapes of the various curves in Fig. 5-3 is not surprising. Birch[45] has suggested an equation of state which is derivable from Murnaghan's theory of finite strain:

$$Pk_0 = \tfrac{3}{2}(y^7 - y^5)[1 - \xi(y^2 - 1)] \tag{5-28}$$

where $y = (V_0/V)^{1/3}$ as before and k_0 is the compressibility at $y = 1$. This equation appears to fit existing room-temperature data for most substances to 100 kilobars with small values of ξ. The earlier alkali-metal data[40] and much of the data on the solidified inert gases have been fitted to this relationship with k_0 and ξ as parameters. The more recent data for sodium appear to show slight deviations from this expression at high temperatures, but not at 20°K.[6] The solid curve in Fig. 5-3 also can be represented by Eq. (5-28) with $\xi = 0$. The deviations from this curve which are found for cesium (Fig. 5-3) and the solidified inert gases (Fig. 5-2) are indicative of the electronic transition in cesium, on the one hand, and of the very large effect of the zero-point energy for the lighter inert gases, on the other.

The Bardeen and Birch expressions represent special cases of a more generalized equation of state. Gilvarry has discussed this at some length, together with a consideration of the effects of temperature on the equation of state.[46]

Finally, the sodium data to 20 kilobars satisfy the empirical assumption that the isothermal compressibility is a linear function of the volume,[6]

$$k_T = A\left(1 - \frac{V}{\nu}\right) \tag{5-29}$$

where A and ν are constants independent of the temperature. This results in an expression for $\Delta V/V_0$,

$$\frac{\Delta V}{V_0} = \frac{\exp AP - 1}{\exp AP - [1 - \nu/V_0(0)]^{-1}} \tag{5-30}$$

[43] J. S. Dugdale, private communication, 1960.

[44] R. M. Sternheimer, The Compressibility of Metallic Cesium, *Phys. Rev.*, vol. 78, pp. 235–243, 1950.

[45] F. Birch, Elasticity and Constitution of the Earth's Interior, *J. Geophys. Research*, vol. 57, pp. 227–286, 1952.

[46] J. J. Gilvarry, Temperature-dependent Equation of State of Solids, *J. Appl. Phys.*, vol. 28, pp. 1253–1261, 1957.

which, it would seem, should also apply to potassium and rubidium at low temperature. If $\Delta V/V_0$ is to be a function of Pk_0 only (Fig. 5-3), the constants which apply to sodium could be used in the above expression to write down a common expression for sodium, potassium, and rubidium:

$$\frac{\Delta V}{V_0} = \frac{\exp(-2.210Pk_0) - 1}{\exp(-2.210Pk_0) - 3.212} \tag{5-31}$$

This expression obviously cannot be used for extrapolation to much higher pressures, since it implies a minimum value of the volume in each case which is greater than the volumes which have been observed by Bridgman at 100 kilobars.[2] Any attempt to correlate these low-temperature data with the higher-pressure room-temperature data is difficult, since there are inconsistencies which are seemingly outside the experimental error for the two sets of existing higher-pressure data on the alkali metals.[6]

5-4c The effects of nuclear zero-point motion. The nuclei have been assumed to be at rest in previous discussions of the solidified inert gases and alkali metals. However, the nuclear zero-point energy may represent an appreciable contribution to the cohesive energy and, hence, to the equation of state at absolute zero. At finite temperatures, nuclear motion (that is, thermal vibrations) is the only effect which alters the equation of state as a function of temperature, and this will be discussed in Sec. 5-5. The observed decrease in compressibility with temperature at constant volume for most solids is due primarily to the excitation of nuclear vibrations (phonons), since the quantum-mechanical electronic states are practically temperature independent under these conditions.

However, even at absolute zero, when no phonons are excited, the nuclear zero-point motion may have important effects on the equation of state of a solid. A rough measure of the importance of these effects can be obtained by the ratio of $k\theta_D/E_0$, where θ_D is the Debye temperature and E_0 is the cohesive energy. Values for this ratio are shown in Table 5-2. It may be concluded from an inspection of this table that nuclear

Table 5-2 Dimensionless Parameters Indicative of Zero-point Effects for the Solidified Inert Gases and the Alkali Metals

Parameter	Ne	A	Kr	Xe	Li	Na	K	Rb	Cs
$k\theta_D/E_0$	0.29	0.088	0.048	0.028	0.003	0.0015	0.0011	0.0008	0.0007
$k\theta_D/B_0V_0$	0.041	0.012	(0.006)	0.003	0.012	0.0053	0.004	0.0025	0.0021

zero-point motion will have a negligible effect on the equation of state of the alkali metals at absolute zero, but may have a large effect on the behavior of the inert gases, especially the lighter ones. This is emphasized by the fact that neither of the isotopes of helium will solidify when cooled under its saturated vapor pressure even to extremely low temperatures. The behavior of helium is unique and, with the many unusual properties of the element, does not fall within the scope of the present discussion.[47–50]

A more quantitative measure of the effect of nuclear zero-point motion on the equation of state can be obtained as follows: Figure 5-4 represents

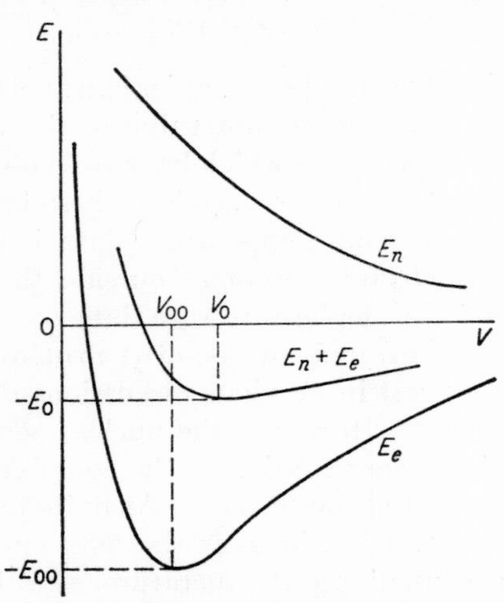

Fig. 5-4 A schematic $E(V)$ relationship for a solid, showing the nuclear zero-point energy E_n, the electronic energy E_e, and the net cohesive energy $E_n + E_e$. The symbols are defined in the text.

schematically the electronic energy $E_e(V)$ and the zero-point energy $E_n(V)$ of a solid as a function of volume. These functions can be written approximately as

$$E_e(V) = -E_{00} + \tfrac{1}{2}\frac{B_{00}}{V_{00}}(V - V_{00})^2 + \tfrac{1}{6}\alpha\frac{B_{00}}{V_{00}^2}(V - V_{00})^3 \quad (5\text{-}32)$$

$$E_n(V) = k\theta_D\left(\frac{V}{V_{00}}\right)^{-\Gamma} \quad (5\text{-}33)$$

where V_{00}, E_{00}, and B_{00} represent the volume, cohesive energy, and bulk modulus at zero pressure and in the absence of nuclear zero-point motion.

[47] C. Domb and J. S. Dugdale, Solid Helium, pp. 338–367 in C. J. Gorter (ed.), "Progress in Low Temperature Physics," vol. 2, Interscience Publishers, Inc., New York, 1957.

[48] N. Bernardes, Theory of the Compressibility of Solid He4 and He3 at 0°K, *Phys. Rev.*, vol. 120, pp. 1927–1932, 1960.

[49] E. R. Grilly and E. F. Hammel, Liquid and Solid He3, pp. 113–152 in C. J. Gorter (ed.), "Progress in Low Temperature Physics," vol. 3, Interscience Publishers, Inc., New York, 1961.

[50] N. Bernardes and D. F. Brewer, Helium 3, *Rev. Mod. Phys.*, vol. 34, pp. 190–214, 1962.

Γ is an average Grüneisen constant which is of the order of unity and $\alpha = -\left(\frac{dB_{00}}{dP}\right)_{V_{00}}$ is usually between -1 and -10. When the effects of nuclear zero-point motion are taken into account, both the volume V_0 and the compressibility $k_0 = B_0^{-1}$ at zero pressure will be somewhat larger than V_{00} and k_{00}, respectively. In the limit in which $\Delta V = V_0 - V_{00}$ is small, it can be shown[51] that at zero pressure,

$$\frac{\Delta V}{V_{00}} = \Gamma\Delta_{00} \tag{5-34}$$

and

$$\frac{\Delta k_0}{k_{00}} = -\frac{\Delta B_0}{B_{00}} = \Gamma\Delta_{00}\,(\Gamma + \alpha + 2) \tag{5-35}$$

where

$$\Delta_{00} = \frac{k\theta_D}{B_{00}V_{00}} \cong \frac{k\theta_D}{B_0V_0}$$

Thus, it may be expected that both the volume and the compressibility of any solid at absolute zero and zero pressure will differ from the static value by an amount which is of the order of $k\theta_D/B_0V_0$. Table 5-2 also gives experimental values for this ratio for the solidified inert gases and for the alkali metals.

The relatively large values of this ratio for the solidified inert gases as compared with the alkali metals again indicate that nuclear zero-point motion will have an appreciable effect on neon and argon, and will have little effect on the alkali metals. The relative importance of the zero-point energy can be seen to decrease with increasing pressure.[28]

Very little can be done along the lines of a more precise treatment of these effects for the alkali metals. A more exact treatment of the effects of nuclear zero-point motion on the equation of state of the solidified inert gases must be based on approximate solutions of the quantum-mechanical equations for the nuclear motion [Eqs. (5-8) and (5-9)]. Several authors[28,29,52–56,56a] have discussed this question using different

[51] N. Bernardes, in a paper to be published.

[52] G. Kane, The Equation of State of Frozen Ne, A, Kr and Xe, *J. Chem. Phys.*, vol. 7, pp. 603–613, 1939.

[53] J. de Boer and B. S. Blaisse, Quantum Theory of Condensed Permanent Gases. II. The Solid State and the Melting Line, *Physica*, vol. 14, pp. 149–164, 1948.

[54] J. H. Henkel, Equation of State and Thermal Dependence of the Elastic Coefficients of Crystalline Argon, *J. Chem. Phys.*, vol. 23, pp. 681–687, 1955.

[55] E. R. Dobbs and G. O. Jones, Theory and Properties of Solid Argon, pp. 516–564 in A. C. Strickland (ed.), "Reports on Progress in Physics," vol. 20, The Physical Society, London, 1957.

[56] T. F. Johns, Calculations of Solid State Data of Neon, and the Vapor Pressure Ratio of Its Isotopes, *Phil. Mag.*, vol. 3, pp. 229–236, 1958.

[56a] I. J. Zucker, Reduced Equation of State of Inert Gas Solids at the Absolute Zero, *Proc. Phys. Soc. London*, vol. 77, pp. 889–900, 1961.

methods and different approximations, with fair agreement among the equations of state at absolute zero. The following discussion will be based on the approach used by Bernardes, which shows in a direct manner the influence of quantum-mechanical effects on the equation of state through the use of a law of corresponding states. Details of this calculation can be found in the original paper.[29]

A good description of the solidified inert gases at absolute zero can be obtained by a single-particle approximation in which every atom is assumed to move in the average field of all the others, with no correlation between the motions of different atoms. The motion of an individual atom can be characterized by the (quantum-mechanical) mean square deviation of an atom from its lattice site. This average deviation affects the energy in two ways: first, there is a zero-point kinetic energy K and second, a correction ΔU to the potential energy of interaction, since the distance between any pair of atoms is not fixed but also has a mean deviation due to zero-point motion. The actual mean square deviation of an atom from its lattice site can be obtained by means of the variational principle of quantum mechanics, which asserts that the best approximate solution to the Schrödinger equation can be obtained by minimizing the expectation value of the Hamiltonian with respect to the parameters describing the quantum-mechanical motion (here, the mean square deviation). When such a variational calculation is carried out, the results can be expressed as a series of powers in λ [Eq. (5-15)]. For a close-packed lattice of atoms interacting according to a 12-6 Mie-Lennard-Jones potential, it is found that[29]

$$V_0(0) = 0.916(1 + 2.02\lambda + 5\lambda^2) \tag{5-36}$$

$$E_0(0) = -8.61(1 - 5.34\lambda + 16\lambda^2) \tag{5-37}$$

$$B_0(0) = 75(1 - 9.4\lambda + 28\lambda^2) \tag{5-38}$$

$$P_0(V) = 24.3V^{-5} - 28.9V^{-3} + 114\lambda V^{-13/3} \tag{5-39}$$

which should be compared with the classical results contained in Eqs. (5-20) to (5-23).

By means of the conversion factors listed in Table 5-1, the predictions of these equations can be compared directly with experimental values. Unfortunately, the data are not all readily available or consistent among themselves when available. For instance, the densities at 4°K for argon and neon as determined by X-ray methods[55,57] and neutron diffraction methods[58] show a systematic difference of about 3 percent, the X-ray

[57] V. S. Kogan, B. G. Lazarew, and R. F. Bulatova, Different Lattice Constants of the Solid Neon Isotopes, *J. Exptl. Theoret. Phys. (USSR)*, vol. 40, pp. 29–31, 1961; *Soviet Physics JETP*, vol. 13, pp. 19–20, 1961.

[58] D. G. Henshaw, Atomic Distribution in Liquid and Solid Neon and Solid Argon by Neutron Diffraction, *Phys. Rev.*, vol. 111, pp. 1470–1475, 1958.

data being higher. Kogan et al.[57] have measured the change in the lattice constant of neon with isotopic content and have shown that the difference between the molar volumes of Ne^{20} and Ne^{22} is $+1.1 \pm 0.5$ percent. This is to be compared with the difference of 0.75 percent predicted from Eq. (5-36) above. Similar work has been done with the lithium isotopes,[59] and the observed difference in lattice constant between Li^6 and Li^7 (0.04 percent) agrees with the value which can be estimated from Eq. (5-34).

The experimental low-temperature P-V data for neon, argon, and xenon are compared with Eq. (5-39) in Fig. 5-5. The agreement is

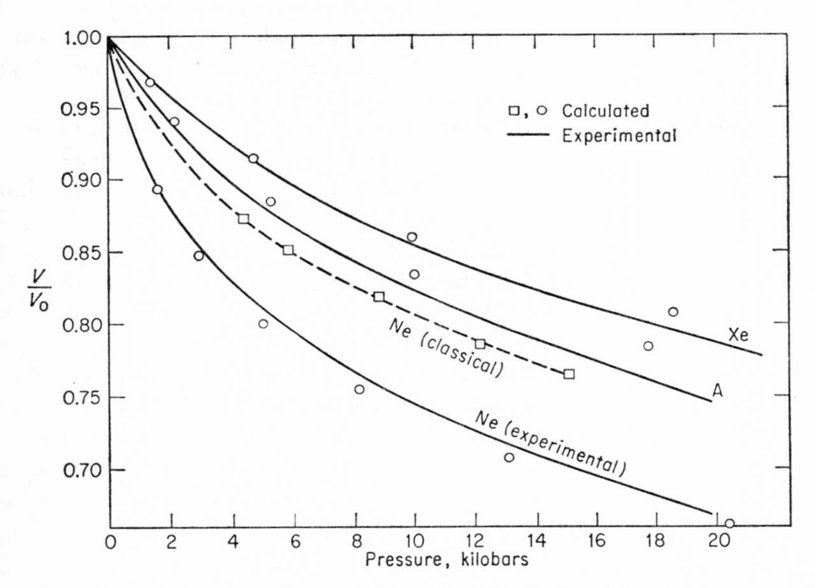

Fig. 5-5 A comparison of the experimental and calculated low-temperature P-V curves for xenon, argon, and neon. The data were obtained as indicated in Fig. 5-2, while the calculations used Eq. (5-39) and the constants in Table 5-1. A slight adjustment of the values of σ was made in the cases of argon and xenon (less than 1 percent in each case) in order to make the experimental and theoretical values of V_0 identical in reduced units and to make the comparison of the two P-V curves more valid.

acceptable for xenon and neon, but not for argon. The reason for the discrepancy is not known. The classical curve [Eq. (5-23)] is shown for neon, and it can be seen clearly how the addition of the zero-point effects improves the agreement between theory and experiment.

[59] E. J. Covington and D. J. Montgomery, Lattice Constants of the Separated Lithium Isotopes, *J. Chem. Phys.*, vol. 27, pp. 1030–1032, 1957.

5-5 The Temperature-dependent Equation of State

It was pointed out in Sec. 5-3 that a knowledge of the ground state of a solid is not necessary for a calculation of its properties as a function of temperature at constant volume. One can, to a good approximation, write the free energy as

$$F(T, V) = E_0(V) + F^*(T, V) = E_0(V) + \sum_{j=1}^{N} F_j^*(T, V) \qquad (5\text{-}40)$$

where the contributions of the excited states have been assumed to be mutually independent. These contributions would include those due to the lattice free electrons, nuclear and quadrupole spins, molecular rotation, magnetic interactions, etc. The temperature dependence of the specific heat or the compressibility at constant volume, for instance, is determined by the F^* contribution. As soon as it is desired to evaluate the temperature dependence at constant pressure of a property such as the thermal expansion or compressibility, however, a knowledge of both the ground state and the excited state is necessary.

In general, the excited-state contribution to the free energy is small, and to a first approximation the compressibility or bulk modulus of a solid may be considered to be dependent on the volume only. This appears to be true for sodium, and perhaps for argon.[2,6] It is not precisely true for some of the more complicated solids (such as copper, silver, gold, and aluminum) where data are available and for which $(\partial \ln k_T/\partial T)_V$ is negative and of the order of 10^{-4} °K^{-1}. This quantity cannot be measured directly, but it can be obtained from a combination of atmospheric-pressure elastic-constant data as a function of temperature and isothermal measurements of the pressure (or volume) variation of the elastic constants as follows:

$$\left(\frac{\partial \ln k_T}{\partial T}\right)_P = \left(\frac{\partial \ln k_T}{\partial V}\right)_T \left(\frac{\partial V}{\partial T}\right)_P + \left(\frac{\partial \ln k_T}{\partial T}\right)_V \qquad (5\text{-}41)$$

A summary of these considerations is given elsewhere.[6]‡

Equation (5-40) implies that the effects of temperature on the pressure and bulk modulus are simply additive at constant volume. Thus,

‡ A reanalysis of the older ultrasonic data by Overton (W. C. Overton, Jr., Relation between Ultrasonically Measured Properties and Coefficients in the Solid Equation of State, *J. Chem. Phys.*, vol. 37, pp. 116–119, 1962) can be used together with Eq. (5-41) to show that the isothermal compressibilities of copper and silver also show no intrinsic temperature dependence. The earlier analyses were based on the temperature and pressure dependence of the adiabatic compressibilities k_s, and indeed an intrinsic temperature dependence must exist for k_s since the ratio k_s/k_T is a function of temperature [Eq. (5-1)].

qualitatively, one can think of a "thermal pressure" which "blows up" the solid, causing thermal expansion and making the substance harder.

Before specific examples are considered, it is of interest to consider the special case in which some (or all) of the F_j^* can be expressed in terms of a reduced equation of state (or law of corresponding states). That is, one assumes that the total volume dependence of this contribution to the free energy appears through a characteristic temperature $\theta_j(V)$ and that $F_j^*/kT = \phi_j[\theta_j(V)/T]$. This leads to the familiar Mie-Grüneisen equation of state for the lattice and similar expressions for other thermally excited properties.[60,61,61a]

In the framework of the above assumption, it follows as a direct consequence that

$$P = P_0(V) + \sum_{j=1}^{N} \frac{\Gamma_j(V) U_j^*(\theta_j/T)}{V} \tag{5-42a}$$

$$\beta = \sum_{j=1}^{N} \frac{\Gamma_j(V) C_{vj} k_T}{V} \tag{5-42b}$$

where $\Gamma_j(V) = -d \ln \theta_j / d \ln V$ is a Grüneisen-type constant.

Two definitions of Γ in terms of thermal quantities are given, with the first [Eq. (5-42a)] being useful when dealing with data expressed as P-V isotherms at various temperatures, and the second [Eq. (5-42b)] being most convenient when dealing with data obtained at atmospheric pressure. Indeed, the two definitions are identical only if the assumption of a law of corresponding states is valid, and thus a comparison of Γ's calculated in these two ways can give direct information about the validity of this simplifying hypothesis. Even if the law-of-corresponding-states hypothesis does not apply, these relationships serve as definitions of the Γ's, which are now functions of both temperature and volume and which allow the equation of state to be expressed in a fairly simple form. The Γ's are typically of the order of 1 to 5 and are positive in many cases, so that Eq. (5-42) can be used to estimate the magnitude of the thermal-expansion contribution due to various terms in the free energy if the heat capacities are known.

[60] F. G. Fumi and M. P. Tosi, On the Mie-Grüneisen and Hildebrand Approximations to the Equation of State of Cubic Solids, *J. Phys. Chem. Solids*, vol. 23, pp. 395–404, 1962. We wish to express our appreciation to the authors for supplying us a copy of the manuscript prior to publication.

[61] R. O. Davies and S. Parke, A Generalization of Grüneisen's Theory of Solids and Its Application to Argon, *Phil. Mag.*, vol. 4, pp. 341–358, 1959.

[61a] G. K. Horton and J. W. Leech, On the Statistical Mechanics of the Ideal Inert Gas Solids, to be published.

The following discussion attempts to summarize the basic theory and results for several specific instances. The framework will be laid in terms of the foregoing summary of the Mie-Grüneisen theory. It must be remembered that if the Γ's are calculated from constant-pressure data, they will display a temperature dependence due to the thermal expansion, even if they have no intrinsic temperature dependence. In general, the Γ's have a practical significance only if the various contributions to the free energy can be separated by different temperature dependences of the specific heats and thermal expansions, for instance. A generalized Γ which is defined from total specific heats and total thermal expansion is of little use.

5-5a Lattice contribution. The free energy of the lattice can be written in the form

$$\frac{F^*}{kT} = \sum_{i=1}^{3N} \ln\left[1 - \exp - \frac{h\nu_i}{kT}\right] + U_0(V)$$
$$= \tfrac{1}{2}\sum_{i=1}^{3N} h\nu_i - \sum_{i=1}^{3N} \ln \frac{2\sinh h\nu_i}{kT} + U_0(V) \qquad (5\text{-}43)$$

The first right-hand term gives the lattice zero-point energy, which is usually lumped together with the static lattice energy $U_0(V)$ to form the ground state E_0 of the system. The definitions of Γ in Eqs. (5-42) can be written as follows:

$$\Gamma_u = \frac{\sum_{i=1}^{3N} \gamma_i u_i}{U^*} \qquad \Gamma_c = \frac{\sum_{i=1}^{3N} \gamma_i c_{vi}}{C_v} \qquad \Gamma_z = \frac{\sum_{i=1}^{3N} \gamma_i v_i}{\sum_{i=1}^{3N} \nu_i} \qquad (5\text{-}44)$$

where the thermodynamic relationships $P = -(\partial F/\partial V)_T$ and

$$U^* = T^2[\partial(-F/T)/\partial T]_V$$

have been used, together with the relationship $\gamma_i = -d \ln \nu_i/d \ln V$ [which assumes $\nu_i(V)$ only]. The third definition will be discussed below.

It is obvious that these definitions of Γ will be identical, and the first two independent of the temperature, only if all the γ_i's are the same, that is, if the frequency spectrum does not change shape upon a change in volume. The third definition Γ_z is of interest for theoretical calculations, since the zero-point energy and its volume dependence often can be calculated directly.[28,62] The zero-point energy is related to the entire frequency spectrum (and, hence, to the high-temperature thermal properties), and its volume dependence should give values for Γ_z which correspond somewhat with the high-temperature thermal values of Γ. In this high-temperature limit, the c_i and u_i contributions of the various oscillators become classical, and $\Gamma_c = \Gamma_u = \sum_{i=1}^{3N} \gamma_i/3N$. This limiting value of the thermal Γ's is not identical with Γ_z, however, since Γ_z is weighted by the volume dependence of the high-frequency part of the spectrum. The zero-point energy and its volume dependence cannot be measured directly, so this quantity is only of theoretical interest.

This discussion is intimately related to calculations of the lattice thermal expansions of solids.[62,63,63a] Barron has given a rather complete discussion of this subject which includes a consideration of various possible definitions of Γ as they relate to the lattice.[62]

For most temperatures, especially those of the same order of magnitude as the characteristic temperature and below it, the thermal definitions of Γ can be expected to be different in magnitude and temperature dependent, since the portions of the vibration spectrum for which $h\nu_i \gg kT$ do not contribute appreciably to the sums involved. The temperature dependence of Γ should give some indication of the change in the shape of the frequency spectrum with volume because of this limitation on the important portions of the spectrum.

It would be of considerable interest to be able to estimate the thermal values for Γ and their volume dependence from other than thermal data. Slater[64] and Dugdale and MacDonald[65] have suggested relationships with which P-V data at constant temperature could be used to obtain Γ. The restrictions were to isotropic solids for which Poisson's ratio does not change with pressure. Unfortunately, the second requirement does not hold for any substance for which data are available.[2] The difficulties can be seen directly for the Debye model, in which θ_D is a function of a suitable average of the longitudinal and transverse sound velocities, which are, in turn, related to the elastic constants. If these two velocities

[62] T. H. K. Barron, Grüneisen Parameters for the Equation of State of Solids, *Ann. Phys. (N.Y.)*, vol. 1, pp. 77–90, 1957.

[63] M. Blackman, On the Lattice Theory of Thermal Expansion, *Proc. Phys. Soc. London*, vol. 74, part 1, pp. 17–26, 1959.

[63a] G. K. Horton, On the Thermal Expansion of Metals at Low Temperatures, *Canad. J. Phys.*, vol. 39, pp. 263–271, 1961.

[64] J. C. Slater, "Introduction to Chemical Physics," pp. 215–220 and 238–240, McGraw-Hill Book Company, Inc., New York, 1939.

[65] J. S. Dugdale and D. K. C. MacDonald, The Thermal Expansion of Solids, *Phys. Rev.*, vol. 89, pp. 832–834, 1953.

change with pressure at different rates, then there may not be a simple relationship between the P-V curve (which is determined by k_T only) and $\Gamma_D = -d \ln \theta_D / d \ln V$.

On the other hand, low-temperature ultrasonic elastic-constant data have been used recently with considerable success to calculate values of θ_D which agree with low-temperature calorimetric values.[66] Hence, one should be able to use the pressure variation of the elastic constants at low temperature (or, approximately, at room temperature) to predict values of Γ which should agree with low-temperature thermal data. The only very-low-temperature thermal-expansion data available at present indicate that Γ is relatively independent of temperature for copper from room temperature to 4°K.[67] One would, then, expect reasonable agreement between calculated elastic-constant and thermal values of Γ in the case of copper.

It is of interest to discuss the available equation-of-state data for solids in terms of the above considerations. Dugdale and Simon[7] found that solid helium under pressures up to 2.5 kilobars and temperatures from 2°K to the melting line obeyed a reduced equation of state, with the characteristic temperature $\phi(V)$ increasing, and its volume dependence, $\Gamma = -d \ln \phi / d \ln V$, decreasing, with increasing pressure. Dugdale[68] has used these results and the 4°K P-V data of Stewart[32] to extrapolate both ϕ and Γ values to 20 kilobars and the melting line. Helium is the only solidified gas for which there are sufficient data available to evaluate the temperature-dependent contribution to the equation of state. The data for argon appear to suggest these contributions are negligible within experimental accuracy (volume changes of roughly $0.001V_0$) for pressures in excess of a few kilobars, even near the triple point.[33] This is undoubtedly due to the high compressibility of argon and the fact that the triple-point temperature (84°K) is approximately the same as the Debye temperature. The high-pressure experiments on the equation of state of solid xenon are more interesting, since here the Debye temperature is roughly one-third of the triple-point temperature, 163°K[5]. Thermal effects are quite important even at 10 kilobars pressure, although even as in the case of sodium, the isothermal compressibility does not appear to contain an intrinsic temperature dependence at constant volume. The shape of the P-V curve at absolute zero is roughly that which would be expected from a Lennard-Jones 6-12 potential, although there appear to

[66] J. A. Rayne and B. S. Chandrasekhar, Elastic Constants of β-Sn, *Phys. Rev.*, vol. 120, pp. 1658–1663, 1960.

[67] G. K. White, Thermal Expansion at Low Temperatures, *Nature*, vol. 187, pp. 927–929, 1960.

[68] J. S. Dugdale, Equation of State of Solid Helium, *Nuovo cimento*, vol. 9, supplement, pp. 27–29, 1958.

be differences in detail. Guggenheim and McGlashan have suggested a more generalized potential function for the solidified inert gases,[68a] but this has not as yet been used to analyze the xenon data.

The Debye temperature for sodium is one-half the melting temperature, and P-V-T data exist for this metal for pressures up to 20 kilobars, from the melting point (370°K) to 20°K.[6] These data have been combined with atmospheric-pressure heat-capacity data to evaluate the various thermodynamic functions over this range of temperature and pressure. Within experimental accuracy, the isothermal compressibility is a linear function of the volume alone [Eq. (5-29)], which simplifies the analysis considerably. Further considerations show that this cannot hold outside the pressure range of the experiments. The results of the various calculations of Γ for sodium are shown in Fig. 5-6. The thermal Γ's [solid

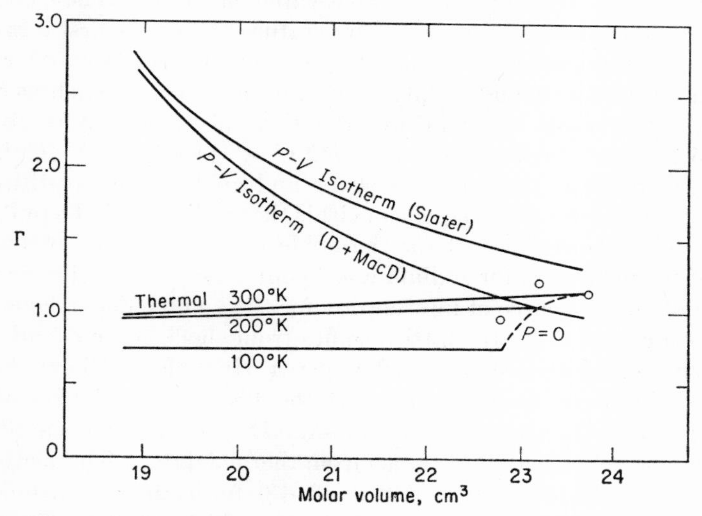

Fig. 5-6 The variation of the Grüneisen constant Γ with volume for sodium. The thermal curves were obtained using Eq. (5-42*a*), while two calculations of Γ from P-V isotherms are shown. The open circles represent values of Γ at zero pressure as calculated from Eq. (5-42*b*) for 300°K, 200°K, and 100°K. (*After Beecroft and Swenson.*[6])

lines, calculated from Eq. (5-42*a*)] decrease slightly with decreasing volume. They agree with Γ's calculated from C_v and β data at atmospheric pressure and room temperature (open circles), where T is of the order of $1.5\theta_D$, but the agreement disappears, as it should, at lower

[68a] E. A. Guggenheim and M. L. McGlashan, Interaction between Argon Atoms, *Proc. Roy. Soc. London*, vol. A255, pp. 456–476, 1960; Equilibrium Properties of Crystalline Argon, Krypton and Xenon, *Molecular Physics*, vol. 3, pp. 563–570, 1960.

temperatures. The volume dependence of Γ as calculated from P-V data (using both Slater's formula[64] and that of Dugdale and MacDonald[65]) is shown also, with very poor agreement at high pressures with the thermal values. The agreement at zero pressure is unexpectedly good. Similar calculations for solid xenon indicate a much closer correlation between the thermal and P-V isotherm definitions of Γ.[5]

Finally, an estimate of the volume dependence of Γ for other substances can be obtained as follows: The definition of Γ involving the specific heat [Eq. (5-42*a*)] can be differentiated with the assumption of a small temperature dependence of Γ to give

$$\left(\frac{\partial \ln k_T}{\partial T}\right)_V = \beta \left\{\left[\frac{\partial \ln (C_v/V)}{\partial \ln V}\right]_T + \frac{d \ln \Gamma}{d \ln V}\right\} \tag{5-45}$$

The term on the left is known from measurements of the elastic constants as a function of both pressure and temperature,[2] while the first term in the braces can be estimated from the Debye theory to be of the order of -1 at room temperature, and $+0.6$ at 80°K, for a substance such as copper. For copper at room temperature, the thermal expansion is given by $\beta = 0.5 \times 10^{-4}$ °C^{-1}, while $(\partial \ln k_T/\partial T)_V = -1.1 \times 10^{-4}$ °C^{-1}. The values are roughly the same for silver and gold. The substitution of these values into the above equation yields the prediction that $d \ln \Gamma/d \ln V$ must be of the order of -1 for the noble metals. This is of the same order of magnitude as for sodium and helium, but of opposite sign.

The only other source of information for the volume dependence of the Grüneisen constant for the lattice comes from shock-wave experiments[69] in which P-V data are obtained along a Hugoniot. These data are analyzed, however, by assuming that the Γ's as derived from the isothermal P-V data, using the Dugdale-MacDonald formula, are identical with those which would be obtained from thermal data. This assumption leads to a value for $d \ln \Gamma/d \ln V$ of $+6$ for copper at atmospheric pressure, in contrast with the above estimate which suggests values of the order of -1.

5-5b The free-electron contribution to the free energy. The available calorimetric data for the nonsuperconducting metals show that a low-temperature heat-capacity contribution exists which is linear in absolute temperature and is of the same magnitude as that which would be obtained if the conduction electrons in the metal were free. This electronic contribution to the heat capacity of a normal metal can be written as $C_n^{el} = \gamma T$, with a contribution to the free energy per mole of

$$F_n^{el*} = \tfrac{1}{2}\gamma T^2 \tag{5-46}$$

[69] M. H. Rice, R. G. McQueen, and J. M. Walsh, Compression of Solids by Strong Shock Waves, pp. 1–63 in F. Seitz and D. Turnbull, (eds.), "Solid State Physics," vol. 6, Academic Press, Inc., New York, 1958.

where γ is a function of volume only and is related to the density of states of the electrons in the metal at the Fermi level $N(0)$.[70] The thermal-expansion contribution due to these electrons can be written down immediately as

$$\beta_n^{el} = C_n^{el}\Gamma^{el}\frac{K_T}{V} = \frac{k_T}{V}\gamma T\frac{d \ln \gamma}{d \ln V} \tag{5-47}$$

$\Gamma^{el} = d \ln \gamma / d \ln V = d \ln N(0)/d \ln V = \frac{2}{3}$ for a free-electron gas[71] and, hence, this thermal-expansion contribution would be positive in this case. There has been some confusion in the literature owing to the occasional use of γ in terms of a specific volume (cubic centimeters) instead of a molar volume. We shall use the molar quantity throughout.

The direct measurement of specific heats as a function of pressure is extremely difficult for a metal and has not been performed. For metals which become superconducting, however, both γ and its volume dependence can be evaluated by measuring the temperature and pressure dependence of the critical field at very low temperatures, if the lattice specific heat does not change at the transition. This assumption has been questioned recently and needs further checks.[72] Indeed, one can obtain from these data (using this assumption) the electronic contributions to the thermal expansion and the heat capacity of both the normal and superconducting states. The details of these experiments and their analysis,[2,9,10] as well as those of the directly related experiments involving the change in length of the superconductor at the transition,[73] have been given elsewhere. It is sufficient to state that the Mie-Grüneisen-type approach can be used in the analysis of these measurements to obtain considerable information about the low-temperature equations of state of both the superconducting and normal states of a metal.[9,10]

The actual values of Γ^{el} given by these measurements vary from $+1$ to $+6$ and are usually larger than the free-electron value of $+\frac{2}{3}$. One can inquire as to the possibility of seeing this contribution directly. For most superconducting metals, the lattice heat capacity is much greater than the electronic; however, the transition metals (such as tantalum) have fairly large Debye θ's (250° and upwards), and also much larger γ's, than free-electron theory predicts. A rather rash estimate of the thermal

[70] C. Kittel, "Introduction to Solid State Physics," 2d ed., chap. 10, John Wiley & Sons, Inc., New York, 1956.

[71] P. G. Klemens, Thermal Expansion of Aluminum at Low Temperatures, *Phys. Rev.*, vol. 120, pp. 843–844, 1960. This paper gives references to earlier work on the electronic contribution to the thermal expansion.

[72] C. A. Bryant and P. H. Keeson, Low Temperature Specific Heat of Indium and Tin, *Phys. Rev.*, vol. 123, p. 491, 1961.

[73] J. L. Olsen and H. Rohrer, The Volume Dependence of the Electron Level Density and the Critical Temperature in Superconductors, *Helv. Phys. Acta*, vol. 33, pp. 872, 1960.

expansion for tantalum (assuming a lattice Grüneisen constant of 2) gives[9]

$$\beta = 10^{-10}T^3 + 10^{-8}T \qquad {}^\circ K^{-1} \tag{5-48}$$

with the two contributions becoming equal at 10°K. The experimental requirement is that changes in length of a 10-cm sample be measured to the order of angstroms at 4°K. Recently, White has reported thermal-expansion measurements which were made with this sensitivity on both copper and iron to 1.5°K.[67] As would be expected, no linear term was found for copper (in which the electronic contribution to the free energy is quite small at 4°K), but one was found for iron, which also has a large value of γ characteristic of transition metals. Aluminum should perhaps also be a suitable subject for investigation. Further work along these lines, preferably with metals which become superconducting, would be quite profitable.[73a]

5-5c Magnetic phenomena. The low-temperature specific heat of a ferromagnetic substance has a $T^{3/2}$ contribution due to spin-wave excitation.[70] One would also expect, therefore, a $T^{3/2}$ contribution to the thermal expansion which would be associated with the pressure dependence of the Curie temperature of the substance in question. The sign of this contribution would, in particular, be directly related to the sign of dT_c/dP. Indeed, magnetic transitions are reflected in both the specific heat and the thermal expansion,[74] and discontinuities in these at T_c are related to the pressure dependence of the Curie temperature directly through thermodynamic arguments.[75,76] This field is virtually unexplored at present.

5-6 Conclusions

The agreement between experimental and theoretical equation-of-state calculations for low temperatures is satisfactory only for the solidified inert gases. While considerable data exist for these solids, most concern the P-V relationship to 20 kilobars at temperatures of roughly 20°K. There is no reason to believe that significantly different data would be obtained in this pressure range at lower temperatures. Further data, however, such as densities as a function of temperature or even at the

[73a] See G. K. White, Thermal Expansion at Low Temperatures; and K. Andres, Thermal Expansion of Some Metals at Low Temperature, in "The Proceedings of the Eighth International Conference on Low Temperature Physics, London, 1962," to be published.

[74] R. R. Birss, The Thermal Expansion Anomaly of Gadolinium, *Proc. Roy. Soc. London*, vol. 255A, pp. 398–406, 1960.

[75] A. B. Pippard, "Classical Thermodynamics," chaps. 8 and 9, Cambridge University Press, New York, 1957.

[76] N. Bernardes, in a paper to be published.

boiling point of helium, are either lacking or show contradictions well outside the estimated experimental uncertainties. The investigation of the reasons for the small discrepancies between theory and experiment for the inert-gas solids described in this paper would involve the use of experimental *P-V* data to derive empirical potentials of the form of Eq. (5-12), for instance. It is gratifying, but not necessary, that the values of ϵ and σ which apply to the atoms in the gaseous phase would apply also to the solid.

A logical extension of the theoretical work would be to the diatomic molecules such as H_2, N_2, and O_2. *P-V* data at 4°K exist for H_2 and D_2 to 20 kilobars,[32] but theoretical calculations are much more difficult for these asymmetric molecules than for the rare gases. It would be expected that at pressures of the order of 10^3 kilobars or greater, solid hydrogen would become atomic and would show metallic behavior. These pressures are well outside current experimental possibilities, although theoretical work is continuing on this problem.[77,77a]

The situation as regards the theory of the equation of state of metals at low temperature is much worse than that for the inert-gas solids, while the experimental situation is perhaps in better shape for the alkali metals, at least. For the present, the major problem here seems to involve the development of theories which can describe the available equation-of-state data.

The amount of data available for the temperature-dependent part of the equation of state of both metals and nonmetals is extremely small. Adequate thermal-expansion data and even heat-capacity data to very low temperatures are not available for many of the simpler solids. High-pressure measurements of the *P-V* relationship as a function of temperature must be complemented by these data in order to calculate the pressure dependence of the thermodynamic functions for a solid. Considerably more information is needed about pressure effects on the thermodynamic functions so that the simpler theoretical assumptions may be tested. In addition, data, as well as theoretical work, are needed which will give the lattice frequency spectrum of a solid as a function of volume. The pressure range need not be large, since for the noble metals significant variations in the elastic constants occur in 10 kilobars.[2]

Finally, solid-solid phase transformations have been observed under pressure at low temperatures in nitrogen[78] (in which the situation is

[77] H. Salwen, private communication and progress report from Gordon McKay Laboratory, Harvard University, Cambridge, Mass., 1958.

[77a] N. F. Mott, The Transition to the Metallic State, *Phil. Mag.*, vol. 6, pp. 287–309, 1961.

[78] C. A. Swenson, New Modification of Solid Nitrogen, *J. Chem. Phys.*, vol. 23, pp. 1953–1954, 1955.

perhaps quite complex) and in helium. The nitrogen transition is probably to a more close-packed structure, while the helium transformations are, in order, from a body-centered cubic to a hexagonal close-packed to a face-centered cubic.[16,17,30] These are not completely understood at present,[31] although the transition between the two close-packed phases involves a very small energy difference which would be difficult to calculate. Experiments on the variation of electrical resistivity with pressure for some semiconductors show a change which may be associated with a transition to a metallic state.[79] The thermodynamics of these transitions would be interesting, although a study would involve a tremendous extension of present techniques. With the extension of the pressure range, the possibility exists that more isomorphic electronic transitions of the type postulated for cesium and cerium[2,44] will be found. The theory of these transitions, in which, presumably, an electron in the solid moves from one orbital to another, has not been worked out in detail as yet.

[79] H. G. Drickamer, private communication, 1961.

6

Some Geophysical Applications of High-pressure Research

FRANCIS BIRCH

Dunbar Laboratory
Harvard University
Cambridge, Massachusetts

6-1 Introduction

The interior of the earth is a domain of compressive stress rising to several megabars‡ at the center; throughout nearly nine-tenths the volume, the mean compressive stress exceeds 100 kilobars. These pressures induce major changes in physical and chemical behavior which

‡ The common units of pressure are the bar and its multiples, the atmosphere, the kilogram per square centimeter, and the pound per square inch, related as follows:

$$1 \text{ bar} = 10^6 \text{ dynes/cm}^2 = 1.01972 \text{ kg/cm}^2 = 0.986924 \text{ normal atm} = 14.5038 \text{ psi}$$

For many purposes, including virtually all geophysical ones, the differences among bar, atmosphere, and kilogram per square centimeter are insignificant. The kilobar (10^3 bar) and megabar (10^6 bar) are useful in eliminating awkward multiples of 10; the megabar is the natural unit for elastic constants and for the pressures deep in the earth.

must be taken into account in interpreting geophysical observations. Present conceptions of the earth's constitution and evolution are closely related to an accumulation of experimental evidence at high pressures, including, in recent years, experiments with shock pressures in the megabar range. It is hardly an exaggeration to say that every aspect of the geophysics and geochemistry of the earth's interior requires consideration of the effects of pressure.

A comprehensive review of geophysical applications of high-pressure research would be too long for the present occasion; instead, an effort has been made to give a connected account of a few topics in which recent work has led to substantial progress. Additional material may be found in other reviews, including "Physics at High Pressure" by Swenson,[1] the contributions in "Researches in Geochemistry" by Clark, Eugster, and Kullerud,[2] "Investigations under Hydrothermal Conditions" by Roy and Tuttle,[3] the conference on rock deformation,[4] and "Progress in Very High Pressure Research."[5]

Most of the following is devoted to a discussion of the bearing of experiments at high pressures on the interpretation of seismic discontinuities: first, the division between mantle and core; then the near-surface division between mantle and crust; finally, the more subtle divisions within the mantle. The relation between certain high-pressure studies and the elusive problem of internal temperatures is briefly indicated. Some familiarity with geophysical fact and theory is required, and to supplement the account given below, the reader may consult the more complete discussions in Jeffreys,[6] Elsasser,[7] Birch,[8] Bullard,[9] and Bullen.[10]

[1] C. A. Swenson, pp. 41–147 in F. Seitz and D. Turnbull (eds.), "Solid State Physics," vol. 11, Academic Press, Inc., New York, 1960.

[2] S. P. Clark, Jr., H. P. Eugster, and G. Kullerud, in P. H. Abelson (ed.), "Researches in Geochemistry," John Wiley & Sons, Inc., New York, 1959.

[3] Rustum Roy and O. F. Tuttle, in Ahrens et al. (eds.), "Physics and Chemistry of the Earth," vol. 1, McGraw-Hill Book Company, Inc., New York, 1956.

[4] David Griggs and John Handin (eds.), "Rock Deformation," memoir 79, Geological Society of America, 1960.

[5] F. P. Bundy, W. R. Hibbard, Jr., and H. M. Strong (eds.), "Progress in Very High Pressure Research," John Wiley & Sons, Inc., New York, 1961.

[6] Sir Harold Jeffreys, "The Earth, Its Origin, History and Physical Constitution," 4th ed., Cambridge University Press, New York, 1959.

[7] W. M. Elsasser, The Earth's Interior and Geomagnetism, *Revs. Mod. Phys.*, vol. 22, no. 1, 1950.

[8] Francis Birch, Elasticity and Constitution of the Earth's Interior, *J. Geophys. Research*, vol. 57, p. 227, 1952.

[9] Sir Edward Bullard, in G. P. Kuiper (ed.), "The Earth as a Planet," University of Chicago Press, Chicago, 1954.

[10] K. E. Bullen, in Ahrens et al. (eds.), "Physics and Chemistry of the Earth," vol. 1, McGraw-Hill Book Company, Inc., New York, 1956.

6-2 Pressure and Density within the Earth

Pressures in the earth are conventionally calculated as in a gravitating liquid sphere having a prescribed density, usually taken to depend upon radius alone. The propagation of shear waves through most of the interior shows, however, that this is solid, with high values of modulus of rigidity. The most general stress in a solid may be resolved uniquely into a "mean stress" having the character of a hydrostatic pressure and equal to one-third the sum of the three principal stresses, plus shear stress. The magnitude of the shear stress is limited by rupture or flow or, loosely, the "strength." The greatest departures (in the relative sense) from hydrostatic stress occur near the surface; below about 100 km, the maximum shear stress is probably always less than 1 percent of the mean stress; the state of stress may then be identified with hydrostatic pressure to this degree of approximation or better. Much the same sort of approximation is made in the discussion of strong shock waves and of static systems employing a solid medium for transmitting pressure.

In a spherical, liquid, gravitating mass at rest, pressure P, density ρ, and radius r are related according to the hydrostatic law $dP = -g\rho\, dr$, where g is the gravitational acceleration at r, given by

$$g(r) = \frac{4\pi G}{r^2} \int_0^r \rho x^2\, dx$$

With $P = 0$ at the outer surface ($r = R$), then

$$P(r) = 4\pi G \int_r^R \frac{\rho}{r^2}\, dr \int_0^r \rho x^2\, dx \qquad (6\text{-}1)$$

For uniform density, $P = (2\pi/3)G\rho^2(R^2 - r^2)$, a parabolic distribution with a central pressure $(2\pi/3)G\rho^2R^2$. Substitution of the earth's mean density (5.52 gm/cm³) and radius (6.37×10^8 cm) leads to 1.7 megabars for the central pressure; this is about one-half the actual central pressure, the difference arising from the increase of density with depth, especially at the core boundary. For an improved pressure distribution, the variation of density with radius has first to be found.

The density function $\rho(r)$ is subject to two integral conditions. First, the mean density in the spherical approximation is

$$5.516 = \frac{3}{R^2} \int_0^R \rho r^2\, dr \qquad \text{gm/cm}^3 \qquad (6\text{-}2)$$

Second, the moment of inertia about the axis of revolution‡ is

$$I = 0.334MR^2 = \frac{8\pi}{3}\int_0^R \rho r^4\, dr \qquad \text{gm-cm}^2 \tag{6-3}$$

These two conditions are insufficient to determine $\rho(r)$ unless this function is arbitrarily restricted to only two adjustable parameters; they indicate that density must be higher somewhere in the interior than near the surface, since the density of common rocks rarely exceeds about 3 gm/cm³, and the moment of inertia of a sphere of uniform density is $0.4MR^2$.

The improvement of the density distribution depends principally upon the use of the seismic velocities (Fig. 6-1). This leads to a division of

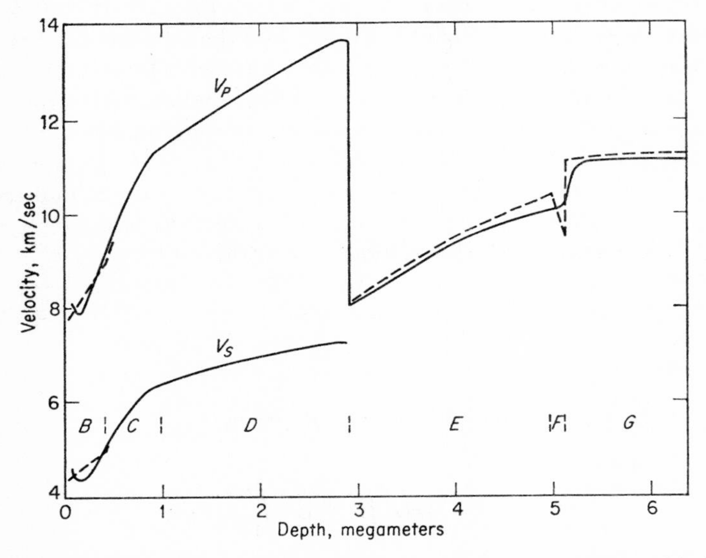

Fig. 6-1 Velocities of seismic waves and major divisions of the earth's interior. (*Solid curves after Gutenberg;*[14] *broken curves after Jeffreys;*[6] *letter designations of layers after Bullen.*[13])

the interior into two major units, "core" and "mantle." Two velocities of propagation of "body waves" are found for the mantle, only one for the core. The velocity of the compressional wave rises to 13.6 km/sec at the base of the mantle, and within a small radial interval drops to 8.1

‡ Recent studies of satellite orbits lead to a value for I/MR^2 close to 0.331, about 1 percent below the figure given above (A. H. Cook, Developments in Dynamical Geodesy, *Geophys. J.*, vol. 2, p. 222, 1959; John A. O'Keefe, discussion of W. A. Heiskanen, The Latest Achievements of Physical Geodesy, *J. Geophys. Research*, vol. 66, p. 1992, 1961). This has the result of increasing core densities by a few percent and decreasing the densities in the mantle by about 0.06 gm/cm³ (see Fig. 6-2).

km/sec in the core. The surface of separation has a mean radius of 3,473 km, and the pressure at this level is about 1.4 megabars. The interpretation of this, the principal feature of the earth's internal structure, is evidently crucial for understanding the evolution of the interior. Most of the increase of density required by the integral conditions of Eqs. (6-2) and (6-3) is assumed to take place at this boundary.

The seismic velocities also provide a means for estimating the rise of density within mantle and core as a result of compression. In terms of the theory of isotropic elasticity, the two velocities are related to incompressibility K and rigidity μ:

$$\rho V_P^2 = K + \tfrac{4}{3}\mu \qquad \rho V_S^2 = \mu$$

Williamson and Adams[11] remarked that these velocities may be combined to yield $K/\rho = V_P^2 - \tfrac{4}{3}V_S^2 = dP/d\rho = \phi$. With the aid of the hydrostatic relation, we then obtain the Adams-Williamson equation for the change of density with radius as a result of (adiabatic) compression:

$$d\rho = -\frac{g\rho\, dr}{\phi} \tag{6-4}$$

This has been used to find the density distribution by numerical integration inward from the surface; solutions with modern values of velocity are given by Bullen,[10,12,13] Bullard,[14] and others.[15] If this were valid throughout the interior of the mantle and core, then only two disposable parameters would remain, the density at the surface of the mantle and the density at the surface of the core, and these would be determined by the integral conditions. The density distribution would then be completely determined.

In Bullen's first application of this procedure,[12] it was supposed that Eq. (6-4) could be applied throughout the mantle, but when the integration reached the boundary of the core, the remaining mass and moment of inertia (for the core) were found to have an unacceptable ratio ($I_c = 0.57M_cR_c^2$); to reduce this to less than $0.4M_cR_c^2$ while retaining the Adams-Williamson relation throughout, it is necessary to assume a density at the upper surface of the mantle of about 3.7 gm/cm^3,[14,15] a

[11] E. D. Williamson and L. H. Adams, Density Distribution in the Earth, *J. Washington Acad. Sci.*, vol. 13, p. 413, 1923.

[12] K. E. Bullen, The Variation of Density and the Ellipticities of Strata of Equal Density within the Earth, *Monthly Notices Roy. Astron. Soc., Geophys. Supplement*, vol. 3, p. 395, 1936.

[13] K. E. Bullen, "An Introduction to the Theory of Seismology," 2d ed., Cambridge University Press, New York, 1953.

[14] Sir Edward Bullard, *Verhandel. Ned. Geol.-Mijnbouwk Genoot.*, vol. 18, p. 23, 1957.

[15] Francis Birch, Uniformity of the Earth's Mantle, *Bull. Geol. Soc. Am.*, vol. 64, p. 601, 1953.

value unacceptably high. With this density in the more probable range of 3.2 to 3.5 gm/cm³, an additional increase of density in the mantle must be introduced, not determined by compressibility alone, and the problem remains indeterminate. With reasonable assumptions about the location of the additional density, however, the distribution may be fixed within narrow limits; two distributions showing probable extremes are shown in Fig. 6-2. Within these limits, the density may be treated as known and may be used for the discussion of composition.

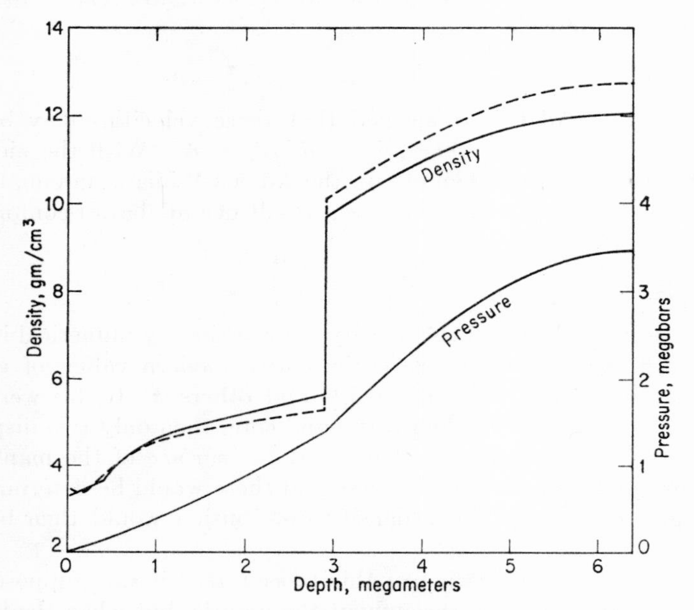

Fig. 6-2 Density and pressure in the earth's interior. The broken curve and density distribution were calculated with $I/MR^2 = 0.3305$, according to the method of Birch.[16] (*Solid curves after Bullard,*[14] *model IV.*)

The Adams-Williamson equation may be generalized to include the effects of nonadiabatic gradients of temperature, of phase changes, and of compositional changes;[8,16] these are probably of greatest importance in layers B and C.

6-3 Equations of State; Elastic Constants

The seismic velocities are found independently of assumptions about the chemical composition of the earth's interior (as are density, pressure,

[16] Francis Birch, Composition of the Earth's Mantle, *Geophys. J.*, vol. 4, p. 295, 1961.

and elastic constants) except for the assumptions regarding uniformity implicit in the Adams-Williamson method. One of the first problems of interpretation is to relate these physical properties to those of known materials. It is necessary to know, for example, how much of the increase of velocity or density may be accounted for by compression alone, and how much must be attributed to phase change or compositional variation. Recent experimental work has brought several major problems close to definitive solution.

6-3a Composition of the core and mantle. The most significant feature of the internal structure is the mantle-core discontinuity, described above. The classical interpretation, suggested by the silicate and metal phases of meteorites and by solar and stellar chemical abundances, is that the core is iron (perhaps with some 10 percent of nickel, like meteoritic iron) while the mantle is a dense silicate. Another hypothesis, suggested by the Wigner-Huntington[17] theory of metallic hydrogen, is that the core is a high-pressure metallic form having essentially the same chemical composition as the mantle.[18] The implications of these two interpretations differ radically, to the point that progress with the theory of the earth's development requires a definite choice between them.

A first question is whether iron has the required density at core pressures. Extrapolations from core pressures to 1 atm have led to conflicting opinions. An equation of state which closely fits Bridgman's experimental compression curves of the alkali metals[19] (for several to twice their ordinary densities) may be used for isothermal extrapolation for iron; this leads to densities perhaps as much as 15 to 20 percent too high, and may be interpreted as indicating the presence of light alloying elements.[8]

The Thomas-Fermi equation of state has also been applied to this problem.[20,21] This suffers from the awkward pressure range of the core, which is below the pressure at which the Thomas-Fermi approximation becomes useful for iron. Interpolation curves may be drawn to connect

[17] E. Wigner and H. B. Huntington, On the Possibility of a Metallic Modification of Hydrogen, *J. Chem. Phys.*, vol. 3, p. 764, 1935.

[18] W. H. Ramsey, On the Constitution of the Terrestrial Planets, *Monthly Notices Roy. Astron. Soc.*, vol. 108, p. 406, 1948; On the Nature of the Earth's Core, *Monthly Notices Roy. Astron. Soc., Geophysical Supplement*, vol. 5, p. 409, 1949; On the Compressibility of the Earth, *Monthly Notices Roy. Astron. Soc., Geophysical Supplement*, vol. 6, p. 42, 1950.

[19] P. W. Bridgman, Rough Compressibilities of Fourteen Substances to 45,000 kg/cm², *Proc. Am. Acad. Arts Sci.*, vol. 72, p. 207, 1938; The Compression of 39 Substances to 100,000 kg/cm², *Proc. Am. Acad. Arts Sci.*, vol. 76, p. 55, 1948.

[20] H. Jensen, Das Druck-Dichte Diagramm der Elemente bei höheren Drucken am Temperaturnullpunkt, *Z. Physik*, vol. 111, p. 373, 1938.

[21] W. M. Elsasser, Quantum Theoretical Densities of Solids at Extreme Compression, *Science*, vol. 113, p. 105, 1951.

the low-pressure data with the Thomas-Fermi curves in different plausible ways. Knopoff and Uffen[22] have used the Murnaghan equation at low to medium pressures to connect with the Thomas-Fermi curve at high pressure. McMillan[23] has proposed a semiempirical relation which guarantees correct behavior in the two limits of high and low pressure. The upshot of these discussions has been to confirm the reasonableness of a predominantly iron core, lightened by some proportion of silicon or other abundant light elements.

Shock-wave measurements for iron and other metals are now available for pressures equaling those of the core.[24–27] Figure 6-3 shows density versus shock pressure for iron compared with the data for the core; the range of uncertainty in the core density is also indicated. The experimental work confirms the earlier surmise that the density of the core may be as much as 15 percent lower than that of iron at the same pressures. Corrections for temperature and for phase change in iron are unlikely to alter this conclusion drastically or alter its corollary that some admixture of lighter elements is required.[28–30] With this modification, the interpretation that the core is mainly iron is consistent with the experimental work at core pressures.

The interpretation in terms of a high-pressure form of silicate cannot be treated so directly, though a brief report of shock compression of dunite (olivine) by Altschuler and Kormer[30] gives the density as 6.8 ± 0.2 gm/cm^3 at 2.4 megabars; this is far below what is required for the core at this pressure, and this point is reasonably consistent with the

[22] L. Knopoff and R. J. Uffen, The Densities of Compounds at High Pressures and the State of the Earth's Interior, *J. Geophys. Research*, vol. 59, p. 471, 1954.

[23] W. G. McMillan, Approximate Compressibilities of Elements on the Statistical Model, *Phys. Rev.*, vol. 111, p. 479, 1958.

[24] L. V. Altschuler, K. K. Krupnikov, B. N. Ledenev, V. I. Zhuchikhin, and M. I. Brazhnik, Dynamic Compressibility and Equation of State of Iron under High Pressure, *Soviet Phys. JETP*, vol. 7, p. 606, 1958.

[25] L. V. Altschuler, S. B. Kormer, M. I. Brazhnik, L. A. Vladimirov, M. P. Speranskaya, and A. I. Funtikov, The Isentropic Compressibility of Aluminum, Copper, Lead, and Iron at High Pressures, *Soviet Phys. JETP*, vol. 11, p. 766, 1960.

[26] M. H. Rice, R. G. McQueen, and J. M. Walsh, Compression of Solids by Strong Shock Waves, pp. 1–63 in F. Seitz and D. Turnbull (eds.), "Solid State Physics," vol. 6, Academic Press, Inc., New York, 1958.

[27] R. G. McQueen and S. P. Marsh, Equation of State for Nineteen Metallic Elements from Shock-wave Measurements to Two Megabars, *J. Appl. Phys.*, vol. 31, p. 1253, 1960.

[28] G. J. F. MacDonald and Leon Knopoff, On the Chemical Composition of the Outer Core, *Geophys. J.*, vol. 1, p. 284, 1958.

[29] Leon Knopoff and G. J. F. MacDonald, An Equation of State for the Core of the Earth, *Geophys. J.*, vol. 3, p. 68, 1960.

[30] L. V. Altschuler and S. B. Kormer, On the Internal Structure of the Earth, *Bull. Acad. Sci. U.S.S.R., Geophys. Series*, vol. 1, p. 18, 1961.

measurements to 700 kilobars by Hughes and McQueen.[31] It is arguable, as remarked by Altschuler and Kormer, that the shock conditions inhibited the postulated phase change which must take place at about 1.4 megabars if it is to coincide with the core boundary. There are, however, systematic relations which emphasize the extreme improbability

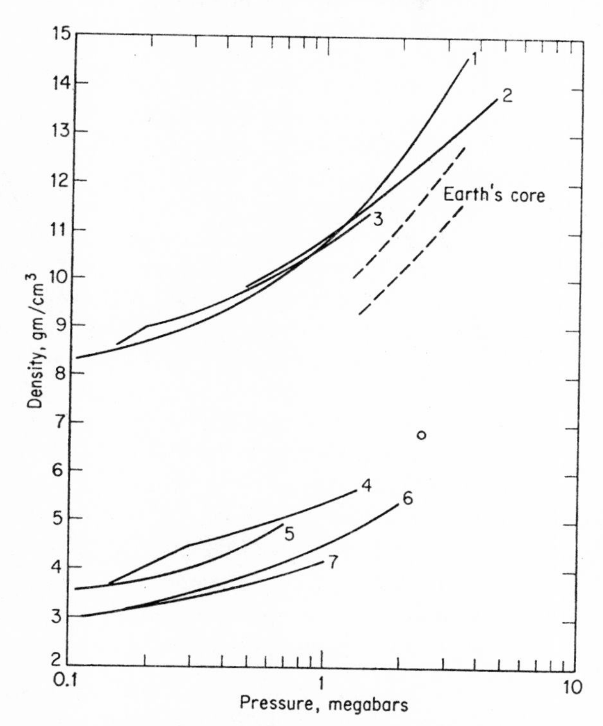

Fig. 6-3 Density versus pressure (logarithmic scale): (1) Murnaghan equation for isothermal compression of iron;[8] (2) and (3) shock compression of iron;[24–27] (4) earth's mantle;[14] (5) shock compression of dunite,[31] with the circle representing the single point for dunite after Altschuler and Kormer;[30] (6) Murnaghan curve for isothermal compression of aluminum; (7) shock compression of aluminum.[26] The broken curves are the limiting densities for the earth's core.

that so light a material as a magnesian silicate will possess the required density at core pressures, regardless of phase change.

A most decisive plot shows the hydrodynamical sound velocity $(\partial P/\partial \rho)^{1/2}$ versus density.[16] When not given in the reports, this velocity may be computed from the tables of P and ρ for the shock curve and will then

[31] D. S. Hughes and R. G. McQueen, Density of Basic Rocks at Very High Pressures, *Trans. Am. Geophys. Union*, vol. 39, p. 959, 1958.

differ somewhat from the adiabatic sound velocity; the difference is not significant for the present purpose. The results for metals up to atomic number 50 are shown in Fig. 6-4; most of these are from McQueen and Marsh.[27] Up to copper these curves occur in a sequence corresponding to the sequence of atomic numbers; beyond the transition metals this is no longer true, but heavy metals are not of present concern. According

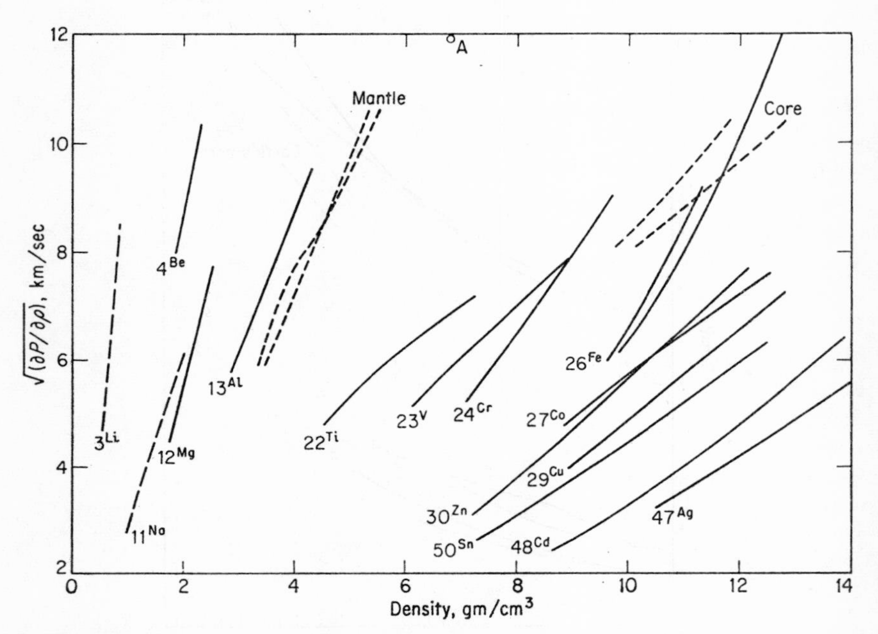

Fig. 6-4 Hydrodynamical velocity $(\partial P/\partial \rho)^{1/2}$ versus density. The solid curves are shock data for metals.[24,27] The broken lines are from isothermal compressions by Bridgman.[19] The dashed curves are from seismic data for mantle and core, combined with limiting density distributions. The circle labeled A represents the point for dunite at 2.4 megabars of Altschuler and Kormer.[30] The straight dashed line for the mantle is the distribution with uniform mean atomic weight.[16]

to the Thomas-Fermi theory, atomic number would be the only parameter; the overlapping of the shock curves for elements beyond $A = 29$ shows that this approximation is still inadequate at pressures of several megabars.

Figure 6-4 also shows the (adiabatic) sound velocity for the core, with limits for the core density, and the corresponding quantity $(K/\rho)^{1/2}$ for the mantle, again with two limiting density distributions. The core values are in the region of the transition metals; the mantle curves are in the region of light metals, close to that of aluminum. Even without information concerning chemical abundances, these relations indicate that the mantle is composed principally of light elements and the core of elements of the iron group.

The data given by Altschuler and Kormer for dunite may also be placed on this diagram if we ignore the difference, usually small, between shock velocity and $(\partial P/\partial \rho)^{1/2}$. Working backwards with the usual Hugoniot relations, one finds a shock velocity of 11.9 km/sec for the reported density of 6.8 gm/cm^3; this point is not far from a prolongation of the mantle curve.

A major increase of density by reason of transformation to a metallic form is a priori highly improbable for such closely packed substances as oxides and silicates. The mean atomic weight of mantle material is probably about 22, yet its density is everywhere greater than that of the metal aluminum of atomic weight 27; the mean atomic volume of the mantle material is less than that of any metal of comparable mean atomic weight at core pressures. This conclusion, based on the experimental evidence, is consistent with the theoretical conclusion by Alder[32] that the transformation of an ionic solid to metallic form is unlikely to be a first-order change. Thus the interpretation of the mantle-core discontinuity as a change of mantle material to a metallic form fails on several counts.

With the conclusion that the mantle and core are chemically distinct, it follows that the evolution of the interior must have included a stage during which separation could occur. Probably this separation can be explained in more ways than one; a persuasive account has been given by Ringwood,[33] who believes that the iron core was formed by reduction of a primitive silicate and that the principal alloying element in the core is silicon, a conclusion reached on other grounds by MacDonald and Knopoff.[28] Shock-wave studies of ferro-silicon alloys should show whether this explanation accounts for the density-pressure relations.

6-3b Mantle and crust: the Mohorovičić discontinuity. Crust and mantle are separated by a seismically determined boundary known as the Mohorovičić discontinuity. This boundary is found at depths of from 30 to 50 km below the continents and about 10 km below sea level in the ocean basins. Below the discontinuity, the velocity of compressional waves is in the range 7.6 to 8.5 km/sec; above the discontinuity this velocity does not exceed about 7 km/sec. Just how "discontinuous" the velocity function is at this boundary is still uncertain, but the change from 7 to 8 km/sec is usually thought to take place within a vertical interval of no more than a few kilometers. As the mean pressure at

[32] B. J. Alder, State of Matter at High Pressure, p. 152 in reference 5.

[33] A. E. Ringwood, On the Chemical Evolution and Densities of the Planets, *Geochim. et Cosmochim. Acta,* vol. 15, p. 257, 1959; Some Aspects of the Thermal Evolution of the Earth, *Geochim. et Cosmochim. Acta,* vol. 20, p. 241, 1960.

35 km is about 10 kilobars, a large amount of experimental data can be applied directly to the interpretation of this discontinuity. The term "crust" antedates the discovery of the seismic boundary; it arose from an older conception of a crystalline layer overlying a generally molten interior; the base of the crust then corresponded to a point on the melting curve with thickness and temperature varying together and composition being essentially the same above and below—in other words, the boundary of the crust was conceived as a phase boundary. It now seems likely that the temperature at the base of the crust is usually well below fusion temperatures, and it is also known that shear waves are propagated in the upper mantle. If the boundary is a phase boundary, it separates two solid phases; the other possibility is a chemical boundary separating solid phases having different chemical compositions. Much recent work on silicate reactions under pressure, as well as the ambitious plan for sampling the mantle by drilling through the thin oceanic crust, is directed toward the solution of this fundamental problem.

(*a*) *The Discontinuity as a Chemical Boundary.* The compressibility of rocks and minerals has been studied by Madelung and Fuchs,[34] L. H. Adams and collaborators,[35–37] Bridgman,[38] Volarovich and others,[39] Yoder and Weir,[40] and Zisman.[41] Velocities of propagation in rocks, under kilobar pressures, have been measured by Birch and Bancroft,[42]

[34] E. Madelung and R. Fuchs, Kompressibilitätsmessungen an festen Körpern, *Ann. Phys.*, vol. 65, p. 289, 1921.

[35] L. H. Adams and E. D. Williamson, The Compressibility of Minerals and Rocks at High Pressures, *J. Franklin Inst.*, vol. 195, p. 475, 1923.

[36] L. H. Adams and R. E. Gibson, The Compressibilities of Dunite and of Basalt Glass and Their Bearing on the Composition of the Earth, *Proc. Natl. Acad. Sci.*, vol. 12, p. 275, 1926; also vol. 15, p. 713, 1929.

[37] L. H. Adams, The Compressibility of Fayalite and the Velocity of Elastic Waves in Peridotite with Different Iron-Magnesium Ratios, *Gerlands Beitr. Geophys.*, vol. 31, p. 315, 1931.

[38] P. W. Bridgman, Linear Compressibility of Fourteen Natural Crystals, *Am. J. Sci.*, vol. 10, p. 483, 1925; The Linear Compressibility of Thirteen Natural Crystals, *Am. J. Sci.*, vol. 15, p. 287, 1928; The High Pressure Behavior of Miscellaneous Minerals, *Am. J. Sci.*, vol. 37, p. 7, 1939; The Compression of 39 Substances to 100,000 kg/cm^2, *Proc. Am. Acad. Arts Sci.*, vol. 76, p. 71, 1948.

[39] M. P. Volarovich, D. B. Balashov, and V. A. Pavlogradsky, Study of the Compressibility of Igneous Rocks at Pressures up to 5000 kg/cm^2, *Bull. Acad. Sci. U.S.S.R., Geophys. Series*, vol. 5, p. 486, 1959.

[40] H. S. Yoder and C. E. Weir, Change of Free Energy with Pressure of the Reaction, Nepheline + Albite = 2 Jadeite, *Am. J. Sci.*, vol. 249, p. 683, 1951.

[41] W. A. Zisman, Compressibility and Anisotropy of Rocks at and near the Earth's Surface, *Proc. Natl. Acad. Sci.*, vol. 19, p. 666, 1933.

[42] Francis Birch and Dennison Bancroft, The Effect of Pressure on the Rigidity of Rocks, *J. Geol.*, vol. 46, pp. 59 and 113, 1938; New Measurements of the Rigidity of Rocks at High Pressure, *J. Geol.*, vol. 48, p. 752, 1940.

Birch,[43,44] Hughes and collaborators,[45–47] Matsushima,[48] Volarovich and Balashov,[49] Tocher,[50] and Balakrishna.[51]

The elastic properties of rocks are commonly much affected by porosity; values useful for the interpretation of seismic velocities, except in near-surface formations, are obtained only after this porosity has been reduced or eliminated by application of pressures of a few kilobars, above which the intrinsic pressure effect upon the crystalline aggregate may be approached. The intrinsic effects appear to be comparable with those found for metals having about the same compressibility, a few percent for 10 kilobars;[52–55] this may be contrasted with changes of as much as 50 percent and frequently 10 percent in the first kilobar as porosity is reduced.

The effect of temperature upon elastic-wave velocities in rocks has also been investigated; again, only those studies in which the rocks have been maintained under pressures of several kilobars are of value for geophysical purposes. Unequal thermal expansions of individual mineral grains may otherwise increase porosity and lead to spuriously large and

[43] Francis Birch, Elasticity of Rocks at High Temperatures and Pressures, *Bull. Geol. Soc. Am.*, vol. 54, p. 263, 1943.

[44] Francis Birch, The Velocity of Waves in Rocks to 10 Kilobars, *J. Geophys. Research*, part 1, vol. 65, p. 1083, 1960; part 2, vol. 66, p. 2199, 1961.

[45] D. S. Hughes and H. J. Jones, Variation of Elastic Moduli of Igneous Rocks with Pressure and Temperature, *Bull. Geol. Soc. Am.*, vol. 61, p. 843, 1950.

[46] D. S. Hughes and J. H. Cross, Elastic Wave Velocities at High Pressures and Temperatures, *Geophys.*, vol. 16, p. 577, 1951.

[47] D. S. Hughes and C. Maurette, Elastic Wave Velocities in Granites, *Geophys.*, vol. 21, p. 277, 1956; Variation of Elastic Wave Velocities in Basic Igneous Rocks with Pressure and Temperature, *Geophys.*, vol. 22, p. 23, 1957; Détermination des vitesses d'onde élastique dans diverses roches en fonction de la pression et de la température, *Rev. Inst. Francais pétrole*, vol. 12, p. 730, 1957.

[48] S. Matsushima, Variation of the Elastic Wave Velocities of Rocks in the Process of Deformation and Fracture under High Pressure, *J. Phys. Earth*, vol. 8, July, 1960.

[49] M. P. Volarovich and D. B. Balashov, Study of Velocities of Elastic Waves in Samples of Rocks under Pressures up to 5000 kg/cm^2, *Bull. Acad. Sci. U.S.S.R., Geophys. Series*, vol. 3, p. 56, 1957.

[50] Don Tocher, Anisotropy in Rocks under Simple Compression, *Trans. Am. Geophys. Union*, vol. 38, p. 89, 1957.

[51] S. Balakrishna, Elasticity of Some Indian Rocks, *Bull. Natl. Inst. Sci. India*, vol. 11, p. 50, 1958; *Current Sci. India*, vol. 27, p. 251, 1958.

[52] P. W. Bridgman, The Effect of Pressure on the Rigidity of Several Metals, *Proc. Am. Acad. Arts Sci.*, vol. 64, p. 39, 1929.

[53] Francis Birch, The Effect of Pressure on the Modulus of Rigidity of Several Metals and Glasses, *J. Appl. Phys.*, vol. 8, p. 129, 1937.

[54] D. Lazarus, The Variation of the Adiabatic Elastic Constants of KCl, NaCl, CuZn, Cu, and Al with Pressure to 10,000 Bars, *Phys. Rev.*, vol. 76, p. 545, 1949.

[55] D. S. Hughes and J. L. Kelly, Second Order Elastic Deformation of Solids, *Phys. Rev.*, vol. 92, p. 1145, 1953.

usually irreversible reductions of velocity. Measurements on single crystals are desirable, but have been discouraged by the low symmetry of rock-forming minerals and by the difficulty of finding specimens of sufficient size. A lowering of velocity of from 2 to 5 percent for a rise of temperature of 500°C, depending upon composition, is indicated by the available work.[43,45–47] Reliable values for the temperature coefficients are needed especially for the discussion of "shadow zones" resulting from downward refraction at certain depths; estimates based on observed temperature effects[8,42,56] have been supplemented by the use of coefficients obtained from solid-state theory.[57–59] The treatment in terms of gradients of temperature and pressure may readily be generalized to include gradients of composition as well.[56]

These studies lead to several general conclusions. The seismic velocities of the crust are in the range of experimental velocities at kilobar pressures for common rocks such as granites, gabbros, and others. The seismic velocities below the Mohorovičić discontinuity are fairly consistent with those found experimentally for relatively rare dense rocks such as dunite, peridotite, and eclogite. The recorded variations from place to place, if real, indicate variability of composition or temperature or both. The generally favored interpretation is that of chemical discontinuity, separating crustal rocks characterized by high feldspar content from underlying dunite or peridotite, essentially magnesium-iron olivines and pyroxenes.

(*b*) *The Discontinuity as a Reaction: Gabbro-Eclogite.* An alternative explanation of the discontinuity as a phase change, which has recently gained favor, may be dated from a series of papers by Fermor beginning in 1912. Fermor[60] recognized that gabbro and eclogite are chemically similar, having essentially the composition of basalt, but that eclogite is

[56] Francis Birch, Interpretation of the Seismic Structure of the Crust in the Light of Experimental Studies of Wave Velocities in Rocks, pp. 158–170 in Hugo Benioff, Maurice Ewing, Benjamin F. Howell, Jr., and Frank Press (eds.), "Contributions in Geophysics in Honor of Beno Gutenberg," Pergamon Press, London, 1958.

[57] P. E. Valle, Sul Gradiente di Temperatura Necessario per la Formazione di "Low Velocity Layers," *Ann. geofis. Rome*, vol. 9, p. 371, 1956.

[58] E. A. Lyubimova, On the Pressure Gradient in the Upper Layer of the Earth and on the Possibility of an Explanation of the Low-velocity Layers, *Bull. Acad. Sci. U.S.S.R., Geophys. Series*, vol. 12, p. 1300, 1959.

[59] Gordon J. F. MacDonald and Norman F. Ness, A Study of the Free Oscillations of the Earth, *J. Geophys. Research*, vol. 66, p. 1865, 1961.

[60] L. L. Fermor, Preliminary Note on the Origin of Meteorites, *J. Proc. Asiatic Soc. Bengal*, vol. 8, p. 315, 1912; Preliminary Note on Garnet as a Geological Barometer and on an Infra-plutonic Zone in the Earth's Crust, *Records Geol. Survey India*, vol. 43, p. 41, 1913; The Relationship of Isostasy, Earthquakes, and Vulcanicity to the Earth's Infra-plutonic Shell, *Geol. Mag.*, vol. 1, p. 65, 1914; Garnets and Their Role in Nature, *Ind. Ass. Cultiv. Sci.*, Special Publication 6, 1938.

about 15 percent denser than gabbro. He was thus led to assume that a pressure-dependent reaction must exist, with eclogite the high-pressure modification. Below the crust, the lower part of which may have a gabbroic composition, he postulated an "infraplutonic" zone of eclogite; this zone was seen as the source of basaltic lavas; the volume change in the reaction was held to account for uplift and depression of portions of the earth's surface without lateral exchange of material, including the foundering of eroded continental blocks below sea level. Implicit in this hypothesis is the assumption that the boundary between the fields of stability of gabbro and eclogite occurs at conditions of pressure and temperature corresponding to the base of the crust; this has been adopted in recent amplifications of Fermor's theory.[61–65]

The principal minerals of gabbro are plagioclase feldspar and pyroxene, usually augite or hypersthene, while those of eclogite are typically magnesium-rich garnet and soda-rich pyroxene (omphacite). Thus the relation between these rocks is not one of simple polymorphism; gabbro must recrystallize completely to form eclogite, no single mineral transforming without chemical change, even though the bulk composition remains fixed. This reaction has not yet been completely worked out experimentally, but several simpler systems related to it have been studied.[66–70] Transition parameters for several univariant equilibrium lines are shown in Table 6-1. One of the most significant results of this

[61] John S. Sumner, Consequences of a Polymorphic Transition at the Mohorovičić Discontinuity, *Trans. Am. Geophys. Union*, vol. 35, p. 385, 1954.

[62] J. F. Lovering, The Nature of the Mohorovičić Discontinuity, *Trans. Am. Geophys. Union*, vol. 39, p. 947, 1958.

[63] George C. Kennedy, The Origin of Continents, Mountain Ranges, and Ocean Basins, *Am. Scientist*, vol. 47, p. 491, 1959.

[64] Gordon J. F. MacDonald and Norman F. Ness, Stability of Phase Transitions within the Earth, *J. Geophys. Res.*, vol. 65, p. 2173, 1960.

[65] Donald C. Noble, Stabilization of Crustal Subsidence in Geosynclinal Terranes by Phase Transition at *M*, *Bull. Geol. Soc. Am.*, vol. 72, p. 287, 1961.

[66] D. T. Griggs and G. C. Kennedy, A Simple Apparatus for High Pressures and Temperatures, *Am. J. Sci.*, vol. 254, p. 722, 1956; see also reference 63; and G. C. Kennedy, in H. E. Landsberg and J. Van Mieghem (eds.), "Advances in Geophysics," vol. 7, Academic Press, Inc., New York, 1961.

[67] F. R. Boyd, Jr., and J. L. England, Phase Equilibria at High Pressure, *Yearbook*, vol. 55, p. 154, Carnegie Institute, Washington, 1956.

[68] E. C. Robertson, F. Birch, and G. MacDonald, Experimental Determination of Jadeite Stability Relations to 25,000 Bars, *Am. J. Sci.*, vol. 255, p. 115, 1957.

[69] S. P. Clark, Jr., E. C. Robertson, and F. Birch, Experimental Determination of Kyanite-Sillimanite Equilibrium Relations, *Am. J. Sci.*, vol. 255, p. 628, 1957; S. P. Clark, Jr., Kyanite-Sillimanite Equilibrium, *Yearbook*, vol. 59, p. 52, Carnegie Institute, Washington, 1960.

[70] Francis Birch and Paul LeComte, Temperature-Pressure Plane for Albite Composition, *Am. J. Sci.*, vol. 258, p. 209, 1960.

Table 6-1 Transition Parameters, $T = T_0 + aP = a(P - P_0)$

Reaction	T_0, °C	P_0, kilobars	a, degrees/kilobar	Experimental range, °C	Reference
β-quartz ⇌ α-quartz	573	...	24	573–800	Yoder[70a]
α-quartz ⇌ coesite	...	10	45	400–600	MacDonald;[78] Dachille and Roy[80]
		20	89	700–1700	Boyd and England[79]
sillimanite ⇌ kyanite	...	5	76	1000–1500	Clark[69]
albite + nepheline ⇌ 2-jadeite	...	1	54	....	Robertson et al.[68]
albite ⇌ jadeite + quartz	...	6	50	600–1000	Birch and LeComte[70]
enstatite + sapphirine (+ sillimanite?) ⇌ pyrope	...	7	(100)	1000–1500	Boyd and England[71]
fayalite ⇌ spinel	...	(25)	(45)	....	Ringwood;[91] Boyd and England[77]

[70a] H. S. Yoder, Jr., High-Low Quartz Inversion up to 10,000 Bars, *Trans. Am. Geophys. Union*, vol. 31, p. 827, 1950.

work is the demonstration of the instability of the feldspars at high pressure, albite, for example, breaking down to jadeite and quartz at 18 kilobars at 600°C. The compatibility of these conditions with those expected at the base of the continental crust is favorable to the explanation in terms of the gabbro-eclogite reaction. A serious difficulty arises, however, in explaining the suboceanic discontinuity by the same reaction, as the conditions here, with a mean pressure of about 2 kilobars and an estimated normal temperature of 150 to 200°C, seem to be well within the field of stability of gabbro. Another awkward feature for this explanation of the discontinuity is the large field of stability of garnet; though the minimum pressure of formation of pure pyrope is 15 kilobars at 800°C,[71] the garnet of eclogite rarely contains more than 70 mole percent of pyrope, and this garnet appears to be stable everywhere in the normal crust.[72]

If the gabbro-eclogite reaction proves unacceptable as the explanation of the Mohorovičić discontinuity, many of the useful features of Fermor's hypothesis may still be retained if an appreciable eclogite component

[71] F. R. Boyd, Jr., and J. L. England, Pyrope, *Yearbook*, vol. 58, p. 83, Carnegie Institute, Washington, 1959.

[72] H. S. Yoder and G. A. Chinner, Almandite-Pyrope-Water System at 10,000 Bars, *Yearbook*, vol. 59, p. 81, Carnegie Institute, Washington, 1960.

exists in the upper mantle. Unpublished experiments by Yoder[73] show that above 20 kilobars, the partial melting of eclogite gives rise to a liquid of nearly the same (that is, of basaltic) composition; thus the origin of basaltic lavas by this process seems possible. Eclogite nodules in diamond pipes, closely associated with the diamonds, are evidence of the presence of eclogite in the mantle; the principal question is the amount of eclogite and its location.

Experimental work in high-pressure mineralogy has been stimulated by the synthesis by Coes[74] of "coesite," a dense form of silica, and of numerous other minerals, and by the synthesis of diamond by Bundy and collaborators and others.[75–77] The equilibrium relations for the α-quartz–coesite reaction have been studied by MacDonald,[78] Boyd and England,[79] and Dachille and Roy.[80] The presence of coesite or diamond is indicative of a high minimum pressure of formation. The diamond pipes have been extruded from depths of the order of 100 km; coesite, unrecognized in nature until produced artificially, has now been identified in the products of meteorite impact.[81] A general conclusion, anticipated by Bridgman,[82] is that few minerals common at the surface are stable in the deep interior. For the geophysics of the Earth's mantle, few studies are more essential than those of the equilibrium curves in the systems of importance and of the physical properties of the high-pressure phases.

(*c*) *The Discontinuity as a Reaction: Olivine-Serpentine.* We return now to the Mohorovičić discontinuity. Another explanation of this phenomenon is the olivine-serpentine reaction proposed by Hess; originally suggested to account for variations and processes taking place below

[73] H. S. Yoder, verbal communication.

[74] L. Coes, Jr., A New Dense Crystalline Silica, *Science*, vol. 118, p. 131, 1953; High Pressure Minerals, *J. Am. Ceram. Soc.*, vol. 38, p. 298, 1955.

[75] F. P. Bundy, H. T. Hall, H. M. Strong, and R. H. Wentorf, Man-made Diamonds, *Nature*, vol. 176, p. 51, 1955; H. P. Bovenkerk, F. P. Bundy, H. T. Hall, H. M. Strong, and R. H. Wentorf, Jr., Preparation of Diamond, *Nature*, vol. 184, p. 1094, 1959.

[76] A. A. Giardini, J. E. Tydings, and S. B. Levin, A Very High Pressure–High Temperature Research Apparatus and the Synthesis of Diamond, *Am. Mineralogist*, vol. 45, p. 217, 1960.

[77] F. R. Boyd, Jr., and J. L. England, Minerals of the Mantle, *Yearbook*, vol. 59, p. 47, Carnegie Institute, Washington, 1960.

[78] G. J. F. MacDonald, Quartz-Coesite Stability Relations at High Temperatures and Pressures, *Am. J. Sci.*, vol. 254, p. 713, 1956.

[79] F. R. Boyd, Jr., and J. L. England, The Quartz-Coesite Transition, *J. Geophys. Research*, vol. 65, p. 749, 1960.

[80] Frank Dachille and Rustum Roy, High-pressure Region of the Silica Isotopes, *Z. Krist.*, vol. 111, p. 451, 1959.

[81] E. C. T. Chao, E. M. Shoemaker, and B. M. Madsen, First Natural Occurrence of Coesite, *Science*, vol. 132, p. 220, 1960.

[82] P. W. Bridgman, Polymorphic Transitions and Geological Phenomena, *Am. J. Sci.*, vol. 243-A, p. 90, 1945.

the discontinuity,[83] it has developed[84] into an explanation of the discontinuity itself. The system $MgO-SiO_2-H_2O$, which contains this reaction, has been studied experimentally by Bowen and Tuttle,[85] with water pressures up to 2 kilobars. Serpentine, which may be formed by hydration of olivine, decomposes above about 500°C, this temperature being nearly independent of water pressure. Hess suggests that the position of the suboceanic discontinuity is determined by the 500° isotherm of an earlier time, "fossilized" at the lower present temperature of 150 to 200°C. This is difficult to reconcile with the dynamical effects supposed to follow from subsequent hydrations and dehydrations. At the same time, 500°C is consistent with estimates of temperature at the base of the normal continental crust, and serpentinization of peridotite can reduce the seismic velocities to values in the range of the lower crust.[44,84] Thus we have several alternatives for the continental discontinuity which encounter difficulties when applied to the oceanic one. Chemical change at the Mohorovičić discontinuity still seems to enjoy the advantage of economy of hypotheses, with phase changes probable at a deeper level.

6-3c Seismic velocities in the mantle. Within the mantle, the principal feature is the rapid rise of velocities, between 300 and 1,000 km of depth, by comparison with the smaller rate of rise at greater depths and the small rise, or even minimum, at shallower depths (Fig. 6-1). These characteristics lead to a subdivision[13] into layers *B*, *C*, and *D*; the boundaries of layer *C* are evidently somewhat indefinite.

Analysis of the behavior of the seismic velocities in these layers[8,86] leads to the following conclusions: The variation in *D* may be consistent with compression of a uniform layer, but the properties of this layer, at zero pressure, are not those of any known silicate ($\rho = 4$ gm/cm^3; $\phi = 50$ km^2/sec^2; $V_P = 9.9$ km/sec); they are comparable with those of corundum or spinel. A minimum in layer *B* may result from the balance between pressure and temperature effects or from compositional changes, but no unknown materials are required. Layer *C* is transitional between the "ordinary" materials of layer *B* and the unknown high-pressure phases of layer *D*; the "abnormal" rate of increase of velocity with depth in *C* results from increasing proportions of the high-pressure forms.

[83] H. H. Hess, Geological Hypothesis and the Earth's Crust under the Ocean, *Proc. Roy. Soc. London*, vol. A222, p. 341, 1954; Serpentines, Orogeny, and Epeirogeny, *Geol. Soc. Am.* Special Paper 62, p. 391, 1955.

[84] H. H. Hess, The AMSOC Hole to the Earth's Mantle, *Trans. Am. Geophys. Union*, vol. 40, p. 340, 1959.

[85] N. L. Bowen and O. F. Tuttle, The System $MgO-SiO_2-H_2O$, *Bull.,Geol. Soc. Am.*, vol. 60, p. 439, 1949.

[86] Francis Birch, The Variation of Seismic Velocities within a Simplified Earth Model in Accordance with the Theory of Finite Strain, *Bull. Seism. Soc. Am.*, vol. 29, p. 463, 1939.

(*a*) *Composition of the Mantle and Transformations within It.* The transformation of olivine to a spinel form was suggested in 1936 by Bernal[87] to explain a now-vanished first-order discontinuity at about 400 km;[88] this transformation has reappeared as a possible explanation of the transition layer and the underlying deep mantle.[8,89,90] There is now experimental evidence of the conditions under which this transformation takes place and of the properties of the spinel phase.

Ringwood has tried to account for the spread of the transition in terms of the binary system Mg_2SiO_4-Fe_2SiO_4. At low pressures, complete solid solution exists between the end members, forsterite and fayalite, having the olivine structure. Ringwood[91] synthesized a spinel of fayalite composition (Fe_2SiO_4) at 600°C and 40 kilobars; he also examined the system Ni_2SiO_4-Mg_2GeO_4, in which the low-pressure forms have the olivine structure and the high-pressure forms have the spinel structure, and obtained the extrapolated pressure of 150 kilobars for the transformation of forsterite at 1500°C. The density of the Fe_2SiO_4-spinel is given as 4.85; by extrapolation, the Mg_2SiO_4-spinel is found to have a density of 3.55, close to that of ordinary spinel ($MgAl_2O_4$). A lower density (3.37) for this form is given by Dachille and Roy,[90] by extrapolation in the system Mg_2SiO_4-Mg_2GeO_4, with a transformation pressure of 100 ± 15 kilobars at 542°C. The slopes of the transition lines are still poorly determined, and synthesis of the spinel form of the end member Mg_2SiO_4 has yet to be accomplished, but the reality of this transformation is no longer in doubt. The principal question is to what extent the properties of this binary system can account for what is known of the transition layer.

A difficulty arises in connection with the density; with Ringwood's values for the spinel forms, a spinel solid solution having a density of 4 would contain about 35 mole percent of Fe_2SiO_4; this may be compared on the one hand with the 37 to 53 mole percent Fe_2SiO_4 proposed by Knopoff and Uffen[22] for the mantle, and on the other with the approximately 10 percent found in peridotites and dunites.

[87] J. D. Bernal, *The Observatory*, vol. 59, p. 268, 1936.

[88] Harold Jeffreys, On the Materials and Density of the Earth's Crust, *Monthly Notices Roy. Astron. Soc., Geophys. Supplement*, vol. 4, p. 50, 1937.

[89] A. E. Ringwood, The Constitution of the Mantle, *Geochim. et Cosmochim. Acta*, I, vol. 13, p. 303, 1958; II, vol. 15, p. 18, 1958; III, vol. 15, p. 195, 1958; IV, vol. 16, p. 192, 1959.

[90] Frank Dachille and Rustum Roy, The Spinel-Olivine Inversion in Mg_2GeO_4, *Nature*, vol. 183, p. 1257, 1959; High Pressure Studies of the System Mg_2GeO_4-Mg_2SiO_4 with Special Reference to the Olivine-Spinel Transition, *Am. J. Sci.*, vol. 258, p. 225, 1960.

[91] A. E. Ringwood, Olivine-Spinel Transition in Fayalite, *Bull. Geol. Soc. Am.*, vol. 69, p. 129, 1958; The Olivine-Spinel Inversion in Fayalite, *Am. Mineralogist*, vol. 44, p. 659, 1959. See also reference 77.

The great spread of layer C, some 600 km or 250 kilobars, remains as a troublesome feature. This problem has been examined by Meijering and Rooymans[92] with the following conclusions: If the binary system is taken arbitrarily to have a spread in pressure comparable with that of layer C, and if the coexisting phases are determined for a uniform gross composition, then most of the change of properties (for example, of density and, by inference, of velocity) would take place in a fairly thin zone near the base of the layer—in other words, the velocity distribution would not look like the seismic one. On the other hand, if the width of the transformation zone is taken from the experimental work as perhaps 50 to 100 kilobars, the transition zone is again much thinner than the observed one. Thus it seems likely that at least a ternary system must be considered and that phases other than spinel are present.

This conclusion, originally based on a discussion of elastic properties,[8] has been strengthened by several recent experimental studies. A high-pressure form of silica (SiO_2) having the rutile structure and a density of about 4.3 gm/cm^3 has been synthesized by Stishov and Popova[92a] at pressures of the order of 100 kilobars, and, following this discovery, identified in the crushed zone about Meteor Crater, Arizona, by Chao and others.[92b] A corundum form of the compound $MgGeO_3$, which at low pressure has the pyroxene structure, has been synthesized by Ringwood and Seabrook[92c] at about 25 kilobars, and found to be denser, by about 15 percent, than the low-pressure form. It is likely that $MgSiO_3$ (enstatite) will also transform to the corundum structure at sufficiently high pressure. Possibly all of these forms play some part in the transition layer. Apparently the highest density is obtained upon breakdown to oxides, if the pressure is high enough for the formation of "stishovite," and the base of the transition layer may correspond to the final conversion to oxides in their high-pressure forms.

(*b*) *Wave-propagation Measurements on Rocks.* Studies of wave propagation in rocks up to 10 kilobars[44] illustrate the difficulties of inferring chemical composition from seismic data. These measurements

[92] J. L. Meijering and C. J. M. Rooymans, On the Olivine-Spinel Transition in the Earth's Mantle, *Proc. Koninkl. Ned. Akad. Wetenschap.*, vol. B61, p. 333, 1958.

[92a] S. M. Stishov and S. V. Popova, New Dense Polymorphic Modification of Silica (trans. from Russian), *Geokhimiya*, vol. 10, pp. 837–839, 1961; C. B. Sclar, A. P. Young, L. C. Carrison, and C. M. Schwartz, Synthesis and Optical Crystallography of Stishovite, a Very High Pressure Polymorph of SiO_2, *J. Geophys. Research*, vol. 67, p. 4049, 1962.

[92b] E. C. T. Chao, J. J. Fahey, Janet Littler, and D. J. Milton, Stishovite, SiO_2, a Very High Pressure New Mineral from Meteor Crater, Arizona, *J. Geophys. Research*, vol. 67, pp. 419–421, 1962.

[92c] A. E. Ringwood and Merren Seabrook, High-pressure Transition of $MgGeO_3$ from Pyroxene to Corundum Structure, *J. Geophys. Research*, vol. 67, pp. 1690–1691, 1962; A. E. Ringwood, Mineralogical Constitution of the Deep Mantle, *J. Geophys. Research*, vol. 67, p. 4005, 1962.

show that the velocity V_P depends principally upon two parameters: density and mean atomic weight. Since most common rocks have mean atomic weights close to 21 or 22 regardless of composition, this leaves density as the controlling variable; but rocks or minerals of very different compositions may have the same densities and velocities. Thus the interpretation of seismic velocities remains indeterminate so far as most of the common elements are concerned. An increase of mean atomic weight above about 22 is associated with an increase of iron content; substitution of iron for magnesium in olivines or pyroxenes increases density but decreases velocity. Consequently, a determination of iron content appears to be a feasible objective.

The measurements show a nearly linear dependence of velocity upon density for rocks and oxides having nearly the same mean atomic weight, over a range of density from about 2.6 to 4.0 gm/cm^3. Mean atomic weight remaining the same, density can change only as the mean volume per atom changes. The observed differences reflect the changes of mean atomic volume associated with different crystal structures, but one may surmise that velocity would change with density in much the same way if the density were changed by compression. Pending more direct information, the line relating velocity to density for rocks of the same mean atomic weight may serve as a compression curve for any of these materials; this line is plotted in Fig. 6-4 and is almost parallel to the shock-wave curve for aluminum. This relation has been used to approach the problem of the mean atomic weight of the mantle;[16] if uniform, it is 22 ± 1, consistent with the value for the silicate phase of chondrites or of average mafic rocks or peridotites. This method is still subject to large uncertainties but further refinement may be possible.

(*c*) *Shock-wave Studies of Silicates.* These should furnish increasingly valuable data; most of the work is still unpublished. The pioneer studies by Hughes and McQueen[31] and by Altschuler and Kormer[30] on dunite have been mentioned above; additional measurements on a variety of rocks are given by Lombard.[93] The scanty data of Hughes and McQueen for dunite were first interpreted as showing a nearly linear increase of density with pressure up to about 600 kilobars, thus a nearly constant sound velocity instead of the increase of about 50 percent shown by the seismic velocities for this pressure. Subsequent (unpublished) work by McQueen and collaborators‡ shows evidence of phase change for virtually all of a wide sampling of rocks, including dunite. At pressures greater than about 400 kilobars, compositional differences, except for iron content, seem to have relatively little effect; furthermore, the densities of most of

[93] David B. Lombard, The Hugoniot Equation of State of Rocks, UCRL report 6311 (1961).

‡ I am greatly indebted to Dr. McQueen for the opportunity to examine the unpublished measurements.

the common rocks are close to the estimated densities for the lower mantle at corresponding pressures. Wackerle[94] has studied the shock compression of quartz and of silica glass to about 700 kilobars; above 400 kilobars, the pressure-volume curve shows a segment which is most plausibly accounted for by supposing it to represent the shock compression of "stishovite," the high-density form of silica mentioned above. The preliminary results for the silicate rocks suggest that a breakdown to the oxides may account for the densities above 400 kilobars, both on the shock curves and in the lower mantle.

6-4 Melting Curves

The problem of the earth's internal temperatures is difficult to approach directly by way of thermal calculations, since the results are sensitive to assumptions concerning initial temperature, distribution of heat sources and thermal transport properties, all of which are highly uncertain.[95,96] Another approach is by way of thermal effects upon physical properties, perhaps the most promising being the analysis of the electrical conductivity of the interior;[97] the data concerning the relevant pressure effects on semiconduction in silicates are still scanty and will not be considered here. Temperature affects density and velocity, but the relatively small changes with temperature cannot be separated with certainty from the large changes with pressure. Useful limits on temperature may be obtainable from melting curves; the silicate mantle is predominantly solid, as shown by its high effective rigidity for seismic and tidal disturbances, while the iron core is liquid in the outer part and probably solid in the inner part.[98–101] Thus the melting curves for iron and its probable alloys furnish lower limits for the temperature of the outer core (and perhaps a fixed point at the boundary of the inner core); the melting curves for probable silicates or oxides provide upper limits for the temperatures in the mantle.

[94] Jerry Wackerle, Shock-Wave Compression of Quartz, *J. Appl. Phys.*, vol. 33, pp. 922–937, 1962.

[95] G. J. F. MacDonald, Calculations on the Thermal History of the Earth, *J. Geophys. Research*, vol. 64, p. 1967, 1959.

[96] J. Verhoogen, Temperatures within the Earth, *Am. Scientist*, vol. 48, p. 134, 1960.

[97] D. C. Tozer, The Electrical Properties of the Earth's Interior, in "Physics and Chemistry of the Earth," vol. 3, Pergamon Press, London, 1959.

[98] Francis Birch, The Alpha-Gamma Transformation of Iron at High Pressures, and the Problem of the Earth's Magnetism, *Am. J. Sci.*, vol. 238, p. 192, 1940.

[99] K. E. Bullen, A Hypothesis on Compressibility at Pressures of the Order of a Million Atmospheres, *Nature*, vol. 157, p. 405, 1946; Compressibility-Pressure Hypothesis and the Earth's Interior, *Monthly Notices Roy. Astron. Soc., Geophysi. Supplement*, vol. 5, p. 355, 1949.

[100] J. A. Jacobs, The Earth's Inner Core, *Nature*, vol. 172, p. 297, 1953.

[101] W. M. Elsasser, Causes of Motion of the Earth's Core, *Trans. Am. Geophys. Union*, vol. 31, p. 454, 1950.

An equation for melting curves proposed by Simon[102] for such materials as helium, neon, argon, and nitrogen has been much employed for representing and extrapolating the observations. The (Kelvin) temperature of melting T at pressure P is given by $(T/T_0)^c = P/P_0 + 1$, where P_0 and c were originally arbitrary constants obtained by adjustment to experimental curves; T_0 is the melting temperature at $P = 0$. The initial slope is then given by $(dT/dP)_{P=0} = T_0/cP_0 = \Delta V/\Delta S$; thus the product cP_0 may be found from the changes of volume and entropy during melting at ordinary pressure.

Simon[103] determined the constants for the melting curves of the alkali metals from Bridgman's observations[104] as shown in Table 6-2 and

Table 6-2 Melting Curves of Alkali Metals*

Metal	P_{max}, kilobars	P_0, kilobars	c	Reference
Sodium...........	12	11	3.8	Simon[103]
		14.5	3.15	Gilvarry[106]
Potassium..........	13	4	4.5	Simon[103]
		4.8	4.21	Gilvarry[106]
Rubidium..........	3.5	3.4	4.2	Simon[103]
		3.95	3.70	Gilvarry[106]
Cesium............	4	2.4	4 8	Simon[103]
		2.65	4.50	Gilvarry[106]

* Experimental data after Bridgman.[104] P_0 and c are the parameters of the Simon equation, $P/P_0 = (T/T_0)^c - 1$, where T is the (absolute) melting temperature at pressure P (kilobars). P_{max} is the maximum pressure of observation. See also Chap. 7.

calculated the melting curve for iron at core pressures on the assumption that the value of c appropriate for iron is not far from the values found for the alkali metals. Salter[105] and Gilvarry[106] have found theoretical interpretations of the constants; in particular, the constant c which determines the curvature is related to Grüneisen's ratio γ for the solid according to

$$c = \frac{6\gamma + 1}{6\gamma - 2}$$

[102] F. E. Simon, On the Range of Stability of the Fluid State, *Trans. Faraday Soc.*, vol. 33, p. 65, 1937.

[103] F. E. Simon, The Melting of Iron at High Pressures, *Nature*, vol. 172, p. 746, 1953.

[104] P. W. Bridgman, Change of Phase under Pressure, *Phys. Rev.*, vol. 3, p. 153, 1914; The Five Alkali Metals under High Pressure, *Phys. Rev.*, vol. 27, p. 68, 1926.

[105] L. Salter, The Simon Melting Equation, *Phil. Mag.*, vol. 45, p. 369, 1954.

[106] J. J. Gilvarry, Equation of the Fusion Curve, *Phys. Rev.*, vol. 102, p. 325, 1956; Temperatures in the Earth's Interior, *J. Atmospheric and Terrest. Phys.*, vol. 10, p. 84, 1957.

if the variation of γ with volume is neglected. As γ is ordinarily between 1 and 3, the constant c given by this relation should not differ greatly from unity (1.2 to 1.8). The determination of c from experimental data thus requires either extremely high precision or a large pressure range relative to P_0.

The melting of iron and several other metals has been followed by Strong and Bundy[107] to nominal pressures of nearly 100 kilobars, and Strong[108] has used the Simon equation for extrapolation of the iron curve to core pressures with $P_0 = 75$ kilobars and $c = 8$ (Table 6-3). These values give the initial slope of 3°/kilobar, as determined from the changes of volume and entropy, but c is greatly in excess of the Salter-Gilvarry value, which, with $\gamma = 1.5$, is 1.4. The latter value has been used by MacDonald[95] to fit Strong's data, but with an initial slope of 2°/kilobar. It seems likely, however, that the pressures above 30 kilobars in this study were overestimated, as suggested by the calibrations of Kennedy and LaMori,[109] and that the relation of melting temperature to pressure is more nearly linear.[110] With this correction of the pressures, the observations become consistent with the values $c = 1.4$ and $P_0 = 430$ kilobars. The extrapolated melting point of iron at the base of the mantle is then 5000°K.

The extrapolation to core pressures is thus notably sensitive to the value of the exponent c; Gilvarry's theory, moreover, predicts a dependence of c on compression, with an appreciable variation even for iron at terrestrial pressures. Beyond about 6 kilobars—a poorly known triple point at which the α, γ, and liquid phases of iron are in equilibrium—the liquid will be in equilibrium with the γ phase instead of the α phase, for which the initial slope of the melting curve is given by the data at 1 atm. The melting curve for γ-iron must have a higher initial slope (dT/dP) than that for α-iron. Finally, the curve of geophysical interest is probably not the melting curve of pure iron, but of some alloy. Silicon, for example, lowers the melting point and restricts the field of the γ phase.

Table 6-3 includes estimates of the melting point of iron by Valle[111] and Zharkov[112] based on developments of Lindemann's melting rule and semiempirical equations of state. A figure of about 4000°K at the core

[107] H. M. Strong and F. P. Bundy, Fusion Curves of Four Group VIII Metals to 100,000 Atmospheres, *Phys. Rev.*, vol. 115, p. 278, 1959.

[108] H. M. Strong, The Experimental Fusion Curve of Iron to 96,000 Atmospheres, *J. Geophys. Research*, vol. 64, p. 653, 1959.

[109] G. C. Kennedy and P. N. LaMori, p. 304 in reference 5; The Pressures of Some Solid-Solid Transitions, *J. Geophys. Research*, vol. 67, p. 851, 1962.

[110] H. M. Strong, p. 182 in reference 5.

[111] P. E. Valle, Una stima del punto di fusione del ferro sotto alte pressioni, *Ann. geofis. Rome*, vol. 8, p. 189, 1955.

[112] V. N. Zharkov, The Fusion Temperature of the Earth's Mantle and the Fusion Temperature of Iron under High Pressures, *Bull. Acad. Sci. U.S.S.R., Geophys. Series*, vol. 3, p. 315, 1959.

Table 6-3 Melting Curve of Iron*

P_0c, kilobars	P_0, kilobars	c	$T_{P=1.37 \text{ megabars}}$, °K	Reference
595	170	3.5	3390	Simon[103]
600	150	4.0	3220	
598	133	4.5	3090	
600	200	3	3590	Bullard[9]
600	150	4	3220	
			4200	Valle[111]
560	350	1.6	4880	Gilvarry[106]
660	347	1.9	4190	
790	343	2.3	3630	
			4500	Zharkov[112]
600	75	8	2610	Strong[108]
900	642	1.4	4080	MacDonald[95]
600	430	1.4	5020	Present

* P_0 and c are the parameters of the Simon equation

$$P/P_0 = (T/T_0)^c - 1 \qquad T_0 = 1805°\text{K}$$

boundary is close to the theoretical consensus, but for geophysical purposes, considering uncertainties of composition and of the shape of the melting curves, we may set the uncertainty of temperature as perhaps $\pm 1000°$K.

Melting is suspected for several low-melting elements under shock-wave conditions.[27] If the beginning of melting could be definitely assigned to a pressure on the Hugoniot curve, the corresponding temperature (and thus a point on the melting curve) could be found.[29,113,114] The estimates of temperature on the Hugoniot curve of iron given by McQueen and Marsh[27] and Strong's original extrapolated melting curve for iron intersect at about 1.5 megabars; with the Kennedy-LaMori reduction of pressures, this is raised to nearly 3 megabars. These pressures have been reached in shock-wave studies; if the beginning of melting could be detected, a powerful method for the extension of the melting curves would result.

The melting of several silicates has been followed to a few tens of kilobars[70,71,115,116] (see Table 6-4), far enough to permit fairly reliable

[113] J. M. Walsh, M. H. Rice, R. C. McQueen, and F. L. Yarger, Shock-wave Compressions of Twenty-seven Metals. Equations of State of Metals, *Phys. Rev.*, vol. 108, p. 196, 1957.

[114] G. B. Benedek, The Temperature of Shock Waves in Solids, Tech. Rept. 316, Cruft Laboratory, Harvard University, Cambridge, Mass., 1960.

[115] H. S. Yoder, Jr., Change of Melting Point of Diopside with Pressure, *J. Geol.*, vol. 60, p. 364, 1952.

[116] F. R. Boyd, Jr., and J. L. England, Melting of Diopside under Pressure, *Yearbook*, vol. 57, p. 173, Carnegie Institute, Washington, 1958.

determination of initial slopes of the melting curves, but insufficient to show curvature. For the extrapolation of these curves, which have served as initial temperature distributions for thermal calculations, MacDonald[95] determined the Simon constants from the observed dT/dP and the Salter-Gilvarry relation. For these materials the Grüneisen ratios are relatively uncertain, as is the applicability of the theory. The results are consistent with the requirement that the mantle remain solid and the core liquid, but the relevance of the behavior of these simple silicates is doubtful. Melting in silicate systems is frequently incongruent; in the deeper mantle, the solid phases are high-pressure forms not yet available for direct study.

Table 6-4 Melting Curves of Compounds, $(T/T_0)^c = P/P_0 + 1$

Compound	T_0, °K	$(dT/dP)_{P=0}$, degrees/kilobar	P_0, kilobars	c	Reference
NaF	1265	16.1	14.3	5.5	Clark[117]
NaCl	1074	23.8	16.7	2.7	
NaBr	1014	28.7	12.2	2.9	
NaI	928	32.7	10.1	2.8	
LiCl	878	24.2	14.5	2.5	
KCl I	1043	26.5	6.9	5.7	
RbCl I	991	24.9	6.6	6	
Albite	1391	11	(45)	(2.8)	Birch and LeComte;[70] MacDonald[95]
Diopside	1664	13	(49)	(2.6)	Yoder;[115] Boyd and England;[116] MacDonald[95]
Pyrope		14 ($P \approx 20$ kilobars)			Boyd and England[71]

The melting curves of the alkali halides, followed by Clark[117] beyond 20 kilobars, provide opportunity for analysis of the thermodynamic significance of the Simon parameters. The observations can be fitted successfully by equations of the Simon form, but the initial slopes do not agree well with those calculated from current values of ΔV and ΔS; nor do the curvature coefficients c agree with those to be expected from the Salter-Gilvarry relation. Reluctance to rely upon extrapolation far beyond the range of observation seems particularly justifiable in the case of melting curves.

[117] Sydney P. Clark, Jr., Effect of Pressure on the Melting Points of Eight Alkali Halides, *J. Chem. Phys.*, vol. 31, p. 1526, 1959. See also R. C. Newton, A. Jayaraman, and G. C. Kennedy, The Fusion Curves of the Alkali Metals up to 50 Kilobars, *J. Geophys. Research*, vol. 67, p. 2559, 1962.

7

Solid-Liquid and Solid-Solid Phase Transitions in Some Pure Metals at High Temperatures and Pressures

George C. Kennedy   Robert C. Newton

Institute of Geophysics
University of California
Los Angeles, California

7-1 Introduction

Knowledge of the phase changes, both solid-solid and solid-liquid, in the pure elements enhances our understanding of the properties of matter and materials. Experimental measurements of the melting curves of the pure elements serve as a test of the validity of Simon's equation of the melting curve and as a check on the independently measured thermodynamic properties of the elements.

7-2 Previous Work

An excellent summary of prior work on melting curves of metals has recently been published by Strong.[1] The first experimental work on the effect of pressure on the melting points of elements was the work of

[1] H. M. Strong, Melting Temperatures of Metals at Very High Pressures, *Am. Scientist,* vol. 48, p. 58, 1960.

Tammann,[2] who studied the fusion curves of tin and bismuth to 3 kilobars. Bridgman[3–5] has reported on the effect of pressure on the melting of sodium, potassium, phosphorus, gallium, mercury, and bismuth to 12 kilobars. He examined lithium, rubidium, and cesium to 8 kilobars.

Simon[6,7] developed an empirical equation to describe his results on the melting of helium, neon, argon, and nitrogen, and he has applied this equation to other substances, including metals, with some success. More recently, Butusov and co-workers[8,9] determined the melting point of tin, lead, bismuth, zinc, cadmium, thallium, and antimony to approximately 30 kilobars. In addition they prepared a phase diagram of bismuth to 30 kilobars which is in fair agreement with the earlier work of Bridgman. In general the work of Butusov agrees, within the region of overlap, with the data presented in this paper.

Strong and Bundy[10] and Strong[1] of the General Electric Company have determined the melting curves of iron, nickel, platinum, rhodium, and rubidium. Bundy[11] has studied the melting curve and subsolidus relationships for bismuth. Hall[12] has determined the effect of pressure

[2] G. Tammann, Uber den Einfluss des Druckes auf den Schmelzpunkt des Zinns und des Wismuts, *Z. anorg. Chem.*, vol. 40, p. 54, 1904; "Kristallisieren und Schmelzen," Johann Ambrosius Barth, Munich, 1904.

[3] P. W. Bridgman, Mercury, Liquid and Solid, under Pressure, *Proc. Am. Acad. Arts Sci.*, vol. 47, pp. 347–441, 1912.

[4] P. W. Bridgman, Change of Phase under Pressure. I. The Phase Diagrams of Eleven Substances with Especial Reference to the Melting Curve, *Phys. Rev.*, vol. 3, pp. 126 and 153, 1914.

[5] P. W. Bridgman, Change of Phase under Pressure. II. New Melting Curves with a General Thermodynamic Discussion of Melting, *Phys. Rev.*, vol. 6, pp. 1 and 94, 1915.

[6] F. E. Simon and G. Glatzel, Bemerkungen zur Schmelzdruckkurve, *Z. anorg. u. Allgem. Chem.*, vol. 178, p. 309, 1929; F. E. Simon, Untersuchungen uber die Schmelzkurve des Heliums, *Z. Elektrochem.*, vol. 35, p. 618, 1929.

[7] F. E. Simon, On the Range of Stability of the Fluid State, *Trans. Faraday Soc.*, vol. 33, p. 65, 1937.

[8] V. P. Butusov, E. G. Ponyatovskii, and G. P. Shakhovskoi, Fusion Temperatures of Zinc, Cadmium, Thallium, and Antimony at Pressures up to 30,000 kg/sq. cm, *Doklady Akad. Nauk. S. S. S. R.*, vol. 109, p. 519, 1954.

[9] V. P. Butusov and M. G. Gonikberg, Determination of the Melting Points of Some Metals at Very High Pressures, *Zhur. Neorg. Khim.*, vol. 1, p. 1543, 1956; V. P. Butusov and E. G. Ponyatovskii, The Melting Point of Indium under Pressures up to 30,000 kg/cm^2, *Kristallografiya*, vol. 1, p. 736, 1956; V. P. Butusov and E. G. Ponyatovskii, Polymorphic Transitions of Bismuth at Super-high Pressures, *Kristallografiya*, vol. 1, p. 573, 1956.

[10] H. M. Strong and F. P. Bundy, Fusion Curves of Four Group VIII Metals to 100,000 Atmospheres, *Phys. Rev.*, vol. 115, p. 278, 1959.

[11] F. P. Bundy, Phase Diagram of Bismuth to 130,000 kg/cm^2, *Phys. Rev.*, vol. 110, p. 314, 1958.

[12] H. T. Hall, The Melting Point of Germanium as a Function of Pressure to 180,000 Atmospheres, *J. Phys. Chem.*, vol. 59, p. 1144, 1955.

on the melting of germanium, and Dudley and Hall[13] have reported melting data for indium and tin.

Some recent revisions in the fixed points on the high-pressure scale, by Kennedy and LaMori,[14] suggest that the pressures indicated by Strong, Bundy, and Hall may have been somewhat overestimated and that their work on melting curves needs reevaluation.

7-3 Present Investigations

In the present investigation the melting curves of bismuth, cesium, sodium, lithium, tin, tellurium, antimony, indium, thallium, cadmium, lead, zinc, silver, and magnesium are reported. In addition we have measured the fusion curve of Pb_2Pt, the pressure coefficient of the eutectic in the system Pb-Pt, the slopes of the transitions Sn I–Sn II and Bi VI–Bi VII. We have also determined the pressure effects on the transitions α-cobalt–β-cobalt, α-iron–γ-iron, and the pressure coefficient of the Curie point in cobalt. These measurements have been carried to pressures of approximately 50 kilobars.

The Simon fusion equation

$$\frac{P + A}{A} = \left(\frac{T}{T_0}\right)^C$$

contains two empirical constants A and C. These are determined from the curvature of the melting curve for a given element, and they describe melting curves of small curvature for moderate pressure intervals. It is apparent that for some elements at high pressure the Simon constants must be changed considerably from those chosen for the low-pressure region. Simon[15] states there can be no security in a high-pressure prediction until the curvature of the melting curve has been determined. Gilvarry[16] states that these considerations "suggest that the Simon equation has more the character of an interpolation formula than a basic fusion equation."

A further disadvantage of the Simon equation is that it does not allow for maxima in melting curves, examples of which are now known from tellurium, cesium, and rubidium. A comparison between the Simon equation and the experimental results for rubidium is shown by Bundy.[17]

[13] J. D. Dudley and H. T. Hall, Experimental Fusion Curves of Indium and Tin to 105,000 Atmospheres, *Phys. Rev.*, vol. 118, p. 1211, 1960.

[14] G. C. Kennedy and P. N. LaMori, Some Fixed Points on the High-pressure Scale, pp. 304–313 in F. P. Bundy, W. R. Hibbard, Jr., and H. M. Strong (eds.), "Progress in Very High Pressure Research," John Wiley & Sons, Inc., New York, 1961.

[15] F. E. Simon, The Melting of Iron at High Pressures, *Nature*, vol. 172, p. 746, 1953.

[16] J. J. Gilvarry, Equation of the Fusion Curve, *Phys. Rev.*, vol. 102, p. 325, 1956.

[17] F. P. Bundy, Phase Diagram of Rubidium to 150,000 kg/cm² and 400°C, *Phys. Rev.*, vol. 115, p. 274, 1959.

7-4 Apparatus

Pressures to 50 kilobars were generated in a piston-cylinder device described by Kennedy and LaMori.[14] Pistons of tungsten carbide, of ½ in. diameter, were used to generate pressure inside a tungsten carbide pressure vessel. The vessel was laterally supported by shrunk-fit retaining rings of hardened steel and vertically supported by a separate 800-ton ram providing end load on the tungsten carbide core. The piston was driven into the carbide pressure vessel by a 1,400-ton ram and also served as the electrical lead by which power was delivered to the internal carbon-resistance furnace. A diagrammatic sketch of the apparatus is shown in Fig. 7-1.

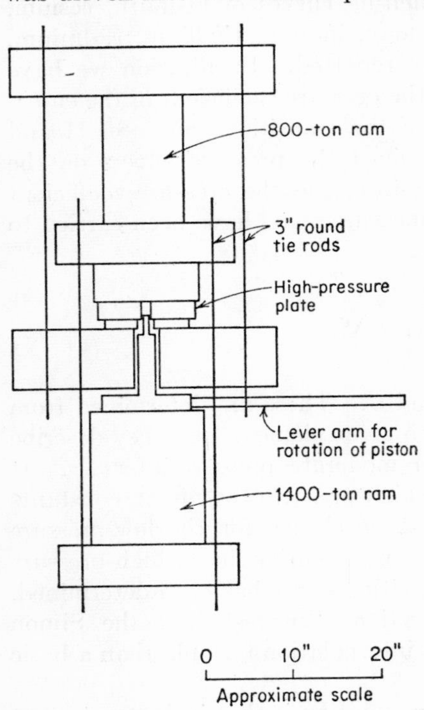

Fig. 7-1 Schematic diagram of high-pressure apparatus.

7-5 Experimental Procedure

The oil pressure on the 1,400-ton ram was measured on a precise 700-bar Heise bourdon-tube gauge. This gauge was previously calibrated against a dead-weight free-piston gauge and was precise to 0.5 bar. Pressure generated in the ½-in.-diameter carbide pressure vessel was determined by a direct force-per-unit-area calculation, with corrections applied for friction. Figure 7-2 shows apparent pressure versus displacement of piston in a typical run. It is clear from this plot that the double value of ram friction plus piston friction is approximately 4 kilobars and is reasonably independent of pressure. Figure 7-2 accounts only for the stop-start friction of the piston against the wall of the pressure container. The carbide piston was lapped to an interference fit with the carbide core of the high-pressure cylinder. The sliding surfaces were lubricated with molybdenum disulfide powder. It is clear that we have not taken into account the internal friction in our talc–boron nitride pressure cell. Runs made on the increasing pressure stroke and on the decreasing pressure stroke, corrected for stop-start piston friction, suggest that the internal friction of our furnace assembly is small. Previous experiments on a recalibration of the pressure scale have indicated that our friction is symmetrical; i.e., the friction on the in stroke is essentially equal to the friction on the out stroke. Thus on a cycle of increasing pressure, the pressure on the sample, based on a force-per-unit-area calculation, is approximately 2 kilobars less than computed, whereas on a cycle of decreasing pressure the pressure on the sample is approximately 2 kilobars more than computed.

In addition to the correction of the pressure measurement for friction, a correction must be made for the pressure generated by expansion of the sample in the pressure cavity as it is heated. The rise in pressure with temperature is shown in Fig. 7-3, which was constructed in the following manner: A furnace assembly was taken on the increasing pressure stroke

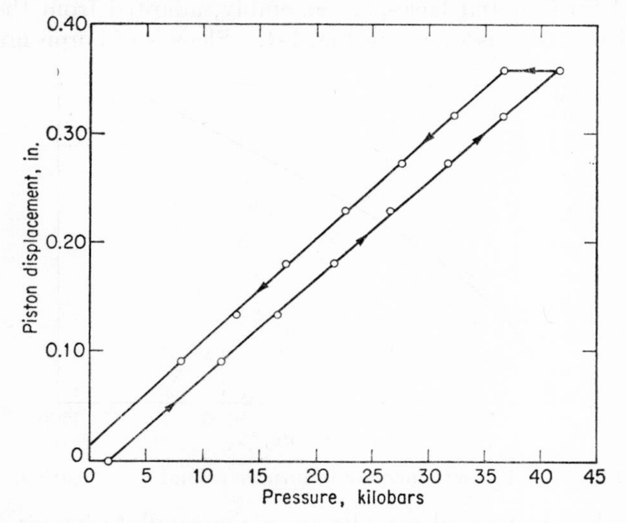

Fig. 7-2 Piston displacement versus ram pressure in dummy furnace assembly.

to approximately 30 kilobars and the temperature was slowly raised. At a temperature of approximately 275°C, the piston began to emerge from the cylinder against the ram pressure, indicating that the pressure rise in the cylinder was equivalent to the double value of stop-start piston friction, approximately 4 kilobars. This gave us the first point in Fig. 7-3. The ram pressure was then increased to keep the piston from emerging from the cylinder as temperature was further raised in the cylinder; the resulting pressure points were plotted as a function of temperature.

These measurements were made by keeping the piston at a constant position in the cavity as the sample was heated. The geometry of our furnace assembly is such that the entire contents of the high-pressure cylinder do not heat up at the same rate; consequently there is more pressure rise for the first 200 to 300° than for subsequent higher temperatures. In most of our runs, the pressure rise from heating approximately compensated for in-stroke piston friction, and the observed pressure computed by force-per-unit-area calculations was used without correction.

Temperatures were measured by chromel-alumel thermocouples connected to a Bristol chart recorder. The accuracy of our recorder and thermocouples was checked several times against the normal melting point of lead. Throughout this work no corrections were made for the pressure effect on the emf of the thermocouples. The pressure correction of thermocouples is currently under investigation in our laboratory, and the data presented in this paper may require revision.

A typical furnace and base-plug assembly, adapted from the work of Boyd and England,[18] is shown in Fig. 7-4. Sleeves of boron nitride were

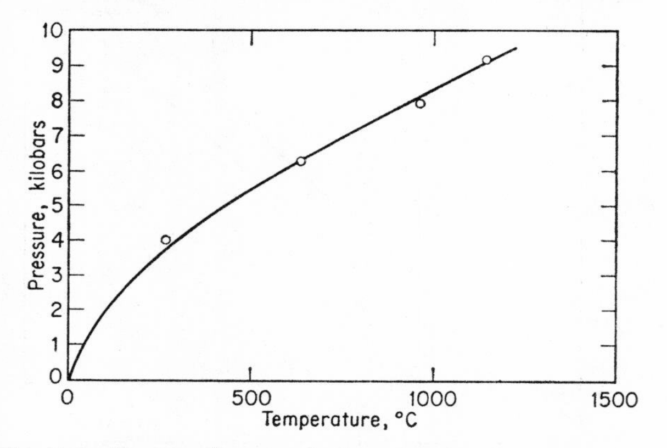

Fig. 7-3 Pressure increase in furnace assembly on heating.

used to insulate our metal samples from the graphite heater. Cups of iron, aluminum, or platinum were used to contain the sample under investigation. The melting points and phase changes were determined by the differential thermal-analysis arrangement shown in Fig. 7-5. Both the differential signal and the true temperature were recorded on a strip chart by a two-pen recorder; a portion of a typical record is shown in Fig. 7-6. It is clear from this record that our DTA signal changed rapidly as temperature varied, because marked temperature gradients existed in our furnace owing to its small length. These gradients changed as furnace temperature was increased or decreased. Nevertheless, the melting and freezing points are clearly marked by spikes on the DTA signal.

Throughout most of these runs, an automatic power drive was used to vary temperature smoothly and slowly.

[18] F. R. Boyd and J. L. England, *J. Geophys. Research*, vol. 65, p. 741, 1960.

In most cases there was a 5 to 10° discrepancy between the melting and freezing temperatures for a given pressure. The freezing points are always lower. This arises from the effects of supercooling of the liquid and superheating of the solid, as well as from the time lag of the sensing thermocouple in detecting the temperature arrest through the metal capsules. Experimentation at 1 atm indicated, however, that the biggest

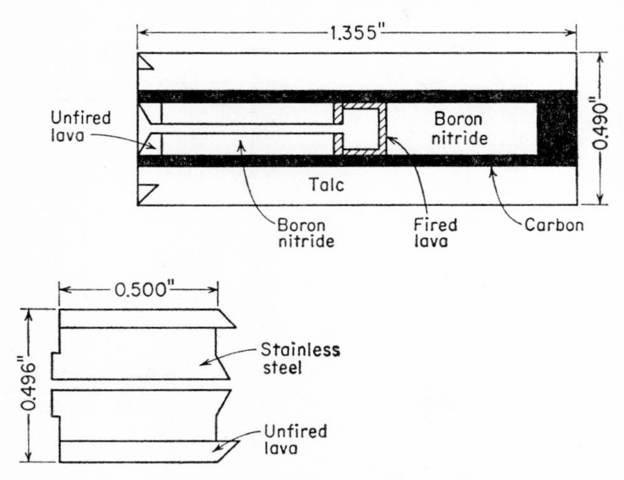

Fig. 7-4 Furnace and base-plug assembly.

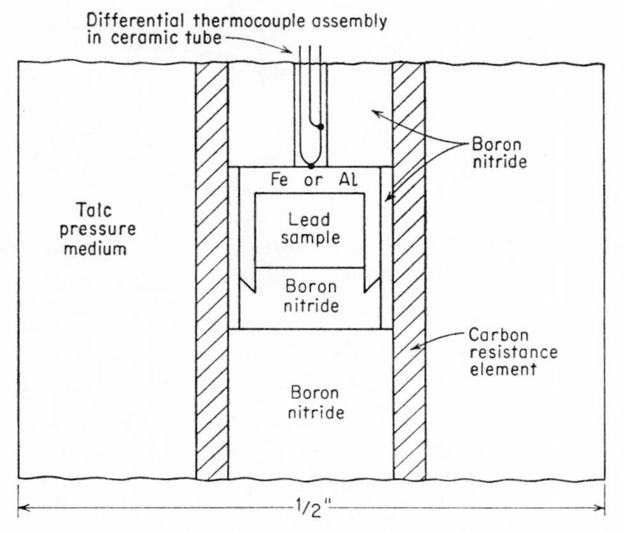

Fig. 7-5 Differential-thermal-analysis arrangement for detection of phase changes in metals at high pressure.

portion of our problem was super-cooling of the melt on the freezing cycle; therefore most of the curves we show are based on melting-point determinations.

We found the method of determining melting points by DTA signal to be rapid and accurate. Barring operational failures, a melting curve could be explored to 50 kilobars in the course of an hour; this calls for three to four traverses at 10 pressure intervals.

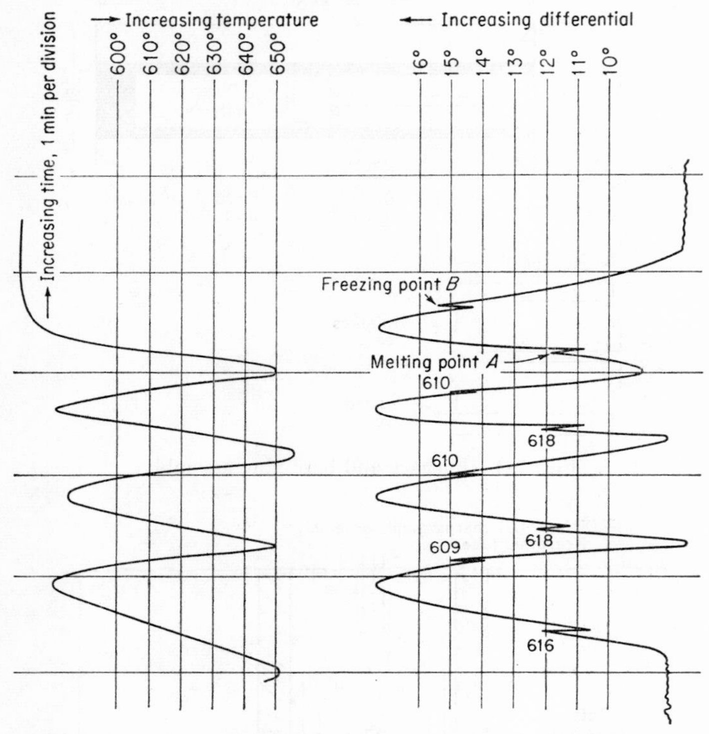

Fig. 7-6 Record showing differential-thermocouple response and true temperature for several traverses of a melting-freezing point.

A number of difficulties are, however, inherent in this method. The first problem is containing the liquid metal under high pressure. Numerous initial failures emphasize the fact that a tight cup must surround the molten metal; otherwise the melt instantaneously escapes to every corner of the furnace and the surrounding pressure medium, shorting out thermocouples, changing the resistance of the carbon furnace, and in other ways completely ruining the setup. This container around the sample must also be thermally conducting, so that the latent heat of freezing or melting may flow from the sample to the thermocouple. It is also apparent that the sample container must be of a substance that will not react or alloy with the sample at temperatures around the sample melting point. Although sealed platinum containers were used for most of these experiments, we found that magnesium, alkali metals, and lead alloy readily with platinum. The melting curve of lead, for instance, was determined in both iron and aluminum capsules with identical results.

Most of the samples used in this investigation were highly refined metals supplied by the McKay Company. We checked the purity of these metals only by measuring their normal melting points at 1 atm pressure.

7-6 Results

The results of this investigation are shown in a number of figures. The melting curves of indium, cadmium, lead, and zinc are shown

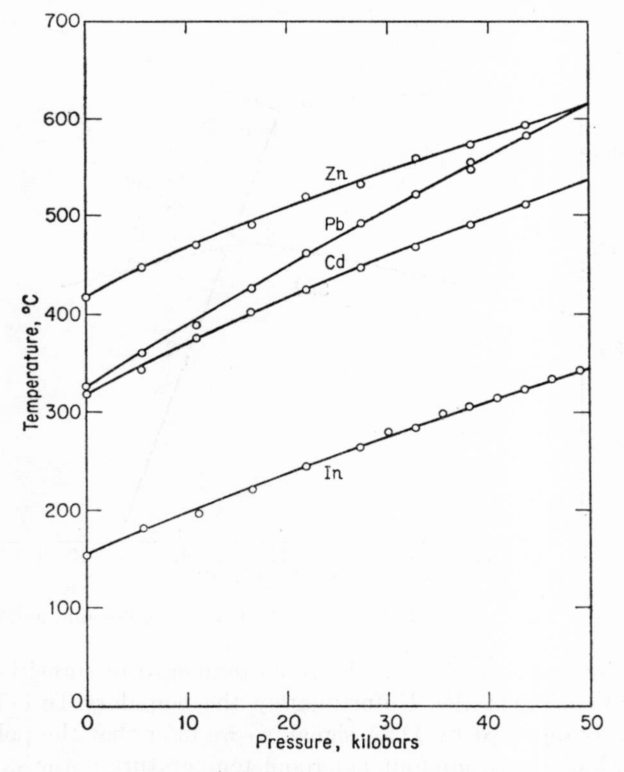

Fig. 7-7 Melting curves of indium, cadmium, lead, and zinc.

in Fig. 7-7. The points show the individual observations where only a single observation was present or, in many cases, are the averages of several observations taken at the same temperature and pressure.

With but one or two exceptions, all our determinations fall within ±5° or ±1 kilobar of a smooth curve. These curves are believed to be precise within these limits. Figure 7-8 shows the melting curves and phase transitions in tin, tellurium, and antimony. The solid-solid boundary of Sn I–Sn II is accompanied by a fairly large latent heat; strong DTA signals were observed as this phase boundary was intersected, in addition to the strong signals which arose at the melting point. The slope of the boundary Te I–Te II was inferred from the minimum found in the

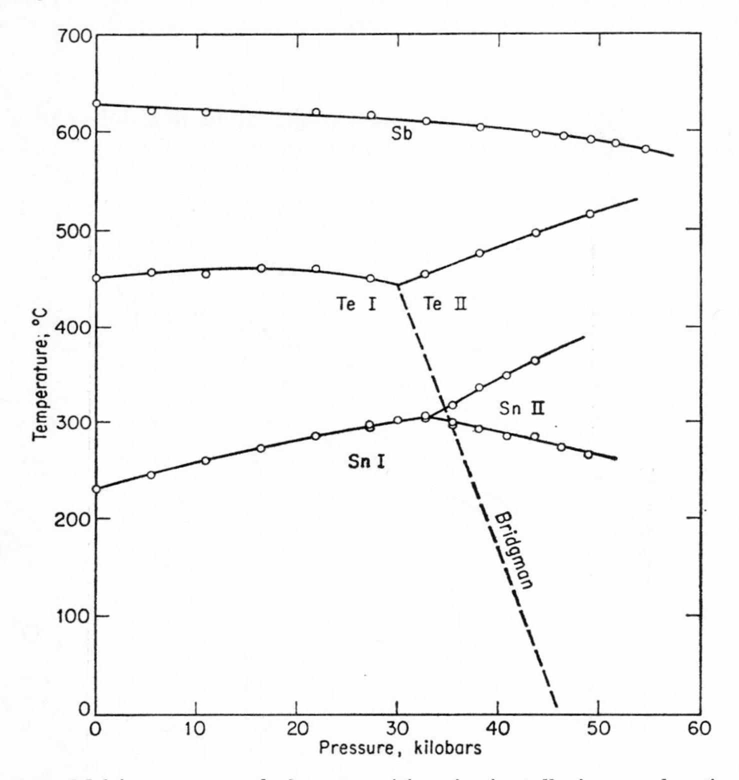

Fig. 7-8 Melting curves and phase transitions in tin, tellurium, and antimony.

melting-point curve and from the room-temperature transition pressure reported by Bridgman.[19] Unfortunately the boundary Te I–Te II could not be clearly detected by DTA signal, so we infer that the polymorph of tellurium which Bridgman found at room temperature is the same one we deduce from the minimum in the melting curve.

It is clear from the behavior of the antimony curve (Fig. 7-8) that a

[19] P. W. Bridgman, Pressure-volume Relations for 17 Elements to 100,000 kg/cm^2, *Proc. Am. Acad. Arts Sci.*, vol. 74, p. 425, 1942.

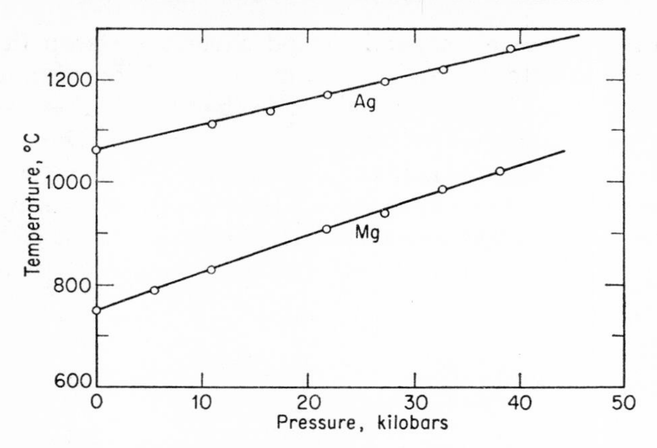

Fig. 7-9 Melting curves of magnesium and silver.

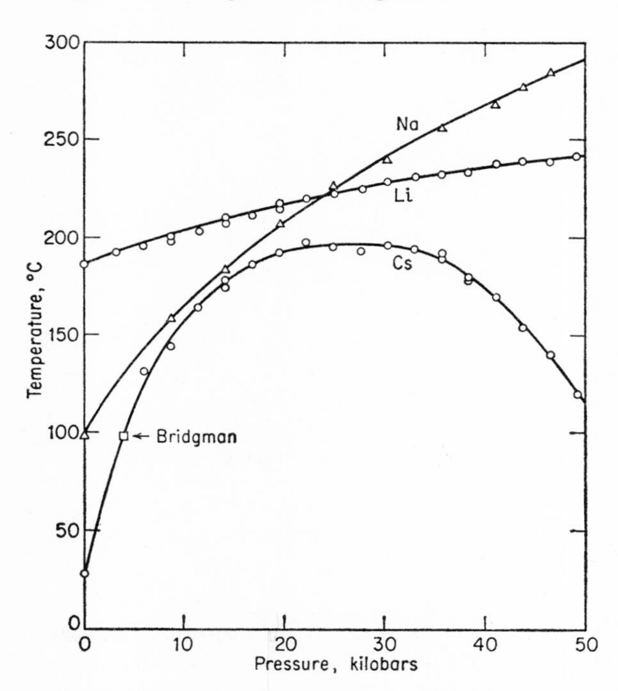

Fig. 7-10 Melting curves of cesium, sodium, and lithium.

phase transition is to be expected somewhat above 50 kilobars. Bridgman, indeed, reports a polymorph of antimony at room temperature at approximately 85 kilobars, and it would be of interest to pursue the melting curve of antimony to a higher pressure in order to locate the transition.

The melting curves of magnesium and silver are shown in Fig. 7-9. They are unusual in that these curves are the only ones (of those investigated) which can best be represented within the limits of the experimental data by a straight line. The Grüneisen constant for these elements is thus infinity if we follow Simon's equation—an obvious impossibility.

Melting curves for cesium, sodium, and lithium are shown in Fig. 7-10. The curve for cesium is most spectacular. The initial value of dT/dP for

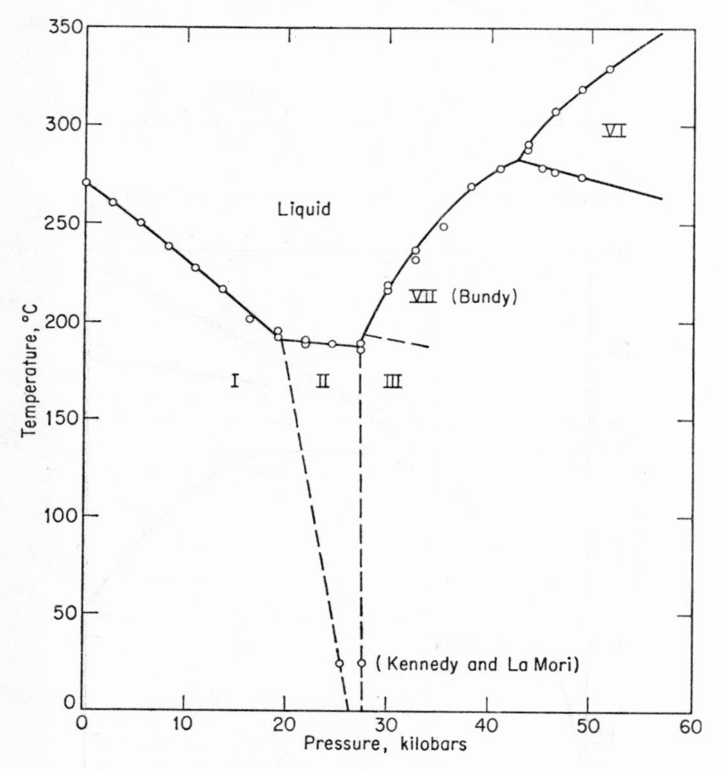

Fig. 7-11 Phase diagram for bismuth.

cesium is the greatest of any element we examined, yet this value drops practically to zero over the pressure interval between 20 and 30 kilobars and then becomes strongly negative above 30 kilobars. Two room-temperature transitions are known in cesium. These are the transitions at 22.6 and 41.7 kilobars. The 22.6-kilobar transition, from Cs I to Cs II is presumed to be associated with the transition to a close-packed structure, whereas the 41.7-kilobar transition, from Cs II to Cs III, is assumed to be associated with the collapse of an electron shell. A complete phase diagram of cesium would be most instructive. The sharp changes in slope of the melting curve may be intersections of solid-solid phase boundaries and the melting curve. It would also be most instructive to carry the work on cesium to higher pressures to determine whether a minimum in the melting curve is encountered (as is the case with bismuth, tellurium, and tin) followed by a reversal of the curve to a normal positive slope. It would also be of the greatest interest to determine the density

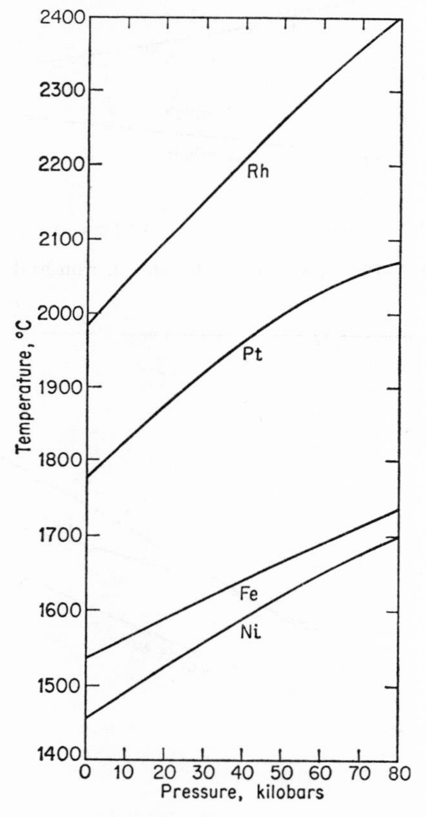

Fig. 7-12 Melting curves of four Group-8 metals.

variations with pressure of molten cesium in the region of the intersection of the electron-shell-collapse phase boundary and the melting curve. Liquid cesium may show a first-order transition or, more likely, two diffuse second-order transitions.

The melting curve of bismuth was carefully explored to 45 kilobars. A large number of points was taken because of the great complexity of this curve. Bi I, Bi II, Bi III, Bi VII, and Bi VI have pressure and temperature intervals in which they are in equilibrium with liquid. It is

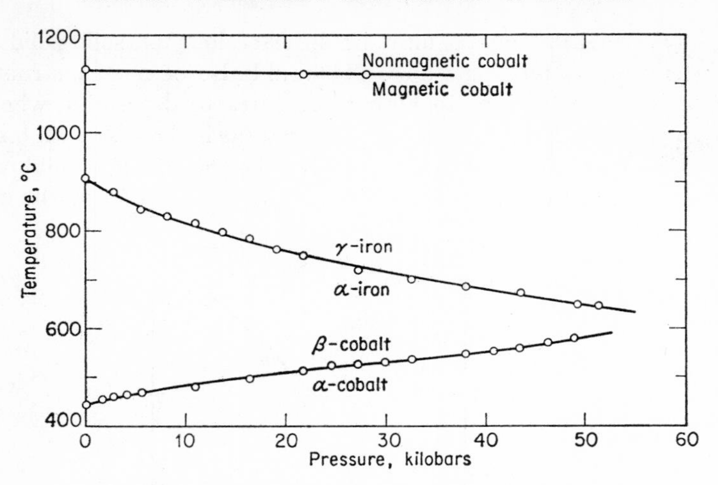

Fig. 7-13 Some phase changes in iron and cobalt.

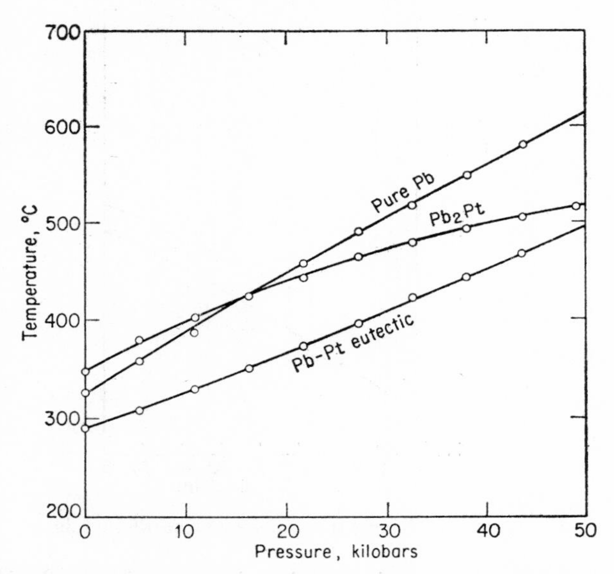

Fig. 7-14 Melting-point curves for lead and Pb_2Pt, and the effect of pressure on the lead-platinum eutectic.

probable that the Bi VIII of Bundy[11] is the same as the Bi VI of Bridgman; we have followed Bridgman's earlier nomenclature. The results of the studies on bismuth are plotted in Fig. 7-11. The boundaries Bi I–Bi II and Bi II–Bi III are shown in Fig. 7-11 as straight lines connecting the known transition pressures at room temperature with the minima found in the melting curve. No signal corresponding to the boundary Bi III–Bi VII, discovered by Bundy,[11] could be detected. However, strong DTA signals were associated with the transition Bi VII–Bi VI. We have been unable to demonstrate by our technique that Bi III is not the same as Bi VII.

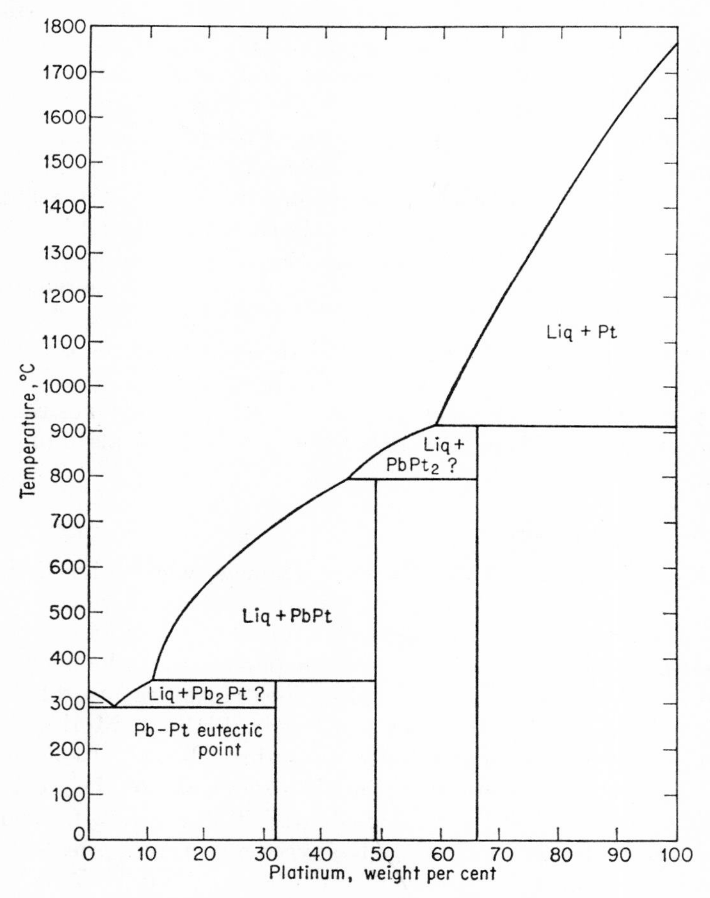

Fig. 7-15 Phase diagram for lead-platinum.

The melting pressures of nickel, iron, platinum, and rhodium are shown in Fig. 7-12. These curves are taken from the work of Strong and Bundy.[10] The data presented by Strong and Bundy have been corrected to lower pressures in the light of recent revisions of the high-pressure scale.

Some phase transitions in cobalt and iron are shown in Fig. 7-13. Strong DTA signals were associated with the α-cobalt–β-cobalt transition and the α-γ transition in iron.

The Curie point in cobalt at 1 atm is reported at 1128°C. To our surprise we found rather large DTA signals associated with this point. This suggests that this transition is a first-order transition and probably is associated with a phase change. It is thus not a "normal" Curie point. This transition is most insensitive to pressure.

The melting curve for pure lead is shown in Fig. 7-14. Essentially identical curves were obtained in using both aluminum and iron capsules as containers for the lead. However, our first measurements were made on lead in platinum capsules. It became immediately apparent that the lead was alloying with the platinum, as two strong DTA signals at a given pressure which did not correlate with the melting point of pure lead were seen. Reference to the phase diagram for lead-platinum (see Fig. 7-15) suggested that these signals were associated with the melting point of Pb_2Pt and with the eutectic point in the system lead-platinum. We therefore traced out the effect of pressure on the eutectic temperature and the melting curve for Pb_2Pt. These are shown in Fig. 7-14. It is interesting to note that the curvature of the eutectic curve is concave to the temperature axis. Such a curvature has not been observed in any of the pure elements. We can only assume that the composition of the eutectic point is shifting toward higher amounts of platinum as the pressure is raised.

7-7 Acknowledgments

Much credit is due to Mr. Terrence Thomas, who designed the temperature-traversing controller which made possible accurate melting-point measurements and who kept the apparatus in working condition. The precision machine work of Mr. Sebastian Schutz, who fashioned the tiny and delicate furnace and sample-holder parts, was essential to this investigation. Thanks are also given to Mr. Philip LaMori and Dr. A. Jayaraman, who made many suggestions throughout the course of the work. Dr. Jayaraman, in particular, is responsible for the work on the pressure effect of the α-cobalt–β-cobalt transition. Funds for constructing the apparatus and conducting the investigation were provided in part by the Office of Naval Research under contract NONR 233(53). Thanks are given to Dr. M. W. Riggs of the Office of Naval Research, who aided in many ways.

8

The Role of Pressure in Semiconductor Research

William Paul
Division of Engineering and Applied Physics
Harvard University
Cambridge, Massachusetts

Douglas M. Warschauer
Research Division
Raytheon Company
Waltham, Massachusetts

8-1 Introduction

In this chapter we shall discuss the effect of hydrostatic and quasi-hydrostatic pressure on the electrical and optical properties of semiconductors. The presently available pressure range for truly hydrostatic pressures such as are developed in shear-free fluids is 30 kilobars.‡ Higher pressures, up to 500 kilobars, may be obtained quasi-hydrostatically by immersing a sample in a soft matrix of silver chloride or some other easily sheared substance to which force can be applied while the material is constrained in volume.

Our particular concern will be to evaluate the extent to which such research has contributed to our present knowledge of semiconductor properties, to examine whether and how further research should be carried out, and to discuss the contribution of a program of research at the extremely high pressures now available.

We shall not discuss nonhydrostatic effects such as those caused by uniaxial tension, although these are very useful in studying semiconductor crystals of high symmetry; nor shall we discuss the properties of those substances which are semiconducting only at pressures or temperatures substantially higher than in our normal environment.

The accuracy of pressure measurement below 30 kilobars is of the order of 1 percent. It is probable that most investigators established their pressures using the value for the freezing pressure of mercury at 0°C of 7,640 kg/cm^2, and the transition pressure Bi I–Bi II of 25,420 kg/cm^2, as determined by Bridgman. Recent work has shown that the first of these values is low, but it is unlikely that this correction will affect even the qualitative conclusions discussed here.

In order to acquaint the reader with the present status of this phase of semiconductor research, we shall give an extensive historical account, starting with the compressibility and resistivity measurements of Bridgman[1] in 1935 and noting the increasing diversity of experiment and

‡ 1 kilobar = 1,000 bars = 1.000×10^9 dynes/cm^2 = 986.92 atm = 1.0197×10^3 kg/cm^2.

[1] P. W. Bridgman, Compressibilities and Electrical Resistance under Pressure, with Special Reference to Intermetallic Compounds, *Proc. Am. Acad. Arts Sci.*, vol. 70, pp. 285–317, 1935. It should be noted that Bridgman had measured the pressure dependence of the resistivity of substances recognized to be semiconductors even earlier, for example, in his measurement of the resistance of black phosphorus at three temperatures. (P. W. Bridgman, Electrical Resistance under Pressure, including Certain Liquid Metals, *Proc. Am. Acad. Arts Sci.*, vol. 56, pp. 126–131, 1921.)

sophistication of interpretation since that time. Among the compounds treated in Bridgman's cited paper were silver sulfide, lead selenide, lead telluride, and germanium. This study was part of a routine survey of a number of materials, and there was no reason for Bridgman to suppose that the results he obtained on a limited number of samples were not characteristic of the pure materials. The resistance of a single crystal of germanium, measured by a four-probe potentiometric method, increased by about 20 percent in 12 kilobars at 30°C. Since the resistivity of the sample was 0.01 ohm-cm, we interpret this result now as a decrease with pressure of the mobility of a constant density of current carriers. At that time the strong influence of impurities on the properties of semiconductors was not appreciated. Thus, in Bridgman's measurements, it is likely that the mobility of the electrons contributing to the measured current flow was controlled by scattering caused by the large number of ionized impurities present in the relatively impure material then available, so that the mobility change with pressure was determined by changes in the effective mass and dielectric constant. Had the impurity concentration been less, it would have been more likely that the mobility was controlled by the scattering due to lattice vibrations only; the magnitude of the changes observed would have been different; the dielectric constant, as one example, would not have entered the analysis, and the measurements would have yielded properties characteristic of germanium itself, rather than of accidental impurities.

It is evident that much subsidiary investigation must be performed to establish exactly what is being measured in any particular pressure experiment. Several of the present-day approaches, therefore, concentrate on the measurement of a large number of semiconductor properties of one crystal under pressure and try to correlate these measurements with each other and with theory.

The particular job under way at present is to systematize the behavior of semiconductors across a wide range of materials extending from the well-known semiconductors of Group 4 in the periodic table to the Group 3–Group 5 and Group 2–Group 6 compounds.‡ We shall find it advantageous, in developing our historical account, to keep in mind some fundamental ideas concerning the properties of semiconductors. Some of these will now be briefly reviewed, with special attention paid to the probable pressure dependences of the quantities involved.

8-2 Fundamental Properties of Semiconductors

8-2a Band structure. The occurrence of allowed and forbidden bands of energy in a solid can be understood if one starts with the model of a solid with the atoms in their proper relative positions but separated by

‡ "Group" here refers to a column of the periodic table. Henceforth Group A–Group B compounds will be referred to as Group A-B compounds.

distances much greater than the equilibrium lattice separation. When the atoms are far apart, the electrons in each atom must have the energies appropriate to the isolated atom; these energies are discrete and are separated by wide bands of forbidden energies. For N identical atoms in such a lattice, N levels exist for each energy represented. As the atoms are brought closer together, there is a broadening of the discrete but degenerate energy levels into bands of levels, each level slightly different in energy from the others. The electrons whose energy levels lie deep in the energy-level structure are hardly affected at all, since the spread of the electronic wave functions corresponding to these energies is so small that there is no overlap of wave function from one atom to the next. This is not so of the wave functions corresponding to higher quantum numbers; the result is that for these the interaction is strong, and there is a large spread of energies forming a quasi-continuous band at the equilibrium lattice separation.

The electrons of the whole crystal are assigned to these energy levels in much the same way as the electrons in the atom are assigned to the discrete energy levels of the atom. If there is just a sufficient number of electrons to fill completely all the bands of allowed energy up to a certain one, and if there is a wide gap in energy between this band and the next higher one, the material will be an insulator at absolute zero and will, if this gap (or *forbidden band*) is wide enough, continue to be an insulator as the temperature is raised. If the uppermost band that contains any electrons is only partly filled at absolute zero, the material will be a metal at this and higher temperatures. On the other hand, if the energy gap between the uppermost completely filled band and the lowest empty band is small at absolute zero, there is the possibility that electrons may be excited across the intervening energy gap at finite temperatures. The material will then properly be classed as an *intrinsic semiconductor*, in which electrical transport can occur not only by way of the excited electrons in the conduction band, but also by movement of the electron vacancies or *holes* in the valence band. The highest filled band is known as the *valence band*, the lowest empty band as the *conduction band*.

From this simple description, one would think that the influence of high pressure would be to decrease the energy gap between the valence band and the conduction band, because one expects the wave-function overlap to broaden with decreasing interatomic spacing, the bands therefore to widen, and the gap to decrease. This has been proved incorrect experimentally, but in order to explain exactly where the model is wrong, it is necessary to describe the energy-band structure in more detail.

The energy-band structure of germanium, which we shall regard as a typical semiconductor, is shown in Fig. 8-1. The electron energy is given as ordinate, and its wave vector, or crystal momentum, as abscissa. The variation of energy with wave vector is illustrated for two of the principal directions in the crystal, namely, the (100) and the (111) directions. We choose to illustrate with these directions because the lowest energies of the conduction band occur for electrons whose wave vector lies in these directions. From the figure, we see that the maximum energy in the valence band corresponds to electrons of wave vector zero. At absolute zero the conduction band is empty of electrons, while the valence band is full.

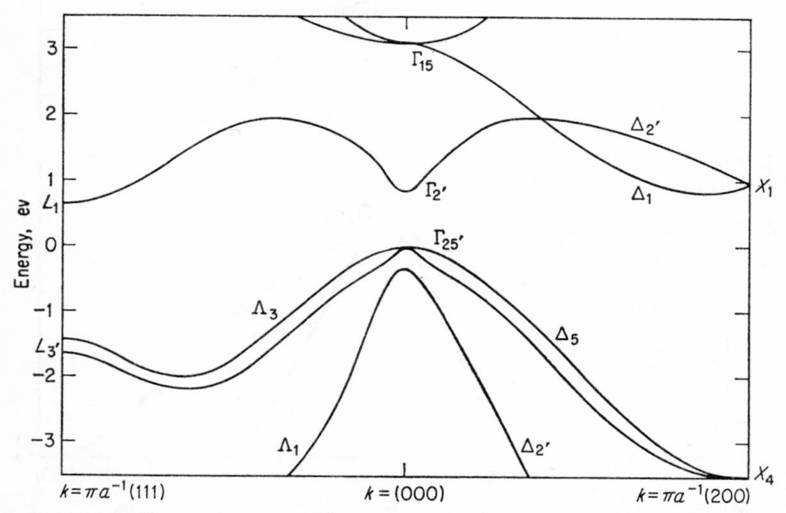

Fig. 8-1 The energy-band structure of germanium, as determined as of December, 1961. The abscissas are the wave vectors in the (111) and (100) directions. Energy is plotted as ordinate. The labeling of states follows the notation of Bouckaert, Smoluchowski, and Wigner. The zero of energy is chosen at the valence-band maximum at $\Gamma_{25'}$. The approximate energy separations at 300°K are $\Gamma_{25'} - L_1$: 0.65 ev; $\Gamma_{25'} - \Delta_1$(min): 0.80 to 0.85 ev; $\Gamma_{25'} - \Gamma_{2'}$: 0.80 ev; $\Gamma_{25'} - \Gamma_{15}$: 3.1 ev; $L_1 - L_{3'}$: 2.1 ev; $X_1 - X_4$: 4.5 ev.

There is a twofold degeneracy in the valence band at $k = (000)$ (actually the degeneracy is fourfold if we remember that two electrons of opposite spin can be accommodated in each electronic state). Still another allowed state for an electron of wave vector zero lies 0.3 ev below the filled state of highest energy. The curvature of these bands close to $k = (000)$ and the separation between the energies at $k = (000)$ are well established by experiment; however, the shape of the rest of the curves is speculative, although their symmetry is established from certain general considerations.

In the conduction band, the three energy minima at $k = (000)$ and in the (111) and (100) directions have been extensively investigated. The properties of the minima at $k = (000)$ and on the boundary at $k = (111)$ have been well established, and the properties of the minima in the $k = (100)$ directions roughly so.

The band structure of silicon, shown in Fig. 8-2, is similar to that of germanium. The lower valence band is split from the upper, by spin-orbit interaction, by about 0.05 ev instead of the 0.3 ev in germanium.

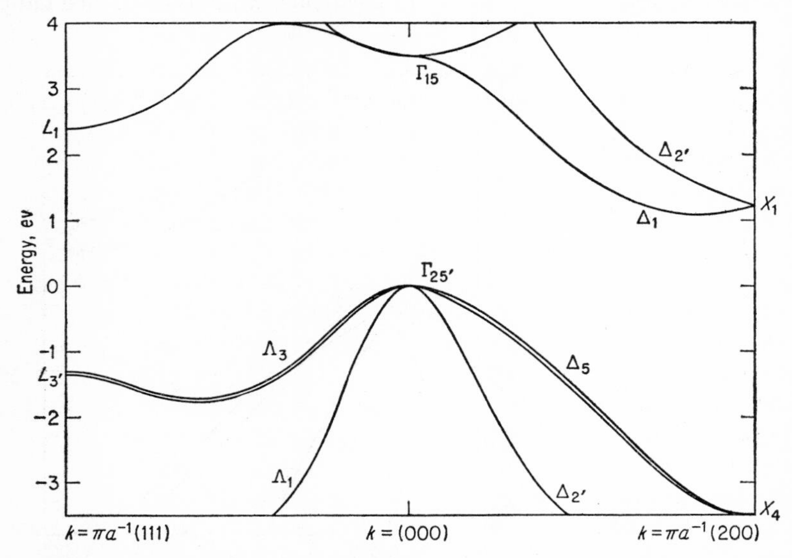

Fig. 8-2 The energy-band structure of silicon, as determined as of December, 1961. The abscissas are the wave vectors in the (111) and (000) directions. Energy is plotted as ordinate. The labeling of states follows the notation of Bouckaert, Smoluchwski, and Wigner. The zero of energy is chosen at the valence-band maximum at $\Gamma_{25'}$. The approximate energy separations at 300°K are $\Gamma_{25'} - \Delta_1(\text{min})$: 1.1 ev; $\Gamma_{25'} - \Gamma_{15}$: 3.5 ev; $L_1 - L_{3'}$: 3.7 ev; $X_1 - X_4$: 4.5 ev.

The lowest energy minima in the conduction band are the six equivalent ones in the (100) directions, and the $k = (000)$ and $k = (111)$ sets are much higher in energy.

Diamond and grey tin probably have band structures similar to those of germanium and silicon, although as of 1962 less was known about them.

The band structures of the Group 3-5 compound[2] are supposed to be

[2] F. Herman, Speculations on the Energy Band Structure of Zinc-blende-type Crystals, *J. Electronics*, vol. 1, pp. 103–114, 1955; J. Callaway, Energy Bands in Gallium Arsenide, *J. Electronics*, vol. 2, pp. 330–340, 1957; Electron Energy Bands in Solids, pp. 100–212 in F. Seitz and D. Turnbull (eds.), "Solid State Physics," vol. 7, Academic Press, Inc., New York, 1958.

perturbations of the scheme for the Group 4 elements. The valence-band maximum energy is again at $k = (000)$, but there is some fine detail near the maximum caused by the absence of inversion symmetry in the crystal lattice. This fine structure is of no significance for any of the phenomena we shall discuss. The conduction-band structures possess the three minima of the type already described.

Certain systematic trends seem to occur as the composition is changed. For example, the (000) conduction-band minimum appears to be lowest for compounds of high average atomic number, while the (100) minimum is lowest for those of low average atomic number. The forbidden-energy gaps and certain other physical properties also change in a regular way as the atomic number and ionicity are changed. Attempts have been made to justify these trends on the basis of bonding or chemical theories[3] and on the basis of a perturbation from germaniumlike behavior. We shall not, however, pursue these ideas in this article.

(*a*) *Effect of Pressure on Band Structure.* The theoretical approach to the calculation of the band structure of semiconductors has been reviewed by Herman.[4] No attempt to recalculate any structure at a value of the lattice constant different from that at atmospheric pressure has been published. However, recent approaches to the calculation of the band structure by perturbation techniques seem to give results sufficiently accurate at the equilibrium lattice constant to warrant recalculation at reduced separations.[5] These approaches are based on the assertion that the valence- and conduction-band electrons move in an effective potential not very different from that of a free electron. The effect of the attractive periodic potential of the atomic cores is partially offset by the result of orthogonalizing the electronic wave functions to the core wave functions. The orthogonalization is simulated by introducing a repulsive pseudopotential that partly cancels the attractive potential due to the core charge. Since the influence of the core is thereby reduced, the band structure approximates that for an electron moving in a small regular potential having the periodicity and symmetry of the particular lattice involved. The band structures of all the Group 4 and Group 3-5 compounds are thus expected to be similar, and this is what is found experimentally.

The difference between the energy of a particular state in the actual

[3] See, for example, E. Mooser and W. B. Pearson, The Chemical Bond in Semiconductors, pp. 103–139 in A. F. Gibson, F. A. Kröger, and R. E. Burgess (eds.) "Progress in Semiconductors," vol. 5, John Wiley & Sons, Inc., New York, 1960.

[4] F. Herman, Theoretical Investigation of the Electronic Energy Band Structure of Solids, *Rev. Mod. Phys.*, vol. 30, pp. 102–121, 1958.

[5] J. C. Phillips and L. Kleinman, New Method for Calculating Wave Functions in Crystals and Molecules, *Phys. Rev.*, vol. 116, pp. 287–294, 1959.

lattice and its energy in this model of a periodic potential of vanishingly small amplitude depends on the symmetry of the state involved, so that we should expect to find states of the same symmetry perturbed to nearly the same extent, or to an extent systematically varying from compound to compound. We should also expect that states of the same symmetry be similarly affected by a change in the lattice constant. This deduction, if correct, vastly simplifies the problem of understanding the pressure variations of the band structure. We shall see later that this discussion justifies to some extent the approximate equality of the pressure coefficients of the energy of the (100) [or the (000) or (111)] minima in the Group 4 and Group 3-5 compounds.

Calculations of the sort mentioned have been carried out by Bassani,[6] and his preliminary results for the band-structure changes in germanium appear to agree well with experimental measurements. It is hoped that further calculations will set the deductions from correlations of the pressure coefficients such as those described in qualitative fashion in the previous paragraph on a firmer foundation.

8-2b Conduction properties. The conductivity of a semiconductor is given by

$$\sigma = e(n\mu_n + p\mu_p) \tag{8-1}$$

where n and p are the electron and hole densities, and μ_n and μ_p are the electron and hole mobilities.

When Maxwell-Boltzmann statistics are obeyed and all the impurities are ionized, the densities are given by

$$n = \frac{n_0}{2} + \left[\left(\frac{n_0}{2}\right)^2 + n_i^2\right]^{1/2} \tag{8-2}$$

$$p = -\frac{n_0}{2} + \left[\left(\frac{n_0}{2}\right)^2 + n_i^2\right]^{1/2} \tag{8-3}$$

where

$$n_0 = n - p = N_d - N_a$$

N_d and N_a are the donor and acceptor impurity densities, and n_i^2, the square of the intrinsic carrier density, is given by

$$n_i^2 = 4A_cA_v \exp\frac{-E_g}{kT} \tag{8-4}$$

A_c and A_v are density-of-states expressions for the conduction and valence bands, and E_g is the energy gap at the temperature T.

The mobilities μ_n and μ_p depend on the scattering mechanisms, the most important of which are scattering by the thermal vibrations of the lattice and scattering by the ionized impurities. When the former is dominant, the mobility decreases with rising temperature in a rather

[6] F. Bassani, private communication, 1961.

complicated way if all the different modes of lattice vibration contribute. At moderate temperatures, and when certain selection rules are obeyed, it may happen that the greatest contribution to the lattice scattering comes from the longitudinal acoustic vibrations. Then the deformation-potential theory of Shockley and Bardeen[7] applies, and the mobility is given by

$$\mu_l = \frac{2(2\pi)^{1/2} e\hbar^4 \rho c^2}{3(kT)^{3/2} m^{*5/2} E_1^2} \tag{8-5}$$

where ρ = density of crystal
c = average phonon velocity
m^* = appropriate average effective mass of carrier

The quantity E_1 is the deformation potential, or the amount by which the energy of an electron at the band edge is changed by unit dilatation of the crystal.

If scattering by the longitudinal acoustic phonons were the dominant scattering mechanism for both electrons and holes (so that the deformation potentials E_{1c} and E_{1v} for the conduction and valence bands could be found from the measured mobilities), then the pressure coefficient of the energy gap could be checked from these measurements of the transport properties. It has been found in all the materials measured so far that the other modes of lattice vibration contribute significantly to the total scattering, so that no such simple check is possible.

At low temperatures and high impurity densities the ionized impurities contribute to the scattering. The relaxation time due to this process is in general a complex function of doping and temperature, but it simplifies when the impurity density is light and the temperature is not too low. Under these conditions, which are equivalent to the condition that the Born approximation holds, the mobility as determined only by ionized impurity scattering would be[8]

$$\mu_i = CN_i^{-1} K^2 m^{*-1/2} T^{3/2} \tag{8-6}$$

where C = constant
N_i = impurity density
K = dielectric constant

When both scattering mechanisms contribute significantly at the same temperature, a rough approximation to the mobility is given by

$$\mu^{-1} = \mu_i^{-1} + \mu_l^{-1} \tag{8-7}$$

[7] W. Shockley and J. Bardeen, Energy Bands and Mobilities in Monatomic Semiconductors, *Phys. Rev.*, vol. 77, pp. 407–408, 1950; Deformation Potentials and Mobilities in Non-polar Crystals, *Phys. Rev.*, vol. 80, pp. 72–80, 1950.

[8] E. M. Conwell and V. F., Weisskopf, Theory of Impurity Scattering in Semiconductors, *Phys. Rev.*, vol. 77, pp. 388–390, 1950.

(*a*) *Effect of Pressure on the Conductivity.* Pressure affects the lattice-scattering mobility through ρ, c, m^*, and E_1. The fractional changes in density[9] and phonon velocity[10] are of the order of 1×10^{-6} bar^{-1}. Changes of E_1 with pressure are second-order effects which have not been established in any actual case. The fractional change in effective mass is approximately equal to the fractional change in energy gap for materials in which the extrema in the conduction and valence bands occur at the same value of wave vector k. Thus effective-mass changes can be large in small-band-gap materials. In germanium, in which the direct energy gap is approximately 0.80 ev at room temperature, the mass change is probably about 1.5×10^{-5} bar^{-1}. These changes imply that for materials such as germanium the effect of a pressure of 10 kilobars on the lattice-scattering mobility will be a change of only a few percent.

The fractional changes in dielectric constant are of the same order of magnitude as the mass changes, since both are caused by changes in the electron energies. This implies that the change in impurity-scattering mobility, and hence in the total mobility when both forms of scattering are present, is also of the order of a few percent in 10 kilobars.

Pressure can also affect the conductivity through a change in impurity-derived or intrinsic carrier density. The ionization energy of hydrogenic impurities in such semiconductors as germanium and silicon is given by

$$E_i = \frac{m^*}{m} K^{-2} E_H \tag{8-8}$$

where E_H is the ionization energy of the hydrogen atom. These impurities are fully ionized above 20°K in germanium and 50°K in silicon. The effect of pressure on the ionization energy, through variation of m^* and K, is of the order of a few percent in 10 kilobars and therefore does not affect the state of complete ionization of the impurities at temperatures above 50°K.

The hydrogenic impurities in germanium and silicon are elements of Groups 5 and 3. Other elements produce energy levels deep in the forbidden gap; their pressure dependence is not as easily estimated. We shall deal with these later as a special case.

The carrier density is more affected by changes in n_i^2 due to pressure. A_c and A_v contain, essentially, only the effective masses of electrons and holes and so change very little. The energy gap, on the other hand, occurs in the exponential, and consequently changes in it rapidly alter

[9] P. W. Bridgman, "Physics of High Pressure," G. Bell & Sons, Ltd., London, 1949. For germanium as a typical semiconductor example, see P. W. Bridgman, Linear Compressions to 30,000 kg/cm, *Proc. Am. Acad. Arts Sci.*, vol. 77, pp. 187–234, 1949.

[10] See, for example, H. J. McSkimin, Elastic Moduli of Single Crystal Germanium as a Function of Hydrostatic Pressure, *J. Acoust. Soc. Am.*, vol. 30, pp. 314–318, 1958.

the carrier density of an intrinsic semiconductor. There seems to be no simple way of estimating a priori what the energy-gap changes will be. Experimentally, they turn out to be about 10 ev per unit dilatation, or 0.1 ev in 10 kilobars. At room temperature such a change in the energy gap causes the carrier density to change by about an order of magnitude, overshadowing all other effects discussed so far.

One other effect found in a number of semiconductors should be mentioned. We saw that it was possible for several energy-band extrema to be close to one another and that these minima very likely would have different pressure coefficients. If pressure inverts the relative positions of two minima in energy, the carriers will change over from one to the other. This may drastically affect the mobility through changes in the effective mass and scattering mechanism and produce conductivity changes comparable with that caused by variation of the energy gap.

8-2c Optical properties. Conservation of energy and crystal momentum demand that transitions produced by photons occur without change of wave vector k, i.e., that they be "vertical" in the band structure of Fig. 8-1 or 8-2. If the transitions at the onset of absorption, i.e., at the band extrema, are also allowed by parity, the absorption coefficient is often taken to be of the form[11]

$$\alpha = A_1(h\nu - E_g)^{1/2} \tag{8-9}$$

where A_1 is a coefficient containing density-of-states masses, the dielectric constant, and the matrix element for the transition. If the transition is disallowed by parity, the appropriate formula is

$$\alpha = A_2(h\nu - E_g)^{3/2} \tag{8-10}$$

Transitions may also occur with emission or absorption of phonons. Such two-step phonon-aided transitions are particularly important when the energy extrema of the conduction and valence bands occur at different points in k space. When this happens, the absorption coefficient is given by a sum of terms involving different phonon energies and different intermediate states for the transition. The intermediate states may lie in either conduction band or valence band, and transitions from the ground state to the intermediate state may be group-theoretically allowed or disallowed. In actual cases the full expression can often be simplified by the argument that the contribution of the intermediate state nearest in energy will be most important, provided the momentum matrix element between it and the ground state is finite. Furthermore, selection rules often reduce the number of possible cooperating phonons whose wave vectors connect the initial and final states. For one intermediate

[11] See, for example, T. P. McLean, The Absorption Edge Spectrum of Semiconductors, pp. 53–102 in A. F. Gibson, F. A. Kröger, and R. E. Burgess (eds.), "Progress in Semiconductors," vol. 5, John Wiley & Sons, Inc., New York, 1960.

state in the conduction band (and ignoring phonon energies that, strictly speaking, should be included in the denominators), the expression for the absorption coefficient becomes

$$\alpha = \sum_i \frac{A_3(h\nu - E_g + \hbar\omega_i)^n}{|E_{cj} - E_c|^2} + \frac{A_4(h\nu - E_g - \hbar\omega_i)^n}{|E_{cj} - E_c|^2} \quad (8\text{-}11)$$

The index n takes the value 2 when the transition to the intermediate state is allowed, and the value 3 when it is disallowed. The sum over i is a sum over phonons $\hbar\omega_i$. E_{cj} is the energy of the intermediate state, and E_c is the energy of the conduction-band minimum. The full expressions for a number of intermediate states can be found in reference 11. The detailed shape of the fundamental absorption edge aids in determining whether such processes occur.

Impurity transitions and lattice vibrations can also contribute to absorption. Electrons or holes on impurities can be excited into higher bound states or ionized into the nearest band. The most characteristic feature of their absorption spectra is the absorption peak or edge corresponding to the appropriate energy difference. The shape of the absorption curve will depend on the details of the states involved.

(*a*) *Effect of Pressure on the Optical Properties.* The most striking effect of pressure on the optical properties of the intrinsic semiconductor is the shift in the fundamental optical absorption edge, easily measurable under normal resolution conditions. A_1 and A_2 change through the coefficients of the mass and dielectric constant, and the resultant change of shape should be observable in narrow-gap materials.

Changes of shape of the absorption edge also occur for indirect transitions. Not only do A_3 and A_4 change, but the energy denominators may also change. These effects complicate the interpretation of the shift of the absorption edge to give changes in the energy gap. The pressure dependence of impurity, lattice-vibration, or free-carrier absorption has not been measured as of 1962.

8-2d Magnetic properties and their pressure dependence. In an extrinsic semiconductor the Hall effect gives the carrier density through

$$R_H = -(nec)^{-1}\langle\mu^2\rangle\langle\mu\rangle^{-2} \quad (8\text{-}12)$$

where $\langle\ \rangle$ denotes an appropriate average.[12]

In an intrinsic sample, this equation becomes, approximately,

$$R_H = -(ec)^{-1}(n\langle\mu_n^2\rangle - p\langle\mu_p^2\rangle)(n\langle\mu_n\rangle + p\langle\mu_p\rangle)^{-2} \quad (8\text{-}13)$$

[12] See, for example, H. Brooks, Theory of the Electrical Properties of Germanium and Silicon, pp. 85–182 in L. Marton (ed.), "Advances in Electronics and Electron Physics," vol. 7, Academic Press, Inc., New York, 1955.

If conditions are such that the carrier density remains constant with pressure, for example, in an extrinsic semiconductor with fully ionized impurities, the change in the Hall coefficient is of the same order of magnitude as changes in $\langle\mu\rangle$. If the same semiconductor were in a lower range of temperature at which the impurity were only partly ionized, the Hall-constant variation would sensitively measure the change in carrier density and, thus, in ionization energy. On the other hand, if the sample is intrinsic, the data can be analyzed to give changes in the energy gap.

The magnetoresistance and magnetoconductance involve more complicated averages over the relaxation times of the carriers, and the results must be expressed as tensor components. The relations between these tensor components are often used to identify the direction in k space in which the energy extrema lie and to find the ratio of certain components of the effective-mass tensor.

The effect of pressure on the magnetoresistance is to change the mobility averages and, so, the magnetoresistance coefficients. However, in the special case in which pressure changes the position in k space at which the minimum in the whole conduction-band structure comes, there will be a radical change in the components of the effective-mass tensor, and the new relations between them will establish the direction in k space of the new extremum in the band.

We shall not consider magnetic susceptibility, since we do not know of any measurements at high pressure, and it is not evident that much can be learned from this sort of study.

When a magnetic field is applied, a rich diversity of magneto-optical effects may be studied.[13] The absorption coefficient is given by

$$\alpha = \sum_n B_n(h\nu - E_n)^{-\frac{1}{2}} \tag{8-14}$$

where $E_n = E_g + (n + \frac{1}{2})(\hbar\omega_c + \hbar\omega_v) + (g_c M_c - g_v M_v)\beta H$ (8-15)

E_g = energy gap with no field applied

n = integer index

$\omega_c = eH/m_c c$

$\omega_v = eH/m_v c$

g_c, g_v = spectroscopic splitting factors for conduction, valence bands

M_c, M_v = total angular momenta of conduction-band electron, valence-band hole

β = gyromagnetic ratio

B_n = coefficient including several constants and matrix element for transition

[13] See B. Lax and S. Zwerdling, Magneto-optical Phenomena in Semiconductors, pp. 221–272 in A. F. Gibson, F. A. Kröger, and R. E. Burgess (eds.), "Progress in Semiconductors," John Wiley & Sons, Inc., New York, 1960.

There are various selection rules on the transitions. For our purpose we note simply that Eq. (8-14) will give infinite absorption when $h\nu = E_n$. In practice, at constant field the absorption oscillates as a function of frequency, peaking when $h\nu = E_n$. Thus a graph of the frequency of an individual peak versus H will give a straight line whose slope depends on the reduced mass $\mu = m_c m_v/(m_c + m_v)$ and on the g factors and angular momenta, and whose intercept at $H = 0$ gives E_g.

The energy gap can thus be very accurately determined, since a number of peaks are usually available. Pressure affects the parameters in the formula for α in the same way as it does when there is no field, but the increased accuracy of the gap determination is transferred to the pressure coefficients. No measurements of this kind under pressure had been reported by 1962.

The spectrum of the indirect-transition absorption is also modified by the field, although less strikingly, but the same general considerations apply to the pressure coefficients.

Related optical phenomena on which magnetic fields should produce effects are photoconductivity, radiative recombination, and reflection at high photon energies. To date, little has been reported in the literature on these phenomena at high magnetic fields, and nothing on how pressure affects them.

8-2e Electrical susceptibility. If $\epsilon' - j\epsilon''$ is the complex dielectric constant of a solid, then $\epsilon' = 1 + 4\chi$ and $\epsilon'' = 4\pi\sigma/\omega$, where χ and σ are the electrical susceptibility and conductivity at the angular frequency ω. The complex refractive index $n' - jn''$ is defined by

$$(n' - jn'')^2 = \epsilon' - j\epsilon''$$

so that $n'^2 - n''^2 = \epsilon'^2$ and $2n'n'' = \epsilon''$. n'' is the extinction index. The intrinsic electrical susceptibility χ_0 is given by [14]

$$\chi_0 = \frac{2e^2\hbar^4}{3m^2} \sum_{k,n,m} \frac{|\int \psi_{nk}^* \nabla \psi_{mk}\, d\Omega|^2}{(E_{nk} - E_{mk})^2} \tag{8-16}$$

where m is the free-electron mass and ψ_{nk} is the wave function in band n, of wave-vector k, with eigenvalue E_{nk}. The double summation is over occupied bands n and unoccupied bands m. ϵ' and ϵ'' are related through

[14] R. de L. Kronig, On the Theory of Dispersion of X-rays, *J. Opt. Soc. Am.*, vol. 12, pp. 547–557, 1926; H. A. Kramers, La Diffusion de la lumière des atomes, *Atti Congresso Intern. Fis.*, vol. 2, pp. 545–557, 1927; see also J. H. Van Vleck, "Relation between the Absorption and Frequency Dependence of Refraction," MIT Radiation Laboratory Report 735, May 28, 1945, or J. H. Van Vleck, E. M. Purcell, and H. Goldstein, Atmospheric Attenuation, pp. 641–692 in D. E. Kerr (ed.), "Propagation of Short Radio Waves," vol. 13, MIT Radiation Laboratory Series, McGraw-Hill Book Company, Inc., New York, 1951.

the Kramers-Kronig relations.[14] Experimental determination of ϵ'' for germanium shows that the vertical transitions contributing most to χ_0 occur at energies between 2 and 5 ev. This is probably typical of the semiconductors we are discussing.

Lattice-vibration absorption may contribute to the susceptibility at finite temperatures. In germanium this contribution is less than 0.1 percent of the static dielectric constant. In polar compounds in which the lattice-vibration absorption is stronger, a correspondingly larger contribution is expected.

In impure semiconductors at finite temperatures, the free electrons and holes contribute to the susceptibility. This effect may be incorporated in Eq. (8-16) by inserting Fermi-Dirac distribution factors. Otherwise we can add a term

$$\chi_c = -\frac{nq^2}{m^*\omega^2}$$

where n and m^* are the electron carrier density and effective mass, to describe the free-electron susceptibility. A similar expression applies for the holes.

(*a*) *Effect of Pressure on the Electrical Susceptibility.* The effect of pressure on χ_0 reflects the behavior of the whole band structure rather than its extrema. We expect fractional changes of ϵ' of the same order of magnitude as the average of the fractional changes in the energy gaps corresponding to different band edges.

The effect of pressure on χ_c is the same as that on m^*, assuming constant n.

8-3 Historical Review

Bridgman's[1] measurements on germanium in 1935 have already been discussed.

In 1949, Miller and Taylor[15] measured the pressure variation of the resistivity of an impure germanium sample. The contribution of the intrinsic carriers, and thus the pressure dependence of the energy gap, was derived from the data. The coefficient found has been confirmed within experimental error by later work.

8-3a The Hall, Bardeen, and Pearson gap measurement. Two years later Hall, Bardeen, and Pearson[16] measured the pressure dependence of the current-voltage characteristic of a *p-n* junction at low

[15] P. H. Miller and J. H. Taylor, Pressure Coefficient of Resistance in Intrinsic Semiconductors, *Phys. Rev.*, vol. 76, p. 179, 1949.

[16] H. H. Hall, J. Bardeen, and G. L. Pearson, The Effects of Pressure and Temperature on the Resistance of *p-n* Junctions in Germanium, *Phys. Rev.*, vol. 84, pp. 129–132, 1951.

bias. In the conventional theory, which assumes low recombination in the transition region between the n and p sides of the junction, the current J is given by

$$J = \left(\frac{kT\mu_p n_i^2}{L_p n_0} + \frac{kT\mu_n n_i^2}{L_n p_0} \right) (e^{e\Delta\varphi_a/kT} - 1) \tag{8-17}$$

where L_p, L_n = diffusion lengths of holes on n side, electrons on p side of junction

n_0, p_0 = thermal equilibrium densities of electrons, holes on the n, p sides of junction

$\Delta\varphi_a$ = applied bias

For low biases,

$$J \approx 4A_c A_v e \left(\frac{\mu_p}{L_p n_0} + \frac{\mu_n}{L_n p_0} \right) \Delta\varphi_a e^{-E_g/kT} \tag{8-18}$$

on expansion of the exponential and substitution for n_i^2 from Eq. (8-4).

Hall, Bardeen, and Pearson ignored changes in μ_n, μ_p, L_n, and L_p and were thus able to deduce a pressure coefficient of the energy gap from their current-voltage measurements in reasonable agreement with the coefficient found by other methods. As this technique seems to give, in principle, a very sensitive determination of the pressure coefficient of the energy gap without requiring that the semiconductor be in its intrinsic range, it is probably worthwhile to pause and comment on it.

The accuracy of the method depends, inter alia, on the insensitivity to pressure of μ_n, μ_p, L_n, and L_p. Separate experiments on the conductivity of homogenous n- and p-type material of the same impurity density as the material of the p-n junction could establish the mobility dependences. Similarly estimates of the pressure dependence of the lifetime could be made, although it would be difficult to simulate exactly the conditions applicable near the p-n junction itself. However, if all these variations are found to be small, as may be expected, a reasonably accurate determination of the energy-gap coefficient may be made from the p-n-junction experiment.

In practice, another difficulty may prevent such a determination from being made. Many p-n junctions do not show the ideal characteristic, so that Eq. (8-18) does not give the accepted value for the energy gap at zero pressure. Such junctions do not give the correct pressure dependence of the energy gap. The departure of the current-voltage characteristic from the ideal may be due to recombination in the transition region; whatever the cause, it appears necessary that the zero-pressure characteristic fits Eq. (8-18). Hall, Bardeen, and Pearson used a junction that obeyed this equation.

8-3b Further measurements by Bridgman. In several papers between 1951 and 1953, Bridgman[17] measured the resistivity of germanium and silicon at pressures up to 100 kilobars at temperatures between 100 and 500°K. A marked difference was found between *n*- and *p*-type germanium. The resistivity of *n*-type germanium of 19 ohm-cm resistivity at room temperature increased by a factor of 4.5 under a pressure increase of 30 kilobars. In the same pressure range, *p*-type samples with room-temperature resistivities between 1.6 ohm-cm and 3.3 ohm-cm showed decreases in resistivity of 5 to 8 percent.

Measurements to 100 kilobars in a soft matrix of silver chloride showed considerable hysteresis, but the *n*-type samples of germanium consistently exhibited a maximum in resistance near 50 kilobars. The hysteresis may have been due to one of three causes: (1) the samples were not as pure as were later available, and long-time trapping effects may have changed the resistance, (2) the nonhydrostatic component of stress in the experiments to 100 kilobars was altered on relieving the pressure, (3) temperature equilibrium, more important for measurements on semiconductors than on metals, was not reestablished after each increment of pressure. The hysteresis, however, was insufficient to obscure the important maximum in the resistivity of *n*-type germanium.

Bridgman also measured several samples at 200°C in the intrinsic range of conductivity and showed that the resistance-pressure relation tended to be the same for all the samples at this temperature and was independent of the starting resistivity of the samples.

8-3c The deformation-potential theory. In 1950, Shockley and Bardeen[7] published their deformation-potential theory for the mobility of semiconductors. The deformation potentials E_{1c} (conduction band) and E_{1v} (valence band) give the change in the energy gap due to unit dilatation through

$$\Delta E_g = \pm E_{1c} \pm E_{1v} \tag{8-19}$$

but the theory does not indicate the correct choice of sign. Actually, working from the band structure of diamond calculated by Kimball,[18] Shockley and Bardeen assumed that the conduction and valence bands would move apart as the lattice constant was decreased, and hence that E_{1c} and E_{1v} were to be added.

[17] P. W. Bridgman, The Effect of Pressure on the Electrical Resistance of Certain Semiconductors, *Proc. Am. Acad. Arts Sci.*, vol. 79, pp. 127–148, 1951; The Electrical Resistance of 72 Elements, Alloys and Compounds to 100,000 kg/cm², *Proc. Am. Acad. Arts Sci.*, vol. 81, pp. 169–251, 1952; Further Measurements of the Effect of Pressure on the Electrical Resistance of Germanium, *Proc. Am. Acad. Arts Sci.*, vol. 82, pp. 71–82, 1953.

[18] G. E. Kimball, The Electronic Structure of Diamond, *J. Chem. Phys.*, vol. 3, pp. 560–564, 1935.

At first, quantitative agreement was found between the predictions of the deformation-potential theory and experimental determinations of the pressure coefficient of the energy gap. However, these agreements were based on the assumption of free-electron masses in both bands, an assumption disproved in 1953 and 1954 by the cyclotron resonance experiments of the Berkeley and Lincoln groups.[19]

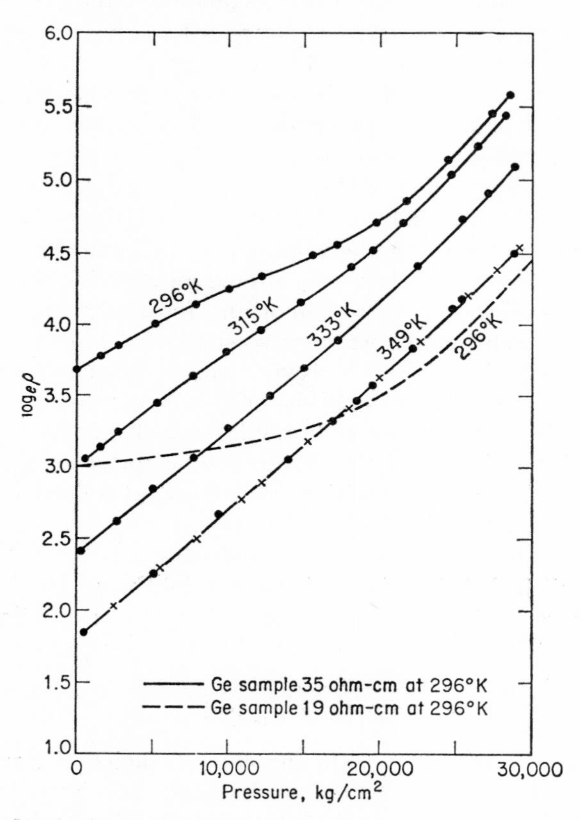

Fig. 8-3 Variation of resistivity with pressure for a sample of n-type germanium at several temperatures. (*Paul and Brooks.*[20])

It was clear also from the "anomalous" temperature dependence of the hole mobility that the deformation-potential theory for the mobilities was insufficient. It is now generally accepted that scattering by other types of lattice vibration must be included in the complete description

[19] See B. Lax and J. Mavroides, Cyclotron Resonance, pp. 261–400 in F. Seitz and D. Turnbull (eds.), "Solid State Physics," vol. 11, Academic Press, Inc., New York, 1960.

of the mobilities of electrons and holes and that only then may the deformation potentials due to dilatation alone be correlated with the pressure coefficients of the energy gap.[12] This correlation has not yet been completed, mostly owing to the difficulty of analyzing the scattering mechanism in the degenerate valence-band structure.

8-3d Measurements of Paul and Brooks. In 1954, Paul and Brooks[20] reported the effect of hydrostatic pressure on the resistivity of a high-purity sample of germanium to 30 kilobars in the temperature range between 300 and 350°K and to 7 kilobars at temperatures down to 77°K. A selection of their experimental results is shown in Fig. 8-3, along with a measurement of Bridgman on a less pure sample. All impure samples tended to give the same resistivity-pressure curve (unless they were excessively impure, when deviations occurred which are now attributed to the influence of impurity scattering on the mobility). Paul and Brooks concluded that the resistivity changes in the impure samples were caused by changes in the electron mobility, and that impurity deionization was not possible. They then assumed that the pressure dependence of the electron and hole mobilities determined at room temperature adequately described the changes in these mobilities at higher temperatures and used these variations to deduce the change of n_i^2 with pressure from Eqs. (8-1) through (8-3). The dependence of E_g on pressure followed from Eq. (8-4). Their value of

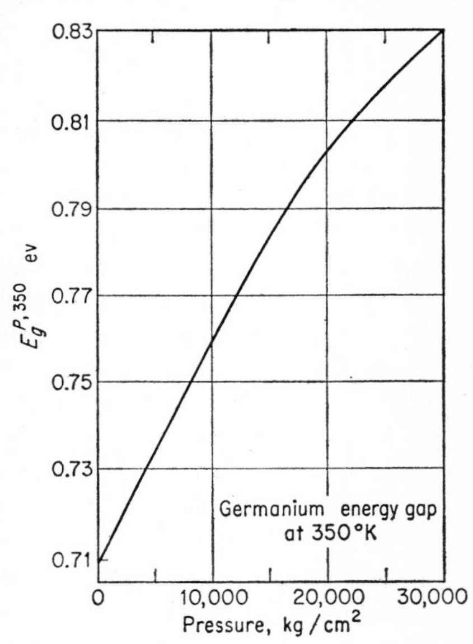

Fig. 8-4 Pressure dependence of the energy gap of germanium. The nonlinearity at the higher pressures is to be noted. (*Paul and Brooks.*[20])

$$\left(\frac{dE_g}{dP}\right)_T = 5 \times 10^{-6} \text{ ev/bar} \tag{8-20}$$

was judged to be correct at least up to 15 kilobars. Above this pressure the rate of increase of E_g decreased according to the variation shown in Fig. 8-4. The sharp decrease in electron mobility in the impure samples

[20] W. Paul and H. Brooks, Pressure Dependence of the Resistivity of Germanium, *Phys. Rev.*, vol. 94, pp. 1128–1133, 1954.

and the departure of the energy-gap variation from linearity occurred at about the same pressure. Paul and Brooks noted that this was consistent with the hypothesis that at high pressures the position in k space of the absolute minimum of energy in the conduction band shifted.

8-3e Smith's drift-mobility measurements. We shall depart from strict historical order to examine certain experiments of Smith[21] that were designed to prove conclusively that the conductivity variation in n-type germanium was caused by a mobility change. Smith measured the drift mobilities of electrons and holes in germanium, modifying the techniques of Haynes and Shockley[22] and of Lawrance and Gibson[22] to suit the geometry of his pressure vessel. The drift-mobility method measures directly the velocity of injected minority carriers moving under the influence of an applied electric field; the density of the carriers affects only the ease of observation of the injected pulse.

Smith concluded that the pressure dependence of the drift mobility and the mobility derived from the resistivity of impure samples were the same to within an experimental error of 2 percent. The agreement is illustrated in Fig. 8-5. We might remark, in passing, that his careful measurements were an experimental tour de force and gave mobility determinations, under difficult experimental conditions, at least the equal in accuracy of many carried out at atmospheric pressure.

Smith's conclusion that impurity deionization was not the cause of the resistivity variation of Fig. 8-3 can also be reached by the argument that the parameters in Eq. (8-8), the expression for the ionization energy of the hydrogenic impurities, change at roughly the same rate as energy gaps do, and that this is not large enough to affect the state of ionization of the impurity at other than very low temperature.

8-3f Measurements on silicon. In 1953, Paul and Pearson[23] measured the pressure dependence of the resistivity of samples of pure silicon at temperatures high enough so that intrinsic carriers dominated the conduction. Their results are illustrated in Fig. 8-6. Curves of the logarithm of resistivity versus $1/T$ (Fig. 8-7) showed that the samples were intrinsic above about 130°C. Despite the hysteresis on reduction of pressure, it was clear that the energy gap of silicon decreased with pressure, in contradistinction to germanium. Paul and Pearson deduced

[21] A. C. Smith, Ph.D. thesis, Harvard University, Cambridge, Mass., 1958, issued as Report HP 2, Division of Engineering and Applied Physics, 1958.

[22] J. R. Haynes and W. Shockley, The Mobility and Life of Injected Holes and Electrons in Germanium, *Phys. Rev.*, vol. 81, pp. 835–843, 1951; R. Lawrance and A. F. Gibson, The Measurement of Drift Mobility in Semiconductors, *Proc. Phys. Soc. London*, vol. B65, pp. 994–995, 1952.

[23] W. Paul and G. L. Pearson, Pressure Dependence of the Resistivity of Silicon, *Phys. Rev.*, vol. 98, pp. 1755–1757, 1955.

that the energy gap changed at the rate

$$\left(\frac{dE_g}{dP}\right)_T = -1.5 \times 10^{-6} \text{ ev/bar} \tag{8-21}$$

This result was entirely unexpected from the early interpretation of the deformation-potential theory, but was consistent with the more sophisticated ideas about the band structure that were being developed as a result of theoretical and experimental studies.

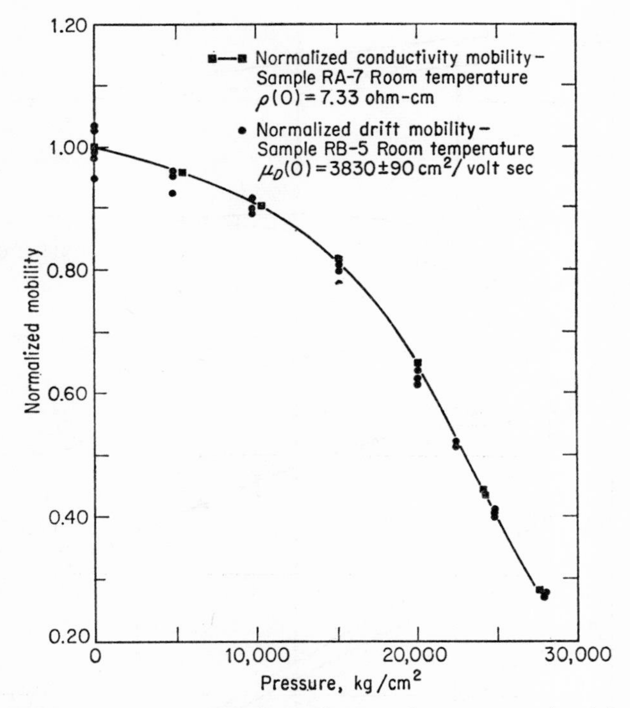

Fig. 8-5 Agreement of pressure dependences of n-type conductivity and drift mobility of electrons in germanium. (*Smith.*[21])

8-3g Band structure of germanium, silicon, and their alloys. A contemporary picture of the band structures of germanium and silicon has been shown in Figs. 8-1 and 8-2. The existence of the three types of minima was demonstrated theoretically by Herman's pioneer work in 1954.[4] Their closeness in energy, rather than the precise energy values, is important for our subsequent arguments.

Experimental measurements of cyclotron resonance and magnetoresistance showed that the lowest minima occurred in the (111) and the (100) directions in k space in germanium and silicon, respectively.

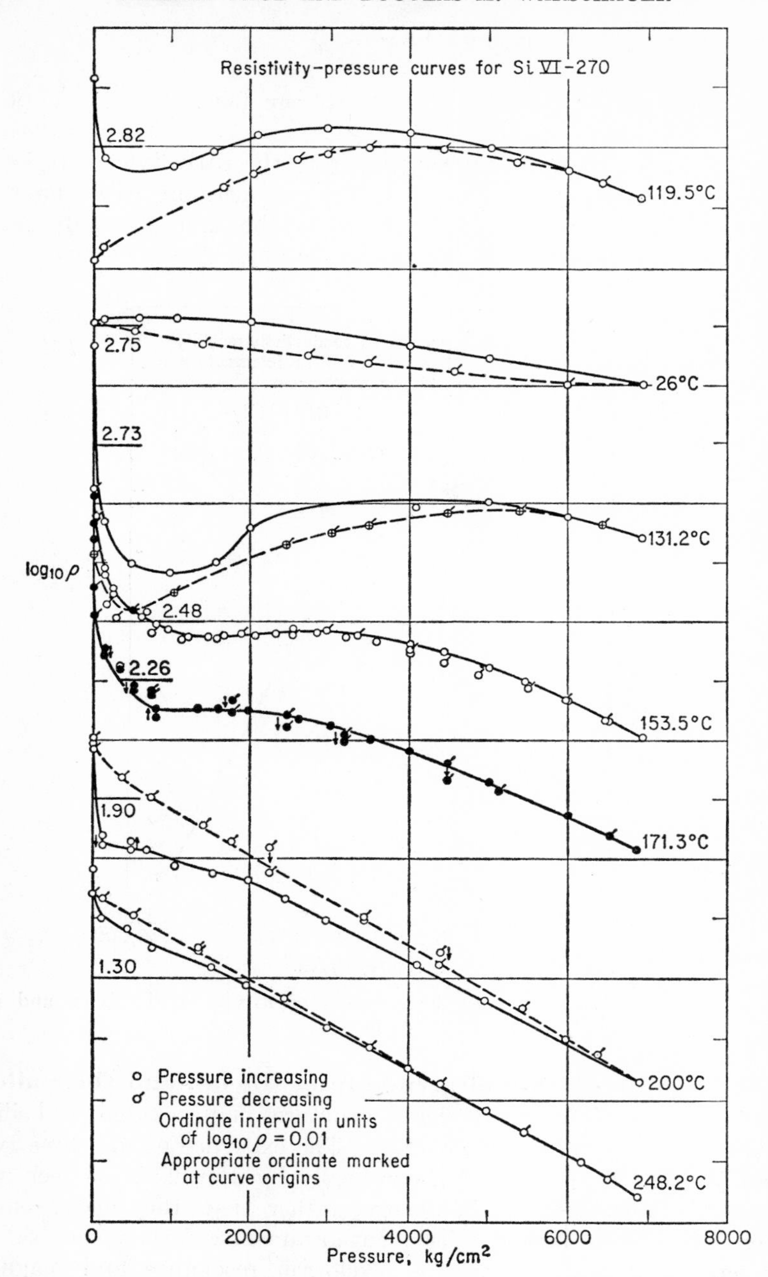

Fig. 8-6 Variation of resistivity with pressure for a sample of n-type silicon at several temperatures. (*Paul and Pearson.*[23])

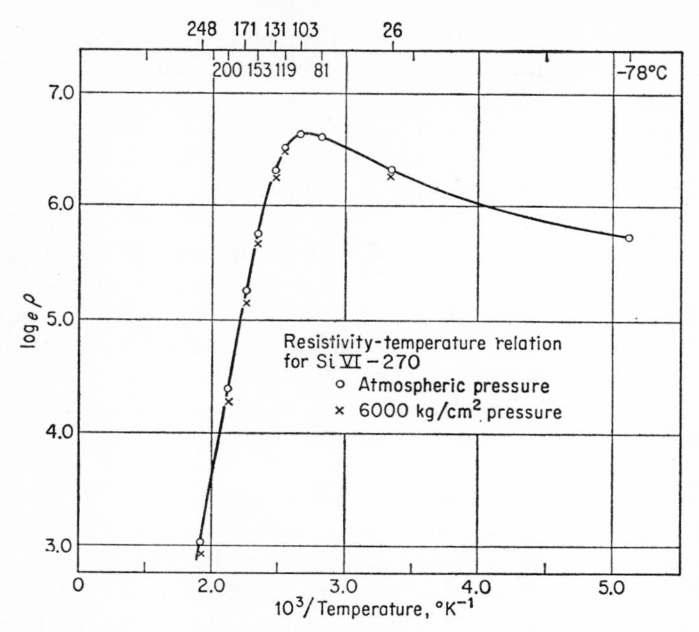

Fig. 8-7 Variation of resistivity with temperature at atmospheric pressure for the samples measured for Fig. 8-6. (*Paul and Pearson.*[23])

Measurements of the change in the optical absorption edge in germanium-silicon alloys by Johnson and Christian,[24] illustrated in Fig. 8-8, were interpreted by Herman as follows: As silicon is added to the germanium lattice, the (111) minima are raised in energy with respect to the valence band, while the (100) minima are raised less rapidly. At roughly 15 percent silicon content the (111) and (100) minima are equidistant from the valence band, while above this content the (100) minima are the lower set. Thus the sharp break in the curve of Fig. 8-8 marks the changeover from germaniumlike to siliconlike behavior.

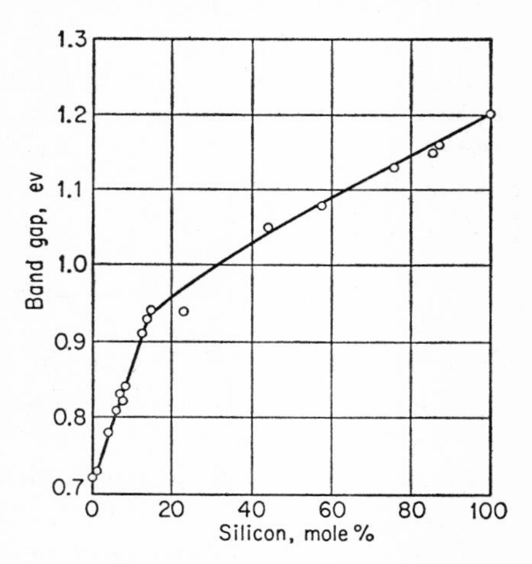

Fig. 8-8 Shift of the optical-absorption-edge energy with composition in germanium-silicon alloys. Note the break at 15 percent silicon composition. (*Johnson and Christian.*[24])

[24] E. R. Johnson and S. M. Christian, Some Properties of Germanium-Silicon Alloys, *Phys Rev.*, vol. 95, 560–561, 1954.

Herman also suggested that the effect of pressure was qualitatively the same as that of adding silicon to the germanium lattice, so that the states in the (100) minima were those required to explain the decrease in mobility and the nonlinearity of the isothermal energy-gap pressure coefficient above 15 kilobars. Implicit in these ideas was the suspicion that the pressure properties of the (100) minima in germanium and silicon might be very similar.

8-3h Quantitative theory of two-band conduction in germanium. In 1956 Brooks and Paul[25] proposed a quantitative explanation of the mobility variation of Fig. 8-3 and the energy-gap variation of Fig. 8-4. This work was later extended and refined by Nathan[26] and Nathan, Paul, and Brooks.[26] Their work represents the first and perhaps the most detailed analysis of conductivity variations with pressure and examines critically all the relevant parameters, so that we shall report it in some detail.

The analysis is based on the supposition that as the pressure is increased, the (111) band moves away from the valence band, whereas another band originally higher [hereafter called the second band or the (100) band, since the data on silicon-germanium alloys identify it quite well] moves slowly towards the valence band. As the pressure is increased, there is a transfer of carriers from the (111) minima into the (100) minima, and an effective energy gap that averages the behavior of the (111) and the (100) minima will first increase with pressure, then decrease. Only the increasing part (and the decrease in its slope) is available to us in the pressure range to 30 kilobars, and this is what is exhibited in Fig. 8-4. Without inquiring about the nature of the scattering process for electrons in this two-band situation, we can analyze the carrier statistics quantitatively to give the pressure variation of parameters connected with both energy gaps. Thus, the electrical conductivity σ is given by

$$\sigma = e(n_1\mu_1 + n_2\mu_2 + p\mu_p) \tag{8-22}$$

where n_1 = number of electrons in minima of type 1 [i.e., (111) minima]
n_2 = number in minima of type 2 [i.e., (100) minima]
p = hole density
μ_1, μ_2, μ_p = associated electron and hole mobilities, respectively

[25] H. Brooks and W. Paul, Interband Scattering in Semiconductors, *Bull. Am. Phys. Soc.*, vol. 1, p. 48, 1956.

[26] M. I. Nathan, Ph.D. thesis, Harvard University, Cambridge, Mass., 1958, issued as Report HP 1, Division of Engineering and Applied Physics, Harvard University, 1958; M. I. Nathan, W. Paul, and H. Brooks, Interband Scattering in n-type Germanium, *Phys. Rev.*, vol. 124, pp. 391–407, 1961.

When Maxwell-Boltzmann statistics apply,

$$\begin{aligned} n_1 &= C_0 C_1 \exp \frac{E_f - E_c}{kT} \\ n_2 &= C_0 C_2 \exp \frac{E_f - E_c - \Delta E}{kT} \\ p &= C_0 C_v \exp \frac{E_v - E_f}{kT} \end{aligned} \tag{8-23}$$

where E_c, E_v = conduction-, valence-band edge energies
ΔE = energy separation of (111) and (100) minima
$C_0 = 2(2\pi kT/h^2)^{3/2}$
$C_1 = m_{d1}^{3/2}\nu_1$
$C_2 = m_{d2}^{3/2}\nu_2$
$C_v = m_{dv}^{3/2}$
m_{di} = density of states effective mass in ith band
ν_i = number of equivalent minima in ith band

The existence of more than one type of hole is taken into account in our lumping them into m_{dv} and C_v.

It is easily shown that the presence of an extra conduction band does not affect the complete ionization of the hydrogenic impurities in germanium. The pressure dependence of the conductivity of an impure n-type sample therefore gives the variation with pressure of an effective mobility:

$$\mu_{\text{eff}} = \frac{n_1\mu_1 + n_2\mu_2}{n_0} \tag{8-24}$$

where

$$\begin{aligned} n_1 &= n_0\left(1 + \frac{C_2}{C_1} \exp \frac{-\Delta E}{kT}\right)^{-1} \\ n_2 &= n_0\left(1 + \frac{C_1}{C_2} \exp \frac{\Delta E}{kT}\right)^{-1} \end{aligned} \tag{8-25}$$

and $n_1 + n_2 = n_0$ = excess donor density, a constant.

For an intrinsic sample we must use

$$n_i^2 = np = C_0^2 C_1 C_v \frac{\exp (E_v - E_c)}{kT}\left(1 + \frac{C_2}{C_1} \exp \frac{-\Delta E}{kT}\right) \tag{8-26}$$

where

$$\begin{aligned} n &= \frac{n_0}{2} + \left[\left(\frac{n_0}{2}\right)^2 + n_i^2\right]^{1/2} \\ p &= -\frac{n_0}{2} + \left[\left(\frac{n_0}{2}\right)^2 + n_i^2\right]^{1/2} \end{aligned}$$

by Eqs. (8-2) and (8-3). The division of n between n_1 and n_2 is given by Eqs. (8-25) with n substituted for n_0.

The pressure variation of the conductivity of impure n- and p-type samples, in which the impurity activation energy and density have been chosen so that there is no change in the total carrier density over the temperature and pressure range of interest, gives the pressure dependence of effective electron and hole mobilities. When lattice scattering predominates, these mobility dependences on pressure can be assumed to hold also for intrinsic samples in which the carrier densities are also changing.

From Eqs. (8-24) to (8-26) we see that

$$\left[\left(\frac{n_0}{2}\right)^2 + n_i^2\right]^{1/2} = \left[\frac{\sigma}{e} - \frac{n_0(\mu_{\text{eff}} - \mu_p)}{2}\right](\mu_{\text{eff}} + \mu_p)^{-1} \tag{8-27}$$

Since σ versus P, μ_{eff} versus P, and μ_p versus P are experimentally determined, so also is n_i^2 versus P. From Eq. (8-26) for n_i^2 and an equation

$$n_i^2 = np = C_0^2 C_1 C_v \exp \frac{-E_{G,\text{eff}}}{kT} \tag{8-28}$$

defining an effective energy gap $E_{G,\text{eff}}$, we obtain the pressure dependence of

$$E_{G,\text{eff}} = E_c - E_v - kT \ln\left(1 + \frac{C_2}{C_1} \exp \frac{-\Delta E}{kT}\right) \tag{8-29}$$

The pressure variation of the smallest energy gap $E_g = E_c - E_v$ is obtained from the low-pressure variation of $E_{G,\text{eff}}$, since the logarithm term is negligible when ΔE is large. If the variation of E_g is then assumed to remain linear in pressure, the pressure coefficient of the logarithm term can be determined from the higher-pressure data. Figure 8-9 gives the deduced pressure dependence of $E_{G,\text{eff}}$, and Fig. 8-10 the variation of $(C_2/C_1) \exp(-\Delta E/kT)$. From Fig. 8-10, if we can assume the C's to be pressure independent, which is fairly accurate, we can deduce $[d(\Delta E)/dP]_T$ and $(C_2/C_1) \exp(-\Delta E_0/kT)$, where ΔE_0 is the value of ΔE at zero pressure.

By this procedure, Nathan found

$$\left[\frac{d(E_c - E_v)}{dP}\right]_T = 5.0 \times 10^{-6} \text{ ev/bar} \tag{8-30}$$

$$\left[\frac{d(\Delta E)}{dP}\right]_T = -5.1 \times 10^{-6} \text{ ev/bar} \tag{8-31}$$

and

$$\frac{C_2}{C_1} \exp \frac{-\Delta E_0}{kT} = 0.014 \tag{8-32}$$

The value for $(C_2/C_1) \exp(-\Delta E_0/kT)$ justifies its neglect in Eq. (8-29) at low pressures. The pressure coefficients imply that the higher (100) conduction band remains essentially static with respect to the valence band. Later pressure measurements by Howard, which we shall discuss presently, imply that the higher conduction band moves toward the valence band at -1.5×10^{-6} ev/bar or with precisely the pressure coefficient of the (100) minima in silicon.

We cannot obtain ΔE_0 and C_2/C_1 from these data alone, but what we have obtained involves few assumptions and gives us clear proof that band edges of different symmetry can have different pressure coefficients, and that those of the same symmetry in different crystals may have

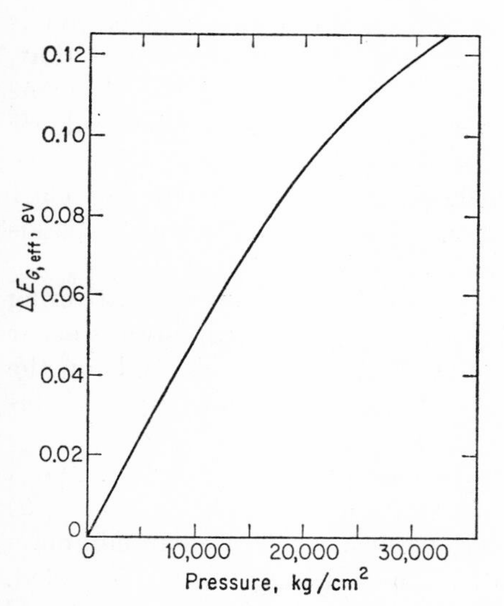

Fig. 8-9 Pressure dependence of the effective energy gap of germanium. (*Nathan, Paul, and Brooks.*[26])

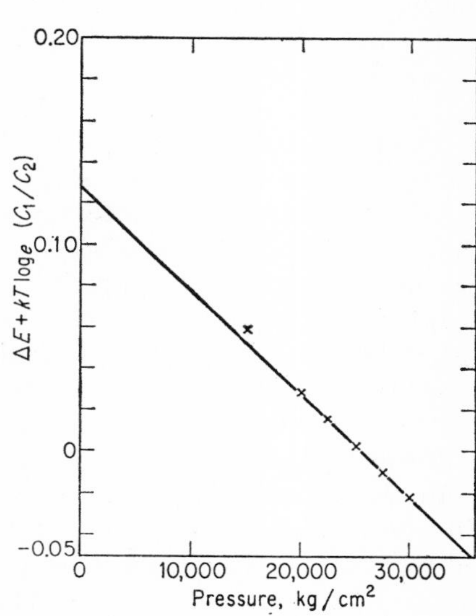

Fig. 8-10 Pressure dependence of the quantity (C_2/C_1) exp $(-\Delta E/kT)$ (see text) from which is derived the pressure dependence of ΔE. (*Nathan, Paul, and Brooks.*[26])

similar coefficients. These ideas are quite important in determining our approach to subsequent investigations.

8-3i Interband-scattering theory for germanium. Our analysis, based on the postulate of the existence of two types of conduction-band minima with different pressure coefficients and supported by the subsidiary evidence on germanium-silicon alloys, Herman's band-structure calculations, and the pressure coefficient of pure silicon, has given a reasonable phenomenological description of the variation of the band gaps in germanium.

We still must explain the variation of the electron mobility in terms of changes of the scattering processes. This analysis is involved, and the reader is referred to the original papers for its details.[26] Here we shall merely recount its qualitative features.

As the two conduction bands approach each other under the influence of pressure, carriers are transferred from one to the other. As a first approximation we might expect the conductivity to be given by an effective mobility that is an appropriate average of the mobilities in the two bands. If this were so, the conductivity would change under pressure from that characteristic of electrons in the (111) minima to that for the same number of electrons in the (100) minima. The maximum in the resistivity found by Bridgman suggests that this explanation is inadequate. A more reasonable theory includes the probability that, as the bands approach, there is increased scattering of the electrons from one band into the other—interband scattering—which reduces the mobility of the carriers in either band from what it would be in the absence of this extra scattering mechanism. It is immediately clear that the effect of the extra scattering will be maximum when the bands are nearly equal in energy, giving a maximum in resistivity.

Interband scattering is qualitatively no different from the scattering that takes place between equivalent (111) minima. It can always occur when two bands are close in energy, but its importance depends on the matrix elements for such scattering transitions and the density of states into which an electron can be scattered.

In the quantitative analysis, various assumptions are made: (1) A direction-independent scattering time $\tau(E)$ is assumed to exist. (2) Scattering by acoustical lattice vibrations inside a particular minimum (intravalley) and from (111) to (100) minima (interband) are included, but not scattering between (111) minima, and not scattering by ionized impurities. (The first exclusion is made because of a selection rule against it, the second by the deliberate choice of fairly pure samples which are used at sufficiently high temperatures in the experimental investigations.) (3) The bands are assumed parabolic in energy. (4) Only the (111) and (100) minima are assumed to possess electrons. (5) The energy of the interacting phonon is neglected. (6) The effective mass in any particular minimum is assumed to be independent of pressure, except when very small changes are being considered.

Then the scattering time $\tau(E)$ is given by

$$\frac{1}{\tau(E)} = \frac{1}{\tau_v(E)} + \frac{1}{\tau_b(E)} \tag{8-33}$$

where $\tau_v(E)$ is the scattering time for intravalley transitions, and $\tau_b(E)$ that for interband transitions.

For $\Delta E \geq 0$, the reciprocal of the scattering time for the (111) minimum can be written

$$\frac{1}{\tau_1(E)} = \begin{cases} A_1C_1'\,E^{1/2} + BC_2'\,(E - \Delta E)^{1/2}\nu_2 & E \geq \Delta E \\ A_1C_1'\,E^{1/2} & E \leq \Delta E \end{cases} \tag{8-34}$$

and the reciprocal of the (100) scattering time is

$$\frac{1}{\tau_2(E)} = A_2C_2'\,(E - \Delta E)^{1/2} + BC_1'\,E^{1/2}\nu_1 \tag{8-35}$$

where E_c = zero of energy
A_i = intravalley scattering probability
B = interband scattering probability
ν_i = number of equivalent minima in ith band
C_i' = density of states factor = $(m_{li}^{1/2}m_{ti})(4\pi 2^{1/2})/h^3$
m_{li}, m_{ti} = longitudinal transverse mass components of band i

Then

$$\mu_1 = e\,\langle\tau_1(E)\rangle\,\frac{1/m_{l1} + 2/m_{t1}}{3}$$
$$\mu_2 = e\,\langle\tau_2(E)\rangle\,\frac{1/m_{l2} + 2/m_{t2}}{3} \tag{8-36}$$

where

$$\langle\tau_i^n(E)\rangle = \frac{4}{3\pi^{1/2}}\int_0^\infty \tau_i^n(y)y^{3/2}\exp(-y)\,dy$$

and

$$y = \frac{E}{kT} \tag{8-37}$$

Certain analytic expressions for these integrals are approximately correct in limiting cases. They are shown in Table 8-1 for $\Delta = \Delta E/kT > 0$.

Table 8-1 Scattering Integrals*,†

n	$\langle\tau_1^n(\Delta)\rangle_N \equiv \dfrac{\langle\tau_1^n(\Delta)\rangle}{\langle\tau_1^n(\infty)\rangle}$	$\langle\tau_2^n(\Delta)\rangle_N \equiv \dfrac{\langle\tau_2^n(\Delta)\rangle}{\langle\tau_2^n(\infty)\rangle}$
1	$1 - \left[\dfrac{S(\Delta+1)}{1+S} - \dfrac{S\Delta}{2(1+S)^2}\right]\exp(-\Delta)$	$\dfrac{1}{1+S'} - \dfrac{S'\Delta}{2(1+S')^2}$
2	$\operatorname{erf}(\Delta^{1/2}) - 2\pi^{-1/2}\Delta^{1/2}\exp(-\Delta) + \dfrac{1}{(1+S)^2[1-\operatorname{erf}(\Delta^{1/2}) + 2\pi^{-1/2}\Delta^{1/2}\exp(-\Delta)]} - \dfrac{2\Delta}{(1+S)^3}[1-\operatorname{erf}(\Delta^{1/2})]$	$\dfrac{1}{(1+S')^2}$
3	$1 - \exp(-\Delta)\left[1 - \dfrac{1}{(1+S)^3}\right]$	$\dfrac{1}{(1+S')^3}$

* $\operatorname{erf}(x) \equiv 2\pi^{-1/2}\int_0^x \exp(-u^2)\,du$.

† All values for $\Delta > 0$.

In the table are tabulated $\langle\tau^n(\Delta)\rangle_N = \langle\tau^n(\Delta)\rangle/\langle\tau^n(\infty)\rangle$; $S = BC_2'\nu_2/A_1C_1'$ and $S' = BC_1'\nu_1/A_2C_2$. For n-type samples chosen so that the holes make a negligible contribution, the conductivity is given by

$$\sigma/\sigma_0 = \frac{1}{n_{10}\mu_{10}}(n_1\mu_1 + n_2\mu_2) = \frac{n_1}{n_{10}}\frac{\mu_1}{\mu_{10}} + \frac{n_2}{n_{10}}\frac{\mu_2}{\mu_2^*}\frac{\mu_2^*}{\mu_{10}^*}\frac{\mu_{10}^*}{\mu_{10}} \tag{8-38}$$

where the subscript 0 refers to zero pressure and the asterisk refers to the mobilities in the absence of interband scattering. In the above we have assumed that only the (111) band contributes at zero pressure, i.e.,

$$\sigma_0 = en_{10}\mu_{10} \tag{8-39}$$

As discussed earlier, n_2, n_1, and $(C_1/C_2) \exp(\Delta E/kT)$ can be determined simply. At very low pressures,

$$\frac{\sigma}{\sigma_0} = \frac{n_1}{n_{10}}\frac{\mu_1}{\mu_{10}} \tag{8-40}$$

Since σ/σ_0 is found experimentally and n_1/n_{10} is known, μ_1/μ_{10} is determined. However μ_1/μ_{10} can be expressed as

$$\frac{\mu_1}{\mu_{10}} = \frac{\mu_1^*}{\mu_{10}^*}\,\frac{1 - \dfrac{S(1+\Delta)}{1+S}\exp(-\Delta) + \dfrac{S\Delta}{2(1+S)^2}\exp(-\Delta)}{1 - \dfrac{S(1+\Delta_0)}{1+S}\exp(-\Delta_0) + \dfrac{S\Delta_0}{2(1+S)^2}\exp(-\Delta_0)} \tag{8-41}$$

The quantity μ_1^*/μ_{10}^* expresses the part of the pressure dependence of μ_1/μ_{10} not caused by interband scattering. At sufficiently low temperature the interband scattering is negligible, so that the pressure dependence of μ_1/μ_{10} is all caused by μ_1^*/μ_{10}^*. In Fig. 8-11 is plotted $\mu_{\text{eff},2.5\text{kilobars}}/\mu_{\text{eff},0}$

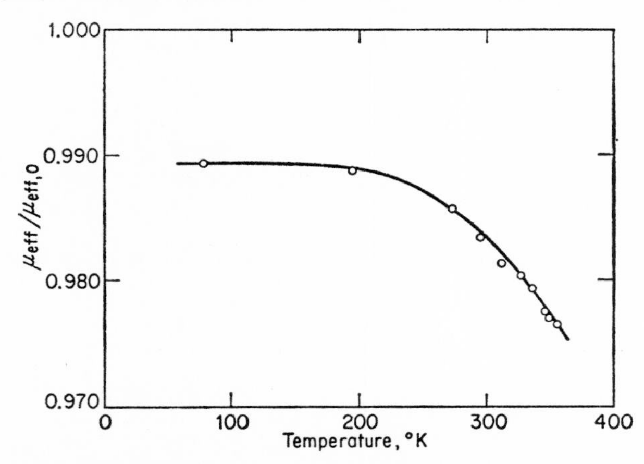

Fig. 8-11 Low-pressure coefficient of resistivity of n-type germanium as a function of temperature. (*Nathan, Paul, and Brooks.*[26])

versus T for n-type germanium. The low-temperature asymptote is clearly consistent with the vanishing of interband scattering at low temperatures. The pressure dependence of μ_1^*/μ_{10}^* thus determined is extrapolated linearly to higher pressures. From the figure,

$$\frac{\mu_1^*}{\mu_{10}^*} = 1 - 4 \times 10^{-6}P \qquad (8\text{-}42)$$

where P is in bars.

Using the variation of μ_1^*/μ_{10}^*, we can plot calculated curves of μ_1/μ_{10} versus Δ_0 for a chosen fixed value of $\Delta - \Delta_0$ with S as a parameter (Fig.

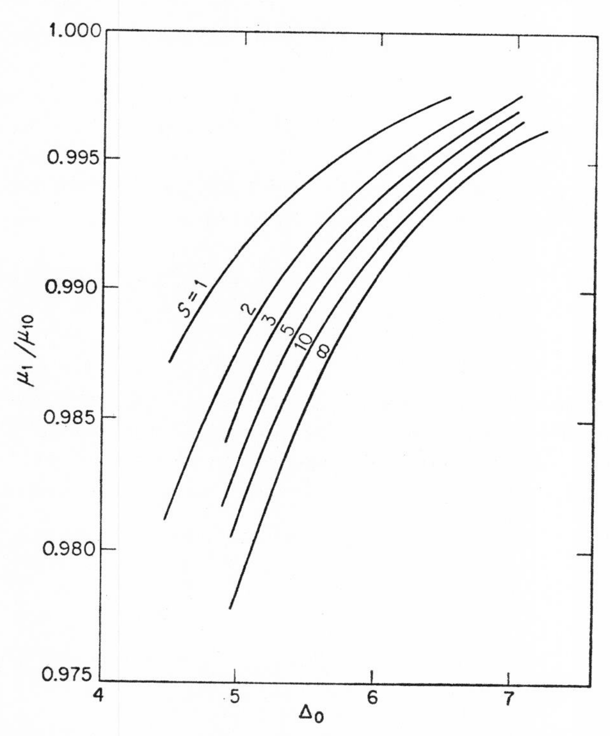

Fig. 8-12 Curves of μ_1/μ_{10} versus Δ_0, with S as parameter. (*Nathan, Paul, and Brooks.*[26])

8-12). These calculated curves can then be compared with experimental values to give parametric relations between S and Δ_0 as shown in Fig. 8-13, and between B/A_1 and S as in Fig. 8-14.

We next turn to the conductivity at the highest pressure. In Eq. (8-38), n_1/n_{10} and n_2/n_{10} are already determined from the analysis of the intrinsic data. If S is chosen, Δ_0 is fixed by Fig. 8-13, and C_2/C_1

by Fig. 8-10, and thus Δ is fixed. Hence, from Eq. (8-38), μ_1/μ_{10} is fixed. Thus, from the experimental determination of $\mu_{\text{eff}}/\mu_{\text{eff},0}$ at a fixed high pressure, the value of the second term of Eq. (8-38) is fixed for a given S.

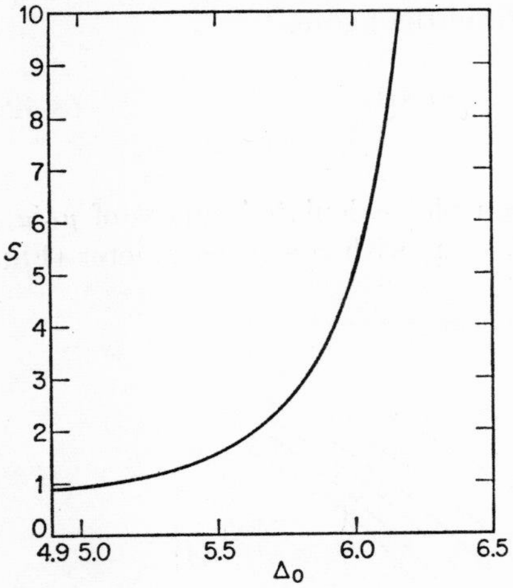

The second term of Eq. (8-38) is

$$\frac{n_2}{n_{10}} \frac{\mu_2}{\mu_2^*} \frac{\mu_2^*}{\mu_{10}^*} \frac{\mu_{10}^*}{\mu_{10}}$$

The quantity n_2/n_{10} is given by the statistics. μ_2/μ_2^* is given by the analytic approximation in Table 8-1; here we assume that to a first approximation μ_2^* is independent of pressure. The parameters S' and Δ are involved in the formula of Table 8-1.

The quantity μ_2^*/μ_{10}^* can be shown to be, after manipulation,

$$\frac{\mu_2^*}{\mu_{10}^*} = \frac{S'}{S} \left(\frac{C_2}{C_1}\right)^{1/3} \left(\frac{K_1\nu_2}{K_2\nu_1}\right)^{2/3} \frac{2K_2 + 1}{2K_1 + 1} \tag{8-43}$$

Fig. 8-13 Parametric relation between S and Δ_0. (*Nathan, Paul, and Brooks.*[26])

where $K_1 = m_{l1}/m_{t1}$, and $K_2 = m_{l2}/m_{t2}$. The numbers of minima ν_1 and ν_2 are assumed to be 4 and 6, respectively. K_1 is known from cyclotron resonance experiments in germanium, as well as magnetoresistance and magnetoconductance; K_2 is assumed to be equal to the K value for silicon. This is not entirely justified but is probably very nearly correct,

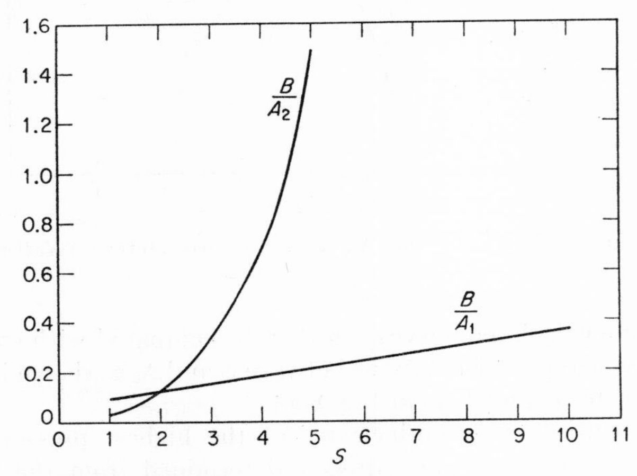

Fig. 8-14 Parametric relation between B/A and S. (*Nathan, Paul, and Brooks.*[26])

since Glicksman[27] has shown that the K ratio for the (100) minima in silicon-germanium alloys is independent of alloy composition. We shall see later that magnetoconductance measurements under pressure, carried out by Howard, show that K_1, at least, is independent of pressure. We shall make the very plausible assumption that K_2 is also.

Thus $(K_1\nu_2/K_2\nu_1)^{2/3}(2K_2 + 1)/(2K_1 + 1)$ of Eq. (8-43) is determined.

Gathering all this information together, we see that if we choose a value for S, the second term of Eq. (8-38) is fixed, and from it S' can

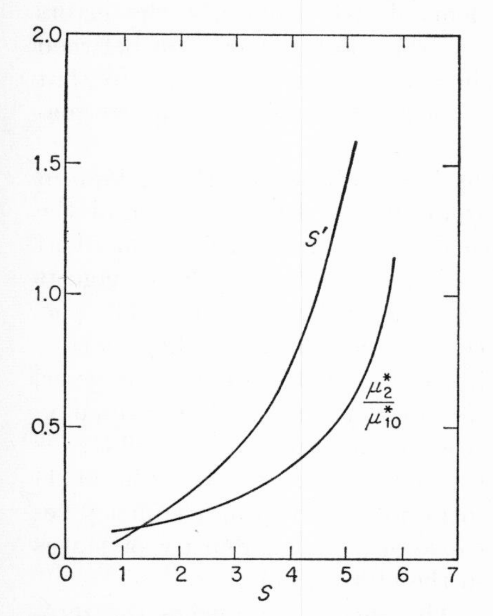

Fig. 8-15 Parametric relation between S' and S, and μ_2^*/μ_{10}^* and S. (*Nathan, Paul, and Brooks.*[26])

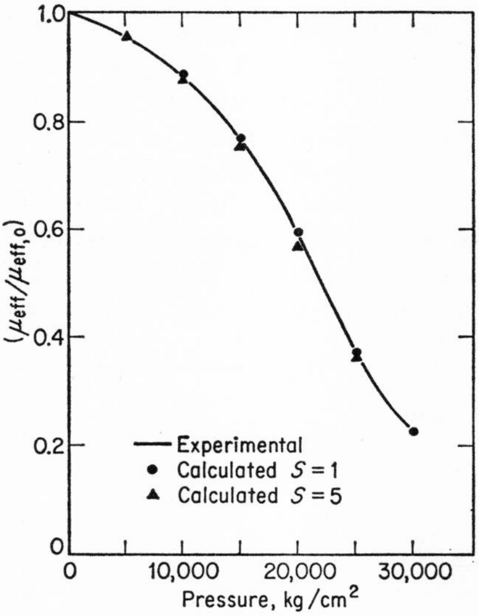

Fig. 8-16 Fit of theory and experiment for the pressure variation of the effective mobility of electrons in germanium. (*Nathan, Paul, and Brooks.*[26])

be evaluated. The dependence of S' and μ_2^*/μ_{10}^* on S is shown in Fig. 8-15. Physical arguments must then be used to choose the most appropriate (S, S', Δ_0). For example, it is clear that S is finite so that $\Delta_0 < 6.2$, from Fig. 8-13. On the other hand, Δ_0 is limited on the low side; otherwise we should have interband effects at very low pressures.

It is inappropriate to give the final details relating to Nathan's choice of the most appropriate parameters here. They are discussed in the paper by Nathan, Paul, and Brooks.[26] The fit obtained between theory and experiment is illustrated in Fig. 8-16; in view of the assumptions, it is very good.

[27] M. Glicksman and S. M. Christian, Conduction Band Structure of Germanium-Silicon Alloys, *Phys. Rev.*, vol. 104, pp. 1278–1279, 1956.

8-3j Summary of the results on interband scattering. The pressure measurements are interpreted as providing conclusive evidence of the existence of a second conduction band in germanium that becomes more and more important as the pressure is increased. Evidence provided by data on silicon-germanium alloys has suggested that the second band has (100) symmetry and is lowest in silicon.

The rate of separation of the (111) minima from the valence band is confirmed as approximately 5×10^{-6} ev/bar. The second band appears to be static with respect to the valence band. Actually the errors involved in the measurement and its analysis allow a variation between 1×10^{-6} and -2×10^{-6} ev/bar. These coefficients are close to that found for silicon, and we shall need to discuss the correctness for germanium again presently.

The necessity for interband scattering is established by the maximum in the resistivity found in n-type germanium by Bridgman,[17] and the present theory provides a quantitative fit of theory and experiment at temperatures between 300 and 375°K. The best fit to the data suggests that the matrix element for interband scattering is between 10 and 30 percent of that for intravalley scattering in the (111) minima. However, the interband scattering frequency, where energetically possible, is greater than or equal to the (111) intravalley scattering frequency because of a higher density of states in the (100) minima.

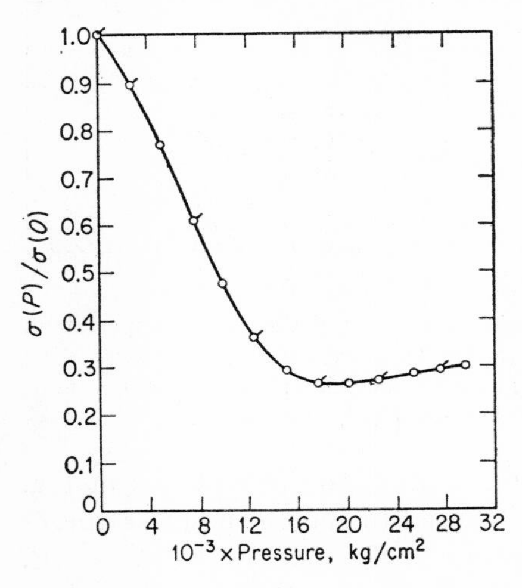

Fig. 8-17 Variation of conductivity with pressure for an n-type silicon-germanium alloy containing 8 percent silicon, showing the expected conductivity minimum at relatively low pressures. (*Bridgman and Paul.*[28])

The theory establishes the zero-pressure separation of the (111) and (100) states as between 0.15 and 0.21 ev.

The data on silicon-germanium alloys suggest that in an alloy with a low percentage of silicon, say 8 percent, the (100) and (111) minima will be energetically closer together than in pure germanium. Thus the interband-scattering phenomena exhibited by pure germanium should appear at lower pressures in the alloy. Figure 8-17 shows a measurement, made by Bridgman and Paul[28] on an 8-percent silicon-germanium alloy, which confirms this speculation.

[28] P. W. Bridgman and W. Paul, unpublished data.

Finally, the interpretation suggests that the mobility of carriers in the (111) minima changes, independent of interband scattering, at a rate given by Eq. (8-42). This change can be interpreted in terms of changes of elastic constants, deformation potentials, and effective masses. We refer the reader to Nathan, Paul, and Brooks[26] for the details, which are consistent with our intuitive ideas that the changes will be at most a few percent in 10 kilobars.

8-3k Later work on the transport properties of germanium and silicon. Later work on the pressure dependence of the resistivity of intrinsic germanium by Michels, van Eck, Machlup, and ten Seldam[29] provided very accurate values for the pressure coefficient of the energy gap, in agreement with those already quoted.

In 1955, Benedek, Paul, and Brooks[30] measured the pressure dependence of the conductivity, Hall effect, and magnetoresistance of n-type germanium to 10 kilobars. This work was extended to 20 kilobars in 1961 by Howard,[30] and we shall now discuss his results, although it takes us a little ahead of our story.

If $\Delta\sigma_l$ is a longitudinal magnetoconductance, i.e., the increment in conductance for electric and magnetic fields, both in a (100) direction in the crystal, and $\Delta\sigma_t$ is a transverse magnetoconductance, i.e., the increment in conductance for electric field in the (100) and magnetic field in the (010) direction, then for (111) minima,

$$\frac{\Delta\sigma_l}{\Delta\sigma_t} = \frac{2(K_1' - 1)^2}{(2K_1' + 1)(K_1' + 2)} \tag{8-44}$$

where $K_1' = (m_{l1}/m_{t1})(\tau_{t1}/\tau_{l1})$, and τ_{l1}, τ_{t1}, and τ_{t1} are the three diagonal components of a relaxation-time tensor diagonal in the same axes as the effective-mass tensor. Taken separately, at low H fields, and still for (111) minima,

$$\frac{\Delta\sigma_l}{H^2} = \frac{-2n_1e^4}{9c^2} K_1'(K_1' - 1)^2 \frac{\langle\tau^3{}_{l1}\rangle}{m^3{}_{l1}} \tag{8-45}$$

and

$$\frac{\Delta\sigma_t}{H^2} = \frac{-n_1e^4}{9c^2} K_1'(2K_1' + 1)(K_1' + 2) \frac{\langle\tau^3{}_{l1}\rangle}{m^3{}_{l1}} \tag{8-46}$$

where

$$\langle\tau^3\rangle = \frac{4}{3\pi^{1/2}} \int_0^\infty \tau^3(y) y^{3/2} \exp(-y)\, dy \tag{8-47}$$

$$y = \frac{E}{kT}$$

[29] A. Michels, J. van Eck, S. Machlup, and C. A. ten Seldam, Pressure Dependence of the Resistivity of Germanium, *J. Phys. Chem. Solids*, vol. 10, pp. 12–18, 1959.

[30] G. B. Benedek, W. Paul, and H. Brooks, Conductivity, Hall Effect, and Magnetoresistance in n-type Germanium, and Their Dependence on Pressure, *Phys. Rev.*, vol. 100, pp. 1129–1139, 1955; W. E. Howard, Ph.D. thesis, Harvard University, Cambridge, Mass., 1961, issued as Report HP 7, Division of Engineering and Applied Physics, Harvard University, 1961.

When the minima lie in the (100) directions, the formulas are different:

$$\frac{\Delta\sigma_l}{H^2} = 0 \tag{8-48}$$

$$\frac{\Delta\sigma_t}{H^2} = \frac{-ne^4}{c^2} K_2'(K_2'^2 + K_2' + 1) \frac{\langle\tau^3{}_{l2}\rangle}{m^3{}_{l2}} \tag{8-49}$$

where c is the velocity of light. Combining these results in the two-band case, we see that

$$\frac{\Delta\sigma_l}{H^2} = \frac{-2n_1e^4}{9c^2} K_1'(K_1' - 1)^2 \frac{\langle\tau^3{}_{l1}\rangle}{m^3{}_{l1}} \tag{8-50}$$

$$\frac{\Delta\sigma_t}{H^2} = \frac{-n_1e^4}{9c^2} K_1'(2K_1' + 1)(K_1' + 2) \frac{\langle\tau^3{}_{l1}\rangle}{m^3{}_{l1}} - \frac{n_2q^4}{c^2} K_2'(K_2'^2 + K_2' + 1) \frac{\langle\tau^3{}_{l2}\rangle}{m^3{}_{l2}} \tag{8-51}$$

Thus, $\Delta\sigma_l/\Delta\sigma_t$ gives the pressure dependence of K_1' at low pressures, where the contribution of the higher band can be neglected. Once K_1' versus P is known, Eq. (8-50) gives the pressure dependence of $n_1 \langle\tau^3{}_{l1}\rangle/m^3{}_{l1}$. Under certain conditions the pressure dependences of n_1 and $\langle\tau^3{}_{l1}\rangle/m^3{}_{l1}$ can be separated out. $n_1(P, T)$ gives $\Delta E(P)$ and $\langle\tau^3{}_{l1}\rangle/m^3{}_{l1}$ gives us information about the amount of interband scattering, since, in the absence of interband scattering,

$$\frac{(\langle\tau^3{}_{l1}\rangle^{1/3}/m_{l1})(P)}{(\langle\tau^3{}_{l1}\rangle^{1/3}/m_{l1})(0)} = \frac{(\langle\tau_{l1}\rangle/m_{l1})(P)}{(\langle\tau_{l1}\rangle/m_{l1})(0)} \tag{8-52}$$

and the right-hand side can be found from the conductivity variation. Howard found that

$$\Delta E(P) = 0.21 \pm 0.03 + (6.6 \pm 1) \times 10^{-6}\, P \qquad \text{ev} \tag{8-53}$$

where P is measured in bars. His $\Delta E(0)$ is within the range found by Nathan, but the most probable value is higher. The pressure dependence of the separation of the higher minima from the valence band given by the difference between the above coefficient and that of Eq. (8-30) for the (111) minima is $(-1.5 \pm 1) \times 10^{-6}$ ev/bar and is almost exactly equal to that for the (100) minima in silicon. The difference between Howard's and Nathan's coefficients is not entirely understood, but it must be remembered that Howard's measurements were made at room temperature and pressures up to 20 kilobars, whereas Nathan's conclusions for this temperature and pressure range were extrapolations based on measurements carried out at a temperature of 375°K and pressures between 15 and 30 kilobars.

Howard found that K_1' varied by only 1 percent in 10 kilobars. He also found that he could not explain his experimental results unless he introduced interband scattering.

Howard's measurements were experimentally limited to pressures below 20 kilobars; this prevented him from identifying the symmetry of the upper band from the symmetry of the magnetoconductance coefficients. Nevertheless his measurements confirmed the predictions of the two-band theory of conduction and gave quite precise values for some of the parameters.

8-31 Optical measurements on germanium: the indirect transition. In parallel with these measurements of the electrical properties, several laboratories were measuring the change in the fundamental absorption spectrum with pressure. Fan, Shepherd, and Spitzer[31] and Paul and Warschauer[31] reported measurements on the spectra of both germanium and silicon at the Photoconductivity Conference of 1954. Fan et al. observed no change in the shape of their absorption spectra with pressure, and so deduced from the translation of the absorption edge in wavelength a pressure coefficient for germanium of 8×10^{-6} ev/bar. Paul and Warschauer, whose measurements extended to 8 kilobars rather than the limit of 1 kilobar used by Fan et al., found a change in the curvature of the absorption edge with pressure. Without correction for the shape change, their results agreed qualitatively with those of Fan et al. In a later publication, Paul and Warschauer[32] analyzed their spectra on the basis of Eq. (8-11), assuming only one intermediate state for the indirect transition, namely, the conduction-band state at $k = 0$, 0.8 ev above the valence band (see Fig. 8-1), and ignoring phonon energies. This analysis yielded a pressure coefficient of the energy gap close to 4×10^{-6} ev/bar, which they judged to be satisfactorily close to the value for the coefficient for the separation between the (111) conduction-band states and the (000) valence-band states determined from the transport measurements.

From the same analysis, Paul and Warschauer were able to find a rough pressure coefficient for the direct energy gap. From Eq. (8-11) we see that, if we ignore all but one intermediate state, neglect the phonon

[31] H. Y. Fan, M. L. Shepherd, and W. G. Spitzer, Infrared Absorption and Energy Band Structure of Germanium and Silicon, pp. 184–203 in R. G. Breckenridge, B. R. Russell, and E. E. Hahn (eds.), "Photoconductivity Conference," John Wiley & Sons, Inc., New York, 1956; W. Paul and D. M. Warschauer, in R. G. Breckenridge, B. R. Russell, and E. E. Hahn (eds.), "Photoconductivity Conference," John Wiley & Sons, Inc., New York, 1956. See comment under the paper by Fan, Shepherd, and Spitzer, pp. 201–202.

[32] W. Paul and D. M. Warschauer, Optical Properties of Semiconductors under Hydrostatic Pressure. I. Germanium, *J. Phys. Chem. Solids*, vol. 5, pp. 89–101, 1958.

energies, and assume the phonons classically excited, we can write

$$\alpha = \frac{A(h\nu - E_g)^2}{(E_{cj} - E_c)^2} \tag{8-54}$$

where E_{cj} refers to the lowest conduction-band state at $k = 0$ ($\Gamma_{2'}$ in Fig. 8-1) and A contains the dielectric constant, effective masses, and the matrix element. The inexactness of the experimentally determined edge in pressure experiments and the crudeness of this approximation to the theory imply that it is pointless to try to estimate the pressure coefficients of the parameters contained in A, which are expected to be small. However we must take account of the possible pressure dependence of $E_{cj} - E_c$. Paul and Warschauer found that the pressure coefficient of $E_{cj} - E_c$ was 10×10^{-6} ev/bar, and we shall see presently that this value agrees with that deduced from a measurement of the absorption edge caused by the direct optical transition between $\Gamma_{25'}$ and $\Gamma_{2'}$.

The measurements of T. P. McLean.[11] show that the most important intermediate state for indirect transitions is indeed the one we have been considering. At zero pressure it is 0.15 ev above the (111) state; at 10 kilobars it is 0.25 ev, so that the energy denominator has changed by a factor of 3. Thus changes in the shape of the absorption edge, all too often ignored, can lead to incorrect pressure coefficients.

Later measurements by Neuringer[33] to approximately 1 kilobar gave results qualitatively the same as those reported above, although Neuringer did not observe a change in the shape of the absorption edge. Slykhouse and Drickamer[34] remeasured this absorption edge to pressures in excess of 100 kilobars. Their results are shown in Fig. 8-18. At low pressures the energy gap increases at a rate in reasonable agreement with the earlier measurements. At higher pressures the energy gap goes through a maximum and then decreases at a rate of -2×10^{-6} ev/bar. Extrapolation of the high-pressure portion of the curve gives a zero-pressure separation of the (111) and (100) minima of about 0.2 ev. All this is in satisfactory agreement with the picture of the band structure we have been drawing up to this point. We shall have occasion to comment on the very powerful technique displayed by these very-high-pressure experiments later in this review.

8-3m Optical measurements on germanium: the direct transition. Pressure investigations of the absorption caused by direct transitions have been reported by Fan, Shepherd, and Spitzer,[31] by Neuringer,[33]

[33] L. J. Neuringer, Effect of Pressure on the Infrared Absorption of Semiconductors, *Phys. Rev.*, vol. 113, pp. 1495–1503, 1959.

[34] T. E. Slykhouse and H. G. Drickamer, The Effect of Pressure on the Optical Absorption Edge of Germanium and Silicon, *J. Phys. Chem. Solids*, vol. 7, pp. 210–213, 1958.

and by Cardona and Paul.[35] All the investigations have been of low spectral resolution, so that no fine structure in the absorption edge, such as that due to excition effects, was observed. No changes of shape of the edge under pressure were observed by any of the investigators, so that the energy-gap change could be estimated directly from the translation of the absorption edge in energy. The coefficient found by Cardona and Paul was 13×10^{-6} ev/bar, in satisfactory agreement with the

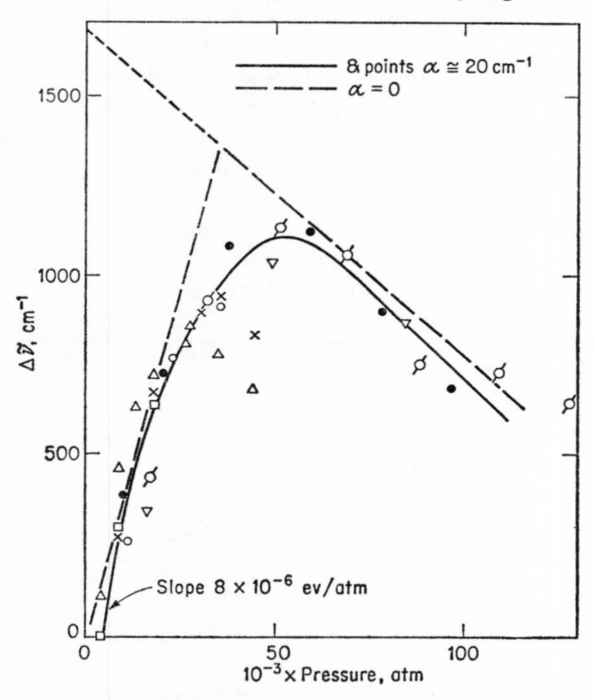

Fig. 8-18 Variation with pressure of the absorption edge for indirect transitions in germanium. (*Slykhouse and Drickamer.*[34])

earlier determinations. Minor discrepancies that do exist are inconsequential for our present purpose (but see reference 35).

We note in passing that the failure to observe a change in the shape of this absorption edge appears to be anomalous, since the pressure coefficients of the mass and dielectric constant predict an observable change. It is not inconceivable that this failure is connected with the parallel failure of other workers to fit the shape of the absorption curve with simple formulas of the form of Eq. (8-9). In this sense we see that the pressure measurements permit us to test theoretical formulas by

[35] M. Cardona and W. Paul, Pressure Dependence of the Direct Energy Gap in Germanium, *J. Phys. Chem. Solids*, vol. 17, pp. 138–142, 1960.

examining in separate experiments the pressure dependence of the parameters entering the formulas. We shall return to this type of application later.

8-3n Optical measurements on silicon. Fan, Shepherd, and Spitzer[31] also measured the pressure coefficient of the energy gap in silicon by the displacement of the absorption edge. They found a coefficient of $+5 \times 10^{-6}$ ev/bar. It is now felt that this result is in error. It has the opposite sign to that reported from the transport measurements of Paul and Pearson.[23] Paul and Warschauer,[36] in measurements carried out at the same time as those of Fan et al., found a coefficient of -1.3×10^{-6} ev/bar. Later they verified this estimate with more precise measurements using a grating spectrometer and found the identical result. Neuringer[33] also verified the negative coefficient.

No change of the shape of the absorption edge was found by any of the investigators. This is consistent with the supposition that the intermediate state for the indirect transition in silicon is widely separated in energy from the valence band (see Fig. 8-2).

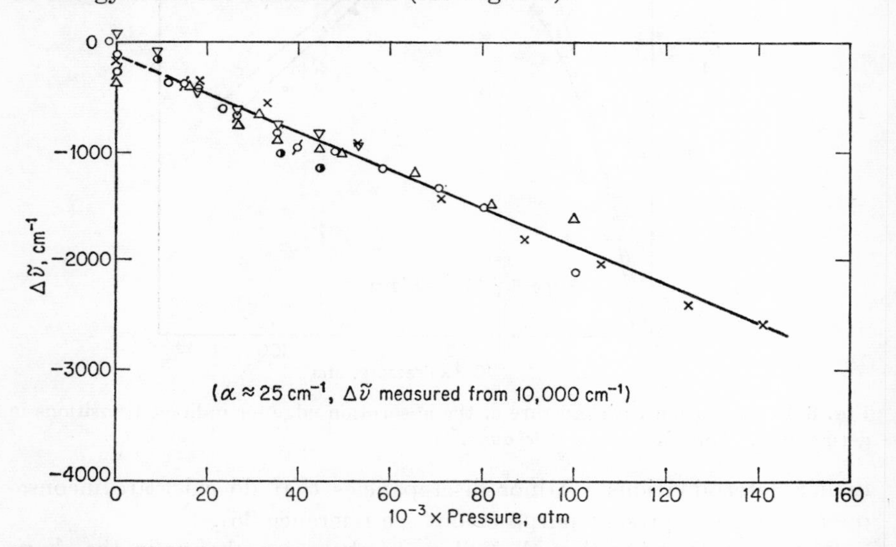

Fig. 8-19 Variation with pressure of the absorption edge in silicon. (*Slykhouse and Drickamer.*[34])

Slykhouse and Drickamer's measurements of the absorption edge are shown in Fig. 8-19, where the direction and magnitude of the shift seem to be established beyond doubt. Their coefficient is also -2×10^{-6} ev/bar.

8-3o Optical measurements on silicon-germanium alloys. Paul and Warschauer have also reported measurements on the displace-

[36] W. Paul and D. M. Warschauer, Optical Properties of Semiconductors under Hydrostatic Pressure. II. Silicon, *J. Phys. Chem. Solids*, vol. 5, pp. 102–106, 1958.

ment of the indirect transition absorption edge in silicon-germanium alloys.[37] A summary of the pressure coefficients they found is given in Fig. 8-20. In germanium-rich alloys the pressure coefficient for the (111) energy gap dominates, while in silicon-rich alloys the measured coefficient is close to that for pure silicon. At intermediate compositions the pressure coefficient is intermediate between these two extremes, the change-over point occurring near 15 percent silicon in germanium, the composition at which the (100) and (111) minima are supposed to be equal in

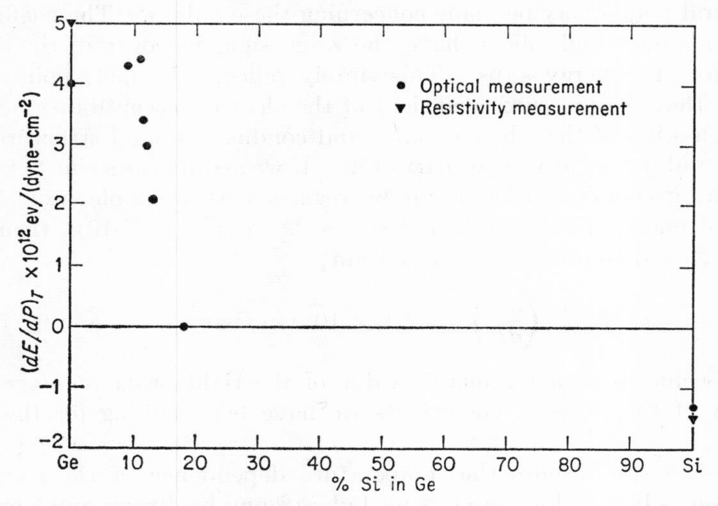

Fig. 8-20 Illustration of the variation in pressure coefficient of the optical absorption edge with the composition of silicon-germanium alloys. (*Paul and Warschauer.*[37])

energy.[24] Thus these data support the picture of the energy-band structure of germanium and silicon as we have described it and the ideas on the structure of silicon-germanium alloys suggested by Herman.

8-3p Other optical measurements on germanium and silicon: refractive index. Cardona, Paul, and Brooks[38] measured the pressure and temperature dependence of the refractive index of silicon and germanium, finding results in agreement with their earlier measurements on the dielectric constant at radio frequencies.[39] The pressure coeffi-

[37] W. Paul and D. M. Warschauer, Optical Properties of Semiconductors under Hydrostatic Pressure. III. Germanium-Silicon Alloys, *J. Phys. Chem. Solids*, vol. 6, pp. 6–15, 1958.

[38] M. Cardona, W. Paul, and H. Brooks, Dielectric Constant of Germanium and Silicon as a Function of Volume, *J. Phys. Chem. Solids*, vol. 8, pp. 204–206, 1959.

[39] M. Cardona, W. Paul, and H. Brooks, Dielectric Constant Measurements in Germanium and Silicon at Radio Frequencies as a Function of Temperature and Pressure, pp. 206–214 in M. Desirant and J. L. Michiels (eds.), "Solid State Physics in Electronics and Telecommunications," vol. 1, Academic Press, Inc., New York, 1960.

cients were estimated from the change in spacing of the interference fringes produced by thin films. For germanium,

$$\frac{1}{\epsilon}\left(\frac{d\epsilon}{dP}\right)_T = -1.4 \times 10^{-6}\ \text{bar}^{-1} \tag{8-55}$$

while for silicon,

$$\frac{1}{\epsilon}\left(\frac{d\epsilon}{dP}\right)_T = -0.6 \times 10^{-6}\ \text{bar}^{-1} \tag{8-56}$$

Several points may be made concerning these values. The coefficients for germanium and silicon have the same sign, in contradistinction to those for the energy gaps. This simply reflects the fact, pointed out earlier, that the pressure coefficient of the electric susceptibility depends on the motion of the whole valence and conduction-band structure with strain, and not on any small part of it. If we assume, as a short exercise, that the germanium lattice can be regarded as a simple oscillator of resonant energy $E = 4$ ev and that $\epsilon \sim E^{-2}$ [see Eq. (8-16)], then from the coefficient quoted above we obtain‡

$$\left(\frac{dE}{dP}\right)_T = 2.4 \times 10^{-6}\ \text{ev/bar} \tag{8-57}$$

which seems to be a reasonable value of the right order of magnitude in view of the pressure coefficients we have been finding for the band edges.

We shall not discuss the temperature dependence of the refractive index found by Cardona et al.,[38] by Lukes,[40] and by Briggs and Konkel.[41] There are quantitative disagreements among the results of the different investigators, which may occur because they used different methods. For our present purpose we note that all the temperature coefficients are much larger than would be predicted from the pressure coefficients and the compressibility and thermal-expansion coefficients.

8-3q Measurements on impurities in germanium and silicon. Holland[42] and Nathan and Paul[26,43] have measured the effect of pressure on the ionization energy of impurities in germanium and silicon.

‡ We are indebted to H. Brooks for pointing out this computation to us.

[40] F. Lukes, On the Theory of the Temperature Dependence of the Refractive Index of Insulators and Semiconductors, *Czechoslov. J. Phys.*, vol. 8, no. 253, pp. 423–434, 1958.

[41] H. B. Briggs and W. H. Konkel, private communication.

[42] M. G. Holland, High Pressure Effects on Impurity Levels in Semiconductors, Ph.D. thesis, Harvard University, Cambridge, Mass., 1958, issued as Report HP 4, Division of Engineering and Applied Physics, Harvard University, 1958; also M. G. Holland and W. Paul, *Phys. Rev.*, vol. 128, pp. 30–38, 43–55, 1962.

[43] M. I. Nathan and W. Paul, Pressure Dependence of the Resistivity of Gold Doped Silicon, *Bull. Am. Phys. Soc.*, vol. 2, p. 134, 1957; also M. I. Nathan and W. Paul, *Phys. Rev.*, vol. 128, pp. 38–42, 1962.

The ionization energy of the so-called hydrogenic impurities in germanium and silicon was discussed earlier (see Sec. 8-2b). In germanium this ionization energy is approximately 0.01 ev, in silicon 0.05 ev. Thus the hydrogenic impurities are approximately completely ionized above about 20°K in germanium and above 50°K in silicon.

Holland measured the change in resistivity of silicon samples near 45°K, where they were only partly ionized; germanium would have required temperatures so low that high hydrostatic pressures could not be applied. He used helium gas as a pressure-transmitting medium, and immersed his pressure vessel at the end of a length of thin stainless-steel high-pressure tubing, in a double Dewar vessel. Strict temperature control was necessary. The changes in resistivity were of the same order as the mobility changes already discussed (Sec. 8-2b), so that the measurements required careful correction for mobility variations before carrier-density changes could be found. These mobility corrections can be made either by extrapolating pressure coefficients of mobility for higher temperatures (where the electron density is unaffected by pressure since all the impurities are ionized) or by calculating the changes from the pressure coefficients of the parameters describing the mobility (when these are known). The pressure coefficients of the ionization energies, determined from the carrier-density changes, are summarized in Table 8-2. These coefficients are small but consistent with those calculated using Eq. (8-8) and the pressure coefficients of mass and dielectric constant found in other experiments. The changes in ionization energy for the p-type impurities cannot really be interpreted using Eq. (8-8), which, strictly speaking, does not apply for these impurities because of the degeneracy of the valence-band edge. On the other hand, it is considered that theory and experiment agree well enough that further experiments on germanium are unnecessary.

The situation regarding the "deep-lying" impurities is quite different. The term "deep-lying" roughly describes all impurities other than those of Groups 3 and 5 of the periodic table. The energy levels are usually separated from the band edges by an amount not negligible compared with the band-gap energy. By contrast with the situation for hydrogenic impurities, our understanding of the energy levels and wave functions for deep-lying impurities is poor. From photoconductivity and transport measurements there is available a wealth of experimental information on the ionization energy and the charge. From spin-resonance measurements we obtain some information on the atomic configuration. In general, however, we know very little above the details of the wave functions, and we have no explanation for the position of the energy levels. Pressure measurements may one day be helpful in constructing a theory for the impurity states. The systems studied so far have been gold in germanium, gold in silicon, and manganese in silicon.

Data concerning the first two of these systems are shown in Table 8-2. Analysis of the carrier statistics to obtain the ionization energy requires knowledge of the energy-level spectrum. In practice, it is assumed that the center can exist in several states of ionization and that each state is described sufficiently accurately by its ground-level energy. By careful counterdoping of the crystal, it can usually be arranged that only two states of ionization of the centers are present in the crystal throughout the pressure range of the measurements. Thus, for example, the lowest gold energy level in germanium is a donor level, 0.05 ev above the valence band. This level is active only when it is partially empty and is acting as a sink for electrons from the valence band. If N_d and N_a are the

Table 8-2 Pressure Coefficients of Ionization Energies of Impurities in Silicon and Germanium

Element	System	Ionization energy (electron volts)	Pressure coefficient (ev-cm²/kg)	Source
Silicon	Arsenic donor	0.05	$\sim -5 \times 10^{-8}$	Holland and Paul[42]
	Aluminum acceptor	0.06	$\sim +1 \times 10^{-8}$	Holland and Paul[42]
	Indium acceptor	0.16	$\sim +5 \times 10^{-8}$	Holland and Paul[42]
	Gold acceptor†	0.54*	-1.2×10^{-6}	Nathan and Paul[43]
	Gold acceptor†	0.62‡	-0.3×10^{-6}	Nathan and Paul[43]
	Gold donor	0.35‡	$\leq \|5 \times 10^{-8}\|$	Nathan and Paul[43]
Germanium	Gold donor	0.04‡	$+0.11 \pm 0.02 \times 10^{-6}$	Holland and Paul[42]
	Gold acceptor	0.15‡	$+0.55 + 0.06 - 0.02 \times 10^{-6}$	Holland and Paul[42]
	Gold acceptor	0.19*	$+2.9 \pm 0.1 \times 10^{-6}$	Holland and Paul[42]
	Gold acceptor	0.04*	$+2.1 \pm 0.1 \times 10^{-6}$	Holland and Paul[42]

* Measured with respect to the conduction band.
† These are the same level.
‡ Measured with respect to the valence band.

compensating hydrogenic donor and acceptor densities and $N_a - N_d > N_{Au} > 0$, then the gold donor electrons are emptied into the acceptor level at 0°K. As the temperature is raised, electrons are excited from the valence band, first into the remaining acceptor impurities, then into the vacated gold donors. In the temperature range in which the gold is acting as a sink for valence-band electrons, it can be shown that the hole carrier density p is given by

$$\frac{p(p + N_{Au} + N_d - N_a)}{N_a - N_d - p} = gC_0C_v \exp \frac{E_v - E_{Au}}{kT} \tag{8-58}$$

where g is a degeneracy factor describing the gold level and E_{Au} is its energy, and C_v describes the density of states in the valence band. Hall-effect measurements give estimates of the comparative sizes of $N_a - N_d$, N_{Au}, and n or p, so that it is often possible to use more tractable expressions for p than Eq. (8-58). Then, measurements of the resistivity as a function of pressure can be interpreted to give the pressure coefficient of the ionization energy. The mobility corrections are small but can be made. Changes in the effective mass affect the state densities, but they can also be estimated.

Similar considerations apply to the other three gold levels.[42] The final results are listed in Table 8-2. We conclude that these coefficients are much larger than those for the hydrogenic impurities. Moreover, the coefficients with respect to the valence band are much smaller than those with respect to the conduction band. There is, as yet, no explanation of even these qualitative differences.

In silicon, gold produces only two levels, one a donor 0.35 ev above the valence band, the other an acceptor 0.54 ev below the conduction band. Presumably these correspond to the lowest two levels produced by gold in germanium and the upper two levels are merged with the conduction band. The statistics for these two cases have their own peculiar difficulties (which can be resolved), and the coefficients listed in Table 8-2 are deduced from measurements of the resistivity as a function of pressure at appropriately low temperatures.

In contradistinction to germanium, the ionization energies decrease with pressure, but again the coefficient with respect to the conduction band is greater than that with respect to the valence band.

Since the acceptor level is so close to the center of the forbidden gap, it is possible to arrange, by careful counterdoping, that this level acts either as a source of electrons for the conduction band, or as a sink for electrons from the valence band. For samples of the first kind, analysis of a logarithmic plot of the resistivity versus $1/T$ gives the separation in energy of the conduction band and impurity level, while for those of the second kind, analysis gives the separation of the valence band and the level. The sum of the separations agrees with the energy gap determined from measurements on the pure material. Similarly, the pressure coefficients for the two ionization energies add to the pressure coefficient of the main gap.[43]

Holland[42] also investigated the properties of manganese impurities in silicon without obtaining conclusive results. Apart from irreproducibility of successive runs, long time changes in resistivity of hours' duration were found. Evidence from spin resonance indicates that manganese forms more than one type of defect in silicon, so that Holland's suggestion that the pressure caused redistribution of the manganese impurities seems plausible.

No measurements of the effect of pressure on the energy levels caused by other impurities in germanium, silicon, or other semiconductors are known to us.

8-3r Optical absorption at very high pressures. We have referred only briefly so far to the measurements of the optical absorption spectra at pressures up to and in excess of 100 kilobars carried out by Drickamer and his colleagues (see Chap. 12). For these measurements the samples are immersed in a soft transparent salt matrix so that the pressure is only approximately hydrostatic. The results of Slykhouse and Drickamer[34] for germanium and silicon are shown in Figs. 8-18 and 8-19. The low-pressure slope of the energy of the absorption edge for germanium (determined by an arbitrary but consistently applied procedure) agrees with the pressure coefficient of the energy gap determined by the analysis of resistivity data. The maximum in the energy gap near 50 kilobars and the subsequent decrease of the gap at a rate of -2×10^{-6} ev/bar agree with the model we have been describing for the energy-band structure. The decrease in energy gap for silicon determined from the curve of Fig. 8-19 is at a rate of -2×10^{-6} ev/bar, which

Table 8-3 Section of the Periodic Table

Periodic table		B	C	N	O	F
		Al	Si	P	S	Cl
Cu	Zn	Ga	Ge	As	Se	Br
Ag	Cd	In	Sn	Sb	Te	I
1	2	3	4	5	6	7

also agrees quantitatively with the electrical measurements of Paul and Pearson[23] and of Nathan and Paul,[43] and with the optical edge determinations at low pressures of Paul and Warschauer[36] and of Neuringer.[33]

We shall refer later to similar measurements on the Group 3-5 compounds and shall comment on the future use of the method. It should be noted that corrections for changes in the compressibility with pressure are necessary before elaborate theoretical interpretation can be made. Apparently the compressibility of these semiconductors can decrease by about a factor of 2 by 100 kilobars, so that quantitative comparison of the coefficients determined at these pressures with the coefficients determined near zero pressure has to be done carefully.

8-3s Measurements on intermetallic compounds. We have already mentioned in cursory fashion the pressure coefficients of energy gaps in the Group 3-5 compounds and the approximate equality of the pressure coefficients corresponding to minima of the same symmetry type. A section of the periodic table is shown in Table 8-3, and the properties of the Group 3-5 compounds in Table 8-4.[45] As we noted earlier, the properties of these compounds are similar to those of the Group 4 elements; the conduction bands exhibit minima of the same symmetry type, and systematic trends exist in such properties as energy gaps, mobilities, and the position of specific minima. Alloys within Group 4 and the Group 3-5 compounds show intermediate properties. The earliest example of these were the silicon-germanium alloys, which showed a radical change of property at 15 percent silicon content, attributed to a change in the type of the lowest conduction-band minimum. The lattice constant, which obeys Vegard's law, decreases as silicon is added, but this is not the primary cause of the change in energy gap. For silicon-germanium alloys of less than 10 percent silicon, the change in lattice constant from germanium causes about 30 percent of the change in energy gap.

The early work of Herman[2] and of Callaway[2] predicted certain changes in conduction-band structure between germanium and the Group 3-5 compounds; however the absolute accuracy of the electron energies predicted from theory is not yet adequate for interpretation of experiment. Thus the differences in energy of the three types of conduction-band minima were so small that calculations could not differentiate them. There were some experimental indications that the minima might be so close in some compounds that multiband conduction occurred under normal conditions of temperature and pressure. Clearly it is very hard to estimate the small contribution of any higher minima to conduction. If the energy and type of these minima can be established, however, careful fitting of data to calculations will determine the properties of the additional minima. Measurements on alloys are invaluable when the lowest conduction-band minima are of different type in the two end members, for extrapolation gives a first estimate of the position of the higher minima (see Fig. 8-8). The pressure measurements are valuable because pressure can invert the positions of the minima, or at least change the separation, so that the properties of the higher minima can be deduced. We shall try to illustrate this with a specific example in a moment.

The first measurements on intermetallic compounds were made by Long[44] and by Keyes[44] in 1955. Long measured the resistivity and Hall effect in indium antimonide to 2 kilobars at 273, 297, and 327°K. The material was p type at low temperatures and began to show intrinsic behavior near 220°K. Long deduced a decrease in electron mobility of the order of 12 percent and an increase in energy gap of 1.45×10^{-5} ev/bar. Keyes's result for the energy-gap coefficient of indium antimonide,

[44] D. Long, Effect of Pressure on the Electrical Properties of Indium Antimonide, *Phys. Rev.*, vol. 99, pp. 388–390, 1955; R. W. Keyes, Effect of Pressure on the Electrical Conductivity of InSb, *Phys. Rev.*, vol. 99, pp. 490–495, 1955.

Table 8-4 Properties of Group 4 Elements and Group 3-5 Compounds[p]

Compound or element	Lattice constant (25°C), Å	Energy gap, ev	Conduction-band minima	$\left(\frac{dE_g}{dP}\right)_T$, ev/kg-cm^{-2}	$\left(\frac{dE_g}{d\ln V}\right)_T$, ev
Carbon......	3.567	5.3 (300°K)	Δ_1(spec.)	$<10^{-6}$ [a]	
Silicon.......	5.43	1.21 (0°K)	Δ_1	-1.5×10^{-6} [b]	+1.5
Germanium..	5.66	0.66 (300°K) 0.803 (300°K) 0.85 (300°K)	L_1 $\Gamma_{2'}$ Δ_1	5×10^{-6} [c] 12×10^{-6} [d] 0 to (-2×10^{-6}) [e]	−3.8 −9 0 to +1.5
Tin.........	6.489	0.08 (0°K)	L_1(spec.)	5×10^{-6} [f]	
AlP.........	5.47	3.1 (300°K)	Δ_1(spec.)		
AlAs........	5.66	2.16 (300°K)	Δ_1(spec.)		
AlSb........	6.10	1.6 (300°K)	Δ_1(spec.)	-1.6×10^{-6} [g]	
GaP.........	5.47	2.2 (300°K) 2.6 (300°K)	Δ_1(spec.) Γ_1(spec.)	-1.7×10^{-6} [h] -1.8×10^{-6} [i]	
GaAs........	5.66	1.53 (0°K) 1.89 (0°K)	Γ_1 Δ_1(spec.)	9.4×10^{-6} [j] 12×10^{-6} [k] negative	−7 −9
GaSb........	6.10	0.81 (0°K)	Γ_1 L_1 Δ_1	16×10^{-6} [l] 12×10^{-6} [g] $\sim 5 \times 10^{-6}$ [m] negative[g]	−9 −6.75 −2.8
InP.........	5.9	1.34 (0°K)	Γ_1 Δ_1(spec.)	4.6×10^{-6} [g] -10×10^{-6} [g]	−6.15 +7.45
InAs........	6.07	0.36 (300°K)	Γ_1	5.5×10^{-6} [n] 8.5×10^{-6} [l] 4.8×10^{-6} [g]	−3.3 −5.1 −2.9
InSb........	6.49	0.27 (0°K)	Γ_1	15.5×10^{-6} [29,o] 14.2×10^{-6} [28]	−6.7 −6.1

[a] F. C. Champion and J. R. Prior, *Nature*, vol. 182, p. 1079, 1958.

[b] W. Paul and G. L. Pearson, *Phys. Rev.*, vol. 98, p. 1755, 1955; M. I. Nathan and W. Paul, *Bull. Am. Phys. Soc.*, vol. 2, no. 2, p. 134, 1957; W. Paul and D. M. Warschauer, *J. Phys. Chem. Solids*, vol. 5, p. 102, 1958; H. Y. Fan, M. L. Shepherd, and W. G. Spitzer, in "Photoconductivity Conference," R. G. Breckenridge, B. R. Russell, and E. E. Hahn (eds.), John Wiley & Sons, Inc., New York, 1956; L. J. Neuringer,

derived from similar measurements to higher pressures, was 1.58×10^{-5} ev/bar.

The most striking thing about these coefficients is that they are very close to the value for the direct energy gap in germanium. We saw earlier that the coefficients for the (100) gaps in germanium and silicon

---

Phys. Rev., vol. 113, p. 1495, 1959; T. E. Slykhouse and H. G. Drickamer, *J. Phys. Chem. Solids*, vol. 7, p. 210, 1958.

[c] P. W. Bridgman, *Proc. Am. Acad. Arts Sci.*, vol. 79, p. 129, 1951; P. H. Miller and J. H. Taylor, *Phys. Rev.*, vol. 76, p. 179, 1949; J. H. Taylor, *Phys. Rev.*, vol. 80, p. 919, 1950; H. H. Hall, J. Bardeen, and G. L. Pearson, *Phys. Rev.*, vol. 84, p. 129, 1951; D. M. Warschauer, W. Paul, and H. Brooks, *Phys. Rev.*, vol. 98, p. 1193, 1955; H. Y. Fan, M. L. Shepherd, and W. G. Spitzer, in "Photoconductivity Conference," R. G. Breckenridge, B. R. Russell, and E. E. Hahn (eds.), John Wiley & Sons, Inc., New York, 1956; W. Paul and D. M. Warschauer, *J. Phys. Chem. Solids*, vol. 5, p. 89, 1958; A. Michels, J. van Eck, S. Machlup, and C. A. ten Seldam, *J. Phys. Chem. Solids*, vol. 10, p. 12, 1959; W. Paul, *Phys. Rev.*, vol. 90, p. 336, 1953; W. Paul and H. Brooks, *Phys. Rev.*, vol. 94, p. 1128, 1954.

[d] L. J. Neuringer, *Phys. Rev.*, vol. 113, p. 1495, 1959; W. Paul and D. M. Warschauer, *J. Phys. Chem. Solids*, vol. 5, p. 89, 1958; M. Cardona and W. Paul, *J. Phys. Chem. Solids*, vol. 17, p. 138, 1960.

[e] H. Brooks and W. Paul, *Bull. Am. Phys. Soc.*, vol. 1, p. 48, 1956; W. E. Howard, thesis, Harvard University, Cambridge, Mass., 1961, available as Report HP 7 from the Division of Engineering and Applied Physics, Harvard University; T. E. Slykhouse and H. G. Drickamer, *J. Phys. Chem. Solids*, vol. 7, p. 210, 1958.

[f] S. H. Groves and W. Paul, *Bull. Am. Phys. Soc.*, vol. 7, p. 184, 1962.

[g] A. L. Edwards and H. G. Drickamer, *Phys. Rev.*, vol. 122, p. 1149, 1961.

[h] A. L. Edwards, T. E. Slykhouse, and H. G. Drickamer, *J. Phys. Chem. Solids*, vol. 11, p. 140, 1959.

[i] R. Zallen and W. Paul, unpublished measurements.

[j] A. L. Edwards, T. E. Slykhouse, and H. G. Drickamer, *J. Phys. Chem. Solids*, vol. 11, p. 140, 1959; see reference *g*.

[k] W. Paul and D. M. Warschauer, unpublished measurements.

[l] J. H. Taylor, *Bull. Am. Phys. Soc.*, vol. 3, p. 121, 1958.

[m] A. Sagar, *Phys. Rev.*, vol. 117, p. 93, 1960; R. W. Keyes and M. Pollak, *Phys. Rev.*, vol. 110, p. 1001, 1960.

[n] J. H. Taylor, *Phys. Rev.*, vol. 100, p. 1593, 1958.

[o] D. Long, *Phys. Rev.*, vol. 99, p. 388, 1955; R. W. Keyes, *Phys. Rev.*, vol. 99, p. 490, 1955.

[p] Compounds containing boron, nitrogen, thallium, and bismuth are not included. Conduction-band minima are labeled "speculative" [(spec.)] if the type is a systematic extrapolation or based on a pressure coefficient and are unlabeled if the type is considered assured through measurement of cyclotron resonance, optical absorption, effective mass, etc. The $\Gamma_{2'}$ minima in the diamond lattice become Γ_1 in the zincblende. The Δ_1 minima in the diamond lattice may shift to the Brillouin-zone edge point X_1 in the zincblende, but we continue to refer to Δ_1 minima. Temperatures of energy gaps are mixed; the room-temperature gaps more easily allow comparisons where higher minima are present. Little attempt has been made to obtain the very latest values of the parameters in columns 1 to 3. On the other hand, columns 4 and 5 represent our best present assessment of the pressure coefficients.

were also very similar. These two sets of observations led to the speculation that energy gaps that correspond to the same levels in Group 4 elements and Group 3-5 compounds might have the same pressure coefficient. This speculation has been examined in detail by Paul,[45] who has concluded from a survey of results on all the Group 4 and Group 3-5 semiconductors that there does exist a strong correlation among the pressure coefficients, which is sufficient to allow extrapolation of results from one semiconductor of the series to another. We cannot reproduce here all the data in Paul's paper, so we shall discuss one or two specific examples only.

Most of the measurements made have been of the types discussed so far—optical absorption, resistivity, Hall effect, and magnetoresistance. Sagar[46] and Keyes and Pollak[47] have used measurements of the piezoresistivity as a function of pressure in interpreting data on gallium antimonide, and recently Sagar and Miller[48] have reported the variation of the Seebeck coefficient. Table 8-4 includes a summary of the pressure coefficients of the three different energy gaps:

1. At $k = (000)$, between $\Gamma_{25'}$ and $\Gamma_{2'}$ states in Group 4 elements, and between Γ_{15} and Γ_1 states in Group 3-5 compounds
2. Between $k = (000)$ valence-band states and $k = (111)$ conduction-band states, i.e., between $\Gamma_{25'}$ and L_1 states or Γ_{15} and L_1 states
3. Between $k = (000)$ valence-band states and $k = (100)$ conduction-band states, i.e., between $\Gamma_{25'}$ and $\Delta_{2'}$ states or Γ_{15} and X_1 states

Looking first at the $k = (000)$ states, we see that nearly the same coefficient is found for this gap in germanium, indium antimonide, gallium arsenide, and gallium antimonide, while somewhat lower coefficients are found in indium arsenide and indium phosphide. The germanium and indium antimonide determinations have already been mentioned. The coefficients for gallium arsenide were determined by Edwards and Drickamer[49] from optical measurements and by Paul and Warschauer[50] at relatively low pressures. The coefficients for gallium antimonide were

[45] W. Paul, Band Structure of Intermetallic Semiconductors from Pressure Experiments, *J. Appl. Phys.*, vol. 32, supplement, pp. 2082–2095, 1961.

[46] A. Sagar, Experimental Investigation of Conduction Band of GaSb, *Phys. Rev.*, vol. 117, pp. 93–100, 1960.

[47] R. W. Keyes and M. Pollak, Effects of Hydrostatic Pressure on the Piezoresistance of Semiconductors: i-InSb, p-Ge, p-InSb, and n-GaSb, *Phys. Rev.*, vol. 118, pp. 1001–1004, 1960.

[48] A. Sagar and R. C. Miller, Study of Band Structure of Intermetallic Compounds by Pressure Experiments, *J. Appl. Phys.*, vol. 32, supplement, pp. 2073–2078, 1961.

[49] A. L. Edwards and H. G. Drickamer, Effect of Pressure on the Absorption Edges of Some III-V, II-VI, and I-VII Compounds, *Phys. Rev.*, vol. 122, pp. 1149–1157, 1961.

[50] W. Paul and D. M. Warschauer, unpublished data.

found from optical measurements by Taylor[51] and Edwards and Drickamer.[49] In all optical measurements the energy coefficients were determined from simple translations of the absorption edge, and no attempt was made to analyze changes in the shape of the absorption curve.

The coefficients for indium arsenide and indium phosphide do not agree well with the idea of strong correlation among the energy-gap coefficients. However, recent measurements by Zallen[52] find larger coefficients than those of Table 8-4, so these discrepancies may not be serious.

From Table 8-4, the correlation for the coefficients corresponding to the energy gap between the k = (000) and k = (100) states seems to be very good. The coefficient for diamond is very poorly defined, but what indications there are give a very small coefficient. The coefficients for silicon and germanium have been discussed. The coefficients for aluminum antimonide, gallium phosphide, indium phosphide, and gallium antimonide have been estimated from the translation of the optical absorption edge. The negative coefficient for gallium arsenide and gallium antimonide has also been deduced from transport measurements. Actually the identification of the minima in some of these compounds is speculative, and the negative pressure coefficient is in some cases the main support of the speculation.

The result for this energy gap in indium phosphide is not in agreement with the postulate of correlated pressure coefficients. However, only one series of measurements has been carried out on this material, and no corrections have been applied for possible changes in the shape of the absorption edge or in the compressibility.

Again from Table 8-4, the correlation for the coefficients corresponding to the (000)-to-(111) energy gaps in gray tin, germanium, and gallium antimonide is seen to be good.

In several of the Group 3-5 compounds the conduction-band minima are so close that two different types may contribute to conduction at atmospheric pressure. This appears to be the case in gallium antimonide, whose suggested band structure is shown in Fig. 8-21. At atmospheric pressure most of the conduction-band electrons occupy states in the (000) minimum. As the pressure is raised, this minimum moves away from the valence band, and some of the electrons are transferred into the (111) minima. The conductivity then depends on the average mobility of the electrons in the two types of minima and is very dependent on pressure. If the pressure is further increased, the electrons disappear entirely out of the (111) minima, but now some of them are transferred into the (100) minima, which approach the valence band

[51] J. H. Taylor, Effect of Pressure on Intrinsic Optical Absorption in Indium Arsenide and Gallium Antimonide, *Bull. Am. Phys. Soc.*, vol. 3, p. 121, 1958.

[52] R. Zallen, unpublished data.

with increasing pressure. At extremely high pressures, the (100) minima will be the lowest set. Figure 8-22 illustrates measurements of the resistivity at pressures up to 30 kilobars. The sharp initial rise is caused partly by a decrease in the mobility of the electrons in the (000) minimum and partly by carrier transfer into the (111) minima. The rise near 30 kilobars, after a plateau has been reached, marks the beginning of carrier transfer into the (100) minima.

The character of the (111) minima was first established by the Hall-effect and piezoresistance measurements versus pressure of Sagar[46] and

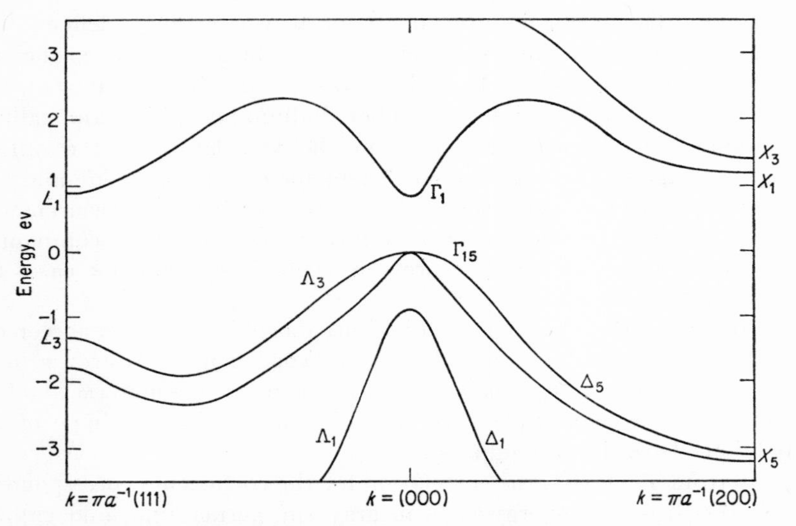

Fig. 8-21 The energy-band structure of gallium antimonide as determined as of December, 1961. The abscissas are the wave vectors in the (111) and (000) directions. Energy is plotted as ordinate. The labeling of states follows the notation of Bouckaert, Smoluchowski, and Wigner. The zero of energy is chosen at the valence-band maximum at Γ_{15}. The approximate energy separations are $\Gamma_{15} - \Gamma_1$: 0.81 ev (4°K); $\Gamma_1 - L_1$: 0.08 ev (300°K); $\Gamma_1 - X_1$: 0.3 to 0.4 ev (300°K); $L_1 - L_3$: 2 ev (300°K); $X_1 - X_5$: 4.2 ev (300°K; speculative).

of Sagar, Keyes, and Pollak.[53] The symmetry relations among the piezoresistance coefficients were found to change from those for a (000) minimum to those for (111) minima above 8 kilobars or so. The identification of the (100) minima is much less direct and depends on an extrapolation from the sort of band structure found in all these compounds and on the negative pressure coefficient of Edwards and Drickamer,[49] found at very high pressures.

Figure 8-23 shows the Hall-coefficient-versus-pressure relation found

[53] A. Sagar, R. W. Keyes, and M. Pollak, Effects of High Hydrostatic Pressure on the Electrical Properties of *n*-type GaSb, *Bull. Am. Phys. Soc.*, vol. 5, p. 63, 1960.

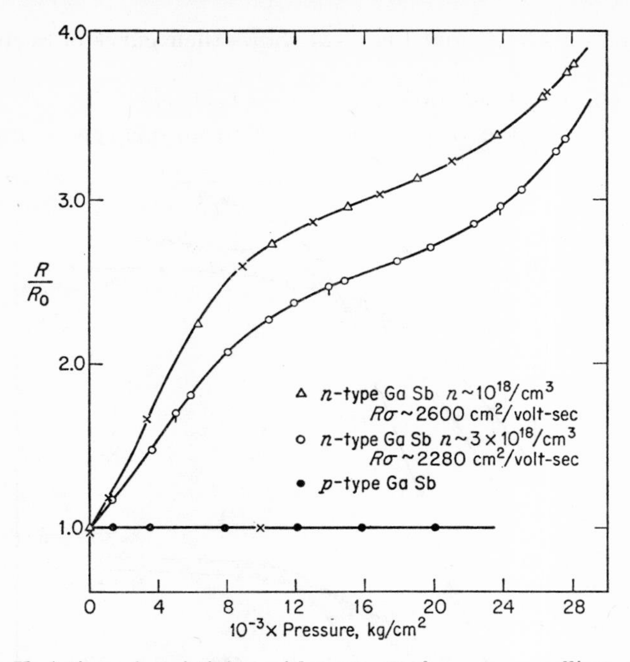

Fig. 8-22 Variation of resistivity with pressure for n-type gallium antimonide. (*Howard and Paul.*[45])

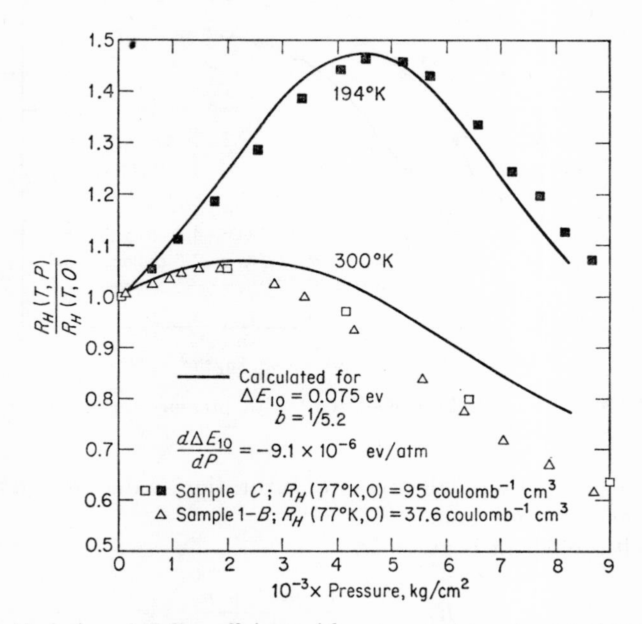

Fig. 8-23 Variation of Hall coefficient with pressure at two temperatures for n-type gallium antimonide. (*Sagar and Miller.*[48])

by Sagar and Miller,[48] and Fig. 8-24 shows their curve of Seebeck coefficient versus pressure.

The increase and saturation of the Seebeck coefficient with pressure is consistent with the transfer of carriers from one type of minimum to

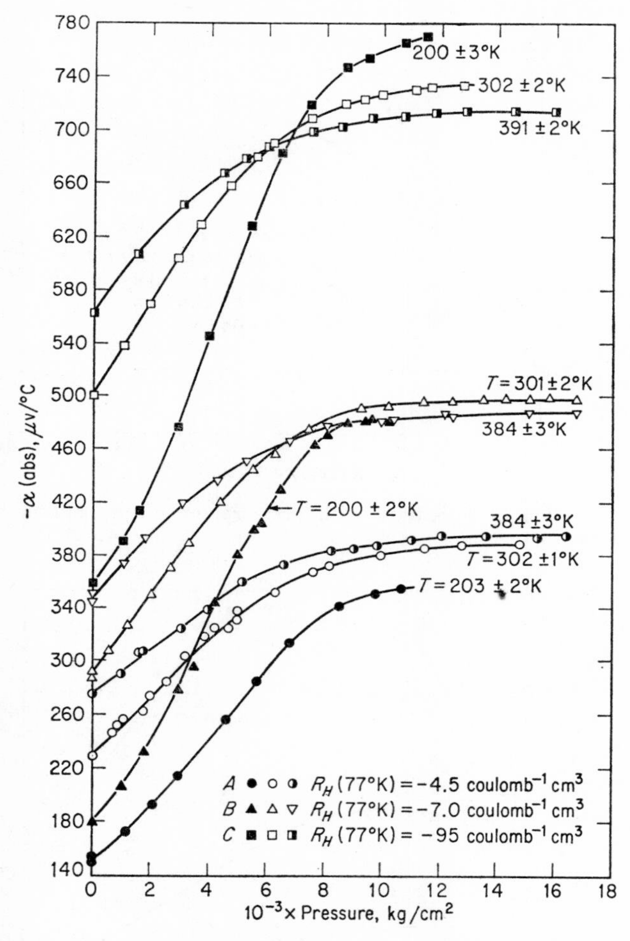

Fig. 8-24 Variation of Seebeck coefficient with pressure for n-type gallium antimonide. (*Sagar and Miller.*[48])

another, so that the high-pressure saturation value is characteristic solely of the (111) minima.

The Hall coefficient is given by

$$R_H = -\frac{1}{ec}\frac{n_1 b^2 + n_2}{(n_1 b + n_2)^2}$$

where n_1 and n_2 are the densities of carriers in the (000) and (111) minima, and $b = \mu_2/\mu_1$ is the ratio of their mobilities. Under the condition that $n_1 + n_2$ is constant but n_1/n_2 decreases with pressure, it can be shown that R_H will give a maximum, as is observed. The data of Fig. 8-23 were fitted by assuming a constant ratio for the mobilities and by ignoring changes in mass and other parameters with pressure.

It is not our intention to describe the fitting of theory and experiment for gallium antimonide in the detail in which we described it earlier for germanium. Less is known concerning the atmospheric-pressure parameters for the bands, so that there are too many adjustable parameters left. The agreement of calculated and experimental curves shown in Fig. 8-23, however, suggests that a reasonable fitting can be made.

The problem of gallium antimonide illustrates again that pressure measurements can contribute to the establishment of the band-structure parameters by bringing into prominence minor but important features of the band structure at atmospheric pressure. The correlation of the pressure coefficients of the energy gaps between extrema of different symmetry, if borne out by further experiments, is a major step toward understanding all the pressure effects in semiconductors and permits us to plan experiments based on known changes of band structure with pressure. We shall return to this subject later.

8-3t Measurements on other materials. While this article is not intended to be a comprehensive review of all pressure work on semiconductors (see reference 45), in this part we shall remark on some investigations of materials other than germanium, silicon, and the Group 3-5 compounds.

In 1938, Bridgman[54] found that the resistance of tellurium decreased rapidly as a function of pressure and ascribed this result to the element becoming more metallic. Using Bridgman's data, Bardeen,[55] in 1949, interpreted the resistance change as a decrease in the forbidden-energy gap of the material.

In 1956 Long[56] extended these measurements and found a rather large coefficient, -1.6×10^{-5} ev/bar, to 2 kilobars maximum pressure. He also studied the effect of pressure on the Hall mobility, parallel and perpendicular to the *c* axis of the crystal, and found a small anisotropy. Later, Robin[57] obtained a coefficient of -1.1×10^{-5} ev/bar at pressures

[54] P. W. Bridgman, Resistance of Nineteen Metals to 30,000 kg/cm², *Proc. Am. Acad. Arts Sci.*, vol. 72, pp. 200–204, 1938.

[55] J. Bardeen, Pressure Change of Resistance of Tellurium, *Phys. Rev.*, vol. 75, pp. 1777–1778, 1949.

[56] D. Long, Effects of Pressure on the Electrical Properties of Semiconductors, *Phys. Rev.*, vol. 101, pp. 1256–1263, 1956.

[57] J. Robin, Variation of the Resistivity of Thin Layers of Ge and Te due to Pressure, *J. phys. radium*, vol. 20, pp. 506–507, 1959.

to 2 kilobars from resistivity measurements on evaporated layers. Neuringer[58] reported, in 1957, measurements of the shift of the absorption edges in tellurium to 2 kilobars. He found that the energy gap for light polarized perpendicularly to the *c* axis decreased more rapidly with pressure than the gap for parallel polarization, the values being -2.8×10^{-5} and -1.8×10^{-5} ev/bar, respectively.

In 1953 Keyes[59] reported a study of the semiconducting form of phosphorus discovered earlier by Bridgman. Keyes's material was *p* type at low temperatures and intrinsic at high temperatures, with a gap width of 0.33 ev at atmospheric pressure. The effect of pressure was to decrease the energy gap. In 1959 Suchan, Wiederhorn, and Drickamer[60] measured the shift of the absorption edge of selenium, white phosphorus, red phosphorus, arsenic, and iodine at pressures up to about 80 kilobars and interpreted their results as a decrease of energy gap in all these materials. Resistance measurements of some of these materials at very high pressures have also been reported,[61] but may only very tentatively be interpreted in terms of band structure (see Chap. 13).

Paul and Soule[62] found that the conductivity of graphite along the basal plane was insensitive to pressure. Deutsch[63] observed a 40 percent increase in the conductivity of pyrolytic graphite measured parallel to the *c* direction when a pressure of 28 kilobars was applied. Samara and Drickamer[63a] have measured the effect of pressure on resistance in these two orientations to pressures above 400 kilobars. They find that the resistance along the *c* axis decreases with increasing pressure and flattens at high pressure, while the basal-plane resistance increases between 90 and 250 kilobars with more-complicated behavior throughout.

Groves and Paul[64] investigated the effect of pressure on the electrical

[58] L. Neuringer, Pressure Induced Changes in the Optical Absorption of Ge, Si, Te, *Bull. Am. Phys. Soc.*, vol. 2, p. 134, 1957; The Effect of Pressure and Temperature on the Intrinsic Optical Absorption of Germanium, Silicon, Tellurium, Tech. Rept. 13, Contract N6-onr-24914, University of Pennsylvania, Philadelphia, Pa., June, 1957.

[59] R. W. Keyes, The Electrical Properties of Black Phosphorus, *Phys. Rev.*, vol. 92, pp. 580–584, 1953.

[60] H. L. Suchan, S. Wiederhorn, and H. G. Drickamer, Effect of Pressure on the Absorption Edges of Certain Elements, *J. Chem. Phys.*, vol. 31, pp. 355–357, 1955.

[61] R. E. Harris, R. J. Vaisnys, H. Stromberg, and G. Jura, Resistance and Thermal Gap Measurements to 400,000 Atmospheres, pp. 165–172 in F. P. Bundy, W. R. Hibbard, Jr., and H. M. Strong (eds.), "Progress in Very High Pressure Research," John Wiley & Sons, Inc., New York, 1961.

[62] W. Paul and D. E. Soule, unpublished data.

[63] T. F. Deutsch, unpublished data.

[63a] G. A. Samara and H. G. Drickamer, Effect of Pressure on the Resistance of Pyrolytic Graphite, *J. Chem. Phys.*, vol. 37, pp. 471–474, 1962.

[64] S. H. Groves and W. Paul, Resistivity of Gray Tin as a Function of Pressure, *Bull. Am. Phys. Soc.*, vol. 7, pp. 184–185, 1962.

properties of gray tin. From the pressure coefficient of the intrinsic resistivity at $-40°C$, and without applying corrections for changes in mobility, they deduced an energy-gap change at precisely the rate for the (111) minima in germanium: 5×10^{-6} ev/bar. This observation supports the contention of Tufte and Ewald,[65] based on magnetoresistance data, that the (111) minima are lowest in this material. Low-temperature measurements of the conductivity-pressure relation, however, show great complexity and suggest that multiband conduction may persist in gray tin below 200°K.

Measurements have also been reported among the Group 2-6 compounds. Höhler[66] measured the shift of the optical absorption edge with pressure up to about 330 bars in cadmium sulfide and obtained $(dE/dP)_T = 9 \times 10^{-6}$ ev/bar in what he claimed was a cubic modification, a structure whose existence in this substance at atmospheric pressure is in grave doubt. Gutsche's[67] measurement of the absorption edge in hexagonal cadmium sulfide yielded $dE/dP = 4.5 \times 10^{-6}$ ev/bar, while Edwards, Slykhouse, and Drickamer[68] obtained 3.4×10^{-6} ev/bar up to 28 kilobars, at which pressure an incompletely reversible transition appeared to occur. This transition is interpreted by Edwards et al. as conversion to the zincblende structure; negligible shift was observed at high pressure after the transition.

Because of selection rules, cadmium sulfide exhibits two absorption edges—one for the electric vector of the radiation perpendicular to the *c* axis and another for the electric vector parallel to this direction in the crystal. Langer[69] measured the shift of each of these edges using polarized light and found that up to 12 kilobars both edges shifted at a rate equivalent to a gap shift of $(4.9 \pm 0.3) \times 10^{-6}$ ev/bar. Langer also measured to 12 kilobars the pressure shift of the reflectivity peak and the green edge-emission spectrum at liquid-nitrogen temperature, obtaining $(4.45 \pm 0.09) \times 10^{-6}$ and $(4.6 \pm 0.23) \times 10^{-6}$ ev/bar, respectively.

[65] O. N. Tufte and A. W. Ewald, Magnetoresistance in Oriented Gray Tin Single Crystals, *Phys. Rev.*, vol. 122, pp. 1431–1436, 1961.

[66] G. Höhler, Pressure and Temperature Shift of the Absorption Edge of Cadmium Sulfide, *Ann. Phys.*, vol. 4, pp. 371–378, 1949.

[67] E. Gutsche, Compressibility and Pressure Displacement of the Absorption Constant of Cadmium Sulfide, *Naturwiss.*, vol. 45, p. 486, 1958.

[68] A. L. Edwards, T. E. Slykhouse, and H. G. Drickamer, The Effect of Pressure on Zincblende and Wurtzite Structures, *J. Phys. Chem. Solids*, vol. 11, pp. 140–148, 1959.

[69] D. Langer, Über die Druckabhängigkeit elektrischer und optischer Eigenschaften von CdS-Einkristallen, Ph.D. dissertation, Technical University, Berlin, 1960; The Effect of Pressure on the Edge Emission and Conductivity in CdS, pp. 1042–1045 in "Proceedings of the International Conference on Semiconductor Physics, Prague, 1960," Publishing House of the Czechoslovak Academy of Sciences, Prague, 1961.

Measurements also were taken by Langer of the variation of the refractive index at wavelengths near the absorption edge and of the room-temperature resistivity of the material as a function of pressure. In later work, Gutsche[70] measured the displacement of the absorption edges and found a slight variation of edge shift between $E \perp c$ and $E \| c$, without change of shape of the edge, of $(4.5 \pm 0.3) \times 10^{-6}$ and $(3.9 \pm 0.3) \times 10^{-6}$ ev/kp-cm^{-2}, respectively.

Thus, with the exception of that measured by Höhler, the energy of optical effects associated with the band gap in cadmium sulfide appears to increase at a rate between 3.4×10^{-6} and 4.6×10^{-6} ev/bar. The reasons for this spread of values, as well as the exact interpretation of the measured effects themselves, remain to be worked out. However, single-crystal conductivity measurements in this material are difficult because of the high resistivity of the pure substance and because of the sensitivity to shear. Langer,[69] for example, detected no change in resistivity not attributable to leakage effects to pressures of 12 kilobars, while Samara and Drickamer[71] observed a very sharp drop in resistance of over three orders of magnitude up to 20 kilobars, perhaps attributable to initial "seasoning," followed by a rise and leveling near 375 kilobars, and finally a sharp cusp of resistance at 465 kilobars.

Other Group 2-6 materials have not received as much attention as of 1962. Samara and Drickamer[71] report high-pressure electrical measurements on zinc sulfide, zinc selenide, zinc telluride, and cadmium telluride, while Edwards et al.[68] performed optical edge measurements on zinc sulfide, zinc selenide, zinc telluride, and zinc oxide, in addition to cadmium sulfide and several Group 3-5 materials. In zinc sulfide, their initial slope of 5.7×10^{-6} ev/kg-cm^{-2} for zincblende structure is to be compared to a slope of 9×10^{-6} ev/kg-cm^{-2} observed by Piper, Marple, and Johnson[72] at low pressure in material of wurtzite structure.

Pressure effects on the electrical properties of the lead chalcogenides have been reported by Sagar and Miller,[48] by Averkin, Moizlies, and Smirnov,[73] by Finegold, DeMeis, and Paul,[45] and by Samara and Drickamer.[73a] Averkin et al. found that in *n*- and *p*-type PbSe the

[70] E. Gutsche, Über den Einfluss hohen Druckes auf die Grundgitterabsorptionskante von Kadmiumsulfid-Einkristallen, *Physica Status Solidi*, vol. 1, pp. 716–725, 1961.

[71] G. A. Samara and H. G. Drickamer, Pressure-induced Phase Transitions in Some II-VI Compounds, *J. Phys. Chem. Solids*, vol. 23, pp. 457–461, 1962.

[72] W. W. Piper, D. T. F. Marple, and P. D. Johnson, Optical Properties of Hexagonal ZnS Single Crystals, *Phys. Rev.*, vol. 110, pp. 323–326, 1958.

[73] A. A. Averkin, B. Ya. Moizlies, and I. A. Smirnov, Change of Electrical Properties of PbSe with Pressure, *Soviet Phys. Solid State*, vol. 3, pp. 1354–1356, 1961.

[73a] G. A. Samara and H. G. Drickamer, Effect of Pressure on the Resistance of PbS and PbTe, *J. Chem. Phys.*, vol. 37, pp. 1159–1160, 1962.

effective mass determined by thermal emf decreases about 1.8 percent per kilobar and the mobility increases about 5 percent per kilobar.

In general, the results confirm the similarity in the band structures of these materials and suggest multiband conduction in the valence band. Finegold, DeMeis, and Paul[45] estimated the pressure coefficient of the energy gap of lead sulfide, from resistivity measurements, to be -7×10^{-6} ev/bar, in agreement with an earlier unpublished determination by Prakash and Paul of -8×10^{-6} ev/bar determined from the shift of the optical absorption edge. An interesting attribute of this coefficient is that it leads to a contribution to the temperature dependence of the energy gap, due to lattice expansion only, of $+2.2 \times 10^{-4}$ ev/°K. The observed temperature coefficient is $+4 \times 10^{-4}$ ev/°K, leaving a *positive* explicit effect of temperature of 1.8×10^{-4} ev/°K. There is as yet no explanation of the sign of this coefficient, which is opposite to that normally observed in semiconductors.

Samara and Drickamer[73a] measured the resistance of lead sulfide and lead telluride to about 500 kilobars. In lead sulfide they observed a drop in resistance as the pressure increased; this was followed by a sharp rise in resistance between 23 and 40 kilobars and then a decrease in resistance up to the highest pressure. They attributed the sharp increase in resistance around 23 kilobars to a phase transition at this pressure.

Measurements of *n*- and *p*-type lead telluride indicated an initial drop in resistance followed in all runs by a sharp rise in resistance attributed to a phase transition around 75 to 80 kilobars.

8-3u Other types of measurement. In Sec. 8-2, we discussed various semiconductor measurements, such as those of magneto-optical phenomena, that gave vital data at atmospheric pressure but which had not been repeated at high pressures. In many cases there is no experimental bar to this extension. We now wish to discuss briefly a type of measurement that promises to yield many new pressure results.

In 1961 and 1962 there appeared to be a resurgence of interest in the examination and interpretation of the reflection spectra of surfaces of semiconductors at energies up to 25 ev[74] and of the transmission spectra of annealed films of the same materials. This renewed interest stems from the identification of several peaks in the reflection spectra of ger-

[74] See, for example, H. R. Philipp and E. A. Taft, Optical Constants of Germanium in the Region 1 to 10 ev., *Phys. Rev.*, vol. 113, pp. 1002–1005, 1959; J. Tauc and A. Abraham, Reflection Spectra of Semiconductors with Diamond and Sphalerite Structures, pp. 375–379 in "Proceedings of the International Conference on Semiconductor Physics, Prague, 1960," Publishing House of the Czechoslovak Academy of Sciences, Prague, 1961; M. Cardona, Fundamental Reflectivity Spectrum of Semiconductors with Zinc-Blende Structure, *J. Appl. Phys.*, vol. 32, supplement, pp. 2151–2155, 1961; H. Ehrenreich, H. R. Philipp, and J. C. Phillips, Interband Transitions in Groups 4, 3-5, and 2-6 Semiconductors, *Phys. Rev. Letters*, vol. 8, pp. 59–61, 1962.

maniumlike semiconductors with the energy separation between specific states. Figure 8-25 is a sketch of several of these reflection spectra. The basis for the interpretation is the observation that absorption edges, as well as peaks in absorption, can give peaks in the reflection. A double peak found at about 2.1 and 2.3 ev in germanium is attributed to the

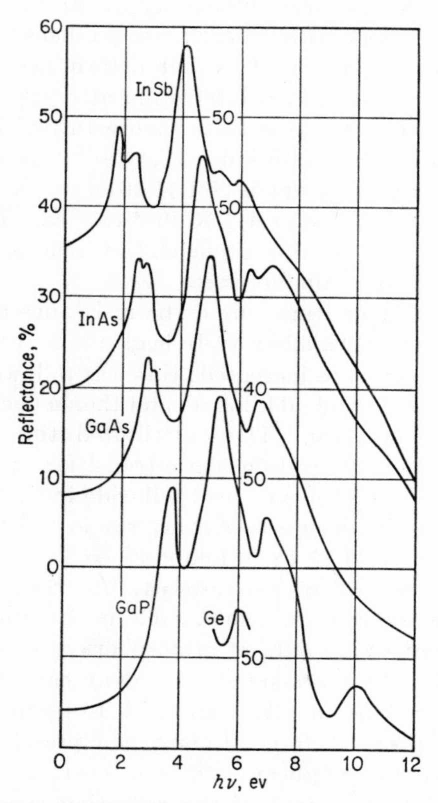

Fig. 8-25 Sketch of the reflection spectra of some Group 3-5 semiconductors. The ordinates have been shifted for clarity. (*Ehrenreich, Philipp, and Phillips.*[74])

$L_{3'}$-to-L_1 transition. The splitting of the peak is associated with the spin-orbit splitting of the $L_{3'}$ state.

It turns out that all Group 4, Group 3-5, and Group 2-6 compounds show the same type reflection spectrum, illustrating once more the basic similarity of these semiconductors. Pressure measurements on the positions of the reflection peaks can now establish finally whether states of the same symmetry respond similarly to changes in lattice constant. It is expected that the behavior will be sufficiently similar so that the pressure coefficient will be usable to identify any unknown transitions.

At the moment, the only alternative methods of identification are splittings caused by the elimination of degeneracies (e.g., spin-orbit splitting) and informed guesswork based on a knowledge of the position of the states in some compounds and ideas of their displacement in others. Thus these pressure experiments may contribute to our knowledge of the band structure at atmospheric pressure.

Measurements of this type have been carried out by Zallen, Paul, and Tauc,[75] who started by measuring the displacement with pressure of the $L_{3'} - L_1$ peaks in germanium, gallium antimonide, and indium arsenide. They found that the pressure coefficients were the same in the three materials within ± 10 percent at about 7×10^{-6} ev/bar. This coefficient is different from that for the energy separation between $\Gamma_{25'}$ and L_1 states and thus seems to show that the valence band does not remain rigid under dilatation. This technique, still in its infancy in 1962, shows great promise of determining the pressure coefficients of the separation in energy of the higher extrema of the band structure. We note also in passing a clever measurement by Philipp, Dash, and Ehrenreich[76] of the reflection spectra of bent germanium and silicon, which can also be interpreted to give reasonably accurate hydrostatic-pressure coefficients.

8-4 Application of Pressure Data to Other Semiconductor Studies

We shall discuss in more general terms in Sec. 8-5 the use of pressure measurements in the understanding of semiconductors at atmospheric pressures. Here we gather together descriptions of several experiments that were designed to apply the results of previous pressure studies to explain new phenomena rather than to derive the pressure dependence of basic parameters from measurements of well-established phenomena.

Our first example is taken from the influence of pressure on the "hot-electron" effect,[77] a phenomenon which demonstrates that it is not always necessary for a given conduction-band minimum to be occupied at atmospheric pressure in order for it to be important in atmospheric-pressure phenomena. Thus, when high electric fields are applied to n-type semiconductors, many of the electrons rapidly gain energy sufficient to excite them 0.2 ev or more above the conduction-band edge. In this case a knowledge of the positions of all higher minima is important for full understanding of the effect. The pressure, by varying the position of

[75] R. Zallen, W. Paul, and J. Tauc, Pressure Dependence of Reflectivity Peaks in Germanium and Related Materials, *Bull. Am. Phys. Soc.*, vol. 7, p. 185, 1962.

[76] H. R. Philipp, W. C. Dash, and H. Ehrenreich, Piezoreflectance of Si and Ge, *Bull. Am. Phys. Soc.*, vol. 7, p. 78, 1962.

[77] S. H. Koenig, M. I. Nathan, W. Paul, and A. C. Smith, Effect of High Pressure on Some Hot Electron Phenomena in n-type Germanium, *Phys. Rev.*, vol. 118, pp. 1217–1221, 1960.

these minima in a known way, can test their contribution to the phenomena of the hot-electron effect. Figure 8-26 is taken from an investigation[77] of the effect of pressure on the current-voltage relation in germanium at high applied fields. It is seen that at the top pressure there is no saturation of the J-V characteristic of the kind evident at the lowest pressure. This feature, and others, can be explained plausibly in terms of the motion of the different conduction-band minima discussed previously and the interband-scattering theory, modified to take account of the details of scattering at high electron energies. We shall not go

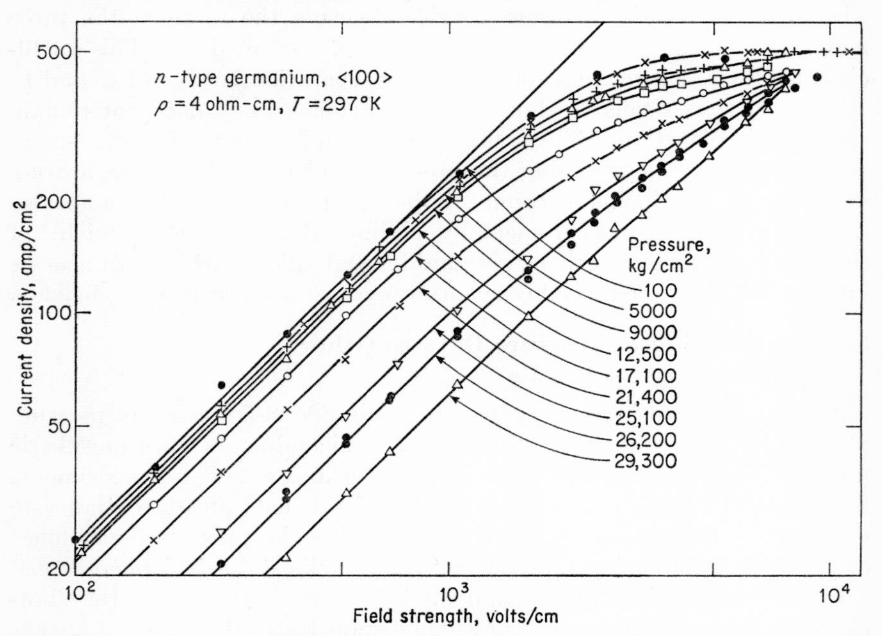

Fig. 8-26 Variation with pressure of the J-V characteristic for n-type germanium illustrating the influence of the (100) minima. (*Koenig, Nathan, Paul, and Smith.*[77])

into the details, but it can be said that the pressure measurements contribute positively to the understanding of a subject whose general features are well known, but whose details are hard to establish.

A second example can be drawn from the physics of tunnel diodes. The band structure for such a diode is shown in Fig. 8-27. Here the doping is so high that the p- and n-type material on either side of the junction is degenerate. The potential drop across the junction takes place in a distance of the order of 100 Å, so that the junction electric field is very large. Electrons can then tunnel (quantum-mechanically) in either direction across the junction. Application of a bias gives forward and reverse current-voltage curves of the form shown in Fig. 8-28.

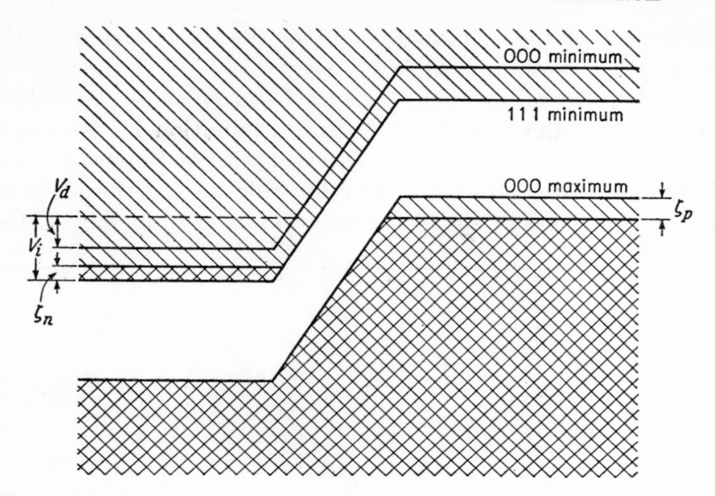

Fig. 8-27 Band structure as a function of position in a tunnel diode.

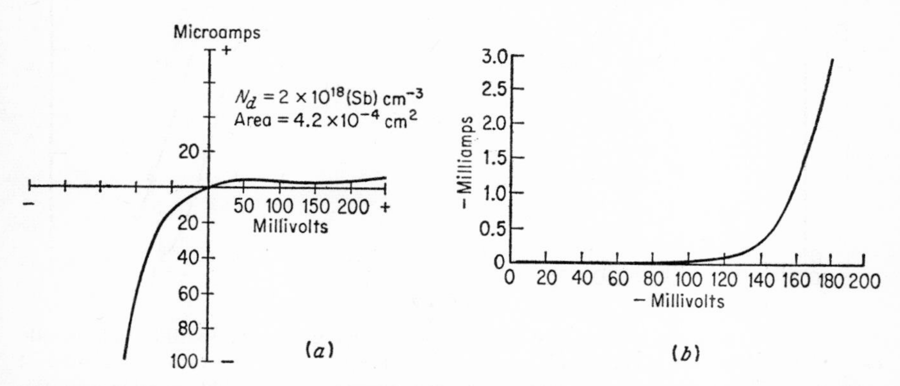

Fig. 8-28 Current-voltage characteristic of a germanium tunnel diode showing the transition from indirect to direct tunneling at 0.13-volt reverse bias. The curves were taken at 77°K. The p-type impurity is gallium at 8×10^{18} cm^{-3}. (a) and (b) are the same specimen with different scales. The peak in the forward direction is less pronounced for this diode than for more heavily doped units.

The pressure dependence of this J-V characteristic has been determined in several sets of experiments.[78] At this point we draw attention to

[78] S. L. Miller, M. I. Nathan, and A. C. Smith, Pressure Dependence of the Current-Voltage Characteristics of Esaki Diodes, *Phys. Rev. Letters*, vol. 4, pp. 60–62, 1960; M. I. Nathan, S. L. Miller, and L. Finegold, Pressure Dependence of the Reverse Characteristic of a Germanium Esaki Diode, *Bull. Am. Phys. Soc.*, vol. 5, p. 265, 1960; M. I. Nathan and W. Paul, The Pressure Dependence of Tunneling in Esaki Diodes, pp. 209–211 in "Proceedings of the International Conference on Semiconductor Physics, Prague, 1960," Publishing House of the Czechoslovak Academy of Sciences, Prague, 1961.

only one aspect of them: measurement of the reverse characteristic in cases such as germanium. At low reverse bias, electrons from the top of the Fermi distribution in the valence band (p side) can only tunnel into the states at the top of the Fermi distribution in the conduction band (n side) if they simultaneously interact with an impurity or a lattice vibration. This is caused by a selection rule on the tunneling process requiring conservation of the electron k vector on tunneling. However,

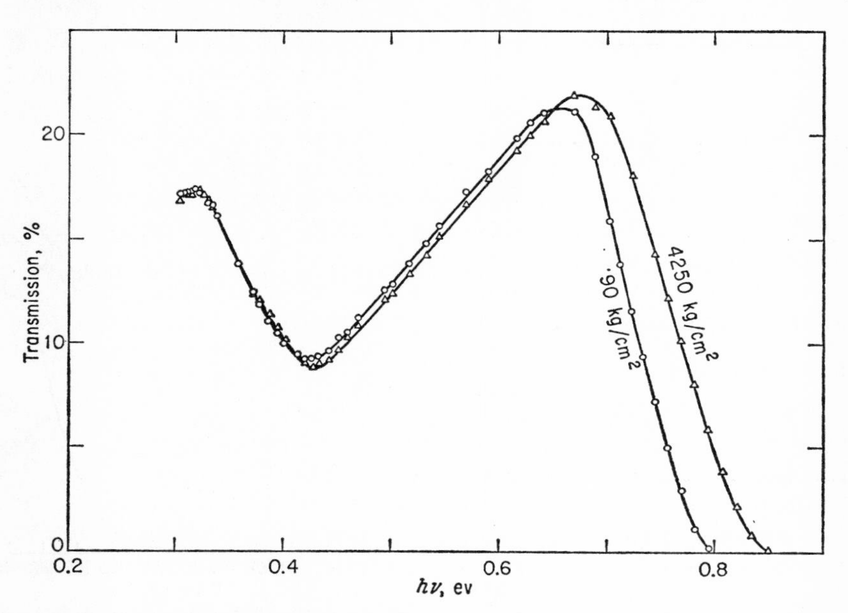

Fig. 8-29 Transmission curves at two pressures for a germanium-gallium phosphide sandwich, illustrating the small pressure coefficient of the transmission near 4 microns. The shift of the germanium edge is in agreement with that found in previous work.[32] The magnitude of the germanium-edge shift (not the energy-gap change) is $\sim 9 \times 10^{-6}$ ev/bar; if the transmission minimum in gallium phosphide were due to a $\Delta_1 \rightarrow \Gamma_1$ transition, its shift would be about 14×10^{-6} ev/bar. See reference 45. (*Zallen and Paul.*)

when the reverse bias is increased above about 0.13 volts, a large increase in tunneling current occurs, presumably caused by direct, unaided tunneling from the valence band $k = (000)$ states ($\Gamma_{25'}$) to the conduction band $k = (000)$ states ($\Gamma_{2'}$) (see Fig. 8-1). Nathan, Miller, and Finegold[78] measured the change with pressure of the reverse bias at which this current increase appeared and found therefrom the pressure coefficient of the energy of the higher ($\Gamma_{2'}$) minimum. This pressure coefficient had been determined otherwise, so that the experiment confirmed the identification of the processes which were occurring. In this particular case, such proof was probably unnecessary, but in general, the positions of higher minima would not be as well established as was the $\Gamma_{2'}$ minimum in germanium.

A third example is afforded by work of Zallen on an absorption peak occurring in n-type gallium phosphide.[45] This peak, illustrated in Fig. 8-29, has been assigned to transitions from the lowest conduction-band state (X_1) into a higher state at Γ_1.[79] If this is correct, and the pressure coefficients of the energies of the states X_1 and Γ_1 are those determined for these states in other compounds (see Table 8-4), the pressure coefficient of the energy difference between X_1 and Γ_1 should be approximately 15×10^{-6} ev/bar. Figure 8-29 shows the transmission characteristic of a sandwich of gallium phosphide and germanium; the germanium is included to illustrate the shift of the germanium edge with pressure at half the above rate. It is evident that the shift of the transmission minimum corresponding to the inter-conduction-band transition is an order of magnitude smaller than predicted. This discrepancy is not yet resolved, but the pressure data seem to establish that X_1-Γ_1 transitions are not the cause of the absorption.

8-5 Prospect

The text of this article has described a much smaller field of research than may be envisaged from its title. This has been a result partly of the background and experience of the authors and partly of a realistic estimate of the present distribution of endeavor. In this section we shall first attempt to answer three pertinent questions that relate particularly closely to the work so far reviewed and then discuss more generally the role of high pressure in semiconductor research.

The questions are:

1. What contributions have the present investigations made to the understanding of the properties of semiconductors at atmospheric pressure?

2. What contribution could they make if the measurements were extended to cover more parameters, through the completion of different types of experiments?

3. To what extent will measurements in the very high range of pressure contribute to our understanding of semiconductors at atmospheric pressure?

We claim that the host of measurements on the germaniumlike semiconductors have made a positive contribution to the understanding of these materials at atmospheric pressure.

In a sense, every pressure measurement, by providing information

[79] W. G. Spitzer, M. Gershenzon, C. J. Frosch, and D. F. Gibbs, Optical Absorption in n-type Gallium Phosphide, *J. Phys. Chem. Solids*, vol. 11, pp. 339–341, 1959.

on the effect of a change in a basic parameter, helps us to understand solids. If the understanding we demand involves a description in terms of less-than-fundamental or even phenomenological parameters, such as one-electron band structure, average mobility, average lifetime—a viewpoint that is usually adequate for an appreciation of phenomena such as optical absorption and electrical conduction under the normal conditions of our environment—then the understanding afforded by an isolated pressure experiment is not apparent.

In fact, if one excludes such fringe cases as determination of a phase transition involving one semiconducting phase, most isolated pressure investigations on poorly understood semiconductors have contributed practically nothing to our understanding of the properties of these materials at atmospheric pressure. Thus, for example, the unpublished pressure measurements of Paul and Soule and of Deutsch tell us little about the conductivity of graphite that we did not know already.

The contribution of a single measurement to understanding is, however, disproportionately increased when more measurements are made to amplify and clarify the first and to dissect out of it the volume dependence of some basic parameters.

Thus, first of all, the pressure measurements allow differentiation between that part of the temperature coefficient of a parameter that is caused by lattice expansion only and any additional contribution that is an explicit effect of temperature. Many of the parameters of semiconductors which are ordinarily measured have such an explicit temperature dependence; in Table 8-5 we show, as illustration of this point, a selection of pressure and temperature coefficients for germanium and silicon taken from a review by Paul and Brooks.[80] There is not as yet a quantitative theory of these effects of electron-phonon interaction.

In the germaniumlike semiconductors, which are by far the set on which most work has been done, the experiments showed that different parts of the energy-band structure changed differently with hydrostatic stress and that a large fraction of the experimental data on the effects of pressure could be explained self-consistently when these changes had been established. However, when this degree of understanding had been reached, it was quite apparent that positive contributions were being made to our appreciation of the properties at hydrostatic pressure—and that these contributions were also positive for those who demand understanding only from the phenomenological viewpoint.

An excellent example of this type contribution is found in the case of gallium antimonide, which we have already discussed to some extent. In this compound the lowest conduction-band minimum is of the (000) (Γ_1) type, and the next lowest is of the (111) (L_1) type. Their separation

[80] W. Paul and H. Brooks, to be published in "Progress in Semiconductors."

Table 8-5 Dependence of Parameters for Germanium and Silicon on Pressure and Temperature

Quantity	$\left(\frac{\partial X}{\partial P}\right)_T$	$-\frac{\alpha}{\beta}\left(\frac{\partial X}{\partial P}\right)_T$ [a]	$\left(\frac{\partial X}{\partial T}\right)_P$
Germanium:			
Energy gap to (111) minima	$+5 \times 10^{-6}$ ev-cm²/kg [b]	-0.7×10^{-4} ev/°K	$\sim -4 \times 10^{-4}$ ev/°K [c]
Energy gap to (000) minimum	$+1.3 \times 10^{-5}$ ev-cm²/kg [d]	-1.8×10^{-4} ev/°K	$\sim -4 \times 10^{-4}$ ev/°K [e]
Average electron effective mass	$\left\|(1/m^*)(\partial m^*/\partial P)_T\right\| \approx 5 \times 10^{-6}$ cm²/kg [f]	0.7×10^{-4} °K⁻¹	$(1/m^*)(\partial m/\partial T)_P = +3.5 \times 10^{-4}$ °K⁻¹ [g]
Dielectric constant ($\epsilon_0 = 16$)	-19×10^{-6} cm²/kg [h]	$+2.7 \times 10^{-4}$ °K⁻¹	$+2.2 \times 10^{-3}$ °K⁻¹ [h]
Silicon:			
Energy gap to (100) minima	-1.5×10^{-6} ev-cm²/kg [i]	$+0.19 \times 10^{-4}$ ev/°K⁻¹	$\sim -2.5 \times 10^{-4}$ ev °K⁻¹ [c]
Average electron effective mass	$\left\|(1/m^*)(\partial m^*/\partial P)_T\right\| \approx 5 \times 10^{-6}$ cm²/kg [j]	0.6×10^{-4} °K⁻¹	$(1/m^*)(\partial m^*/\partial T)_P = +4.5 \times 10^{-4}$ °K⁻¹ [g]
Dielectric constant ($\epsilon_0 = 12$)	-4.8×10^{-6} cm²/kg [h]	$+0.6 \times 10^{-4}$ °K⁻¹	$+1.0 \times 10^{-3}$ °K⁻¹ [h]

[a] M. E. Straumanis and E. J. Aka, *J. Appl. Phys.*, vol. 23, p. 330, 1952; P. W. Bridgman, *Proc. Am. Acad. Arts Sci.*, vol. 77, p. 187, 1949.
[b] W. Paul and H. Brooks, *Phys. Rev.*, vol. 94, p. 1128, 1954.
[c] J. R. Haynes, M. Lax, and W. F. Flood, *J. Phys. Chem. Solids*, vol. 8, p. 329, 1959.
[d] M. Cardona and W. Paul, *J. Phys. Chem. Solids*, vol. 17, p. 138, 1960.
[e] S. Zwerdling, L. M. Roth, and B. Lax, *J. Phys. Chem. Solids*, vol. 8, p. 397, 1959.
[f] M. I. Nathan, thesis, Harvard University, Cambridge, Mass., 1958, Report HP 1 of Division of Engineering and Applied Physics, Harvard University.
[g] M. Cardona, W. Paul, and H. Brooks, in "Solid State Physics in Electronics and Telecommunications," vol. 1, M. Desirant and J. L. Michiels (eds.), Academic Press, Inc., New York, 1960; *J. Phys. Chem. Solids*, vol. 8, p. 204, 1959; *Helv. Phys. Acta*, vol. 33, p. 329, 1960.
[h] M. Cardona, W. Paul, and H. Brooks, "Solid State Physics in Electronics and Telecommunications," vol. 1, M. Desirant and J. L. Michiels (eds.), Academic Press, Inc., New York, 1960; *J. Phys. Chem. Solids*, vol. 8, p. 204, 1959.
[i] W. Paul and G. L. Pearson, *Phys. Rev.*, vol. 98, p. 1755, 1955.
[j] A. C. Smith, thesis, Harvard University, Cambridge, Mass., 1958, Report HP 2 of Division of Engineering and Applied Physics, Harvard University.

is a scant 0.08 ev, so that, for the average density of donor impurities found in n-type gallium antimonide, at room temperature, some of the electrons are to be found in the (111) minima. The number is, in fact, quite high, even though $\Delta E = 0.08$ ev $\approx 3\,kT$, because the (000) mass is low and this minimum has few states, which are rapidly filled, associated with it. Nevertheless, most measurements aimed at examining the properties of the conduction-band electrons in order to determine their location in k space will discover only those at the (000) position. For example, the magnetoresistance measurements bias heavily the contributions from electrons of high mobility (and thus of low mass). Experiments at high impurity densities and high temperatures show the presence of carriers in high minima, but such experiments determine their k vectors and other properties only roughly. The application of pressure brings the higher (111) minima below the (000) minimum and thus allows examination of the properties of the (111) minima. When these properties are extrapolated back to atmospheric pressure, a better theory for the small but significant contribution of carriers in these minima can be derived.

Other examples are furnished in Sec. 8-4, which we carefully separated from the main review because its investigations were applications based on pressure results rather than quests after pressure variations of fundamental parameters. Thus these cases allow us to answer our first question concerning the contribution of pressure measurements to the understanding of semiconductors at atmospheric pressure in the affirmative. However, it is also clear that a fair number of separate measurements were necessary before positive gain was apparent. The similarities in properties, including pressure properties, of all the Group 4, Group 3-5, and Group 2-6 compounds have meant, in fact, that a truly large number of pressure measurements has been taken on the type of band structure they possess in common.

This brings us to our second question, which really has two parts to it: the first concerns what additional information might be gleaned from more measurements on the already well-investigated semiconductors; the second concerns what initial information might be obtained from further experiments on those semiconductors so far subjected only to isolated measurements.

The answer to the first part is, we believe, that more sophisticated experiments on the Group 4 and Group 3-5 semiconductors may well give vital new information immediately. We already have such a store of pertinent pressure data that there is a fair chance that the pressure coefficients of single parameters can immediately be isolated. An example of such experiments being carried out is the reflectivity measurement; one possible new experiment is the remeasurement of magneto-optical absorption at high pressures.

The answer to the second part of the question is that, starting "from scratch," a number of experiments is usually necessary before the dependence on pressure of single basic parameters is obtainable. Fortunately, however, the prognosis for the immediate contribution that pressure measurements may make to other semiconductors is more favorable than this might imply. In the first place, extrapolations concerning the order of magnitude of changes may be made from the germaniumlike semiconductors. In the second place, the basic theory of all semiconductors has advanced, so that more immediately informative experiments may be planned. And, in the third place, many of the techniques of experiment and interpretation have been worked out. In summary, we are hopeful that a much smaller number of experiments than have been necessary heretofore should suffice to establish models of behavior under pressure complete enough to be useful in the understanding of systems such as lead sulfide, selenide, and telluride, the selenium-tellurium system, the other elemental semiconductors, and the more complicated semiconductors such as Bi_2Te_3 which still nevertheless probably possess "band-type" conduction.

What of question 3, concerning the extension of such measurements to still higher pressures, in the range of hundreds of kilobars?

With a few exceptions, measurements of semiconductors in the pressure range above 30 kilobars have been carried out by Drickamer's group at the University of Illinois. Drickamer has measured the optical absorption spectra of the Group 4, Group 3-5, and Group 2-6 compounds to pressures above 100 kilobars. Where comparison is possible, his results agree with those of investigators working in the lower pressure ranges. The accuracy of pressure coefficients has not been improved by the extension of range because of the attendant decrease in optical resolution and precision of pressure calibration. Moreover, changes in compressibility with pressure, which are not known quantitatively, prevent quantitative comparison with pressure coefficients determined at low pressures. These objections to the utility of the very-high-pressure investigations are well taken if the investigator at lower pressures already knows precisely what his experiments are measuring. They are completely invalid in physical situations which require, preferably first, a panoramic view of the gross effects of pressure—a wide-field, low-magnification view—which may then be followed by a precise examination of the details of the behavior in a smaller pressure range. Thus, although the resistivity measurements of Paul and Brooks on germanium contained all the information necessary to establish a higher set of minima that could ultimately dominate the conductivity (at sufficiently high pressures) and could be analyzed quite exactly to give accurate estimates of the parameters of the upper minima, it took them considerable time and thought to reach the correct conclusions; how much easier when the data of Fig. 8-17 are presented, demonstrating ad oculos that very-high-pressure behavior is *qualitatively* different from that at lower pressure and that the most obvious postulate is the existence of other minima?

We conclude that the most profitable scheme is a combination of the relatively low (hydrostatic) pressure data and the very high (quasi-hydrostatic) pressure measurements. It would be desirable to extend the range of hydrostatic pressures, say, to 50 kilobars. Beyond that, since we suspect that the compressibilities and the dilatational coefficients of the band edges may change, the present type of quasi-hydrostatic measurement is entirely adequate for its most useful purpose of mapping out the gross behavior of the energy minima.

This, we hope, answers the questions posed near the beginning of this section. We now want to expand our horizon and discuss in more general terms the role of pressure in semiconductor research.

Most of the work described has been on the high-mobility semiconductors—substances in which the electron mean free path extends over several interatomic distances. Semiconduction, loosely defined as a condition in which the conductivity increases with temperature (not, of course, a good general definition for impurity semiconduction), is more ubiquitous than this. In substances like nickel oxide, the conduction apparently proceeds through the electron's hopping from one site to a neighbor. The interatomic spacing should be an important parameter in this process, and pressure experiments on such substances should therefore give vital information concerning it.

Little work has been done on the effect of pressure on semiconduction in organic semiconductors, although a start has been made.[81] Here the crystal structure is very complicated indeed, and the conduction process is not well understood. If electron hopping is involved, then the high compressibility of many of these substances may cause very drastic effects of pressure on conductivity.

We have said relatively little about semiconduction at very high pressure, except as it taught us about low-pressure behavior. Much of the matter in the physical universe, including the earth, exists under very high pressure; it is possible that some semiconducting form of olivine is present in the earth's mantle. Scattered pressure investigations on olivine have been carried out, but the results have not been definitive. This is perhaps not too surprising when we realize that the process of semiconduction at atmospheric pressure has not been established. It is not known, for example, what bands (if any) are involved, or whether

[81] H. Inokuchi and H. Akamata, Electrical Conductivity of Organic Semiconductors, pp. 93–141 in F. Seitz and D. Turnbull (eds.), "Advances in Solid State Physics," vol. 12, Academic Press, Inc., New York, 1961.

the conduction involves discrete electron jumps between ions. There is, therefore, a great challenge in this whole field which has not yet been adequately met.

We have hardly mentioned the possibility of the synthesis of new semiconducting forms. That this is possible has been demonstrated by the synthesis of black phosphorus by Bridgman; we should mention in passing that it has been shown that this material can be produced at atmospheric pressure.[82] The growth of diamond at high pressure and temperature offers the possibility of selective doping that might make diamond a reasonably valuable high-temperature transistor or phosphor.

This brings us to the question of the use of these high-pressure effects in devices. It was clear some time ago that semiconductors may be used as very efficient strain transducers, relying on a very large effect of non-hydrostatic pressure to alter the average mobilities of current carriers. The large pressure effect on the fundamental energy gap and on the ionization energy of deep-lying impurities may also be utilizable in sensing pressure variations, especially in liquids. Most such detectors in the past have relied on changes in carrier mobilities. However, it is quite clear that the more sensitive mode of operation is at a temperature at which carrier-density changes can be caused by the pressure. For some purposes the extreme temperature sensitivity in this mode may be a drawback; this can probably be overcome by using the pressure effect on the tunnel diode, operated where its temperature sensitivity is very low. Yet another example of possible device application is afforded by the shifts of absorption and photoconductivity edges with pressure. In substances whose energy gap decreases with pressure (e.g., lead sulfide), the wavelength of maximum sensitivity may be tunable by hydrostatic or quasi-hydrostatic pressure. These ideas, which are only some of several possibilities for devices, have not to our knowledge been tested.

In summary, we hope we have demonstrated that the pressure measurements carried out so far have been useful at several levels of understanding of the behavior of solids, and of semiconduction in particular. We see no reason why similar experiments on other semiconducting systems should not be equally fruitful. There is no difficulty in pointing out semiconductors that look qualitatively different from those so far intensively investigated, and these appear to be interesting, challenging, and informative. Very-high-pressure research can be used to complement that at lower pressures and can be integrated with it, in addition to providing new phenomena of its own. And finally, it does not seem to be outside possibility that devices of limited but decided usefulness may be the result of such investigation.

[82] H. Krebs, H. Weitz, and K. H. Worms, Die katalytische Darstellung des schwarzen Phosphorus, *Z. anorg. u. allgem. Chem.*, vol. 280, pp. 119–133, 1955.

9

Magnetic Resonance in Solids under High Pressure

George Benedek

Department of Physics
Massachusetts Institute of Technology
Cambridge, Massachusetts

9-1 Introduction

The first magnetic-resonance experiment under high pressure was proposed to me by Prof. E. M. Purcell in the fall of 1952. Purcell had noted that in all Bridgman's high-pressure experiments, one of the most striking changes was to be found in the viscosity of liquids. Bridgman had observed that on compression to 10 kilobars the viscosity of liquids increased by factors as large as 100. Previous experiments by Bloembergen, Purcell, and Pound[1] had shown that the nuclear-relaxation times of liquids were inversely proportional to the viscosities. In their experiments the viscosity of the liquid was changed by changing the temperature or the composition of the liquid. It was by no means obvious that this inverse proportionality would be maintained for viscosity changes produced by high pressure, because the application of pressure could be expected to inhibit primarily the translational diffusion, while leaving

[1] N. Bloembergen, E. M. Purcell, and R. V. Pound, Relaxation Effects in Nuclear Magnetic Resonance Absorption, *Phys. Rev.*, vol. 73, pp. 679–712, 1948.

the rotational diffusion of the molecules less affected. Thus it seemed worthwhile to investigate the effect of pressure on the nuclear-relaxation times of liquids. However, two experimental problems had to be solved. The first was the problem of developing a high-pressure electrical plug which would permit the introduction of radio-frequency power into the high-pressure region. The second was the problem of finding a nonmagnetic material capable of containing pressures of the order of 10 kilobars.

Prof. Bridgman pointed the direction in which to proceed on both these problems, and in so doing opened the door not only to the magnetic-resonance experiments which I shall describe, but also to studies of galvanomagnetic effects in solids under high pressure.[2] In Fig. 9-1 is shown the radio-frequency plug, which the reader will recognize as nearly identical with the electrical plug that Bridgman used for d-c measurements.

Bridgman also was responsible for the use of beryllium copper as the material for a high-pressure vessel. At his suggestion, a small BeCu test cylinder was prepared and tested using indium as a pressure-transmitting medium. The first test was conducted in a corner of Bridgman's laboratory by Mr. Charles Chase and myself, with Bridgman watching out of the corner of his eye. Impatient with our cautious increase of the pressure, Bridgman walked over and without a word manned the hand pump himself. Within a few minutes he increased the pressure inside the cylinder to 18 kilobars without cylinder failure. At this point Bridgman stopped pumping with the comment, "That looks like pretty good stuff you've got there," and walked off. This was the end of the test and the solution of the problem of the nonmagnetic high-pressure vessel. Later experiments[3] showed that BeCu could be taken to 30 kilobars using liquid pressure transmitters. Figure 9-1 shows the high-pressure cylinder used in the first magnetic-resonance experiment under pressure.[4] Its great length permitted it to be hung from the bottom of a press into the air gap of an electromagnet. In Fig. 9-2 is shown a high-pressure cylinder and rf electrical plug now used in magnetic-resonance experiments. The flexible stainless-steel tubing connection which was developed by Paul and Warschauer permits the use of the very small pressure cylinder.

[2] G. Benedek, W. Paul, and H. Brooks, Conductivity, Hall Effect, and Magnetoresistance on *n*-type Germanium, and Their Dependence on Pressure, *Phys. Rev.*, vol. 100, pp. 1129–1139, 1956.

[3] W. Paul, G. Benedek, and D. Warschauer, Nonmagnetic High-pressure Vessels, *Rev. Sci. Instr.*, vol. 30, pp. 874–880, 1959.

[4] G. Benedek and E. M. Purcell, Nuclear Magnetic Resonance in Liquids under High Pressure, *J. Chem. Phys.*, vol. 22, pp. 2003–2012, 1954.

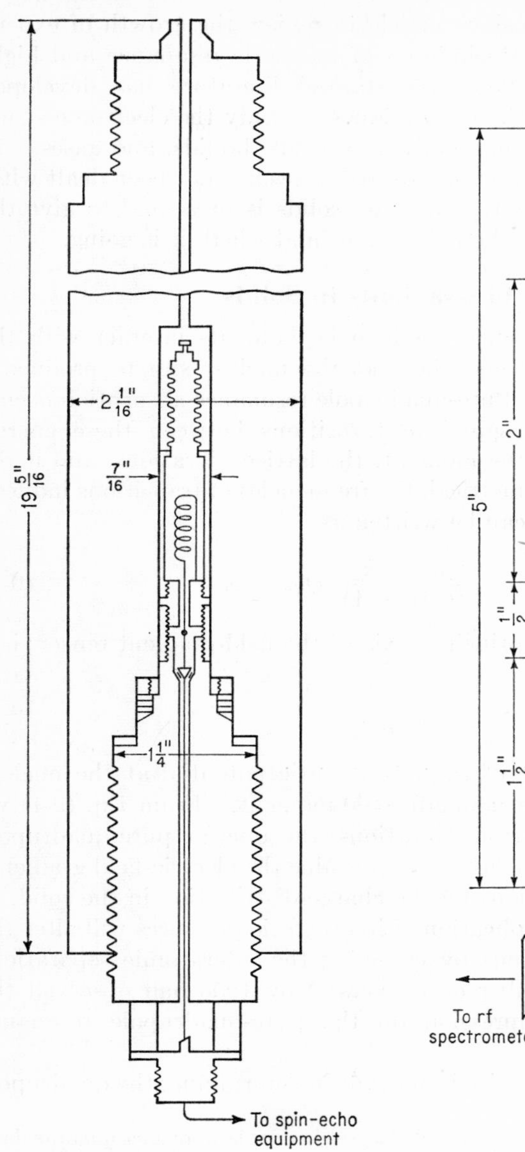

Fig. 9-1 Early design of a radio-frequency electrical plug and a high-pressure beryllium copper bomb.

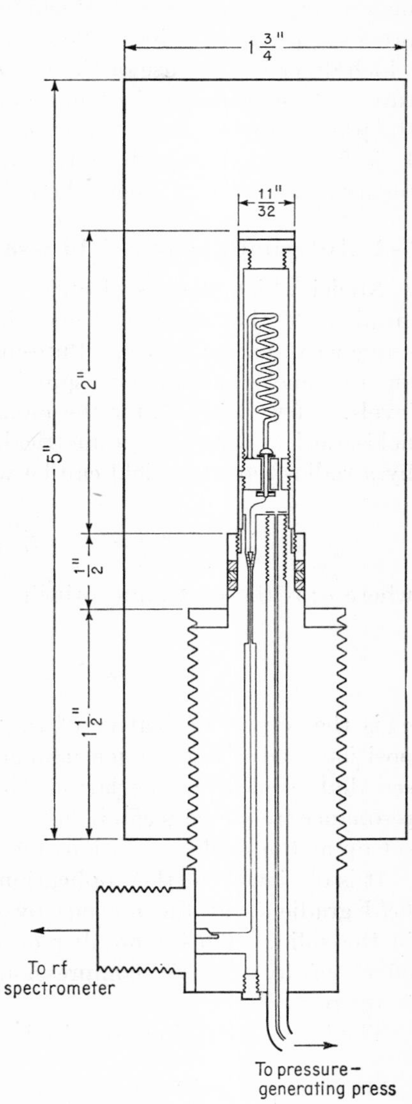

Fig. 9-2 Recent design of a radio-frequency plug and bomb assembly. Note the small dimensions of the bomb and the use of a single lead-in plug for both the rf power and pressure-transmitting medium.

It is the purpose of this short article to review the growth of experiments employing the joint techniques of magnetic resonance and high-pressure physics. Since 1953 a substantial literature has developed which describes the use of these techniques to study the electronic structure and molecular and atomic motion of solids, liquids, and gases. In the present review the work on liquids and gases has not been dealt with. It is hoped that enough of the work on solids is presented to give the reader some sense of where the field is now and where it is going.

9-2 Internal Electric-field Gradients in Solids

Nuclei which possess electric quadrupole moments interact with the gradient of the internal electric field at the nuclear site to produce a sequence of energy levels. Pure-quadrupole resonance absorption occurs at frequencies which correspond to transitions between these energy levels. If we neglect, for the moment, the lattice vibrations, and if the field-gradient tensor is symmetrical, the frequencies of transitions induced by a radio-frequency field can be written as

$$\nu_{m_z \leftarrow m_z - 1} = \frac{3/2\, m_z - 3/2}{2I(2I - 1)} eQq_0 = \nu_0 \tag{9-1}$$

where q_0 is the maximum principal axis of the field-gradient tensor; i.e.,

$$q_0 = \frac{\partial^2 V}{\partial z^2} \tag{9-2}$$

q_0 is the second derivative of the electrostatic potential at the nuclear position, and Q is the nuclear quadrupole moment. From Eq. (9-1) we see that, neglecting the lattice vibrations, the nuclear pure-quadrupole resonance frequencies can be used to determine the electric-field gradients set up at the nuclear positions by the charge distribution in the solid.

It is obvious that the application of hydrostatic pressures will alter the field gradients at the nucleus by changing the interatomic separations in the solid. Thus a number of workers[5–8] by 1955 had observed the effect of hydrostatic compression on the pure-quadrupole resonance frequency.

The lattice vibrations are also important in determining the quadrupole

[5] D. Dautreppe and B. Dreyfus, Effet de la pression sur la résonance quadropolaire nucléaire, *Compt. rend.*, vol. 241, pp. 795–798, 1955.

[6] C. Dean and E. Lindstrand, Polymorphism of Para-Dichlorobenzene, *J. Chem. Phys.*, vol. 24, p. 1114, 1956.

[7] R. Livingston, private communication.

[8] G. Benedek, N. Bloembergen, and T. Kushida, Effect of Hydrostatic Pressure on the Nuclear Quadrupole Coupling in Crystalline Fields, *Bull. Am. Phys. Soc.*, series II, vol. 1, p. 11, 1956.

resonance frequency. Following the observation that the pure-quadrupole resonance frequency ν was a strong function of the temperature, Bayer[9] produced a simple theory to explain this effect.

In the presence of lattice vibrations the components of the field-gradient tensor ϕ_{ij} in a fixed coordinate system will fluctuate. This fluctuation is at a higher frequency than that corresponding to the energy levels of the system, so that only the average value of these fluctuating components will enter into a determination of the energy. Bayer considered a simple model of the vibration in which the field-gradient tensor components did not change in magnitude, but the tensor as a whole oscillated in an angle θ around some equilibrium direction. In such a model the value of q_0 is reduced owing to the averaging process to $q_0(1 - \frac{3}{2}\overline{\theta^2})$, assuming $\theta \ll \pi/2$. In Bayer's picture the observed decrease in ν as T increases was due to the increase in the amplitude of the thermal vibrations. The Bayer theory was successful in qualitatively explaining the observed temperature variation of ν, but failed quantitatively. Kushida later generalized[10] Bayer's theory to include the effects of all the modes of vibration of the lattice and was able to show that the resonance frequency could be written as

$$\nu = \nu_0 \left(1 - \frac{3}{4} \sum_i \frac{\xi_i^{0^2}}{\Theta_i}\right) \tag{9-3}$$

where ξ_i^0 is the amplitude of the ith normal mode of lattice vibration and $1/\Theta_i$ is essentially a coefficient which describes the effect that a particular mode of vibration has on the magnitude and orientation of the field-gradient tensor. For simple geometries Θ_i can be interpreted as the moment of inertia of the particular mode of motion. Since the amplitude of the ith normal mode is determined by the mean energy of the corresponding oscillator, i.e.,

$$\frac{1}{2}\omega^2 \xi_i^{0^2} = h\nu_i \left(\frac{1}{2} + \frac{1}{e^{h\nu_i/kT} - 1}\right) \tag{9-4}$$

it is again possible to predict the temperature variation. But even Kushida's generalization of the Bayer theory was incapable of predicting the observed temperature variation quantitatively. The reason was that neither theory included the effect of thermal expansion on the magnitude of the components of ϕ_{ij}. To put it more quantitatively, if we consider a temperature range greater than some minimum temperature $T_{\min}$, then all those modes of vibration of frequency $h\nu_m < kT_{\min}$

[9] H. Bayer, Zur Theorie der Spin-Gitterrelaxation in Molekülkristallen, *Z. Physik*, vol. 130, pp. 227–238, 1951.

[10] T. Kushida, *J. Sci. Hiroshima Univ.*, vol. A19, p. 327, 1955.

produce a temperature dependence of the form

$$\nu = \nu_0\left(1 + bT + \frac{c}{T}\right) \tag{9-5a}$$

$$b = \frac{-3k}{2}\sum_{1}^{m}\frac{1}{\Theta_i\omega_i^2} = -\frac{3k}{2}\,m\left\langle\frac{1}{\omega^2\Theta}\right\rangle \tag{9-5b}$$

$$c = \frac{-\hbar^2}{8k}\sum_{1}^{m}\frac{1}{\Theta_i} = \frac{-\hbar^2}{8k}\,m\left\langle\frac{1}{\Theta}\right\rangle \tag{9-5c}$$

The minimum temperature is chosen high enough so that the contribution of frequencies higher than ω_m is small (high ω modes contribute less because of the $1/\omega$ dependence of ξ_i^{02}). From the definitions of b and c it is seen that they contain information as to the vibration frequencies and effective moment of inertia of various vibration modes of the lattice. ν_0 contains information as to the magnitude of the principal axis of the field-gradient tensor $\partial^2V_e/\partial z^2$. The failure of previous attempts to fit Eq. (9-5a) to the experimental data was because ν_0, b, and c were considered as constants independent of the volume of the solid. In fact, of course, they are not. One can estimate roughly, using $\delta\nu_0/\nu_0 \sim \delta V/V$, that between $0 < T < 300$ the frequency should change approximately 2 percent owing to the volume effect alone. Also if ν_0, b, and c were independent of volume, the pressure dependence of the resonance frequency would be zero. Actually, though, looking at Fig. 9-3, which shows measurements of ν versus pressure for Cu_2O,[11] we see that this is far from true. To apply the theory of Kushida correctly

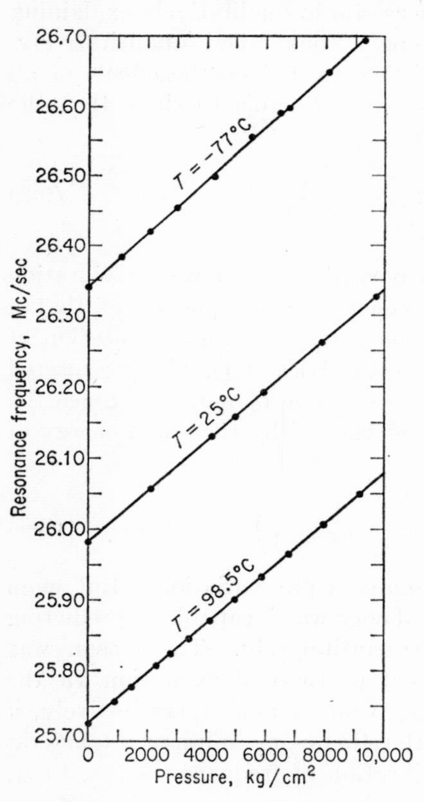

Fig. 9-3 Pressure dependence of the pure-quadrupole resonance frequency for Cu_2O at three temperatures.

[11] T. Kushida, G. B. Benedek, and N. Bloembergen, Dependence of Pure Quadrupole Resonance Frequency on Pressure and Temperature, *Phys. Rev.*, vol. 104, pp. 1364–1377, 1956.

to the experimental data, it is necessary to plot ν-versus-volume isotherms for a range of temperatures. It is presumed that a knowledge of V as a function of P for various temperatures is known. Then at each volume ν_0, b, and c can be determined. To check whether the temperature variation at $P = 0$ can be explained, one must determine the volume at each temperature for which $P = 0$ and put into Eq. (9-5*a*) the corresponding values of ν_0, b, and c. If this procedure is carried out, it is possible to explain the temperature variation of the resonance frequency quantitatively.

But notice that here we have also obtained the volume dependence of the internal field gradients from $\nu_0(V)$, and from $b(V)$ and $c(V)$ we have the volume dependence of the vibration frequencies and their magnitudes. This is rather detailed information which casts considerable light on the internal electric fields and the lattice vibrations.

The analysis described above has been carried out[11] for three solids, Cu_2O, $KClO_3$, and paradichlorobenzene, in experiments to 10 kilobars using temperatures as low as $-77°C$ and as high as $100°C$. The Cu^{63} nucleus was observed in Cu_2O; the Cl^{35} nucleus was studied in $KClO_3$ and p-$C_6H_4Cl_2$.

In Cu_2O it was found that ν_0 varies reciprocally with the volume $[\nu(V) = \nu_0(V/V_0)^{-0.96 \pm 0.04}]$. This is precisely what one would expect if the neighbors set up a coulomb $(1/r^2)$ electric field at the nucleus, for in such a case $q_0 \propto (\partial/\partial r)(1/r^2) \propto 1/V$. This fact confirms the belief that Cu_2O is an ionic crystal. Furthermore, from the volume dependence of b and c it was found that $\gamma = \langle -\partial \ln \omega_i/\partial \ln V\rangle$ is negative; that is, the vibration frequencies decrease with decreasing volume. This result is not too surprising when it is remembered that the thermal-expansion coefficient for Cu_2O is negative in certain temperature ranges, thus suggesting a negative Grüneisen constant for certain normal modes of vibration. In $KClO_3$, q_0 changes from a $(V/V_0)^{-0.022}$ dependence at $V/V_0 = 0.98$ to a $(V/V_0)^{-0.028}$ at $V/V_0 = 1.06$. In this substance the field gradient arises primarily from the ClO_3 covalent bond with a contribution of several percent from the potassium ions. The weakness of the observed volume dependence of q_0 is consistent with the view that the compression of the crystal changes the K^+ and ClO_3^- distances without appreciably affecting the dimensions of the ClO_3 group. In $KClO_3$, γ has the reasonable value of about 1.8 (1.4 at $V/V_0 = 0.98$ and 2.2 at $V/V_0 = 1.06$). The experimental results on paradichlorobenzene are so unusual that they are given in Figs. 9-4 to 9-6. These data contain, in the same specimen, two phenomena dear to the heart of the high-pressure physicist: the presence of polymorphic transitions and a maximum in the ν-versus-pressure curve. At room temperature and atmospheric pressure the α phase is observed, its frequency increasing with pressure until at

1.6 kilobars the line quickly disappears. The line is found again 436 kc higher, with intensity and line width about the same as in the α phase. This new phase can be identified as a "γ phase."[12] On further increase in pressure, the ν-versus-pressure curve flattens, until at 8.5 kilobars there is a suggestion that $d\nu/dp$ may become negative. With a decrease in pressure, the ν phase can be followed below 1.6 kilobars until at about 0.750 kilobar it disappears, to reappear once again in a β phase[12] 27 kc below the α phase. The β phase is metastable relative to the α phase at room temperature, returning to it in a time which is very sensitive to the pressure.[11]

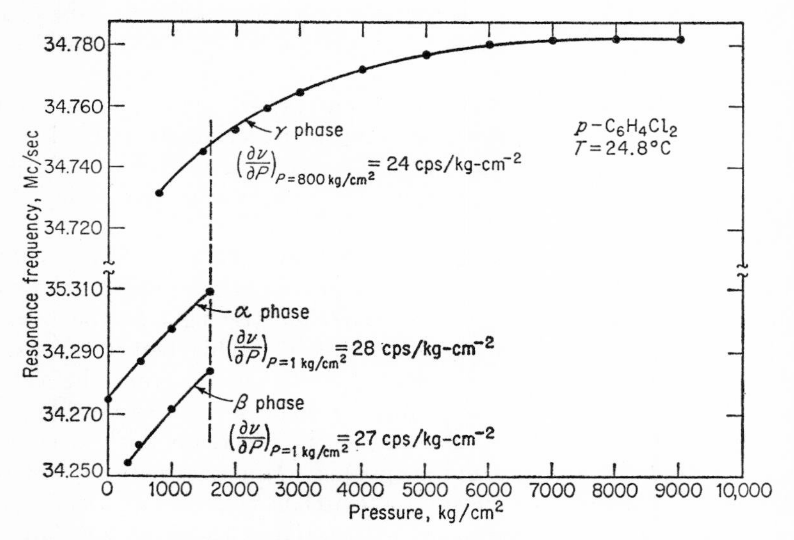

Fig. 9-4 Pressure versus volume for three phases of paradichlorobenzene at 24.8°C. The α phase is stable at 1 kg/cm². The γ phase appears at 1,600 kg/cm². The β phase appears at 750 kg/cm² on pressure release.

At lower temperatures we observe very clearly that the γ-phase ν-versus-pressure curve does possess a maximum, which can be understood as follows: With a decrease in volume, the amplitude of vibration decreases, that is, $\overline{\theta^2}$ decreases, thus tending to produce an increase in the resonance frequency. On the other hand, at low pressures ν_0 is roughly independent of volume. This is because the field gradient at the Cl^{35} nucleus is produced by the C—Cl covalency bonding. Since, in the zeroth approximation, the application of pressure to a molecular crystal changes only the intermolecular distances, q_0 can be expected to be independent of volume at the lowest pressures. However, as the volume gets smaller, the covalency bonding decreases by inter-

[12] C. Dean, unpublished Ph.D. thesis, Harvard University, Cambridge, Mass., 1952.

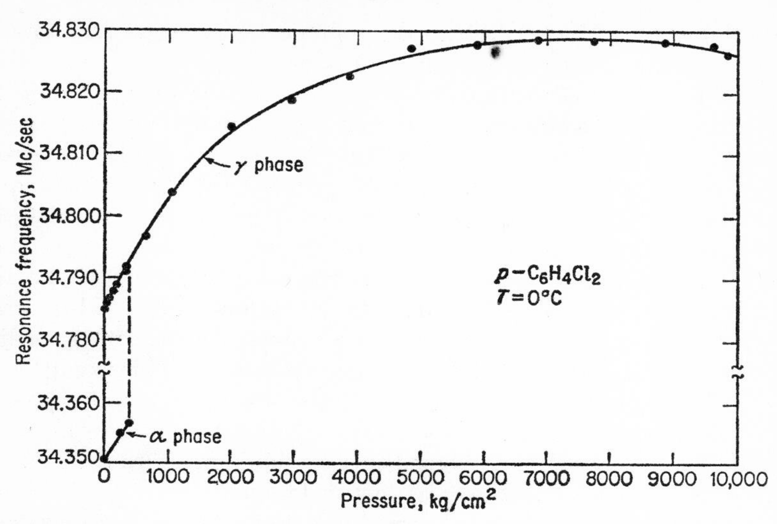

Fig. 9-5 Pressure versus volume for the γ and α phases of paradichlorobenzene at 0°C.

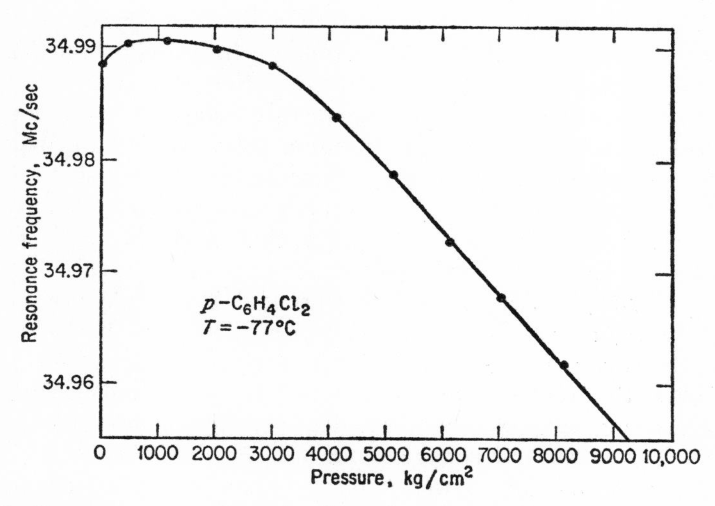

Fig. 9-6 Pressure versus volume for the γ phase of paradichlorobenzene at -77°C.

molecular hybridization with neighboring molecules. This reduces the field gradient, thereby tending to *reduce* the resonance frequency. The competition between these two effects causes the maximum in ν. The maximum shifts to lower pressures as the temperature is dropped, because $\overline{\theta^2}$ starts small at low temperatures and is therefore more easy to overcome. Quantitatively, it is observed that q_0 varies with volume as $V^{0.0}$ to $V^{0.035}$ as the volume varies from 1.04 to 0.94. γ is about 1 and is roughly independent of volume.

Recently, T. Fuke, working in Professor Koi's laboratory at Tokushima University, has observed[13] the pure-quadrupole resonance spectra of the I^{127} nucleus in SnI_4 and the Br^{81} nucleus in p-$C_6H_4Br_2$ under pressures up to 10 kilobars. In both these crystals Fuke found results quite similar to those mentioned above for p-$C_6H_4Cl_2$. The bromine and iodine resonances occur at about 200 Mc and 116 Mc, respectively. Nevertheless he found it possible simply to adapt the conical electrical lead for operation in this frequency region. Fuke also found that petroleum ether could be used as a pressure-transmitting medium to about 1 kilobar at liquid-oxygen temperatures! This result, combined with the previous observation[11] that a 50-50 mixture of n-pentane and 2-methyl butane will not freeze below 10 kilobars at 196°K, means that a high-pressure system designed to use a liquid pressure-transmitting medium can be used effectively as low in temperature as 90°K. Fuke also studied the As^{75} resonance in As_5O_6 and the Br^{81} resonance in $KBrO_3$ and analyzed all his results along the lines described above.

The negative slopes $d\nu/dP$ which we have noted for the γ phase in p-$C_6H_4Cl_2$ are about 10 times smaller than those observed for the Cl^{35} resonance in $HgCl_2$[14] and the Br^{81} resonance in $TiBr_4$.[15] In the latter compound, Barnes and Engardt[15] concluded that this negative pressure dependence can explain the strange temperature dependence of the quadrupole resonance frequency. In titanium tetrabromide the resonance frequency *increases* with increasing temperature from -250 to -50°C, until at the latter temperature it starts to behave normally and decreases with increasing temperature. They argue that thermal expansion causes the resonance frequency to increase as the temperature is raised, because $d\nu/dV = (d\nu/dP)(dP/dV) > 0$. This product is positive because both $d\nu/dP$ and dP/dV are negative. However, the lattice vibrations tend to *lower* the resonance frequency. This effect dominates above -50°C, while below this temperature the thermal-expansion effect dominates.

By measuring the pressure dependence of the quadrupole splitting of the nuclear-magnetic-resonance lines of Na^{23} in $NaClO_3$ and $NaBrO_3$, Gutowsky and Williams[16] were able to show that the electric-field gradient at the sodium nuclei varies approximately as V^{-2}. It was

[13] T. Fuke, Nuclear Quadrupole Resonance under High Pressure I, *J. Phys. Soc. Japan*, vol. 16, pp. 266–277, 1961.

[14] D. Dautreppe and B. Dreyfus, Effet de la pression sur la résonance quadrupolaire nucléaire de Cl dans $HgCl_2$, *Compt. rend.*, vol. 242, pp. 766–768, 1956.

[15] R. G. Barnes and R. D. Engardt, Unusual Temperature Dependence of Bromine Quadrupole Resonance in $TiBr_4$, *J. Chem. Phys.*, vol. 29, pp. 248–249, 1958.

[16] H. S. Gutowsky and G. Williams, Sodium Nuclear Quadrupole Interactions in $NaClO_3$ and $NaBrO_3$, *Phys. Rev.*, vol. 105, pp. 464–468, 1957.

pointed out in this work, and in a later study of $NaNO_3$,[17] that in order to analyze this result it was important to keep in mind the fact that the distortions in the unit cell will not in general be specified by a single parameter V, the volume of the unit cell, even though the compression is hydrostatic. The authors realized that in order to calculate theoretically the pressure dependence of the field gradient it is necessary to know how the pressure affects the internal parameters which describe the position of each of the atoms within the unit cell. This point was also made by W. M. Walsh[17] in his study of the effect of pressure on the crystalline-field splitting of the ground state of Ni^{++} in $NiSiF_6H_2O$. These observations make it clear that concomitant measurements of the pressure dependence of the X-ray-structure factors could make a valuable contribution to studies of the pressure dependence of the pure-quadrupole spectra.

The effect of pressure on the quadrupole resonance in a metal has been studied in the case of gallium.[18] Despite the complexity of the crystal structure of this metal, unpublished analysis of the data indicates that the field gradient of the gallium nucleus varies roughly as $1/V$.

Quadrupole splitting in metallic indium is an extremely strong function of the temperature.[19] The crystal is face-centered tetragonal; the unit cell has dimensions $(a, a, 1.078a)$. The relative structural simplicity of indium suggests that measurements of the pressure dependence of the resonance frequency might help to account for the observed temperature dependence of ν.

9-3 Crystalline Electric Fields: Higher Multipole Moments of the Electrostatic Potential

It is possible, as we saw in Sec. 9-2, to obtain information on the quadrupole moment of the electrostatic potential by means of its interaction with the nuclear quadrupole moment. In the present section we shall briefly treat methods of obtaining information on higher multipole moments of the crystalline electric fields. This can be done by means of an indirect interaction between the spin of an ion and the electrostatic field in which the ion is placed. Physically, one may describe the origin of this interaction as follows:

The energy of a free ion is in part determined by the orientation of the spin magnetic moment relative to the orbital moment because of the spin-

[17] W. M. Walsh, Jr., Stress and Temperature Dependence of the Paramagnetic Resonance Spectrum of Nickel Fluosilicate, *Phys. Rev.*, vol. 114, pp. 1473–1490, 1959.

[18] T. Kushida and G. Benedek, Pressure Dependence of Pure Quadrupole Resonance Frequency in Metallic Gallium, *Bull. Am. Phys. Soc.*, vol. 3, p. 167, 1958.

[19] W. W. Simmons and C. P. Slichter, Nuclear Quadrupole Absorption in Indium Metal, *Phys. Rev.*, vol. 121, pp. 1580–1590, 1961.

orbit coupling. If the ion is placed in a crystalline electric field of low symmetry, the orbital angular momentum is quenched in first order. However, in second order there still remains an interaction between the spin and the orbital angular momentum whose magnitude depends in detail on the splittings of the orbital angular-momentum states by the crystalline fields. The combined effect of the spin-orbit coupling and the crystalline electric field is to make the energy of the ion depend on the angle between the spin and the crystal axes. This angular dependence produces "zero-field splittings" which can be detected in the paramagnetic resonance spectrum of the ion. Conversely, from observed spectra one may deduce information about the symmetry and strength of the crystalline fields at the site of the ions.

By analogy with the case of the nuclear-quadrupole-resonance experiments, it is clear that information on the detailed origin of the crystalline electric fields can be obtained by studying the temperature and pressure dependence of the paramagnetic resonance spectra.

The extension of high-pressure magnetic-resonance techniques to the X-band microwave region was made by W. M. Walsh, Jr., and N. Bloembergen,[20] using a subtle modification (see Fig. 9-7) of the radio-frequency electrical plug. A rather different design using transmission through a sapphire window has been developed by Lawson and Smith[21] and used at 24 kilomegacycles up to 10 kilobars.

The first microwave-resonance experiment under pressure was a study of the Ni^{++} ion in nickel fluosilicate.[22] In this crystal the Ni^{++} is located in a predominantly cubically symmetric crystal field with a weak component having trigonal symmetry superposed. This trigonal field produces a splitting in the microwave region of the ground levels of the ion. The magnitude of the trigonal-field splitting is described by a parameter D. In Fig. 9-8 we see Walsh's results[22] for the effect of pressure on D. The trigonal component of the field decreases linearly with pressure until at about 6 kilobars the symmetry around the ion becomes perfectly cubic and $D = 0$. Walsh also made an analysis of the effects on D of both the change in shape of the unit cell and the thermal vibrations. Despite the absence of *detailed* knowledge of the displacements of the atoms inside the unit cell, he was able to show that the thermal vibrations play an important role in determining the magnitude of D. This result was quite different from the previous view that the tempera-

[20] W. M. Walsh, Jr., and N. Bloembergen, Paramagnetic Resonance of Nickel Fluosilicate under High Hydrostatic Pressure, *Phys. Rev.*, vol. 107, pp. 904–905, 1957.

[21] A. W. Lawson and G. E. Smith, High-pressure Microwave Window, *Rev. Sci. Instr.*, vol. 30, pp. 989–991, 1956.

[22] W. M. Walsh, Jr., Stress and Temperature Dependence of the Paramagnetic Resonance Spectrum of Nickel Fluosilicate, *Phys. Rev.*, vol. 114, pp. 1473–1490, 1959.

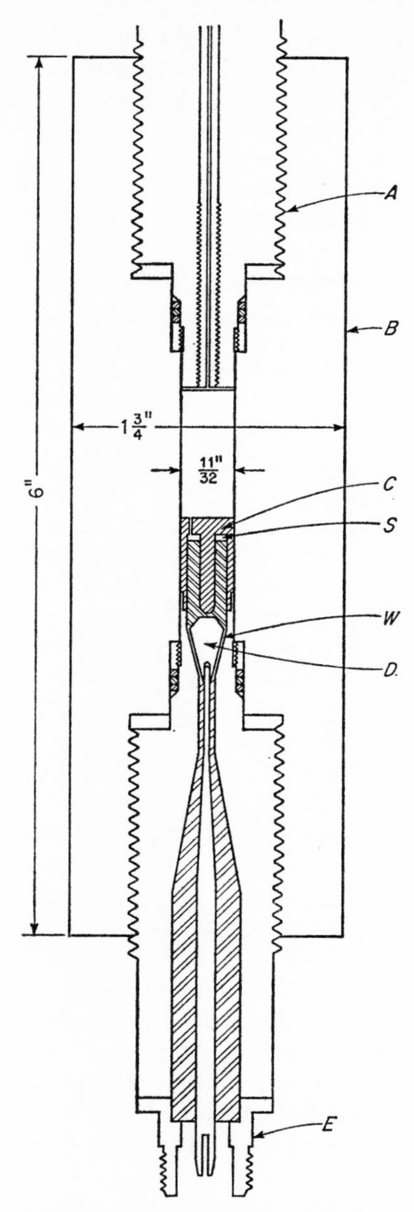

Fig. 9-7 High-pressure bomb and microwave transmission plug. (*A*) Pressure plug; (*B*) BeCu vessel; (*C*) microwave cavity; (*D*) sealing cone; (*E*) type *N* connector; (*S*) sample position; (*W*) synthetic-mica washer. (*After W. Walsh and N. Bloembergen.*[20])

ture dependence of the crystal-field splittings is due solely to thermally induced changes in the geometry of the unit cell.

Walsh also studied the Cr^{3+} ion in the ionic crystal ammonium aluminum alum.[22] The paramagnetic resonance spectrum of this ion, *covalently* bonded in the complex $[Cr(CN_6)]^{3-}$, was also studied by substituting Cr^{3+} into potassium cobalticyanide. Again the effect of temperature and pressure on the zero-field splittings was studied. In addition to this, a new effect was found in $[Cr(CN_6)]^{3-}$, namely, a strong dependence of the effective magnetic moment of the ion on pressure. In the free ion, the magnetic moment results from both the spin and orbital magnetic

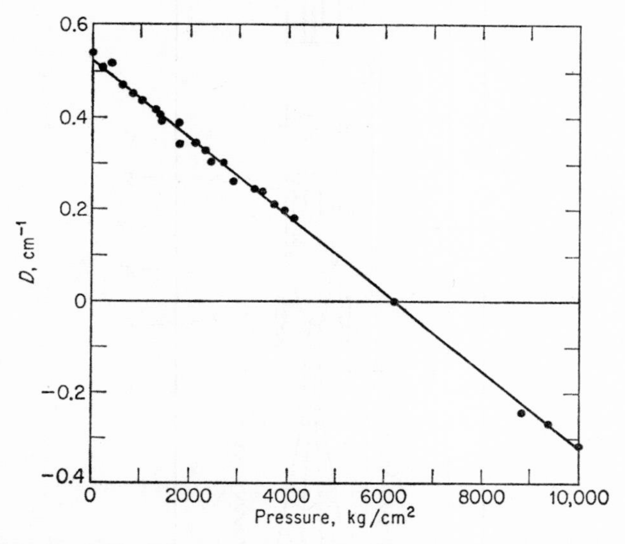

Fig. 9-8 Pressure dependence of the zero-field splitting D in $NiSiF_6 \cdot 6H_2O$ at 300°K. (*After W. Walsh and N. Bloembergen.*[19])

moments. In a crystal, the orbital contribution to the moment is partially, but not entirely, quenched. The spin-orbit coupling again prevents complete removal of the orbital contribution to the magnetic moment. As a result, the interaction between the magnetic moment of the ion and the external magnetic field may be written as $\mathbf{S} \cdot \mathbf{g}\beta \cdot \mathbf{H}$, where $\mathbf{g}$ is in general a tensor, and β is the Bohr magneton. The departure of $\mathbf{g}$ from isotropy and from the value 2.0032 gives information on the crystal-field strength and symmetry. It also involves the magnitude of the spin-orbit coupling parameter. Walsh's measurements show that one of the components of the $\mathbf{g}$ tensor is a very strong function of the pressure. In fact the curve of $\mathbf{g}$ versus pressure passes through a minimum at about 7 kilobars.

Walsh realized that a detailed theoretical calculation of the effects he had observed would not be possible until the paramagnetic ion was placed in an environment that was so simple that one could estimate with confidence the displacements of the surrounding ions solely from measurements of the thermal expansion and compressibility. This problem was solved by a study of the paramagnetic resonance spectra of Cr^{3+}, Mn^{++}, Fe^{3+}, and Ni^{++} present substitutionally in the cubic crystals MgO and ZnS.[23]

In an outstanding paper,[23] Walsh described these experiments and analyzed the volume dependence of the orbital contribution to the magnetic moments of the F-state ions Cr^{3+} and Ni^{++}. He also determined the volume dependence of the cubic-field splitting of the S-state ions Mn^{++} and Fe^{3+}.

9-4 Hyperfine Interactions in Feebly Paramagnetic Metals

A nucleus which possesses a magnetic moment

$$\boldsymbol{\mu} = g_N \beta_N \mathbf{I}$$

where g_N = nuclear gyromagnetic ratio
β_N = nuclear magneton
$\mathbf{I}$ = nuclear spin

interacts with a magnetic field $\mathbf{H}$ at the nuclear site to produce energy levels

$$E_n = g_N \beta_N H m_I$$

where $m_I = -I, \ -I + 1, \ . \ . \ . \ , \ I$. By measuring the separation between these levels, one may obtain the magnetic field at the nuclear site.

In the absence of an externally applied magnetic field, the time-average magnetic field at a nucleus in a feebly paramagnetic metal is zero. However, if a magnetic field H_0 is applied, the field at the nucleus is no longer zero, but it is not equal to H_0. If we measure the internal field at the nuclear site in a metal and compare it with the field at the nuclear site in a solution of a salt of that metal, then we see that a difference in field ΔH can be measured.[24] This shift, the "Knight shift," arises out of the paramagnetic alignment of the spins in the metal and is enhanced by the hyperfine interaction, that is, the lumping of spin density of

[23] W. M. Walsh, Jr., Effects of Hydrostatic Pressure on the Paramagnetic Resonance Spectra of Several Iron Group Ions in Cubic Crystals, *Phys. Rev.*, vol. 122, pp. 762–771, 1961.

[24] W. V. Knight, Electron Paramagnetism and Nuclear Magnetic Resonance in Metals, pp. 93–136 in F. Seitz and D. Turnbull (eds.), "Advances in Solid State Physics," vol. 2, Academic Press, Inc., New York, 1956.

electrons in s states around the nucleus. The Knight shift K can be written as[25]

$$K = \frac{\Delta H}{H_0} = \frac{8\pi}{3} \chi_p \Omega P_F \tag{9-6}$$

where $P_F = |\psi_F(0)|^2$ = probability density for finding a conduction electron, with energy equal to Fermi energy, at nucleus (wave function is presumed normalized over unit cell)

χ_p = paramagnetic susceptibility per unit volume

Ω = atomic volume

The Knight shift, in that it includes the P_F term, provides us with one of the few relatively direct means of obtaining information on the electronic wave functions in the metal.

It is clearly of theoretical interest to obtain information on the volume dependence of the Knight shift. If K and χ_p could be measured separately, P_F could be deduced. While the paramagnetic susceptibility has been measured at atmospheric pressure[26] for lithium and sodium, the method is of insufficient accuracy to determine the volume dependence of χ_p. Instead, one may use for the alkali metals a theoretical calculation by Pines[26a] which is successful in calculating the magnitude of χ_p in lithium and sodium.

The pressure dependence of K has been measured[27] in lithium, sodium, rubidium, copper, and aluminum at room temperature over the pressure range of 1 to 10 kilobars. The measurements consist in the determination of the change in nuclear resonance frequency ν when hydrostatic pressure is applied to a sample placed in a constant external field H_0. The changes in ν are very small in lithium and sodium. At 10 kilobars the change in ν is only about 30 cps for lithium and 110 cps for sodium. Hence stringent requirements are placed on the stabilization of the external field and the frequency stability of the spectrometer. To meet these requirements, a system then unprecedented in accuracy was developed which enabled stabilization of both spectrometer and magnetic field to a few parts in 10^7 over long periods (8 to 10 hours) of time. The results for sodium are shown in Fig. 9-9. It will be noted that the center of the resonance line is determined to within ± 1 cps at each pressure. When the results for the pressure dependence of K are combined with

[25] G. Pake, Nuclear Magnetic Resonance, p. 56 in F. Seitz and D. Turnbull (eds.), "Advances in Solid State Physics," vol. 1, Academic Press, Inc., New York, 1956.

[26] R. T. Shumacher and C. P. Slichter, Electron Spin Paramagnetism of Lithium and Sodium, *Phys. Rev.*, vol. 101, pp. 58–65, 1955.

[26a] D. Pines, Electron Interaction in Metals, in F. Seitz and D. Turnbull (eds.), "Advances in Solid State Physics," vol. 2, Academic Press, Inc., New York, 1956.

[27] G. Benedek and T. Kushida, The Pressure Dependence of the Knight Shift in the Alkali Metals and Copper, *J. Chem. Phys. Solids*, vol. 5, pp. 241–255, 1958.

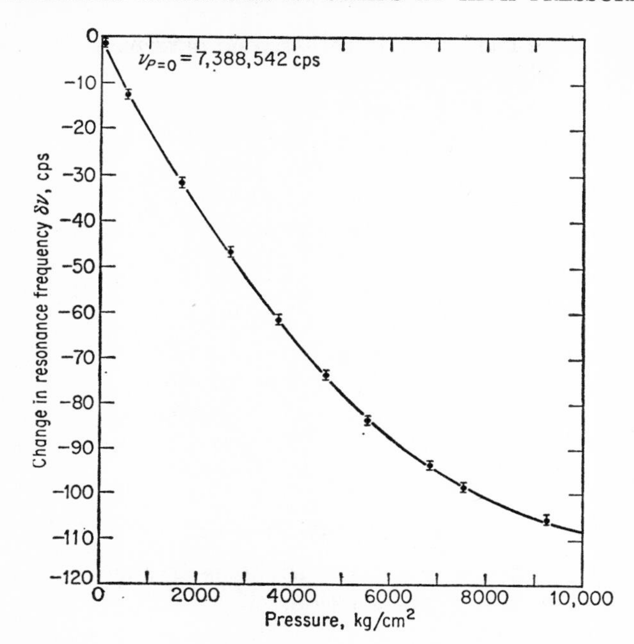

Fig. 9-9 The change in Na^{23} resonance frequency with pressure at 24.4°C. The accuracy of the determination of the frequency is ± 1 cps at each pressure.

Bridgman's measurements[27a] of the volume compression of the solid, we obtain the volume dependence of K.

In Table 9-1 we list the fractional volume changes produced by approximately 10 kilobars, along with the accompanying changes in $\chi_p\Omega$ and P_F.

Using the quantum-defect method,[28] H. Brooks has calculated the volume dependence of P_F, and his results are given in the last column

Table 9-1 The Fractional Change in the Knight Shift and P_F with Change of Volume of the Solid by the Fraction $\Delta V/V$

Metal	$\frac{\Delta V}{V}$	$\frac{\Delta \chi_p \Omega}{\chi_p \Omega}$	$\frac{\Delta P_F}{P_F}$	$\frac{\Delta P_F}{P_F}$ (theoretical)
Lithium	−0.08	−0.0116	−0.005	
Sodium	−0.13	−0.0131	+0.072	+0.062
Rubidium	−0.23	+0.068	+0.22	+0.21
Cesium	−0.24	+0.415	+0.57	+0.34

[27a] P. W. Bridgman, "The Physics of High Pressure," G. Bell & Sons, Ltd., London, 1949.

[28] H. Brooks and F. Ham, Energy Bands in Solids—The Quantum Defect Method, *Phys. Rev.*, vol. 112, pp. 344–361, 1958.

of Table 9-1. The results are in rather good agreement for sodium and rubidium. In lithium the theory gives the correct sign, but the theoretical expansion for the wave function diverges too near the observed value of the radius of the Wigner-Seitz sphere to permit any quantitative results. In cesium the theory clearly gives too small a result.

From the measurements of the volume dependence of the Knight shift, it was possible to check whether or not the observed temperature dependence of the Knight shift[29] was due to thermal expansion alone. It was found that thermal expansion could not explain the observations and that the Knight shift is an *explicit* function of the temperature at constant volume. A theory was proposed to explain this effect in terms of the modulation of P_F by the lattice vibrations. Semiquantitative calculations[27] based on this model were in agreement with experimental results. A more rigorous and very recent treatment of this problem has been given by Muto and associates.[30]

9-5 Hyperfine Interaction in Antiferromagnetic MnF_2

Manganous fluoride, MnF_2, is a nearly ionic crystal. On forming the crystal lattice, in first approximation, the manganese atoms become doubly ionized magnetic Mn^{++} ions with the configuration $^6S_{5/2}$, while the fluorine atoms become singly charged nonmagnetic F^- ions in the closed-shell configuration $^1S_0$. The magnetic moments on the manganese sites are responsible for the paramagnetism of MnF_2 at temperatures above the Néel temperature T_N. Below T_N, the superexchange interaction and anisotropy fields produce an antiferromagnetic ordering of the Mn^{++} spins. In Fig. 9-10 we see the arrangement of nearest-neighbor Mn^{++} spins around each fluorine site. The nucleus under study is the F^{19} nucleus. In this crystal there are two types of fluorine sites. In the antiferromagnetic state one type of fluorine sees the spin arrangement shown in Fig. 9-10, while the other site sees a reversed orientation of spins. To examine the magnetic effect of the near-neighbor Mn^{++} spins on the F^{19} nucleus, we employ the Heitler-London, or atomic-orbital, description of the wave functions in the crystal. If we neglect entirely the effect of overlap between the fluorine and manganese orbitals, then we may expect that the field H which the fluorine nucleus sees is due entirely to the magnetic-dipole field of the Mn^{++} ions. At $T = 0°K$, for the case of complete antiparallel alignment, this would produce a magnetic field of 12,500 gauss; 12,800 gauss of this is due to the nearest-

[29] B. R. McGarvey and H. S. Gutowsky, Nuclear Magnetic Resonance in Metals. II. Temperature Dependence of the Resonance Shifts, *J. Chem. Phys.*, vol. 21, pp. 2114–2119, 1953.

[30] T. Muto, S. Kobayasi, M. Watanabe, and H. Kozima, Temperature Effect of Knight Shifts in Alkali Metals, *J. Phys. Chem. Solids*, vol. 23, p. 1303, 1962.

neighbor ions, -300 gauss being contributed by the further neighbors. Jaccarino and Shulman,[31] who were the first to observe the F^{19} nuclear resonance in MnF_2, found that at $T \simeq 0$ the field at the fluorine site was actually 40,470 gauss. They proposed that this large field was due to an indirect hyperfine interaction between the spin of the Mn^{++} ions and the F^{19} nucleus. They also suggested that the mechanism for this hyperfine interaction was covalent bonding which produces a transfer of spin-up electrons in s states on the fluorine onto the spin-down d orbitals on the manganese ions. However, no quantitative evidence was presented to support this view.

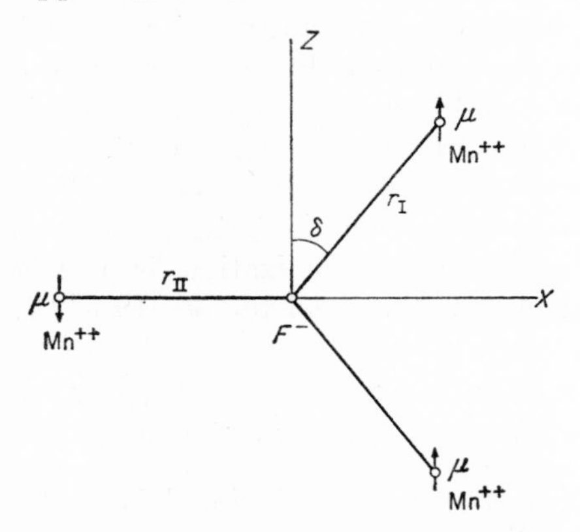

Fig. 9-10 The arrangement of nearest-neighbor Mn^{++} ions around a fluorine nucleus. The arrows represent the magnitude and relative orientation of the time-averaged magnetic moment of the Mn^{++} ions. A second type of fluorine site sees the same configuration as above, except that the direction of the manganese spins is reversed.

At temperatures other than $T = 0$ the resonance frequency can be expected to have the same temperature dependence as the sublattice magnetization. This follows from the fact that the nucleus responds only to the time-average spin orientation of the neighbor manganese spins. This time-average spin orientation in turn is proportional to the sublattice magnetization $M(T)$. Thus we may write that the resonance frequency ν is related to $M(T)$ by

$$\nu = AM(T) \tag{9-7}$$

The constant of proportionality includes the effects of both the hyperfine coupling and the dipole-dipole interaction.

Well below the Néel temperature, $M(T)$ becomes a constant, independent of the temperature and very nearly independent of the volume.

[31] V. Jaccarino and R. G. Shulman, Observation of Nuclear Magnetic Resonance in Antiferromagnetic $Mn(F^{19})_2$, *Phys. Rev.*, vol. 107, pp. 1196–1197, 1957.

Thus, by measurements of the pressure dependence of the resonance frequency ν at very low temperatures and in zero external field, one can determine the pressure dependence of A and hence the pressure dependence of the hyperfine coupling constant. Furthermore, if the change in lattice dimensions produced by the pressure is known, one may determine how the hyperfine coupling constant depends on the distance between the manganese and fluorine ions. This information in turn can be expected to cast light on the detailed origin of the hyperfine coupling between the Mn^{++} ions and the fluorine nucleus.

Measurement of the pressure dependence of ν has been performed[32] at 4.2°K using liquid helium as a pressure-transmitting medium. The pressure range was limited to only 100 bars, but the accuracy with which the line center could be determined was sufficient to specify that $(1/A)(\partial A/\partial P) = (1.9 \pm 0.1) \times 10^{-6}\ (\text{kg/cm}^2)^{-1}$.

At higher temperatures at which $M(T)$ is not a constant, the pressure dependence of ν arises also from the pressure dependence of the magnetization. The sublattice magnetization is a function of pressure through its dependence on the Néel temperature T_N. We may therefore write

$$\frac{1}{\nu}\left(\frac{\partial \nu}{\partial P}\right)_T = \frac{1}{A}\left(\frac{\partial A}{\partial P}\right)_T + \frac{1}{M}\frac{\partial M}{\partial T_N}\frac{\partial T_N}{\partial P} \tag{9-8}$$

If we take $M = M(T/T_N)$ as the functional form of the dependence of M on T and T_N, it follows that

$$\frac{1}{\nu}\left(\frac{\partial \nu}{\partial P}\right)_T = \frac{1}{A}\left(\frac{\partial A}{\partial P}\right)_T - \frac{T}{T_N}\left(\frac{\partial \ln M}{\partial T}\right)_{T_N}\frac{\partial T_N}{\partial P} \tag{9-9}$$

Since $(\partial \ln M/\partial T)_{T_N} = (\partial \ln \nu/\partial T)_P$, we may obtain $\partial T_N/\partial P$ by measuring the pressure dependence of ν at a temperature at which the second term on the right-hand side of Eq. (9-9) is appreciable compared to the first. This measurement has been carried out at 35.7°K, yielding a determination of

$$\frac{\partial T_N}{\partial P} = (0.298 \pm 0.02) \times 10^{-3}\ {}^\circ\text{K}/(\text{kg/cm}^2)$$

where $T_N = 68.5$°K. As a self-consistent check we can measure $(1/\nu)(\partial \nu/\partial P)$ at some other temperature and compare the result with the prediction of Eq. (9-8) obtained by using the values of $\partial \ln A/\partial P$ and $\partial \ln T_N/\partial P$ given above. At 20°K, Eq. (9-9) predicts

$$\frac{1}{\nu}\left(\frac{\partial \nu}{\partial P}\right)_T = (2.2 \pm 0.1) \times 10^{-6}\ (\text{kg/cm}^2)^{-1}$$

[32] G. Benedek and T. Kushida, Nuclear Magnetic Resonance in Antiferromagnetic MnF_2 under Hydrostatic Pressure, *Phys. Rev.*, vol. 118, pp. 46–57, 1960.

whereas we found $(2.21 \pm 0.04) \times 10^{-6}$ $(\text{kg/cm}^2)^{-1}$. This satisfactory agreement lends support to the use of Eq. (9-9).

With the aid of measurements of the compressibility of MnF_2, these determinations of $\partial T_N/\partial P$ show how the superexchange interaction between manganese ions depends on the distances and angles which characterize the Mn—F—Mn geometry. No theoretical calculations have yet been made to predict the dependence of the superexchange integral on the Mn—F—Mn distances and angles.

On the other hand, a theory has been proposed[32,33] to account for the magnitude and pressure dependence of the hyperfine interaction between the manganese ions and the fluorine nucleus. In essence, this theory proposes that the unpairing of the core electron in s states around the fluorine nucleus arises out of Pauli, or exchange, repulsion between fluorine and manganese spins which have the same orientation. Because of orthogonality, this exchange repulsion does not act on those fluorine electrons whose spin is antiparallel to the direction of the neighbor Mn^{++} spin. As a result, spin-up and spin-down s and p orbitals around the fluorine nucleus are slightly different.

With this model of Pauli, or exchange, repulsion first proposed by Mukherji and Das[34] and Marshall's estimate of the alteration of the Hartree-Fock free-ion wave functions when the ions are in the solid,[33] calculations of the magnitude and pressure dependence of A were made which were in excellent agreement with observations.[32] However, subsequent refinements of the theory[33,35] showed that a cross term between the $2s$ and $1s$ orbitals reduces the magnitude of the theoretical prediction of the hyperfine coupling constant by a factor of 2. This difficulty may be due to inadequate knowledge of the details of the $3d$ Mn^{++} wave functions near the F^- ion. However, it is possible that covalency between F^- and Mn^{++} ions may indeed play a significant part in determining the hyperfine interaction. Thus, while the importance of the exchange repulsion for the hyperfine interaction between Mn^{++} and F^- ions has been clearly established, it is possible that other mechanisms may make significant contributions.

9-6 Hyperfine Interactions in Magnetic Ions Located in Diamagnetic Host Crystals

In the previous section we saw the effect of magnetic electrons at the nuclear sites of *neighboring* ions. In the present section we shall discuss

[33] W. Marshall and R. N. Stuart, Theory of Transition in Iron Complexes, *Phys. Rev.*, vol. 123, pp. 2048–2058, 1961.

[34] P. N. Mukherji and T. P. Das, F^{19} Hyperfine Interaction in the Paramagnetic Resonance Spectrum of Mn^{++} Ions in ZnF_2, *Phys. Rev.*, vol. 111, pp. 1479–1482, 1958.

[35] A. J. Freeman and R. E. Watson, Origin of the F^{19} Hyperfine Structure in Transition Element Fluorides, *Phys. Rev. Letters*, vol. 6, pp. 343–345, 1961.

briefly the effect of magnetic electrons at the nucleus of *their own* ion. The ions which have been studied under pressure are iron-group ions present in very low concentration in diamagnetic host crystals. The magnetic electrons of these ions are situated in d orbitals around the nucleus. Since d electrons have no probability density at the nucleus, one expects no hyperfine interaction between nucleus and electrons. Nevertheless the paramagnetic resonance spectra show that strong hyperfine interactions do exist. This indicates that the spin-up and spin-down probability densities for electrons at the nucleus are not equal. The mechanism for this inequality is discussed very completely in a recent paper by Watson and Freeman.[36] Briefly, the effect results from the fact that spin-up and spin-down s electrons see different exchange potentials, depending upon whether their spin is parallel or antiparallel to the spin of the d electrons. Thus, the two electrons in each s orbital have slightly different radial distributions, so that the spin densities are slightly different at the nucleus. This effect is known as "exchange polarization."

The hyperfine interaction between nucleus and electron reveals itself as a splitting of the electron spin-resonance line into $2I + 1$ lines, since the orientation of the nuclear spin relative to the electron spin can have $2I + 1$ values. The splitting of the resonance line gives the hyperfine-interaction constant A. This quantity is a very sensitive measure of the details of the d wave function in the crystal, since the exchange polarization depends in detail on the shape of the d wave functions. Alteration of the interatomic distances affects the shape of the d wave function and thereby affects A. Thus information on the pressure dependence of A is valuable in determining how the d wave functions are affected by the presence of the neighbor nonmagnetic ions in the crystal.

Walsh[23] has measured the pressure dependence of the hyperfine coupling constant of Mn^{++} ions in the cubic crystals MgO and ZnS. Using Bridgman's measurements of the compressibilities, Walsh found that A depends on the volume of the crystal in MgO as

$$A = -81.11 \times 10^{-4} \left(\frac{V}{V_0}\right)^{0.06} \qquad \text{cm}^{-1}$$

Thus, in this ionic crystal the hyperfine interaction depends only slightly on the distance between the magnetic ion and the neighboring nonmagnetic ions. However, in the more covalent crystal ZnS, it was found that

$$A = -63.73 \times 10^{-4} \left(\frac{V}{V_0}\right)^{0.35} \qquad \text{cm}^{-1}$$

[36] R. E. Watson and A. J. Freeman, Origin of Effective Fields in Magnetic Materials, *Phys. Rev.*, vol. 123, pp. 2027–2047, 1961.

Thus the hyperfine interaction here is a very strong function of the interatomic distances. This suggests the importance of covalency in determining the detailed spreading of the d orbitals of the impurity ion.

9-7 Hyperfine Interactions in Ferromagnetic Metals

The alignment of the spins of d electrons in a ferromagnet produces a large magnetic field at the position of the nuclei. Since this field is proportional to the time-average electron-spin orientation, which in turn is proportional to the magnetization M, we see that the nuclear-resonance frequency ν is related to the magnetization by

$$\nu(T) = AM(T) \tag{9-10}$$

where T is the temperature. By far the largest contribution to the constant A is the hyperfine interaction which is proportional to the difference between spin-up and spin-down probability densities at the nucleus.

Marshall[37] has presented a theory which describes in detail how the alignment of d electrons in a ferromagnet produces a spin-unpairing of s electrons at the nucleus. Briefly we may describe the three mechanisms he has proposed. The first is the exchange polarization of the core s electrons by the aligned d electrons. The second is the paramagnetic alignment of the s-like conduction electrons. The alignment of these electrons is produced by the magnetic field set up by the d electrons. The third effect is the admixture of s-like wave functions into the d band. It has proved difficult to determine quantitatively the relative importance of these three effects.

The first measurements of the pressure dependence of the nuclear-resonance frequency in a ferromagnet were made by Jones and Kaminow[38] and Koi et al.[39] in cobalt. Interpretation of the data was difficult because of the absence of information on the compressibility and thermal expansion of the observed *cubic* phase of cobalt.

In ferromagnetic iron, however, the compressibility and thermal expansion are accurately known. Furthermore in iron an important departure from Eq. (9-10) has been observed by Robert and Winter.[40] These workers measured the temperature dependence of ν at constant pressure

[37] W. Marshall, Orientation of Nuclei in Ferromagnets, *Phys. Rev.*, vol. 110, pp. 1280–1285, 1958.

[38] R. V. Jones and I. P. Kaminow, *Bull. Am. Phys. Soc.*, Series II, vol. 5, p. 175, 1960.

[39] Y. Koi, T. Tsuzimura, and Y. Yukimoto, The Temperature and Pressure Dependence of the Nuclear Resonance of Co^{59} in Face-centered-cubic Cobalt Metal, *J. Phys. Soc. Japan*, vol. 15, p. 1342, 1960.

[40] C. Robert and J. M. Winter, Observation de la résonance nucléaire du fer 57 dans le fer metallique naturel en l'absence de champ extérieur, *Compt. rend.*, vol. 250, pp. 3831–3833, 1960.

and compared their results with Fallot's[41] measurements of the temperature dependence of the magnetization M at constant pressure. They found that $(1/\nu)(\partial\nu/\partial T)_P$ was smaller than $(1/M)(\partial M/\partial T)_P$. This was a serious challenge to workers in this field who felt that by the accurate nuclear-resonance measurements of ν versus the temperature T one could obtain precise information on the temperature dependence of M. This latter information is of course vital in the theory of magnetism. Robert and Winter[40] suggested that the difficulty arose not because A was an explicit function of the temperature, but only because of the effect of the thermal expansion on A. Their thought may be put more quantitatively as follows: From Eq. (9-10) we see that

$$\left(\frac{\partial \ln \nu}{\partial T}\right)_P - \left(\frac{\partial \ln M}{\partial T}\right)_P = \left(\frac{\partial \ln A}{\partial T}\right)_V + \left(\frac{\partial \ln A}{\partial \ln V}\right)_T \left(\frac{\partial \ln V}{\partial T}\right)_P \tag{9-11}$$

The supposition of Robert and Winter was that the first term on the right-hand side of Eq. (9-11) is zero and that the entire effect is due solely to the last term. Measurements of the pressure dependence of M and ν can settle this matter since

$$\left(\frac{\partial \ln A}{\partial \ln V}\right)_T = \left(\frac{\partial \ln \nu}{\partial P}\right)_T \left(\frac{\partial P}{\partial \ln V}\right)_T - \left(\frac{\partial \ln M}{\partial P}\right)_T \left(\frac{\partial P}{\partial \ln V}\right)_T \tag{9-12}$$

Thus measurements of $(1/\nu)\partial\nu/\partial P$, $(1/M)\partial M/\partial P$, and the compressibility $(\partial P/\partial \ln V)^{-1}$ enable the volume dependence of A to be determined. This can then be used in Eq. (9-11) to determine $(\partial \ln A/\partial T)_V$. Benedek and Armstrong[42] have measured $\partial\nu/\partial P$ in iron, while Kouvel[43] and Galperin[44] have measured $\partial M/\partial P$. The analysis outlined above has been carried out,[42] and it has been found that the coupling constant A is indeed an explicit function of the temperature at constant volume, i.e., $(\partial \ln A/\partial T)_V \neq 0$. In fact, A depends on the temperature as follows:

$$A = A_0(1 - 0.77 \times 10^{-7}T^2) \tag{9-13}$$

This observation, while it implies that the temperature dependence of ν does not accurately mirror the temperature dependence of M, presents us with the problem of finding an explanation for the temperature

[41] M. Fallot, Ferromagnetism of Iron Alloys, *Ann. Phys.*, vol. 6, pp. 305–387, 1936.

[42] G. Benedek and J. Armstrong, Pressure and Temperature Dependence of the Fe^{57} Nuclear Magnetic Resonance Frequency in Ferromagnetic Iron, *J. Appl. Phys.*, vol. 32, supplement, pp. 106S–110S, 1961.

[43] J. Kouvel and R. H. Wilson, General Electric Research Laboratory Report 60-RL-2421 M. See also E. Tatsumoto, T. Kamigaichi, H. Fujiwara, Y. Kato, and H. Tange, *J. Phys. Soc. Japan*, vol. 17, p. 592, 1960.

[44] F. Galperin, S. Larin, and A. Shishkov, Investigation of the Effect of Uniformly Distributed Pressure on the Magnetic Saturation of Iron at the Temperature of Liquid Nitrogen, *Doklady Akad. Nauk S. S. S. R.*, vol. 89, pp. 419–422, 1953.

dependence of A. The data provide a hint in the T^2 temperature dependence of A. Such a temperature dependence would in fact arise from the excitation of electrons in d states higher into the d band. Since the shape of the d wave functions changes markedly as one goes higher into the d band,[45] the contribution to A of the d electrons in the upper part of the band will be different from the contribution of those in the lower part. What is observed experimentally is an average over all the d band. As the temperature is changed, this average is altered by the redistribution of electrons. A theory based on such a mechanism has been worked out.[42] It gives, of course, a T^2 temperature dependence as a result of the application of Fermi statistics to the problem. However, numerical calculation of the coefficient of the T^2 term has not yet been possible. Nevertheless there is in this effect an indication that the d electron in a ferromagnet may have to be treated as occupying band states.

Recently Kushida[46] has measured the pressure and temperature dependence of the nuclear-resonance frequency in ferromagnetic nickel. When his results are combined with measurements of the pressure dependence of the magnetization M, we shall see whether the same situation arises in nickel as we have observed in iron.

9-8 Conclusions

In specifying the state of a solid, thermodynamics tells us that the volume and the temperature stand on equal footing. The comparative ease with which the temperature can be changed has long made it the more frequently studied variable. However, the development and refinement of high-pressure techniques, first pioneered by Bridgman, have permitted the experimentalist to study the interaction of the solid under pressure with energy in the radio-frequency, microwave, optical, X-ray, and even γ-ray regions of the electromagnetic spectrum. In the present article we have seen briefly how the effect of pressure on the nuclear and microwave spectra has cast light on the electronic structure and atomic motions within the solid.

Despite the variety of solids and spectra studied, one general feature stands out in all the experiments discussed. We have seen again and again that in order to understand the temperature dependence of a particular property of the solid, it is necessary to know also the effect on that property of changing the volume. This arises simply because thermal expansion is always present. This thermodynamic aspect of magnetic-resonance experiments under pressure stands out very clearly

[45] J. H. Wood, Wave Functions for Iron D Band, *Phys. Rev.*, vol. 117, pp. 714–718, 1960.

[46] T. Kushida, private communication.

in the quadrupole-resonance experiments and in the study of ferromagnetic metals. Thus, for thermodynamic reasons alone, pressure experiments are needed for a detailed understanding of the properties of solids.

Aside from this thermodynamic necessity, however, advances in rf and microwave spectroscopy permit the experimentalist to obtain detailed information on the electronic structure of atoms and ions in the solid. The pressure experiments then show the theoretician how this structure depends on the fundamental parameter in the theory of solids: interatomic distance. This particular aspect of the resonance experiments stands out most clearly in the experiments on MnF_2 and on the paramagnetic resonance spectra of iron-group ions in diamagnetic crystals.

Looking to the future, we note that a number of nuclear-resonance experiments already have been performed on solidified gases under pressure. Two groups[47,48] have studied solid hydrogen, while Scott[49] has studied the pure-quadrupole resonance frequency in solid nitrogen. Also Goodkind and Fairbank[50] have studied solid He^3. Further activity in this area should be very fruitful. It should also be observed that in ferromagnets, ferrimagnets, and antiferromagnets, the magnetic field in which the nuclei resonate can be provided by the electronic spins in the solid. Thus for these materials one can dispense with an external magnetic field and use the massive equipment now available for the generation of pressures in the range up to 100 kilobars. Magnetic-resonance experiments in this greatly extended pressure range are thus not only possible, but quite likely. Recently J. D. Litster and G. Benedek[51] have observed the Fe^{57} resonance in iron to 65,000 bars using a belt-type press.

[47] G. W. Smith and C. F. Squire, Pressure Studies on the Nuclear Magnetic Resonance of Solid Hydrogen between 1.2° and 14°K, *Phys. Rev.*, vol. 111, pp. 188–193, 1958.

[48] W. Fairbank and W. D. McCormack, Nuclear Resonance Experiments on Solid Hydrogen at High Pressures, *Bull. Am. Phys. Soc.*, series 2, vol. 3, p. 166, 1958.

[49] T. A. Scott, Quadrupole Resonance of N^{14} in Nitrogen and in Clathrates at Low Temperatures, unpublished Ph.D. thesis, Harvard University, Cambridge, Mass., 1959.

[50] J. M. Goodkind and W. M. Fairbank, Nuclear Spin Relaxation in Solid He^3, *Phys. Rev. Letters*, vol. 4, pp. 458–460, 1960.

[51] J. D. Litster and G. Benedek, Observation of the Fe^{57} Nuclear Resonance in Ferromagnetic Iron to 65,000 Atmospheres, *J. Appl. Phys.*, in press for March, 1963.

10

Magnetic Properties of Solids under Pressure

J. S. Kouvel

General Electric Research Laboratory
Schenectady, New York

10-1 Introduction

Technological interest in ferromagnetic materials has often centered on properties that are extremely sensitive to the gross structure of these materials. Prominent examples are the "soft" ferromagnets, such as the nickel-iron Permalloys and some of the ferrites, whose magnetic permeabilities at very low fields can be increased enormously by proper control of crystal texture, structural defects, and other macroscopic factors. Similarly, the "hard" ferromagnets, such as the Alnico-type alloys, derive their optimum permanent-magnet properties from suitable conditions of fabrication and annealing. Hence, many of the methods now used in improving these materials for specific applications are based not only on fundamental knowledge of magnetism, but also on fairly sophisticated understanding of other physical and chemical processes, e.g., the kinetics of atomic diffusion, crystal growth, and phase transformations in both metallic and ceramic systems. A relatively new variable in the study of these latter processes is pressure (hydrostatic or otherwise), and many of the pressure effects recently investigated (and discussed in other parts of this book) indicate some promising directions for future development of new materials. It seems inevitable that many of these new materials prepared under specific pressure conditions will have magnetic properties of scientific as well as technological importance.

However, our principal concern here is the more immediate contribution to our basic understanding of magnetism made by the study of various intrinsic magnetic properties of solids under hydrostatic pressure. In contrast with the properties mentioned above, which are governed largely by macroscopic conditions, the intrinsic magnetic behavior of a material is determined by forces operating on an atomic scale. Among the most powerful of these forces are the quantum-mechanical exchange interactions between electrons. It is often convenient, though not rigorously valid, to make a conceptual separation of the exchange interactions in a magnetic material into two parts: (1) an *intra-atomic* part which prevents the complete antiparallel pairing of electron spin moments within the unfilled d or f shell of a transition-group atom and thus produces a net magnetic moment on this atom and (2) an *interatomic* part which acts as a coupling between the atomic moments and tends to align them parallel (ferromagnetically) or antiparallel (antiferromagnetically) to each other. Below some critical temperature, the interatomic interactions become comparable to the disruptive thermal forces and give rise to a cooperative magnetic state characterized by a spontaneous alignment of the atomic moments.

Thus, for a simple ferromagnet or antiferromagnet which has only one type of interaction (i.e., parallel or antiparallel, but not both) between its atomic moments, the Curie or Néel temperature is a direct measure of the interatomic exchange forces. The nature of this exchange mechanism can therefore be probed by measurements of magnetic ordering temperatures as a function of different experimental variables, of which one of the most promising is hydrostatic pressure. It has long been theoretically contended that the effective exchange coupling between the atomic moments of a transition-group metal or alloy is dependent on the atomic separation distance. This has led to the now famous Bethe-Slater interaction curve,[1] which is shown in its usual schematic form in Fig. 10-1. The exchange coefficient J, which is positive or negative for ferromagnetic or antiferromagnetic interactions, respectively, is the ordinate, and the ratio of the nearest-neighbor atomic separation to the diameter of the unfilled electron shell is the abscissa. The closed circles in this figure correspond to the ferromagnetic elements in their normal room-temperature crystal forms and to antiferromagnetic, face-centered-tetragonal manganese, obtained by extrapolation from the manganese-rich manganese-copper alloys.[2] The values of J

[1] J. C. Slater, Atomic Shielding Constants, *Phys. Rev.*, vol. 36, no. 1, pp. 57–64, 1930; H. Bethe, Ferromagnetism, pp. 595–598 in A. Smekal (ed.), "Handbuch der Physik," vol. 24, part 2, Springer-Verlag, Berlin, 1933.

[2] G. E. Bacon, I. W. Dunmur, J. H. Smith, and R. Street, The Antiferromagnetism of Manganese Copper Alloys, *Proc. Roy. Soc. London*, series A, vol. 241, no. 1225, pp. 223–238, 1957.

for these materials relate directly to the Curie or Néel temperatures and therefore represent the approximate strengths of the interatomic exchange interactions (specifically, those between nearest-neighbor atom pairs, as indicated by the labeling of the points).

Although all the closed circles in Fig. 10-1 have been joined together by a single curve, this is probably not justified, since the materials are quite different in crystal form. Nevertheless, this interaction curve has been a useful guide to the sign, if not the magnitude, of the expected pressure dependence of the magnetic ordering temperature of any of these pure metals. In this qualitative use of the curve, it has been generally assumed that only the atomic spacings, and not the dimensions of the

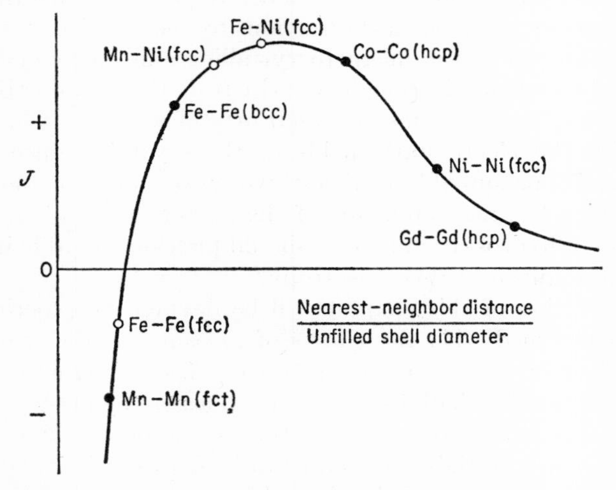

Fig. 10-1 Exchange coefficient J as a function of the ratio of nearest-neighbor distance to the diameter of the unfilled electron shell.

unfilled electron shell, respond to a change in pressure. As we shall show later, the interaction curve of Fig. 10-1 has been particularly helpful in the interpretation of the effects of pressure on the Curie temperatures of certain ferromagnetic alloys.

In the simple ferromagnet defined earlier (which presumably includes the pure metals iron, cobalt, and nickel), all the atomic moments are aligned parallel to each other at absolute zero temperature. In such a case, any pressure dependence of the saturation magnetization measured at very low temperatures will correspond to an effect of pressure on the magnitude of the atomic moments and, ultimately, on the strength of the intra-atomic exchange forces. This correspondence will also obtain for a simple ferrimagnet, such as magnetite, with an ordered antiparallel arrangement of unequal moments. However, for any system whose compression alters the alignment as well as the magnitude of its atomic moments, any change in saturation magnetization with pressure requires a very different interpretation. Recent pressure experiments indicate that the face-centered-cubic iron-nickel alloys and several other atomically disordered alloys may be examples of such a system, as later discussion will show.

In addition to the exchange interactions, there is another important, though generally much smaller, interaction in a ferromagnetic crystal which acts as an effective coupling between the atomic moments and the crystal lattice. As a consequence, the atomic moments (and, hence, the total magnetization of the material) are preferentially aligned along particular crystal directions. The energy required to turn the magnetization from these so-called easy directions by means of an external magnetic field is known as the magnetocrystalline anisotropy energy. This anisotropy phenomenon is thought to arise from the coupling between the spin moments of the electrons and their orbital moments which, in turn, interact with the electrostatic fields of the crystal. Since a uniform compression will presumably change the intensity but not the symmetry of the crystal fields, measurements of the magnetocrystalline anisotropy as a function of hydrostatic pressure should provide valuable information about the mechanism of this anisotropy.

The next section of this chapter will be devoted to experiments that have been concerned with the effects of pressure on the magnetization or on the magnetic transition temperature of various magnetic substances. In the final section we shall discuss the few measurements that have been made of the pressure dependence of the magnetocrystalline anisotropy of ferromagnetic materials. Several brief reviews[3] of pressure work in magnetism have been very helpful to this author's perspective on these topics.

An inherent requirement of all the experiments to be discussed has been that the specimen inside the pressure apparatus be subjected to a magnetic field. Since this field has usually been produced by an external electromagnet, the pressure cell has had to be built out of a strong nonferromagnetic material (e.g., various austenitic stainless steels and beryllium-copper alloys) which would allow penetration by the field and yet withstand moderately high pressures (up to about 10 kilobars). In some recent experiments in which the fields were produced inside the

[3] P. W. Bridgman, "The Physics of High Pressure," pp. 373–375, G. Bell & Sons, Ltd., London, 1931; J. C. Jamieson and A. W. Lawson, Solid State Studies under High Pressure, chap. 6 in K. Lark-Horovitz and V. A. Johnson (eds.), "Methods of Experimental Physics," vol. 6, part A, Academic Press, Inc., New York, 1959; C. A. Swenson, Physics at High Pressure, pp. 41–147 in F. Seitz and D. Turnbull (eds.), "Solid State Physics," vol. 11, Academic Press, Inc., New York, 1960.

pressure vessel (which was therefore made from a stronger ferritic steel), hydrostatic pressures of over 25 kilobars could be theoretically attained. In practice, however, many reliable magnetic measurements have been made at pressures considerably below the theoretical upper limit for the apparatus. The uniformity of the pressure, rather than its magnitude, has been the critical factor; deviations from truly hydrostatic pressure can cause large spurious changes in magnetization, whereas a narrow operating range of hydrostatic pressures can often be compensated for by an increased sensitivity to small magnetic changes. It is very reasonable to expect that improvements in the precision of various magnetic measurements and the development of convenient hydrostatic-pressure techniques for many temperatures of operation will be more effectively combined in future pressure research in magnetism. Even today, in many cases in which the pressure dependence of a magnetic property is thermodynamically related to some constant-pressure property (e.g., volume magnetostriction and anomalous temperature coefficient of expansion), the pressure experiment is the simpler one to perform.

10-2 Magnetic Moments and Transformations

10-2a Pure metals. The very first experiments on the effects of pressure on magnetic materials were prompted by the interest of Nagaoka and Honda[4] in checking the results of their volume-magnetostriction measurements on iron and nickel. The thermodynamic equation they used can be expressed as

$$V^{-1}\frac{\partial V}{\partial H} = -D\frac{\partial \sigma}{\partial P} \tag{10-1}$$

where the volume magnetostriction is related to the pressure dependence of σ, the magnetization per unit mass, and D is the density. The magnetization changes observed in hydrostatic pressures up to 250 bars were too small to be determined quantitatively, but the authors found that $\partial\sigma/\partial P$ was negative for iron and positive for nickel, in agreement with their magnetostriction results. However, a subsequent repeat of these measurements gave negative values for this pressure effect in nickel.[5] Although nickel has continued up to the present day to defy consistent pressure measurements of its magnetization, the experiments of Nagaoka and Honda were particularly handicapped by the use of magnetizing fields of less than 100 oersted, which were incapable of saturating any of the ferromagnetic specimens. A similar range of low magnetizing fields

[4] H. Nagaoka and K. Honda, On Magnetostriction, *Phil. Mag.*, series 5, vol. 46, no. 280, pp. 261–290, 1898.

[5] H. Nagaoka and K. Honda, On the Magnetostriction of Steel, Nickel, Cobalt and Nickel Steels, *Phil. Mag.*, series 6, vol. 4, no. 19, pp. 45–72, 1902.

was used in other early pressure work.[6,7] Yeh's experiments were specifically aimed at finding changes in magnetic permeability with pressure. Steinberger, however, also chose to interpret his low-field magnetization results for various iron-nickel alloys under compression in terms of more intrinsic behavior. His oft-quoted discovery that the 30 percent nickel alloy under a 12.5-kilobar pressure "becomes nonmagnetic" at room temperature was made with fields no higher than 7.5 oersted, which left his polycrystalline specimen magnetically unsaturated. Hence, this dramatic pressure effect cannot be attributed with any certainty to a change in saturation moment; nor can it be attributed unambiguously to a Curie-point variation on the basis of low-field measurements at a single temperature.

The need for fairly high magnetizing fields in any reliable measurement of the effect of pressure on saturation moment was clearly demonstrated by the experiments of Ebert and Kussman[8] on iron, nickel, and various ferromagnetic alloys. Reserving discussion of the alloys for later, we note that the values they obtained for the pressure dependence of the magnetization of iron fluctuated (and even changed sign) as a function of the applied field before settling down to a more or less constant value for fields over approximately 1,000 oersted. A similar behavior was observed in nickel, except that lower fields were required for saturation of the pressure effect. Their results at these moderately high fields (up to about 2,000 oersted), expressed as relative changes of saturation magnetization with pressure, $\sigma_s^{-1}(\partial\sigma_s/\partial P)$, were -6×10^{-7} bar^{-1} and -2.8×10^{-7} bar^{-1}, for iron and nickel, respectively. Both these measurements were made on annealed specimens at room temperature with a maximum hydrostatic pressure of about 3 kilobars. The nickel specimen was also studied before annealing, when it was still in a cold-worked state; in this case, the magnetization change with pressure never reached a steady value, but was still varying at the maximum available field of about 2,000 oersted. Since this field is more than sufficient to overcome the magnetocrystalline anisotropy of nickel, the result indicates the extraordinarily large additional forces that can inhibit the magnetization process in a highly strained material and which must be avoided in a pressure experiment of this kind.

Room-temperature measurements of the saturation moment of iron under hydrostatic pressure have been made more recently by Galperin

[6] Chi-Sun Yeh, The Effect of Hydrostatic Pressure on the Magnetic Permeability of Iron, Cobalt, and Nickel, *Proc. Am. Acad. Arts Sci.*, vol. 60, no. 12, pp. 503–533, 1925.

[7] R. L. Steinberger, Magnetic Properties of the Iron-Nickel Alloys under Hydrostatic Pressure, *Physics*, vol. 4, no. 4, pp. 153–161, 1933.

[8] H. Ebert and A. Kussman, Änderung der Sättigungsmagnetisierung durch allseitigen Druck, *Physik. Z.*, vol. 38, no. 12, pp. 437–445, 1937.

et al.[9] and by Kouvel and Wilson;[10] the values obtained for $\sigma_s^{-1}(\partial\sigma_s/\partial P)$ were, respectively, -1.70×10^{-7} bar^{-1} and -2.78×10^{-7} bar^{-1}. The latter quantity, determined at fields up to 12 kilo-oersted, appears to be favored by a comparison with the values -4.4, -4.0, and -2.9 (in 10^{-7} bar^{-1}) computed by means of Eq. (10-1) from the results of volume-magnetostriction measurements at room temperature.[5,11,12] Despite the differences among these room-temperature values for the $\sigma_s^{-1}(\partial\sigma_s/\partial P)$ of iron, there is at least general agreement on its negative sign and on its very small order of magnitude.

There is no such agreement on nickel, however, at the present time. Subsequent to Ebert and Kussman's work, Stacey[13] attempted a different type of experiment in which a thin disk of nickel was squeezed by direct piston action of the poles of an electromagnet which formed part of a permeameter circuit. By this technique, he obtained values of $+360 \times 10^{-7}$ bar^{-1} and $+50 \times 10^{-7}$ bar^{-1} for $\sigma_s^{-1}(\partial\sigma_s/\partial P)$ at pressures of 1 and 10 kilobars, respectively. However, pressures generated in this way are only very approximately hydrostatic and produce considerable plastic deformation of the specimen, which, as indicated previously, can cause serious departures from magnetic saturation, even at the high fields generally achieved by this technique. A similar method was later used by Gugan,[14] but in this case the permeameter assembly was placed inside a hydrostatic-pressure vessel and was relied on only for magnetic measurements, which for annealed and cold-rolled nickel specimens gave $(0 \pm 4) \times 10^{-7}$ bar^{-1} and -31×10^{-7} bar^{-1}, respectively, for $M_s^{-1}(\partial M_s/\partial P)$. A zero result ($\pm 1.2 \times 10^{-7}$ bar^{-1}) for $M_s^{-1}(\partial M_s/\partial P)$ was also obtained by von Klitzing and Gielessen[15] from hydrostatic-pressure measurements on annealed nickel in a maximum field of 6,400 oersted.

The results of the latter two experiments are given, as they were in

[9] F. Galperin, S. Larin, and A. Shishkov, A Study of the Effect of Pressure on the Magnetic Saturation of Iron at Liquid Nitrogen Temperature (translated from Russian), *Doklady Akad. Nauk S. S. S. R.*, vol. 89, no. 3, pp. 419–422, 1953.

[10] J. S. Kouvel and R. H. Wilson, Magnetization of Iron-Nickel Alloys under Hydrostatic Pressure, *J. Appl. Phys.*, vol. 32, no 3, pp. 435–441, 1961.

[11] M. Kornetzki, Über die Abhängigkeit der Volumenmagnetostriktion und des Weissschen Faktors von der Temperature und der Gitterkonstante, *Z. Physik*, vol. 98, nos. 5 and 6, pp. 289–313, 1935.

[12] J. L. Snoek, Volume Magnetostriction of Iron and Nickel, *Physica*, vol. 4, no. 9, pp. 853–862, 1937.

[13] F. D. Stacey, The Behavior of Ferromagnetics under Strong Compression, *Can. J. Phys.*, vol. 34, no. 3, pp. 304–311, 1956.

[14] D. Gugan, The Change of Spontaneous Magnetization with Hydrostatic Pressure, *Proc. Phys. Soc. London*, vol. 72, part 6, pp. 1013–1026, 1958.

[15] K. H. von Klitzing and J. Gielessen, Die Sättigungsmagnetisierung von Nickel unter hohem hydrostatischem Druck, *Z. Physik*, vol. 146, no. 1, pp. 59–64, 1956.

the original papers, as relative changes of M_s, the saturation magnetization per unit volume. However, it is preferable that such results be converted to the corresponding changes of σ_s by means of the identity

$$\sigma_s^{-1}\frac{\partial\sigma_s}{\partial P} = M_s^{-1}\frac{\partial M_s}{\partial P} - \kappa$$

where the volume compressibility $\kappa = -V^{-1}(\partial V/\partial P)$; $\sigma_s^{-1}(\partial\sigma_s/\partial P)$ is more directly related to the variations of the average atomic moment. Since the compressibility of nickel is about 5.5×10^{-7} bar^{-1}, it follows that the latter two results for annealed nickel give the negative of this quantity for $\sigma_s^{-1}(\partial\sigma_s/\partial P)$. More recent hydrostatic-pressure measurements by Kouvel and Wilson[10] gave $\sigma_s^{-1}(\partial\sigma_s/\partial P) = +1.31 \times 10^{-7}$ bar^{-1} for an annealed polycrystalline specimen of nickel, but a negative value (of about the same magnitude) was later obtained for a similarly annealed nickel crystal. Although the former result is very close to the value $+1.15 \times 10^{-7}$ bar^{-1} deduced from the most recent volume-magnetostriction measurements,[16] the latter is more consistent, not only with the previous pressure results described above, but also with the values -2.4×10^{-7} bar^{-1} and -1.96×10^{-7} bar^{-1} obtained from earlier volume-magnetostriction experiments.[5,12]

All the pressure measurements discussed thus far were made at room temperature, where the experimental techniques are relatively simple. However, the experimental convenience is largely offset by the fact that the pressure dependence of the saturation magnetization at room temperature is not in itself a fundamental property. Under the simplifying assumptions that the magnetization-versus-temperature curve of a ferromagnet may be expressed as

$$\sigma_s = \sigma_0 f\left(\frac{T}{\theta}\right) \tag{10-2}$$

and that the form of the function f is unaffected by changes in pressure, it follows that an observed change of σ_s with pressure at temperature T can be the result of a corresponding variation of σ_0, the saturation moment at 0°K, and/or of θ, the Curie temperature. The relationship between the pressure dependences of these different quantities may be expressed as[10]

$$\sigma_s^{-1}\frac{\partial\sigma_s}{\partial P} = \frac{\sigma_0^{-1}(\partial\sigma_0/\partial P) - (T/\sigma_s)(\partial\sigma_s/\partial T)_P\theta^{-1}(\partial\theta/\partial P)}{1 + (3\alpha T/\kappa)\theta^{-1}(\partial\theta/\partial P)} \tag{10-3}$$

where α is the temperature coefficient of linear expansion. According to this expression, or to an analogous but more complicated one derived

[16] K. Azumi and J. E. Goldman, Volume Magnetostriction in Nickel and the Bethe-Slater Interaction Curve, *Phys. Rev.*, vol. 93, no. 3, pp. 630–631, 1954.

from molecular field theory,[17] a measurement of $\partial\sigma_s/\partial P$ at a single temperature can determine either one of the basic quantities $\partial\sigma_0/\partial P$ and $\partial\theta/\partial P$, but only when the other is known.

The effects of pressure on the Curie temperatures of iron and nickel, as well as of several other materials, were measured by Patrick[18] by a method in which the ferromagnetic specimen formed a section of an alternating-current transformer inside the pressure vessel. This method was devised for accurate determination of changes in Curie temperature but was less reliable for values of the Curie temperatures themselves. In the experiments on nickel and other materials having Curie points under 400°C, a liquid pressure medium and external heating were used, whereas the materials with higher Curie points, such as iron, were compressed by argon gas and heated internally. Despite substantial scatter of the data taken at the higher temperatures, Patrick was able to assign the value 0 ± 0.1 degree/kilobar to the pressure dependence of the Curie temperature of iron. This essentially zero result is in contrast to the value -5 to -10 degrees/kilobar calculated earlier by Kornetzki.[11] In his calculation, Kornetzki used Eq. (10-1) to convert his room-temperature volume-magnetostriction result for iron into a $\partial\sigma_s/\partial P$ value which he then substituted into Eq. (10-3) and solved for $\partial\theta/\partial P$, assuming that $\partial\sigma_0/\partial P = 0$. The only direct measurement of $\partial\sigma_s/\partial P$ for iron at low temperatures was made by Galperin et al.,[9] whose result at 77°K (where pressures up to 2 kilobars were transmitted by a gaseous medium) was not very different from what they obtained at room temperature. It would therefore appear that Kornetzki's assumption that $\partial\sigma_0/\partial P = 0$ in iron is questionable and that Patrick's result, $\partial\theta/\partial P \simeq 0$, is probably correct. However, Patrick's result disagrees with the interaction curve of Fig. 10-1, whose large positive slope at the point for bcc iron would imply a sizable decrease of the Curie temperature with increased pressure.

For nickel, Patrick's measurements[18] gave $\partial\theta/\partial P = +0.35$ degree/kilobar, with a very satisfactory degree of accuracy. The sign of this effect is in agreement with the interaction curve of Fig. 10-1. Moreover, Döring[19] has pointed out that the volume magnetostriction of nickel measured adiabatically just below its Curie point, when corrected for magnetocaloric effects, yields a negative value for the isothermal $V^{-1}(\partial V/\partial H)$, which is the appropriate quantity for substitution into Eq. (10-1). The positive value for $\partial\sigma_s/\partial P$, thus obtained, is indicative

[17] R. Smoluchowski, On the Theory of Volume Magnetostriction, *Phys. Rev.*, vol. 59, no. 3, pp. 309–317, 1941.

[18] L. Patrick, The Change of Ferromagnetic Curie Points with Hydrostatic Pressure, *Phys. Rev.*, vol. 93, no. 3, pp. 384–392, 1954.

[19] W. Döring, Über die Temperaturabhängigkeit der Magnetostriktion von Nickel, *Z. Physik*, vol. 103, nos. 9 and 10, pp. 560–582, 1936.

of a positive $\partial\theta/\partial P$. Another indirect estimate of $\partial\theta/\partial P$ for nickel was made by Michels and de Groot,[20] who used the Ehrenfest relation

$$\theta^{-1}\frac{\partial\theta}{\partial P} = \frac{3\Delta\alpha}{D\Delta C_m} \tag{10-4}$$

which is valid for the second-order magnetic transition that occurs at the Curie temperature. In nickel, $\Delta\alpha$ and ΔC_m, the abrupt changes in the temperature coefficient of expansion and in the specific heat (per unit mass) at the Curie temperature, are both negative,[21] and it follows from Eq. (10-4) that $\partial\theta/\partial P$ should be positive. In fact, by substituting experimental values for $\Delta\alpha$, ΔC_m, and D (the density) for nickel into this equation, Michels and de Groot computed a positive value for $\partial\theta/\partial P$ identical with that found directly by Patrick. If $\partial\theta/\partial P$ for nickel is indeed positive, then the negative $\partial\sigma_s/\partial P$, obtained in the majority of the pressure- and volume-magnetostriction measurements at room temperature, would indicate that $\partial\sigma_0/\partial P$ must also be negative. Hence, from existing experimental evidence, one may tentatively conclude that for nickel as well as iron there is a small decrease of the saturation magnetization at 0°K with increasing pressure.

There have been very few experiments on the magnetic properties of other ferromagnetic elements under pressure. The only measurement of the effect of pressure on the magnetization of cobalt was made by Gugan,[14] whose result, converted to $\sigma_s^{-1}(\partial\sigma_s/\partial P)$, is about -13.5×10^{-7} bar^{-1}, which disagrees with the value -3.5×10^{-7} bar^{-1} deduced from earlier volume-magnetostriction measurements.[22] The latter value is probably more dependable since it was obtained in fields high enough to overcome the large anisotropy forces in the polycrystalline cobalt specimens. Patrick's attempt[18] to measure the very high Curie temperature of cobalt as a function of pressure was unsuccessful. The low Curie point (289°K) of gadolinium was much less of an obstacle, and Patrick[18] determined its pressure dependence as -1.2 degrees/kilobar. This negative value for $\partial\theta/\partial P$ is inconsistent with the positive effect predicted for gadolinium from the interaction curve of Fig. 10-1.

10-2b Alloys and compounds. The alloy system whose magnetic properties as a function of pressure has attracted by far the most experimental attention is that of iron and nickel. As mentioned in Sec. 10-2a,

[20] A. Michels and S. R. de Groot, Influence of Pressure on the Curie Point, *Physica*, vol. 16, no. 3, pp. 249–252, 1950.

[21] R. M. Bozorth, "Ferromagnetism," pp. 447 and 735, D. Van Nostrand Company, Inc., Princeton, N.J., 1951.

[22] M. Kornetzki, Über die Magnetostriktion von ferromagnetischen Ellipsoiden. II. Messungen an Eisen und Kobalt, *Z. Physik*, vol. 87, nos. 9 and 10, pp. 560–579, 1934.

it has long been known that the alloys of about 30 percent nickel exhibit an unusually large positive volume magnetostriction at room temperature.[5,11,23] Large decreases in the magnetization of these iron-nickel compositions with increasing pressure could therefore be anticipated by virtue of Eq. (10-1); they were first observed by Steinberger.[7] However, as discussed previously, Steinberger's pressure experiments involved very low magnetizing fields, and, hence, his results cannot be interpreted unambiguously. Hydrostatic-pressure measurements on iron-nickel alloys were subsequently made under magnetic-saturation conditions by Ebert and Kussman[8] and by Gugan,[14] whose room-temperature values for $-\sigma_s^{-1}(\partial\sigma_s/\partial P)$ are plotted against alloy composition in Fig. 10-2.

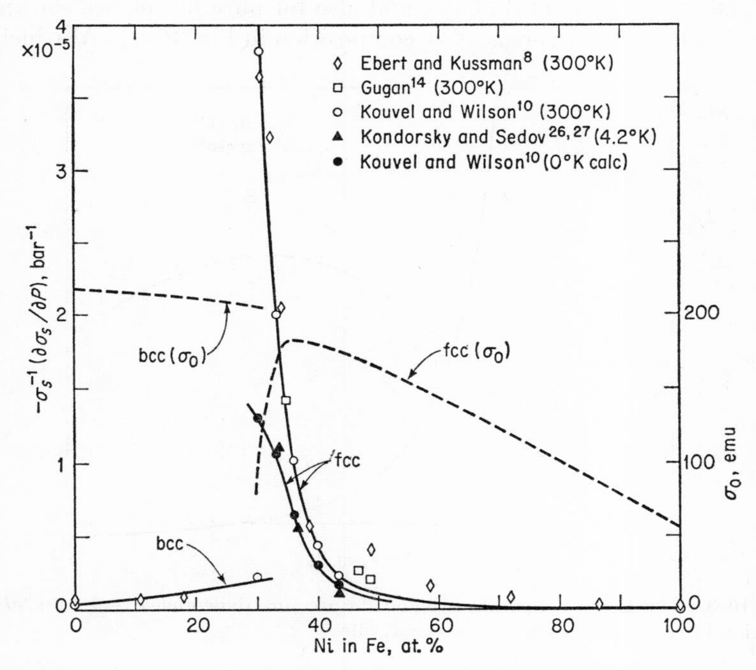

Fig. 10-2 Values of $-\sigma_s^{-1}$ $(\partial\sigma_s/\partial P)$ and σ_0 as a function of the composition of iron-nickel alloys.

Higher values of $-\sigma_s^{-1}(\partial\sigma_s/\partial P)$ reported for alloys of just under 30 percent nickel[8] lie outside the figure; nevertheless, this figure adequately demonstrates the enormous increase in the magnitude of this negative pressure effect at these compositions.

The possibility that the low Curie points of the alloys of about 30 per-

[23] Y. Masiyama, On the Magnetostriction of Iron-Nickel Alloys, *Sci. Repts. Tôhoku Imp. Univ.*, vol. 20, pp. 574–593, 1931.

cent nickel in iron may be sufficiently pressure sensitive to give rise to the large pressure dependence of the room-temperature magnetizations was argued against by Ebert and Kussman on the basis of the small magnetization-pressure effects observed in many other alloys of low Curie point.[8] Indeed, from an analysis of their magnetization-pressure data at various temperatures for the alloy of 30 percent nickel in iron, Ebert and Kussman[24] later concluded that the pressure dependence of the Curie point of this alloy was essentially zero. This, however, was not borne out by Patrick's more direct measurements,[18] which revealed a substantial decrease of the Curie temperature with increased pressure for an alloy of approximately this composition. Patrick's results for this and other iron-nickel alloys, and also for pure nickel, are shown in a plot of $-\theta^{-1}(\partial\theta/\partial P)$ versus alloy composition in Fig. 10-3. Also included

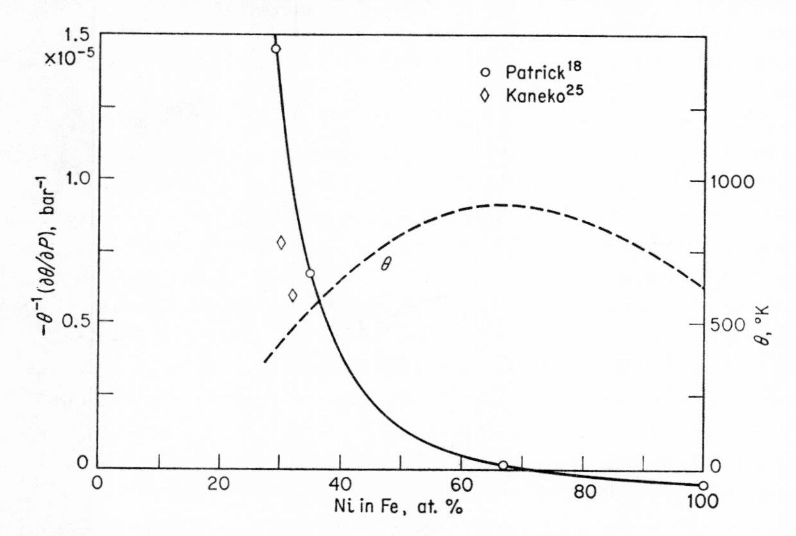

Fig. 10-3 The Curie temperature θ and its pressure dependence $-\theta^{-1}(\partial\theta/\partial P)$ as a function of the composition of iron-nickel alloys.

in this figure are the more recent results of Kaneko.[25] It should be noted that the change in the sign of $\partial\theta/\partial P$ from positive to negative with decreasing nickel concentration is consistent with the experimental fact that $\Delta\alpha$, which appears in the Ehrenfest relation [Eq. (10-4)], changes correspondingly from a negative to a positive quantity,[21] while ΔC_m remains negative.

[24] H. Ebert and A. Kussman, Über den Einfluss allseitigen Druckes auf die Curietemperatur, *Physik. Z.*, vol. 39, no. 16, pp. 598–605, 1938.

[25] T. Kaneko, The Change of the Curie Temperatures of Iron-Nickel Alloys due to Hydrostatic Pressure, *J. Phys. Soc. Japan*, vol. 15, no. 12, pp. 2247–2251, 1960.

Recent work has indicated that the large changes of magnetization with pressure in the alloys of about 30 percent nickel in iron (Fig. 10-2) cannot be attributed solely to the large pressure dependence of their Curie temperatures (Fig. 10-3). Using pressures created at very low temperatures by freezing water in a beryllium-bronze bomb, Kondorsky and Sedov[26] found large decreases in saturation magnetization with increasing pressure in alloys of about 38 and 45 percent nickel in iron. Moreover, the observed magnetization changes were independent of temperature from 77°K down to 4.2°K. Similar results were later obtained by the same workers[27] with helium gas as their low-temperature pressure medium. Their values for $-\sigma_0^{-1}(\partial\sigma_0/\partial P)$ are plotted in Fig. 10-2, where they lie consistently just below the $-\sigma_s^{-1}(\partial\sigma_s/\partial P)$ values obtained at room temperature (which include the recent results of Kouvel and Wilson[10]). Furthermore, Kouvel and Wilson substituted their room-temperature values for $-\sigma_s^{-1}(\partial\sigma_s/\partial P)$ and values for $-\theta^{-1}(\partial\theta/\partial P)$ taken from the curve in Fig. 10-3 into Eq. (10-3), and they thus computed $-\sigma_0^{-1}(\partial\sigma_0/\partial P)$ for each of their iron-nickel alloys. These also are plotted in Fig. 10-2, and the curve drawn through them shows very good agreement with the $-\sigma_0^{-1}(\partial\sigma_0/\partial P)$ values measured directly at very low temperatures.[27] Hence, it follows from this figure that σ_0, as well as θ, becomes increasingly pressure-sensitive as the nickel concentration in these alloys decreases toward 30 percent and that both these effects contribute additively [in the manner shown in Eq. (10-3)] to the large pressure dependence of σ_s observed at room temperature.

Kouvel and Wilson[10] also measured the room-temperature $\sigma_s^{-1}(\partial\sigma_s/\partial P)$ for their 30 percent nickel in iron specimen after it had been almost completely and irreversibly transformed to a bcc structure by cooling to 77°K, which is well below the martensite-start temperature of this alloy. The value obtained was -22×10^{-7} bar^{-1}, compared to -382×10^{-7} bar^{-1} for the same alloy in its original fcc state; both these values are shown in Fig. 10-2. The two states of this 30 percent nickel alloy are also very different in saturation moment and Curie temperature. For the bcc alloy, σ_0 and θ are only slightly below those for pure iron, i.e., about 200 emu and 1000°K, whereas those shown in Figs. 10-2 and 10-3 for the fcc alloy are considerably smaller and decrease rapidly with decreasing nickel concentration.

This difference in the variation of σ_0 and θ with composition has sug-

[26] E. I. Kondorsky and V. L. Sedov, Variation de l'aimantation à saturation et de la résistance électrique d'alliages fer-nickel sous l'effet d'une compression isotrope aux basses températures, *J. phys. radium*, vol. 20, nos. 2 and 3, pp. 185–191, 1959.

[27] E. I. Kondorsky and V. L. Sedov, Antiferromagnetism of Iron in Face-centered Crystalline Lattice and the Causes of Anomalies in Invar Physical Properties, *J. Appl. Phys.*, vol. 31, supplement, no. 5, pp. 331–335, 1960.

gested to Kondorsky and Sedov[27] and to Kouvel and Wilson[10] that while the bcc iron-nickel alloys are probably simple ferromagnets with all their atomic moments aligned parallel, the fcc alloys of low nickel content have some of their atomic moments aligned antiferromagnetically. This partial antiferromagnetic alignment was considered to be the result of exchange forces between nearest-neighbor iron-iron atom pairs which in the fcc alloys were antiferromagnetic, in contrast to the ferromagnetic iron-iron interactions in the bcc alloys. The iron-nickel and nickel-nickel nearest-neighbor interactions were taken to be ferromagnetic in both bcc and fcc alloys. It was then argued that all the interactions in the fcc iron-nickel alloys can be plotted on the same Bethe-Slater type of curve as shown in Fig. 10-1, and that the effect of compression on each interaction can be represented by a shift to the left along this curve. Thus, an increase of pressure will result in a gradual strengthening of the nickel-nickel couplings and a more rapid weakening of the iron-nickel couplings, and the pressure dependence of the Curie temperature will therefore change from a positive to a negative quantity when the iron concentration in the fcc alloys is high enough; this is borne out by the experimental results plotted in Fig. 10-3. However, since the iron-nickel and nickel-nickel interactions are assumed to be ferromagnetic, the parallel alignment of the atomic moments will remain essentially unchanged in the nickel-rich fcc alloys, even under compression. Consequently, any variation in the saturation magnetization of these alloys with pressure will reflect a change only in the magnitudes of the atomic moments; this effect is indicated by Fig. 10-2 to be quite small. The same qualitative argument applies for the small $\partial\sigma_s/\partial P$ observed in the bcc iron-nickel alloys. In the iron-rich fcc alloys, however, the rapid strengthening of the antiferromagnetic iron-iron interactions with increases of pressure not only gives rise to very large negative values for $\partial\theta/\partial P$, but also causes the antiferromagnetic alignment of an increasing number of atomic moments. Thus, according to this interpretation, the anomalously large negative values for $\partial\sigma_0/\partial P$ exhibited by the fcc alloys of about 30 percent nickel are quite different in origin from the smaller pressure effects in other iron-nickel alloys.

It has also been suggested[10] that the large pressure dependence of saturation magnetization at room temperature observed in atomically disordered fcc nickel-manganese alloys of about 20 percent manganese[8] can be attributed to a change in the directions (and not just the magnitudes) of the atomic moments. In this case, as indicated in Fig. 10-1, it is the manganese-manganese nearest-neighbor interactions which are assumed to be antiferromagnetic and to increase in strength as the alloy is compressed, whereas the manganese-nickel and nickel-nickel interactions are assumed to be ferromagnetic. Upon suitable heat treatment, these alloys develop a high degree of Ni_3Mn atomic order, which drastically reduces the number of nearest-neighbor manganese-manganese atom pairs. Experimentally, the ordered nickel-manganese alloys are found to have a higher saturation magnetization and a lower pressure dependence of magnetization than the same alloys in a disordered state;[8] both these effects of ordering are consistent with a reduced number of antiferromagnetic interactions.

Other binary alloys whose pressure dependences of saturation moment were measured at room temperature by Ebert and Kussman[8] include those of nickel with aluminum, cobalt, chromium, and copper and those of iron with cobalt and chromium. In all these materials, the pressure effects were negative and about as small as those in pure iron and nickel. A small negative value of $\partial\sigma_s/\partial P$ for a nickel-copper alloy was also obtained at room temperature by Gugan.[14] Moreover, since Patrick[18] observed no change with pressure in the Curie point of a nickel-copper alloy, it appears that the low values of $\partial\sigma_s/\partial P$ at room temperature can be attributed to variations of σ_0 with pressure, which in turn are probably associated with small changes in the magnitudes of the atomic moments. Ebert and Kussman[8] also investigated several fcc platinum-iron alloys and found that with an increasing percentage of iron the room-temperature value for $\sigma_s^{-1}(\partial\sigma_s/\partial P)$ became increasingly negative, reaching -207×10^{-7} bar^{-1} in the 44 percent iron alloy. In these alloys, and in the ternary iron-cobalt-chromium alloy for which the same workers obtained a room-temperature $\sigma_s^{-1}(\partial\sigma_s/\partial P)$ value of -600×10^{-7} bar^{-1}, it seems quite likely that the large pressure effects are the result of changes in direction, as well as in magnitude, of the atomic moments.

Very little work has been done on the effects of hydrostatic pressure on the magnetic properties of ionic compounds. Patrick's[18] measurements of the Curie temperatures of a manganese-zinc ferrite and of a perovskite (approximate formula: $La_{0.75}Sr_{0.25}MnO_3$) as a function of pressure gave +0.9 and +0.6 degree/kilobar, respectively, for $\partial\theta/\partial P$. More recently, Werner[28] obtained a $\partial\theta/\partial P$ value of +0.85 degree/kilobar for a nickel-zinc ferrite.

In each of the materials whose Curie-temperature pressure dependence has been discussed earlier, the magnetic transition occurring at this temperature is thermodynamically second-order. Pressure studies have also been made of the ordered alloys Au_2Mn and MnAs, for which first-order magnetic transitions have been reported. Magnetic measurements[29] have indicated that below about 360°K, Au_2Mn is antiferro-

[28] K. Werner, Der Einfluss hydrostatischen Druckes auf den Curiepunkt eines Ni-Zn Ferrites, *Ann. Physik Leipzig*, series 7, vol. 2, nos. 7 and 8, pp. 403–405, 1959.

[29] A. J. P. Meyer and P. Taglang, Propriétés magnétiques, antiferromagnétisme et ferromagnétisme de $MnAu_2$, *J. phys. radium*, vol. 17, no. 6, pp. 457–465, 1956.

magnetic in fields less than about 10 kilo-oersted; its antiferromagnetism in low fields has been confirmed by neutron-diffraction experiments,[30] which furthermore revealed a helical arrangement of atomic moments.

In higher fields, the magnetization of Au_2Mn rises very rapidly and then levels off at what appears to be a ferromagnetic saturation value. This remarkable so-called metamagnetic behavior is illustrated in Fig. 10-4 by the magnetization-versus-field curves obtained recently by

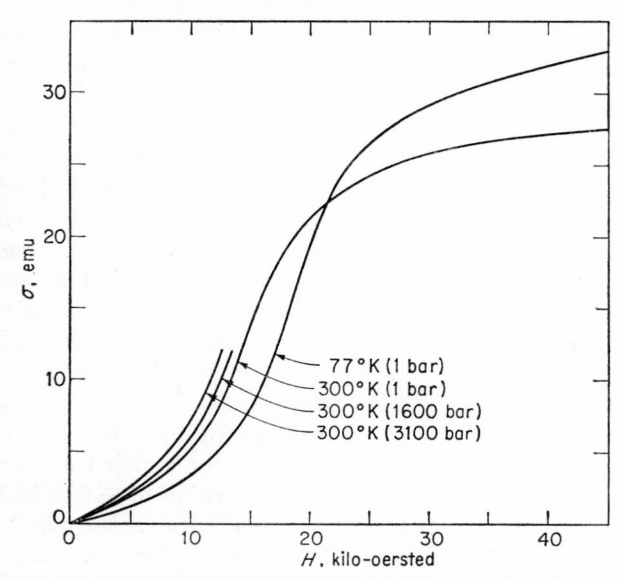

Fig. 10-4 Magnetization of Au_2Mn at room and liquid-nitrogen temperatures as a function of field.

Rodbell[31] at liquid-nitrogen and room temperatures at atmospheric pressure. Also shown in this figure are Rodbell's results for Au_2Mn under various hydrostatic pressures at room temperature, which indicate a lowering of the critical field required for this transition with increasing pressure; these results are consistent with previous hydrostatic-pressure measurements by von Klitzing and Gielessen.[32] If this transition can be regarded as first-order, the critical field at a given temperature should

[30] A. Herpin, P. Mériel, and J. Villain, Structure magnétique de l'alliage $MnAu_2$, *Compt. rend.*, vol. 249, no. 15, pp. 1334–1336. 1959.

[31] D. S. Rodbell, pp. 283–286 in F. P. Bundy, W. R. Hibbard, Jr., and H. M. Strong (eds.), "Progress in Very High Pressure Research," John Wiley & Sons, Inc., New York, 1961.

[32] K. H. von Klitzing and J. Gielessen, Über den Einfluss allseitigen Drucks auf die Magnetisierbarkeit von Au_2Mn, *Z. Physik*, vol. 150, no. 4, pp. 409–414, 1958.

vary with applied pressure according to the thermodynamic expression

$$\frac{\partial H_c}{\partial P} = \frac{V^{-1}\,\Delta V}{D\,\Delta\sigma} \tag{10-5}$$

where ΔV and $\Delta\sigma$ are the changes in volume and magnetic moment (per unit mass) at the transition and D is the density. For Au_2Mn, in which $\partial H_c/\partial P$ is negative and $\Delta\sigma$ (for increasing field) is positive, Eq. (10-5) would predict a volume contraction as this material transforms from antiferromagnetic to ferromagnetic; this volume change has not yet been measured. It has also been noted[31] that the observed decrease of H_c with increasing pressure removes the possibility that the lowering of H_c with increasing temperature (indicated in Fig. 10-4) is simply a thermal-expansion effect.

The intermetallic compound MnAs is a less ambiguous example of a material that undergoes a first-order magnetic transformation. It is ferromagnetic below 312°K, at which temperature its spontaneous magnetization abruptly disappears. This transition is accompanied by a discontinuous volume contraction[33] of about 1.9 percent and by a latent heat[34] of about 1.8 cal/gm. According to the Clausius-Clapeyron equation

$$\theta^{-1}\frac{\partial \theta}{\partial P} = \frac{V^{-1}\,\Delta V}{D\,\Delta Q_m} \tag{10-6}$$

the volume change ΔV and the latent heat per unit mass ΔQ_m, at a first-order transition, are related to the pressure dependence of the transition temperature θ. When the above values for θ, $V^{-1}\,\Delta V$, ΔQ_m and the density D of 6.3 gm/cm^3 are inserted into Eq. (10-6), it is found that $\partial\theta/\partial P \simeq -12$ degrees/kilobar. Rodbell[31] recently made direct measurements of the pressure dependence of θ in MnAs. In this experiment, the magnetization in a 12-kilo-oersted field was measured at several temperatures as a function of hydrostatic compression. The results are shown in Fig. 10-5, and it is evident that at each temperature there is a rapid decrease of the magnetization at some critical value of pressure. Moreover, the pressure required to induce this transition from ferromagnetism increases monatonically with decreasing temperature or, conversely, the transition temperature decreases with increasing pressure. Quantitatively, the value for $\partial\theta/\partial P$ that Rodbell obtained from these data is in excellent agreement with the value computed from Eq. (10-6).

[33] B. T. M. Willis and H. P. Rooksby, Magnetic Transitions and Structural Changes in Hexagonal Manganese Compounds, *Proc. Phys. Soc. London*, series B, vol. 67, part 4, pp. 290–296, 1954.

[34] L. F. Bates, Magnetic Properties of Some Compounds of Manganese, *Phil. Mag.*, series 7, vol. 8, no. 52, pp. 714–732, 1929.

A difference between the data for increasing and decreasing pressure was observed at all these temperatures and is shown for 307°K in Fig. 10-5; it is analogous to the irreversibility of this first-order transition which occurs with increasing and decreasing temperature at constant pressure. A pressure hysteresis of this kind has not yet been encountered (and reported) in any pressure studies of the more usual second-order magnetic transitions in various other ferromagnets.

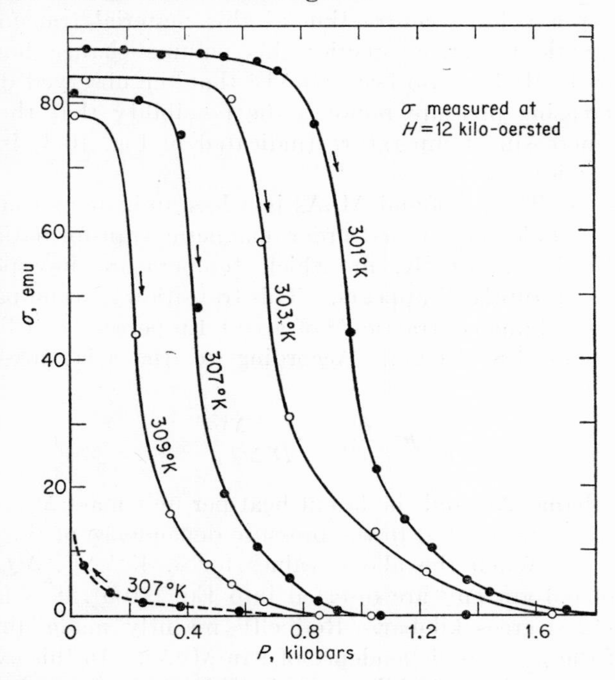

Fig. 10-5 Magnetization of MnAs at 12 kilo-oersted as a function of applied hydrostatic pressure.

First-order transitions from antiferromagnetism to ferromagnetism (with increasing temperature) have recently been reported[35,36] for the ordered alloys FeRh and chromium-modified Mn_2Sb. Both materials exhibit abrupt changes in volume as well as in magnetization; hence, the effect of hydrostatic pressure on these magnetic transitions would appear to be a very promising subject for future study.

[35] F. Debergevin and L. Muldawer, Ferromagnetic-Antiferromagnetic Transformation in FeRh, *Bull. Am. Phys. Soc.*, series 2, vol. 6, no. 2, p. 159, 1961.

[36] T. J. Swoboda, W. H. Cloud, T. A. Bither, M. S. Sadler, and H. S. Jarrett, Evidence for an Antiferromagnetic-Ferrimagnetic Transition in Cr-modified Mn_2Sb, *Phys. Rev. Letters*, vol. 4, no. 2, pp. 509–511, 1960.

10-3 Magnetocrystalline Anisotropy

The most reliable nonresonance method for determining the magnetic anisotropy of a ferromagnetic crystal is that of torque measurements in very high fields. However, this technique presents obvious experimental difficulties when the crystal specimen is located inside a pressure cell, and it has not yet been used in any measurements of a pressure-induced effect on the magnetocrystalline anisotropy. Alternatively, such an effect can be evaluated from measurements of the magnetization as a function of pressure at various fields up to those required for ferromagnetic saturation. Several versions of this general method have been resorted to, and in all of them it has been assumed that the magnetization of any part of the specimen can be regarded as a vector quantity of fixed magnitude σ_s which rotates smoothly into the direction of an increasing field against only the restraining forces of magnetic anisotropy. For these simplifying conditions, the equation that relates σ, the net magnetization parallel to the field, and the field H has the general form

$$H\sigma_s = K_1 f_1\left(\frac{\sigma}{\sigma_s}\right) + K_2 f_2\left(\frac{\sigma}{\sigma_s}\right) + \cdots \qquad (10\text{-}7)$$

where K_1, K_2, . . . are the magnetocrystalline anisotropy coefficients per unit mass appropriate to the crystal structure of the material. For a single crystal, the forms of the functions f_1, f_2, . . . are set by the field direction relative to the crystal axes; for a polycrystalline specimen, they represent complicated averages over all crystal orientations. In all cases, the functional forms of f_1, f_2, . . . have been assumed to be unaffected by variations in hydrostatic pressure.

It must be emphasized that in any measurements of K_1 and K_2 at different pressures it is very important that the pressures be truly hydrostatic; otherwise, any linear component of stress will induce an additional anisotropy (proportional to this stress and to the linear magnetostriction of the material) and thus give rise to extraneous results. In all the experiments described here, this possible pitfall has been avoided by the use of hydrostatic pressure fluids. The earliest of these experiments are those of Gugan and Rowlands[37] on polycrystalline specimens of nickel and of an iron-nickel alloy of 48 percent nickel. Their measurements were based on a theoretical relationship that can be derived by differentiation of Eq. (10-7) with respect to field and to pressure; terms in K_2 and higher-order anisotropy coefficients are neglected. By means

[37] D. Gugan and G. Rowlands, The Pressure Dependence of the Ferromagnetic Anisotropy Energy, *Proc. Phys. Soc. London,* vol. 72, part 2, pp. 207–213, 1958.

of this relationship,

$$K_1^{-1}\frac{\partial K_1}{\partial P} = \frac{\sigma_s^{-1}(\partial\sigma_s/\partial P)[\sigma + H(\partial\sigma/\partial H)_P] - \partial\sigma/\partial P}{H(\partial\sigma/\partial H)_P} \tag{10-8}$$

the pressure dependence of K_1 can be determined from experimental values of $\partial\sigma/\partial P$, $(\partial\sigma/\partial H)_P$, and σ obtained at a given field H, and from values of $\partial\sigma_s/\partial P$ and σ_s obtained at a high saturating field. The expression actually used by Gugan and Rowlands was exactly analogous to Eq. (10-8), but involved per-unit-volume quantities (i.e., K_{1_v}, M, and M_s, instead of K_1, σ, and σ_s). In this way, from their magnetization measurements at pressures up to about 5 kilobars, they evaluated $K^{-1}{}_{1_v}(\partial K_{1_v}/\partial P)$ at several different fields. Although the values thus obtained for both specimens varied rapidly at the lowest fields rather than being constant as theoretically expected, there was some tendency at the maximum field (about 10 to 30 oersted) toward a leveling off at approximately -6×10^{-6} and $+20 \times 10^{-6}$ bar^{-1} for nickel and for the iron-nickel alloy, respectively. Under the circumstances, these values can only be regarded as having order-of-magnitude significance.

Another method of determining the pressure dependence of the magnetic-anisotropy coefficients from magnetization measurements at different fields and pressures was recently applied by Kouvel and Wilson[38] to their data on an iron-silicon-alloy crystal. In principle, this method is valid for polycrystalline materials as well as for single crystals (this is also true for the method of Gugan and Rowlands). Hence, it will be interesting to compare these two methods on the basis of very recent data[39] on polycrystalline specimens of pure iron and an iron-silicon alloy (of about 6 atomic percent silicon) and then compare the results for the alloy with those of the single-crystal experiments mentioned above.

The magnetization-versus-field curves for both materials are shown in Fig. 10-6; the magnetizations have been normalized to the saturation values, 218 and 204 emu, for iron and the iron-silicon alloy, respectively. Subject to the assumption that the approach to ferromagnetic saturation is impeded only by magnetocrystalline anisotropy forces, the area bounded by the σ/σ_s-versus-H curve and the σ/σ_s axis (shaded area A in Fig. 10-6) is directly related to the anisotropy coefficients. This relationship, derivable from Eq. (10-7), may be written as

$$n_1K_1 + n_2K_2 + \cdots = \int_0^{\sigma_s} H\,d\sigma = \sigma_s\left(H' - \int_0^{H'} \frac{\sigma}{\sigma_s}\,dH\right) \tag{10-9}$$

[38] J. S. Kouvel and R. H. Wilson, Effects of Pressure on Magnetic Interactions in Metals, pp. 271–282 in F. P. Bundy, W. R. Hibbard, Jr., and H. M. Strong (eds.), "Progress in Very High Pressure Research," John Wiley & Sons, Inc., New York, 1961.

[39] J. S. Kouvel and R. H. Wilson, unpublished data.

where H' is any field above that required for saturation and $n_1, n_2, \ldots$ are numerical quantities that depend on the crystal texture of the specimen.

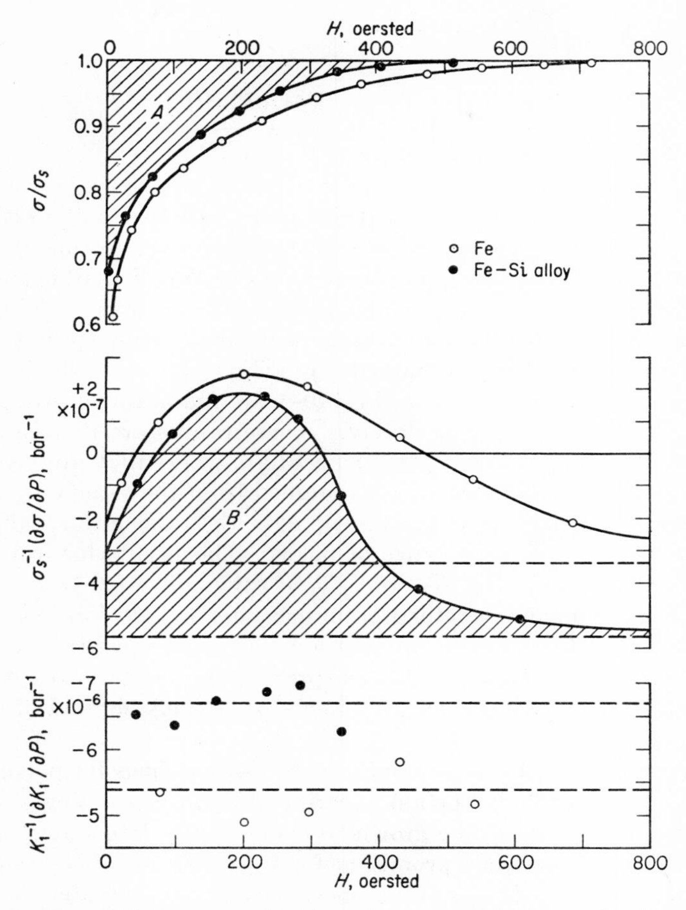

Fig. 10-6 Top: Relative magnetization σ/σ_s versus field curves for iron and iron-silicon alloy; middle: pressure dependence of the magnetization σ_s^{-1} $(\partial\sigma/\partial P)$ as a function of field; bottom: pressure dependence of the anisotropy coefficient K_1^{-1} $(\partial K_1/\partial P)$ as a function of field.

Also shown in Fig. 10-6 are values for $\sigma_s^{-1}(\partial\sigma/\partial P)$ obtained experimentally from changes of magnetization with pressure (up to about 5 kilobars) at various fields. At high fields, $\sigma_s^{-1}(\partial\sigma/\partial P)$ was found to level off at saturation values of -3.4×10^{-7} and -5.6×10^{-7} bar^{-1}, for iron and the iron-silicon alloy, respectively; these $\sigma_s^{-1}(\partial\sigma_s/\partial P)$ values are represented by the horizontal dashed lines in Fig. 10-6. The area enclosed by each of these lines and the corresponding $\sigma_s^{-1}(\partial\sigma/\partial P)$-versus-$H$ curve (shaded area B in the figure) is related to the pressure dependence of the anisotropy coefficients by the expression

$$\frac{n_1(\partial K_1/\partial P) + n_2(\partial K_2/\partial P) + \cdots}{n_1K_1 + n_2K_2 + \cdots} = \frac{(H'\sigma_s)^{-1}(\partial\sigma_s/\partial P) - \int_0^{H'} \sigma_s^{-1}(\partial\sigma/\partial P)\,dH}{H' - \int_0^{H'} (\sigma/\sigma_s)\,dH} = -\frac{\text{area } B}{\text{area } A} \qquad (10\text{-}10)$$

which follows from Eq. (10-9). If it is further assumed that $n_1(\partial K_1/\partial P)$ and n_1K_1 are the dominant terms in the ratio on the left-hand side of Eq. (10-10), this ratio then simplifies to $K_1^{-1}(\partial K_1/\partial P)$, which is independent of the crystal orientations within the specimen. When this assumption is made for the iron and the iron-silicon-alloy specimens, the values for $K_1^{-1}(\partial K_1/\partial P)$, obtained from Eq. (10-10) from graphical estimates of the different areas in Fig. 10-6, are found to be -5.4×10^{-6} and -6.7×10^{-6} bar^{-1}, respectively. These results are represented by the dashed lines in the lower part of Fig. 10-6, where they are compared and found to agree with the values obtained from the same data by the Gugan-Rowlands method [Eq. (10-8)]; note that the latter values are fairly constant over a wide range of fields. The results for iron are in close agreement with the $K_1^{-1}(\partial K_1/\partial P)$ value of -5.6×10^{-6} bar^{-1} deduced from volume-magnetostriction measurements at low fields;[40] the $K_1^{-1}(\partial K_1/\partial P)$ values for the iron-silicon alloy are consistent with the result -6.4×10^{-6} bar^{-1}, obtained previously by the area method [Eq. (10-10)] from pressure measurements on a single crystal of similar composition.[38]

The agreement between the results of the two methods for polycrystalline iron is particularly important experimentally, because single crystals of pure iron cannot easily be grown to conveniently large size. Hence, both methods appear very promising for future study of the effects of pressure on K_1 in polycrystalline specimens of other materials whose single crystals are not readily accessible. Both these methods, however, require that higher-order anisotropy coefficients and their pressure dependences be negligibly small and that there be essentially no forces other than those of magnetic anisotropy opposing the magnetization process.

When the pressure dependences of more than one anisotropy coefficient are desired, magnetization measurements must be made on single crystals with the magnetizing field along different crystallographic directions.

[40] R. Becker and W. Döring, "Ferromagnetismus," p. 298, Springer-Verlag, Berlin, 1939.

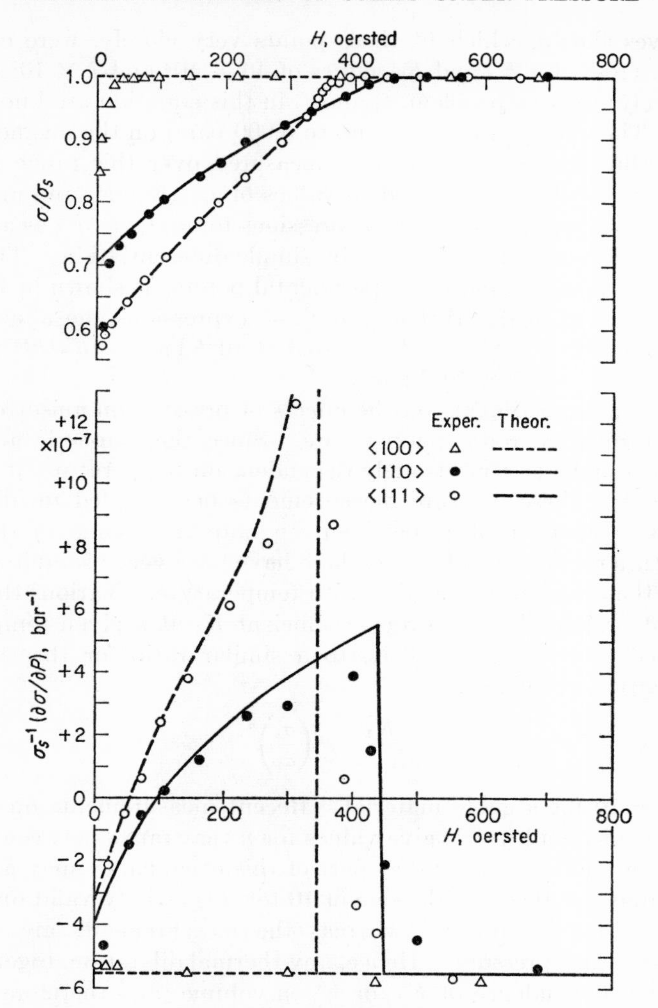

Fig. 10-7 Top: magnetization σ/σ_s as a function of field for single-crystal 6 atomic percent silicon in iron; bottom: $\sigma_s^{-1}\ (\partial\sigma/\partial P)$ as a function of field for three different crystal orientations.

This method was recently demonstrated by Kouvel and Wilson[41] for single crystals of the alloy of 6 atomic percent silicon in iron; the crystals were magnetized along the (100), (110), and (111) directions. The experimental points obtained for σ/σ_s versus H are plotted in Fig. 10-7.

[41] J. S. Kouvel and R. H. Wilson, Magnetocrystalline Anisotropy of Fe-Si Alloy Crystals under Hydrostatic Pressure, *J. Appl. Phys.*, vol. 32, supplement, no. 3, pp. 276–277, 1961.

The curves shown, which fit these points very closely, were computed from Eq. (10-7) for K_1 and K_2 values of 46×10^3 and 7×10^3 ergs/gm, respectively; for this problem, f_1 and f_2 in this equation are known functions.[42] The effects of pressure (up to 5,000 bars) on the magnetizations in these three directions were also measured over this range of fields; the results have been converted to values of $\sigma_s^{-1}(\partial\sigma/\partial P)$ and are plotted in the same figure. Theoretical expressions for $\sigma_s^{-1}(\partial\sigma/\partial P)$ as a function of H were derived from Eq. (10-7) by simple differentiation. The curves which best approximated the experimental points, as shown in Fig. 10-7, were obtained by substituting into these expressions the above values for K_1 and K_2, $K_1^{-1}(\partial K_1/\partial P) = -6.0 \times 10^{-6}$ bar^{-1}, $\partial K_2/\partial P \simeq 0$, and $\sigma_s^{-1}(\partial\sigma_s/\partial P) = -5.5 \times 10^{-7}$ bar^{-1}.

To date, all experiments on the effects of pressure on anisotropy have been performed at room temperature. Since the magnetic anisotropy of most materials is very strongly dependent on temperature, it is highly desirable that these pressure measurements be extended to other temperatures. However, it is pertinent to note that some of the room-temperature pressure results given here have been very useful in a critical study of the anisotropy variation with temperature. Various theoretical treatments relate the anisotropy coefficient K_1 at a given temperature, normalized to its value at 0°K, to a similar ratio for the saturation magnetization as follows:

$$\frac{K_1}{K_{1(0)}} = \left(\frac{\sigma_s}{\sigma_0}\right)^n \tag{10-11}$$

where $n = 10$ for a cubic material. Recent measurements on iron and some iron-silicon alloys[43,44] give values for n that range between 4 and 6. It has been pointed out[45,46] that part of this discrepancy may arise from the fact that the theoretical value of 10 for n is strictly valid only under constant-volume conditions, whereas the measurements are normally made at constant pressure. Hence, any thermal dilatation, together with any explicit dependence of K_1 (or σ_s) on volume (and therefore on pressure), will contribute to the measured variation of K_1 (or σ_s) with temperature. When the effects of these contributions are taken into account

[42] K. H. Stewart, "Ferromagnetic Domains," pp. 20–21, Cambridge University Press, New York, 1954.

[43] C. D. Graham, Jr., Magnetocrystalline Anisotropy Constants of Iron at Room Temperature and Below, *Phys. Rev.*, vol. 112, no. 4, pp. 1117–1120, 1958.

[44] C. D. Graham, Jr., Magnetocrystalline Anisotropy Constant of 3.1% Si-Fe at Room Temperature and Below, *J. Appl. Phys.*, vol. 30, no. 3, pp. 391–392, 1959.

[45] R. Brenner, Remarks on Zener's Classical Theory of the Temperature Dependence of Magnetic Anisotropy Energy, *Phys. Rev.*, vol. 107, no. 6, pp. 1539–1541, 1957.

[46] W. J. Carr, Jr., Explanation for the Low-temperature Behavior of the Anisotropy of Iron, *J. Appl. Phys.*, vol. 31, no. 1, p. 69, 1960.

(to first order), the result is a constant-pressure expression identical to Eq. (10-11), but whose exponent is now

$$n \simeq 10 + \frac{\omega}{\kappa\xi}\left(K_1^{-1}\frac{\partial K_1}{\partial P} - 10\sigma_s^{-1}\frac{\partial \sigma_s}{\partial P}\right) \tag{10-12}$$

where $\omega \equiv (V - V_0)/V_0$
$\xi \equiv (\sigma_0 - \sigma_s)/\sigma_0$
$\kappa =$ volume compressibility

For iron, Carr[46] computed the pressure dependences of K_1 and σ_s from volume-magnetostriction data[40] and found that $n \simeq 8.2$. From the results of their pressure measurements on iron-silicon-alloy crystals (Fig. 10-7), Kouvel and Wilson[41] found from Eq. (10-12) that $n \simeq 9.8$. Thus, for these two materials, the effects of thermal expansion can account for only a small part of the discrepancy between theory and experiment in the matter of the temperature dependence of K_1; the source of most of this discrepancy must therefore be sought elsewhere.

The situation in which the theory has been developed for constant-volume conditions but the experiments are performed at constant pressure is characteristic of many problems, not only in magnetism, but in other areas of solid-state physics as well. It is therefore certain that hydrostatic-pressure measurements will often be called upon to play the useful but subsidiary role of bringing theory and experiment to the point of valid comparison.

11

Phase Equilibria and Transformations in Metals under Pressure

LARRY KAUFMAN

Research Division
Man Labs, Inc.
Cambridge, Massachusetts

11-1 Introduction

The effects of hydrostatic pressure on phase equilibria in metallic systems have been studied by various investigators for nearly a century.[1] Extensive measurements of the physical properties of metals and alloys under hydrostatic conditions, culminating in the work of Tammann, Lussana, and Bridgman,[1] have been carried out. In recent years, advances in high-pressure technology have expanded the scope of high-pressure studies to cover a wide range of temperatures at pressures up to 100 kilobars.

Indeed, pressures of the order of several hundred kilobars can be attained if certain restrictions on temperature and volume ar eaccepted.[2-4] In addition to static high-pressure studies, there has been a rapid expansion of research into the effects of the dynamic pressures produced by intense shock waves on the properties of metallic systems.[5] The pressure range available for dynamic studies is currently of the order of several megabars,[6] and ambient temperatures up to 1000°C have been used successfully in shock-wave experiments.[7] Correlation of the effects of static and dynamic pressures on the compressibility of metals has yielded satisfactory results;[6] however, comparison of static and dynamic effects on phase transformations in metals appears to be much more difficult. This difficulty arises primarily from the short duration of the dynamic pressure pulse (of the order of 10^{-6} sec) and the finite time required for the occurrence of phase transformations in metals.

The subject of equilibria in metallic systems at high pressure has long been a central area of interest to workers in the field of high-pressure research. Bridgman, in his textbook,[1] devotes two chapters to the subjects of melting phenomena and polymorphic transitions under pres-

[1] P. W. Bridgman, "The Physics of High Pressure," G. Bell & Sons, Ltd., London, 1952.

[2] H. G. Drickamer, Optical Studies at High Pressure, pp. 16–27 in F. P. Bundy, W. R. Hibbard, and H. M. Strong (eds.), "Progress in Very High Pressure Research," John Wiley & Sons, Inc., New York, 1961.

[3] A. Balchan and H. G. Drickamer, High Pressure High Temperature Optical Device, *Rev. Sci. Instr.*, vol. 31, pp. 511–513, 1960.

[4] R. E. Harris, R. J. Vaisnys, H. Stromberg, and G. Jura, Resistance and Thermal Gap Measurements to 400,000 Atmospheres, pp. 165–172 in F. P. Bundy, W. R. Hibbard, and H. M. Strong (eds.), "Progress in Very High Pressure Research," John Wiley & Sons, Inc., New York, 1961.

[5] M. H. Rice, R. G. McQueen, and J. M. Walsh, Compression of Solids by Strong Shock Waves, pp. 1–60 in F. Seitz and D. Turnbull (eds.), "Solid State Physics," vol. 6, Academic Press, Inc., New York, 1959.

[6] R. G. McQueen and S. P. Marsh, Equation of State for Nineteen Metallic Elements from Shock-wave Measurements to Two Megabars, *J. Appl. Phys.*, vol. 31, pp. 1253–1269, 1960.

[7] P. Johnson, B. Stein, and R. S. Davis, Temperature Dependence of the Shock-induced Transformation in Iron, *J. Appl. Phys.*, vol. 33, p. 557, 1962.

sure. In addition, recent papers by Lawson,[8] Swenson,[9] and Hilliard[10] provide excellent reviews of this field. In view of the availability of rather complete discussions of phase transformations and equilibria under pressure, an attempt will be made here to approach this subject from an alternative viewpoint.

The central theme of the present paper will be an attempt to correlate the information obtained from high-pressure studies of phase equilibria in metals with 1-atm thermodynamic data. Such an approach is by no means unique, and perhaps the current level of knowledge concerning thermodynamic and high-pressure effects in metals may doom this sort of an approach to failure. However, the correlation of high-pressure results within the thermodynamic framework does offer the possibility of learning more about high-pressure effects and thermodynamics by "a reiterative combination of theory and experiment." The subject matter of this paper will therefore be concerned with a thermodynamic correlation of the effects of pressure on phase equilibria in condensed metallic systems.

Since the thermodynamics of phase equilibria in metals is generally discussed in a complex symbolic form which is far from universal, a table of the symbols used in this paper is presented in the Appendix.

11-2 One-component Systems

It is appropriate to consider initially the effects of temperature and pressure on phase transformations in a pure metal A. If the stable crystal modification of A at 1 atm between absolute zero and the melting temperature $\bar{T}_A^\alpha$ is the α form,‡ then the free energy of α-A at atmos-

‡ The subject of the symbolism of metallic phases has a rather long and confused history.[11] Although it is customary to use Greek symbols to denote the crystal structure of a phase, there is no standard scheme in which a given symbol is used for a particular phase (i.e., β for bcc or α for fcc). In most cases the stable room-temperature 1-atm form is called α irrespective of the structure, and other phases are given various designations as they arise. This haphazard situation naturally raises havoc with any attempt to discuss the crystal structures of different metals in a systematic way. At the risk of further confusing the issue, the following symbolism will be used in the present paper: the *fcc crystal* structure, which is usually considered to be the most dense arrangement, *will be designated as* α in all cases. Having stated this rule, we proceed immediately to state an *exception* for the case of *iron* and iron alloys, where *γ will be used for the fcc form and α for the bcc form.* The phase connotation for iron, illogical as it may seem, will probably remain as such "forever."

[8] A. W. Lawson, The Effect of Hydrostatic Pressure on the Electrical Resistivity of Metals, pp. 1–44 in B. Chalmers and R. King (eds.), "Progress in Metal Physics," vol. 6, Pergamon Press, New York, 1956.

[9] C. A. Swenson, Physics at High Pressure, pp. 41–148 in F. Seitz and D. Turnbull (eds.), "Solid State Physics," vol. 11, Academic Press, Inc., New York, 1960.

[10] J. E. Hilliard, ASME Paper 60-WA-271, New York, December, 1960.

[11] M. Hansen and K. Anderko, "Constitution of Binary Alloys," 2nd ed., McGraw-Hill Book Company, Inc., New York, 1958.

pheric pressure is $F_A{}^\alpha(T)$. At some pressure P the free energy of α-A is

$$F_A{}^\alpha(T, P) = F_A{}^\alpha(T) + \int_{P_0}^{P} V_A{}^\alpha \, dP \qquad \text{cal/mole} \qquad (11\text{-}1)$$

where P_0 is atmospheric pressure. If the α modification of A is the most dense or close-packed form, then the melting curve of pure A under pressure, i.e., $\bar{T}_A{}^\alpha(P)$, may be represented by writing an equation for the free energy of liquid A,

$$F_A{}^L(T, P) = F_A{}^L(T) + \int_{P_0}^{P} V_A{}^L \, dP \qquad \text{cal/mole} \qquad (11\text{-}2)$$

and subtracting from Eq. (11-1) we obtain

$$\Delta F_A{}^{\alpha\to L}(T, P) = \Delta F_A{}^{\alpha\to L}(T) + \int_{P_0}^{P} \Delta V_A{}^{\alpha\to L} \, dP \qquad \text{cal/mole} \quad (11\text{-}3)$$

where $\Delta V_A{}^{\alpha\to L}$ will in general be temperature and pressure dependent. The melting curve is then defined by the condition

$$\Delta F_A{}^{\alpha\to L}(\bar{T}_A{}^\alpha, P) = 0 \qquad (11\text{-}4)$$

In general the free-energy and volumetric differences between the α and liquid phases are not known over a wide range of temperature and pressure, so that $\bar{T}_A{}^\alpha(P)$ cannot be predicted precisely. However, Eq. (11-3) can be differentiated to obtain the Clausius-Clapeyron equation,

$$\left(\frac{dT}{dP}\right)_{\bar{T}_A{}^\alpha}^{\alpha\to L} = \left(\frac{\Delta V}{\Delta S}\right)_{\bar{T}_A{}^\alpha}^{\alpha\to L} = \bar{T}_A{}^\alpha \left(\frac{\Delta V}{\Delta H}\right)_{\bar{T}_A{}^\alpha}^{\alpha\to L} \qquad (11\text{-}5)$$

Equation (11-5) can be used in cases in which the entropy and volume change associated with the melting of α have been measured to compute the initial slope of the melting curve. At present there is no reliable method for accurately predicting ΔV or ΔS, although the collection of data on fusion of metals has suggested some empirical methods of estimating these changes.[12–14] In addition there have been several attempts[15–17] to derive semiempirical relationships for the $\bar{T}_A{}^\alpha(P)$ curve in terms of an

[12] O. Kubaschewski, The Change of Entropy, Volume, and Binding State of the Elements on Melting, *Trans. Faraday Soc.*, vol. 45, pp. 931–940, 1949.

[13] A. Schneider and G. Heymer, "The Physical Chemistry of Metallic Solutions and Intermetallic Compounds," H. M. Stationery Office, London, 1959.

[14] J. Lumsden, "Thermodynamics of Alloys," Institute of Metals, London, 1952.

[15] F. Simon, Untersuchungen über die Schmelzkurve des Heliums, *Z. Electrochem.*, vol. 35, p. 618, 1929; On the Range of Stability of the Fluid State, *Trans. Faraday Soc.*, vol. 33, p. 65, 1937.

[16] J. Gilvarry, The Lindemann and Grüneisen Laws, Grüneisen's Law and the Fusion Law at High Pressure, Equation of the Fusion Curve, *Phys. Rev.*, vol. 102, pp. 308–331, 1956.

[17] L. Salter, The Simon Melting Equation, *Phil. Mag.*, vol. 45, pp. 369–378, 1954.

"internal pressure" and the Grüneisen constant. The parametric form of these equations is found to be compatible with the shape of the $\bar{T}_A{}^\alpha(P)$ curve, but the empirical values of the parameters bear little relation to the predicted values.[18,19] Consequently the theoretical usefulness of this approach in predicting or understanding the fusion of metals under pressure appears uncertain.

The above-mentioned case, in which the α modification is the stable form of A for $0°K \leq T \leq \bar{T}_A{}^\alpha$ and the most dense form, is perhaps the simplest situation. Polymorphism is observed in many metals which exhibit higher density in the high-temperature form than in the modification which is stable near 0°K, e.g., in tin and iron. In order to discuss the effects of pressure on transformations in metals, it is necessary, unfortunately, to understand polymorphism under atmospheric conditions. At present this subject is not fully understood.

Metals are observed to crystallize in many forms which differ from the closed-packed fcc or ideal hcp $[c/a = (8/3)^{1/2}]$ structures. The difficulty in predicting the temperature or pressure range over which a metal can exist in a given crystal form arises from the small differences in energy between different modifications. For example, the free-energy difference between the fcc and the more stable bcc form of iron at absolute zero is only 1,200 cal/mole[20] or 0.052 ev/atom; similarly the difference between hcp and bcc titanium and zirconium is[21] 0.052 ev/atom. The free-energy difference between the diamond cubic form of tin and the tetragonal form, which is stable above 286°K, is only about 0.022 ev/atom at absolute zero.[22] These values are an order of magnitude smaller than the expected errors in quantum-mechanical calculations of the cohesive energy of a metal; moreover in some metals, e.g., cobalt with 0.0026 ev/atom, energy differences are still smaller.[22]

Another method of estimating the magnitudes of free-energy differences among various crystal forms of metals is to compute the product $P\,\Delta V$ for an observed high-pressure transition at room temperature, ignoring the differences in compressibilities between the two phases as a second-order effect. This has been done in Table 11-1 for a number of

[18] H. Strong, Melting and Other Phase Transformations at High Pressure, pp. 182–194 in F. P. Bundy, W. R. Hibbard, Jr., and H. M. Strong (eds.), "Progress in Very High Pressure Research," John Wiley & Sons, Inc., New York, 1961.

[19] J. D. Dudley and H. T. Hall, Experimental Fusion Curves of Indium and Tin to 105,000 Atmospheres, *Phys. Rev.*, vol. 118, pp. 1211–1216, 1960.

[20] L. Kaufman and M. Cohen, Thermodynamics and Kinetics of Martensitic Transformations, pp. 165–247 in B. Chalmers and R. King (eds.), "Progress in Metal Physics," vol. 7, Pergamon Press, New York, 1958.

[21] L. Kaufman, The Lattice Stability of Metals. I. Titanium and Zirconium, *Acta Met.*, vol. 7, pp. 575–587, 1959.

[22] D. R. Stull and G. C. Sinke, "Thermodynamic Properties of the Elements," American Chemical Society, Washington, 1956.

metals for which transitions have been observed by Bridgman. The values of the transition pressure and volume change have been taken from Lawson's recent review[8] of Bridgman's work. Here again it is seen that the magnitudes of the energy differences are small. Notwithstanding the small magnitudes of the differences in free energy between the various crystal forms, it is precisely these differences which determine the temperature-pressure range of stability of metallic phases. In view of the energetic situation perhaps it is not surprising to find

Table 11-1 Estimation of the Difference in Free Energy between High- and Low-pressure Forms of Various Metals at Room Temperature

Metal	Structure, volume[23] (ambient conditions), cm³/mole	Transformation[8] pressure, kilobars	Volume[8] change, cm³/mole	Free-energy difference, cal/mole
Barium	bcc, 39.0	17	0.234	95
		60	0.741	1,070
Bismuth	rhombohedral, 21.3	26	1.83	1,125
		45	0.127	135
		65	0.106	165
		90	0.254	550
Calcium	fcc, 25.9	64	0.337	520
Strontium	fcc, 34.0	25	0.374	225
		65	0.272	425
Antimony	rhombohedral, 18.4	85	0.681	1,390
Thallium	hcp, 17.24	37	0.121	105
Cerium	fcc, 20.0	7	3.2	535

[23] "Metals Handbook," 8th ed., American Society for Metals, Cleveland, Ohio, 1961.

metastability and hysteresis with respect to temperature and pressure occurring in experimental studies of transformations under pressure.

In spite of the small free-energy differences among the various crystal forms, it is instructive to consider formally a situation slightly different from the above-mentioned case, in which the most dense form of metal A, the α structure, was stable over the range $0 \leq T \leq \bar{T}_A{}^\alpha$.

We now consider a second possible structure for metal A, i.e., β-A, where $V_A{}^\beta > V_A{}^\alpha$. In order to simplify the various alternatives in the present considerations, we impose the further conditions that $V_A{}^L > V_A{}^\beta > V_A{}^\alpha$ and that $\Delta V_A{}^{\alpha\to L}$ and $\Delta V_A{}^{\alpha\to\beta}$ are independent of temperature and pressure. We can now envision several different ways in which the application of hydrostatic pressure would alter the stability of the α and β forms of metal A.

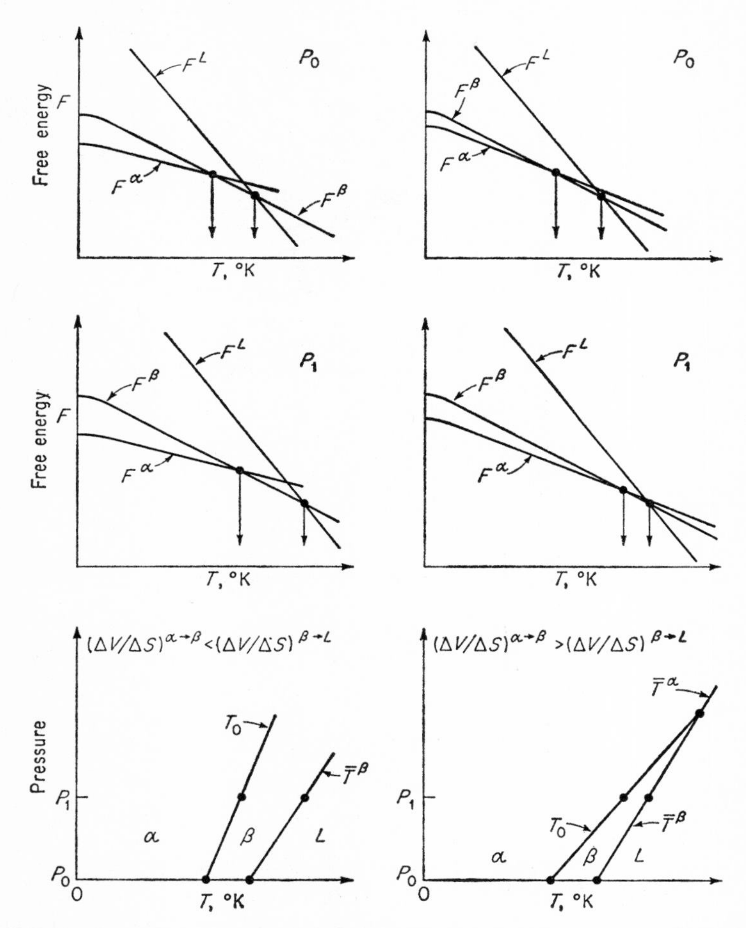

Fig. 11-1 Schematic representation of high-pressure transitions in a metal exhibiting 1-atm polymorphism, where $\Delta V^{\alpha\to L} > \Delta V^{\beta\to L} > 0$ and the volume changes are constant.

Case A. Metal A exhibits polymorphism at atmospheric pressure with the α phase stable for $0°K \leq T \leq T_0$ and the β form stable for $T_0 \leq T \leq \bar{T}_A{}^\beta$. This case is shown schematically in Fig. 11-1. The free energies of the α, β, and liquid forms of A can be estimated from measurements of the latent heat of transformation $\Delta H_A{}^{\alpha\to\beta}(T_0)$, the heat of fusion $\Delta H_A{}^{\beta\to L}(\bar{T}_A{}^\beta)$, and the volume changes attending the

$\alpha \rightarrow \beta$ and $\beta \rightarrow L$ reactions. These data would be sufficient to apply the Clausius-Clapeyron equation for the purpose of calculating $(dT/dP)^{\alpha\rightarrow\beta}$, $(d\bar{T}/dP)^{\beta\rightarrow L}$, and $(d\bar{T}/dP)^{\alpha\rightarrow L}$ and to predict with some confidence the qualitative features of the T-P diagram. A more accurate

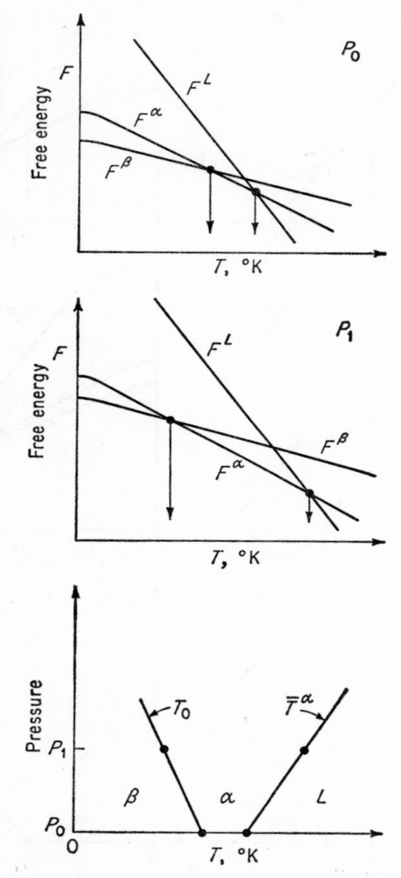

Fig. 11-2 Schematic representation of high-pressure transitions in a metal exhibiting 1-atm polymorphism to a denser high-temperature phase, where $\Delta V^{\alpha\rightarrow L} > \Delta V^{\beta\rightarrow L} > 0$ and the volume changes are constant.

diagram could be calculated if specific-heat, volumetric, and compressibility data were available for each phase. As shown in Fig. 11-1, a triple point will occur only if

$$\left(\frac{\Delta V}{\Delta S}\right)^{\alpha\rightarrow\beta} > \left(\frac{\Delta V}{\Delta S}\right)^{\beta\rightarrow L}$$

Case B. Metal A exhibits polymorphism at atmospheric pressure with the β phase stable for $0°K \leq T \leq T_0$ and the α phase stable for $T_0 \leq T \leq \bar{T}_A{}^{\alpha}$. This situation is similar to case A in that atmospheric-pressure calorimetric and volumetric data can be used to predict quantitatively the features of the T-P diagram. In this case, as shown in Figure 11-2, triple-point phenomena are not indicated.

Case C. Metal A is stable as β-A for $0°K \leq T \leq \bar{T}_A{}^{\beta}$ at atmospheric pressure, i.e., there is no polymorphism at 1 atm. Figures 11-3 and 11-4 show the alternative possibilities for this case in the situations in which $\Delta S_A{}^{\alpha\to\beta}$ at atmospheric pressure is positive and negative. In this case triple-point phenomena are observed. However, apart from calculations of the $\bar{T}_A{}^{\beta}(P)$ curve, there are other characteristics of the P-T diagram which cannot be directly estimated from 1-atm data concerning pure A.

The cases described above are idealized descriptions of what might occur when a real metal is exposed to hydrostatic pressure. Restricting our consideration to situations in which the liquid is least dense, the volume differences are constant, and the 1-atm free-energy curves are nearly linear is not overly realistic. However, the behavior indicated by these simple examples should be representative of the more complex behavior of real systems. We shall now turn to a consideration of real metallic systems.

11-2a Melting in metals at high pressure. The melting curves of a number of pure metals have been determined as a function of pressure over a fairly wide pressure range, up to 10 kilobars in certain instances, 50 kilobars in others, and in a few cases to pressures of the order of 100 kilobars. In most cases the melting curve is not linear, and gradual changes in slope are observed as the pressure increases. In a first consideration of melting data it is of interest to compare the measured initial slope of the melting curve with the calculated slope based on the Clausius-Clapeyron equation.

Recently Schneider and Heymer[13] published an excellent review of the volume and entropy changes attending the fusion of metals which incorporates some of the earlier work of Kubaschewski[12] with more recent data.

In considering the entropy and volume changes attending the fusion of metals, Kubaschewski suggested that the product $V\,\Delta S/\Delta V$, where V is the molar volume of the solid at the melting point and ΔS and ΔV are the entropy and volume changes attending fusion, should be a constant for close-packed metals. He suggested that the value of this product was 57 cal/mole °K for these metals. The 1-atm volumetric and calorimetric data on fusion collected in Table 11-2 for 11 fcc and

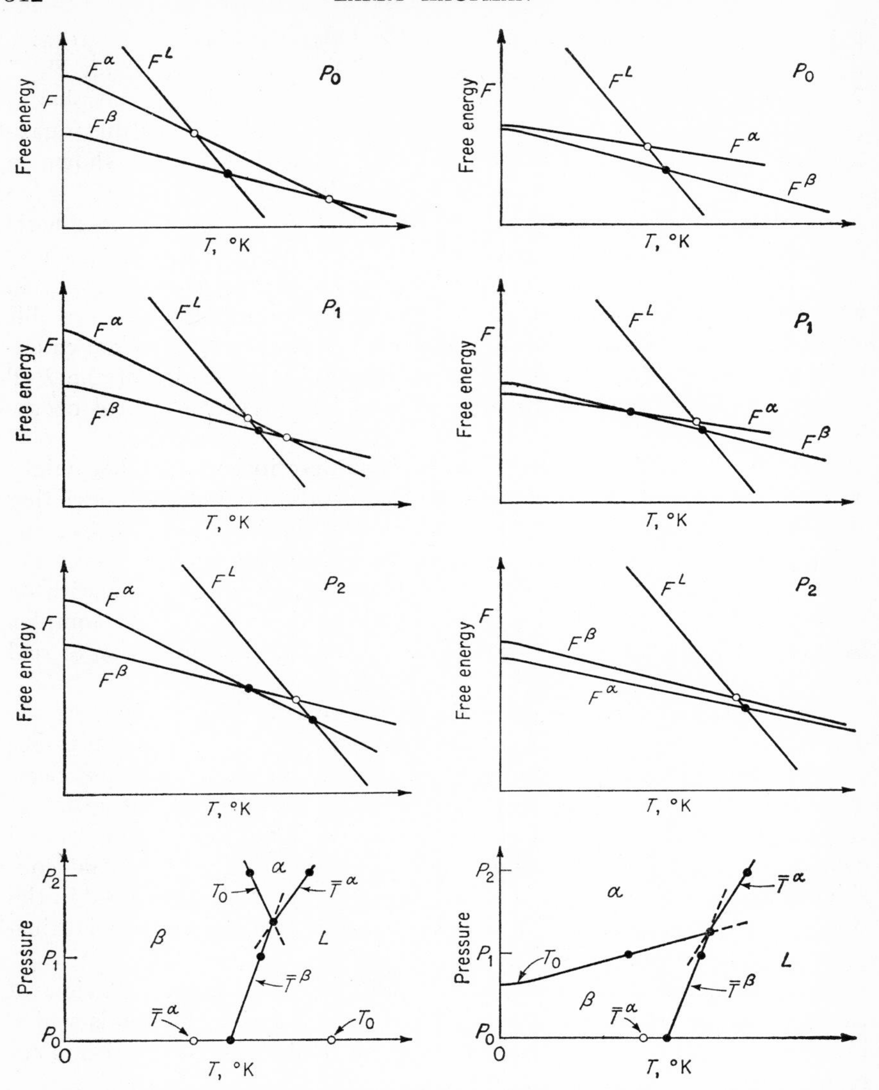

Fig. 11-3 Schematic representation of high-pressure transitions in a metal exhibiting no transitions at 1 atm, where $\Delta S^{\alpha\to\beta} < 0$ and $\Delta V^{\alpha\to L} > \Delta V^{\beta\to L} > 0$. Volume changes are constant.

Fig. 11-4 Schematic representation of high-pressure transitions in a metal exhibiting no transitions at 1 atm, where $\Delta S^{\alpha\to\beta} > 0$ and $\Delta V^{\alpha\to L} > 0$ and $\Delta V^{\beta\to L} > 0$. Volume changes are constant.

hcp metals have been used to evaluate this product. The average value found is 60 cal/mole °K. Apart from aluminum (46 cal/mole °K), gold (43 cal/mole °K), and fcc thallium (86 cal/mole °K), the parameter determined for the individual metals lies within 10 percent of 60 cal/mole °K. Thus the approximation

$$\frac{V\,\Delta S}{\Delta V} \sim 60 \text{ cal/mole °K} \tag{11-6}$$

should be a useful relationship for estimating the initial slope of the melting curve for close-packed metals when entropy and volume-change data are not available. Equation (11-6) has been applied in the calculation of $d\bar{T}/dP$ for rhodium and platinum in Table 11-2.

By use of Schneider and Heymer's[13] review as a primary source of volumetric data and Stull and Sinke's[22] thermodynamic compilation as a source of entropy data, $d\bar{T}/dP$ was calculated for various metals as follows:

$$\frac{d\bar{T}}{dP} = 23.9\,\frac{\Delta V}{\Delta S} \qquad \text{°K/kilobar} \tag{11-7}$$

where P = pressure, kilobars
ΔV = volume change, cm³/mole
ΔS = entropy of fusion, cal/mole °K

For the case of iron, in which $d\bar{T}/dP$ was measured by Strong,[18] the calculation was performed in two ways—treating the solid as α (bcc) and γ (fcc). Both calculations yield the same initial slope. The results of the calculation are compared in Table 11-2 with the data of Bridgman,[1] Butuzov,[24] Strong,[18] Kennedy,[25] Hall,[26] and Dudley and Hall.[19]

In general, the agreement between the calculated and observed initial slopes is fair; there are, however, some notable exceptions. Nevertheless, in view of the difficulty of making accurate measurements of the volume change of fusion,[27,28] the agreement shown in Table 11-2 appears satisfactory.

[24] V. P. Butuzov, Study of Phase Transformations at Very High Pressures, *Soviet Phys. Cryst.*, vol. 2, pp. 536–543, 1957.

[25] See Chap. 7.

[26] H. T. Hall, The Melting Point of Germanium as a Function of Pressure to 180,000 Atmospheres, *J. Phys. Chem.*, vol. 59, pp. 1144–1146, 1955.

[27] G. Urbain, Viscosity and Density Measurements on Molten Metals, p. 1F in "The Physical Chemistry of Metallic Solutions and Intermetallic Compounds," H. M. Stationery Office, London, 1959.

[28] G. Cavalier, Measurements of the Viscosity of Undercooled Mother Metals, p. 1D in "The Physical Chemistry of Metallic Solutions and Intermetallic Compounds," H. M. Stationery Office, London, 1959.

Table 11-2 Comparison of the Initial Slope of the Melting Curves of Metals with the Slope Calculated from 1-atm Fusion Data

Metal[23]	Volume[23] at $\bar{T}$, cm^3/mole	ΔS,[22] cal/mole °K	$\Delta V/V$[13]	dT/dP calculated, °K kilobar^{-1}	dT/dP observed, °K kilobar^{-1}
Lithium (bcc)	13.3	1.59	0.0165	3.3	3.3[1] 1.5[25]
Sodium (bcc)	24.1	1.68	0.025	8.6	7.8[1] 6.5[25]
Potassium (bcc)	46.0	1.65	0.0255	16.9	13.3[1] 8.5[25]
Rubidium (bcc)	56.1	1.79	0.025	18.7	18.0[1]
Cesium (bcc)	70.0	1.69	0.026	25.7	20.0[1] 19.0[25]
Aluminum (fcc)	10.5	2.74	0.060	5.5	6.4[24]
Copper (fcc)	7.6	2.30	0.0415	3.3	4.2[24]
Silver (fcc)	10.9	2.19	0.038	4.5	5.5[25]
Gold (fcc)	10.7	2.21	0.051	5.9	
Nickel (fcc)	7.1	2.44	0.037*	2.6	3.7[18]
Platinum (fcc)	9.5	2.30	(0.038)†	(3.8)	5.0[18]
Rhodium (fcc)	8.7	(2.32)	(0.039)†	(3.5)	5.9[18]
Lead (fcc)	18.9	1.90	0.035	8.3	10.0[18] 6.6[25]
Iron (fcc)	7.7§	(2.20)‡	(0.032)§	2.7	3.0[18]
Iron (bcc)	7.7[4]	2.03	0.030	2.7	
Thallium (bcc)	17.8	1.77	0.022	5.3	9.0[18] 5.0[25]
Thallium (fcc)	17.8	(1.98)[14]	(0.023)¶	4.9	
Magnesium (hcp)	14.8	2.31	0.041	6.3	7.5[25]
Zinc (hcp)	9.5	2.55	0.042	3.7	4.5[18] 4.8[25]
Cadmium (hcp)	13.4	2.44	0.040	5.3	9.0[18] 5.6[25]
Indium (fct)	16.2	1.82	0.020	4.3	4.8[25] 5.6[29]
Tin (bct)	16.5	3.41	0.028	3.2	2.8[18] 4.3[19] 2.7[25]
Tellurium (hexagonal)	21.0	5.78	(0.020)	1.7	0.1[25]
Antimony (rhombohedral)	18.7	5.25	−0.0095	−0.8	−0.50[18] −0.44[25]
Bismuth (rhombohedral)	21.5	4.78	−0.0335	−3.6	−3.8[1]
Germanium (diamond cubic)	13.9	6.28	−0.050	−2.7	−3.3[26]
Gallium (orthorhombic)	11.8	4.41	−0.032	−2.0	−2.1[1]

* Reference 29 measured $V^L_{Ni} = 7.384$ cm^3/mole at the melting point.
† Calculated from Eq. (11-6).
‡ Reference 30 measured $\Delta S^{\gamma \to \alpha}_{Fe} = 0.165$ cal/mole °K at 1668°K.
§ Reference 31 measured $\Delta V^{\gamma \to \alpha}_{Fe} = 0.04$ cm^3/mole at 1668°K.
¶ Reference 1 found $\Delta V^{\beta \to \epsilon}_{Tl} \sim 0.01$ cm^3/mole, and $\Delta V^{\epsilon \to \alpha}_{Tl}$ is approximately -0.03 cm^3/mole.

[29] C. Benedicks, Bestimmung des spezifischer Volumens von Eisen, Nickel, und Eisenlegierungen im geschmolzenen Zustand, *Arch. Eisenhüttenw.*, vol. 3, pp. 473–486, 1930.

[30] M. Olette and H. Ferrier, "The Physical Chemistry of Metallic Solutions and Intermetallic Compounds," H. M. Stationery Office, London, 1959.

[31] Z. S. Basinski, W. Hume-Rothery, and A. L. Sutton, The Lattice Expansion of Iron, *Proc. Roy. Soc. London,* vol. A229, pp. 459–467, 1955.

11-2b Polymorphism in metals at high pressure. As indicated earlier, there are many examples of high-pressure phase transformations in metals. Unfortunately, however, the identity of the high-pressure phase is usually unknown. Although considerable progress has been made in conducting X-ray investigations of substances under pressure, current techniques are limited to pressures below 30 kilobars.‡ The most notable success in determining high-pressure phases in metals is the work of Lawson and co-workers[32,33] with beryllium and diamond high-pressure X-ray windows. Vereshagin and co-workers,[34,35] Jamieson,[36,37] and Kasper[38] have experimented with X-ray windows designed for pressures up to 30 kilobars. These workers have attempted to determine the crystal structure of the high-pressure form of bismuth produced at approximately 26 kilobars. To date, however, this structure has not been identified.

Although in most instances the crystal structure of the high-pressure phase has not been determined, there are a few in which the high-pressure structure is known.

(*a*) *Case A: Cerium.* Cerium falls into the category discussed earlier under case *A*. At atmospheric pressure,[39] cerium exists in a fcc cubic

‡ In the two-year interval between submission of this paper and publication, several notable advances in high-pressure X-ray techniques have been reported. Jamieson and Lawson[31a] have succeeded in obtaining X-ray patterns at 150 kilobars while Piermarini and Weir[31b] have successfully obtained patterns at pressures up to 60 kilobars.

[31a] J. C. Jamieson and A. W. Lawson, X-ray Diffraction Studies in the 100 Kilobar Range, *J. Appl. Phys.*, vol. 33, pp. 786–780, 1962.

[31b] G. J. Piermarini and C. E. Weir, Diamond Cell for X-ray Diffraction Studies at High Pressures, *J. Res. Natl. Bur. Std.*, vol. 66A, p. 325, 1962.

[32] A. Lawson and N. A. Reiley, An X-ray Camera for Obtaining Powder Pictures at High Pressures, *Rev. Sci. Instr.*, vol. 20, pp. 763–765, 1949.

[33] A. Lawson and T. Y. Tang, A Diamond Bomb for Obtaining Powder Pictures at High Pressure, *Rev. Sci. Instr.*, vol. 21, p. 815, 1950.

[34] L. F. Vereshagin and I. V. Brandt, X-ray Investigations of Structure of Substances under Pressures of up to 30,000 Atmospheres, *Doklady Akad. Nauk S. S. S. R.*, vol. 108, pp. 423–442, 1956.

[35] L. F. Vereshagin and S. S. Kabalkina, Исследование кристалической структуры галосенидов рубидия при высоком давлении, *Doklady Akad. Nauk S. S. S. R.*, vol. 113, p. 797, 1957.

[36] J. C. Jamieson, Introductory Studies of High-pressure Polymorphism to 24,000 Bars by X-ray Diffraction with Some Comments on Calcite II, *J. Geol.*, vol. 65, p. 334, 1957.

[37] J. C. Jamieson, Diamond Cells for X-ray Diffraction Studies under High Pressure, pp. 10–15 in F. Bundy, W. R. Hibbard, and H. M. Strong (eds.), "Progress in Very High Pressure Research," John Wiley & Sons, Inc., New York, 1961.

[38] J. S. Kasper, X-ray Diffraction by Substances at High Pressures, *J. Metals*, vol. 12, p. 732, 1960.

[39] W. B. Pearson, "Handbook of Lattice Spacings and Structures of Metals," Pergamon Press, New York, 1958.

form for 263°K ≤ T ≤ 1077°K with a lattice parameter of 5.1612Å at 263°K.[39,22] Below 263°K the fcc form transforms partially into a close-packed hexagonal structure[40] ($c/a = 1.65$).[39] On further cooling below 100°K, the untransformed fcc phase converts to a denser fcc structure[39] whose lattice parameter is 4.82Å. A high-pressure transition was first discovered by Bridgman[41] at 7 kilobars and room temperature. Subsequently Lawson and Tang[42] carried out X-ray measurements at 15 kilobars and room temperature which showed that the high-pressure phase was a dense fcc form with a lattice parameter of 4.84Å. The large change in volume associated with the cerium transformation, of the order of 16 percent, ranks with the transformation in tin (diamond cubic to bct 27 percent) as the largest exhibited during solid phase transformations. Both these transformations have been regarded as manifestations of changes in electronic structure.

The cerium transition has been studied extensively over a wide range of temperatures by various techniques,[9] and the transformation pressure and volume change, measured by several different methods, are in good agreement. Swenson[9] has reviewed the P-T-ΔV data for the cerium transition, which indicates a value of about 900 cal/mole for $\Delta H^{\alpha\to\alpha'}{}_{Ce}$ (α = low-temperature dense fcc; α' = high-temperature fcc). The atmospheric-pressure transition temperature of 150°K suggested by Swenson yields an entropy change of $\Delta S^{\alpha\to\alpha'}{}_{Ce} \approx 6.0$ cal/mole °K at low temperatures for this transition. This value for the entropy change is five or ten times larger than the entropy change generally observed for allotropic transformations in metals at 1 atm. Calorimetric determination of the latent heat of the $\alpha \to \alpha'$ reaction at 1 atm would yield useful data for comparison with the values determined from the P-T-ΔV measurements. However, such measurements would be complicated by the sluggishness of the transformation and the intervention of the hcp phase.[40]

(*b*) *Case B: Tin.* Tin undergoes a phase transformation at 1 atm and 286°K.[43] The high-temperature form (white tin) is body-centered tetragonal with $V^{\tau}{}_{Sn} = 16.28$ cm³/mole at 286°K,[39] while the low-temperature form is diamond cubic (grey tin) with $V^{\delta}{}_{Sn} = 20.71$ cm³/mole at the same temperature.[39] Thus the white-grey tin transformation

[40] C. J. McHargue and H. L. Yakel, Phase Transformations in Cerium, *Acta Met.*, vol. 8, p. 637, 1960.

[41] P. W. Bridgman, Effects of High Shearing Stress Combined with High Hydrostatic Pressure, *Phys. Rev.*, vol. 48, pp. 825–847, 1935; *Proc. Am. Acad. Arts Sci.*, vol. 76, pp. 55 and 71, 1948.

[42] A. W. Lawson and L. Y. Tang, Concerning the High-pressure Allotropic Modification of Cerium, *Phys. Rev.*, vol. 76, pp. 301–302, 1949.

[43] G. A. Busch and R. Kern, Semiconducting Properties of Grey Tin, pp. 1-40 in F. Seitz and D. Turnbull (eds.), "Solid State Physics," vol. 11, Academic Press, Inc., New York, 1960.

corresponds to case B of the general discussion. The free energy and enthalpy differences, $\Delta F^{\delta\to\tau}{}_{\text{Sn}}$ and $\Delta H^{\delta\to\tau}{}_{\text{Sn}}$, have been measured as a function of temperature by emf[44] and calorimetric techniques[45,46] at atmospheric pressure.[47] These data yield a value of $\Delta S^{\delta\to\tau}{}_{\text{Sn}} = 1.88$ cal/mole °K at the transition temperature. Combination with the value of $\Delta V^{\delta\to\tau}{}_{\text{Sn}} = 4.43$ cm³/mole suggests that

$$\left(\frac{dT}{dP}\right)^{\delta\to\tau}_{\text{Sn}} = -56°\text{K/kilobar}$$

This is more than twice the experimental value of -20°K/kilobar measured by Enz.[48,43]

(*c*) *Case B: Iron.* Another example of the case-B transition is the bcc (α) → fcc (γ) transition in iron. This transformation occurs at 1183°K under atmospheric conditions. The low-temperature α phase transforms to the more dense γ phase at this temperature attended by an enthalpy change, $\Delta H^{\alpha\to\gamma}{}_{\text{Fe}} = 215$ cal/mole[49] (i.e., $\Delta S^{\alpha\to\gamma}{}_{\text{Fe}} = 0.182$ cal/mole °K), and a volume change, $\Delta V^{\alpha\to\gamma}{}_{\text{Fe}} = -0.075$ cm³/mole.[31] These data yield[49a]

$$\left(\frac{dT}{dP}\right)^{\alpha\to\gamma}_{\text{Fe}} = -9.8°\text{K/kilobar}$$

Thermodynamic studies of the $\alpha \rightleftarrows \gamma$ phase transformations in iron[49–53] have shown that $\Delta H^{\alpha\to\gamma}{}_{\text{Fe}}$ and $\Delta S^{\alpha\to\gamma}{}_{\text{Fe}}$ are strongly temperature depend-

[44] E. Cohen and C. van Eijk, Physikalisch-chemische Studien am Zinn, *Z. physik. Chem.*, vol. 30A, p. 601, 1899.

[45] F. Lange, Untersuchungen über die spezifische Wärme bei tiefen Temperaturen, *Z. physik. Chem.*, vol. 110A, pp. 313–362, 1924.

[46] J. N. Bronsted, Berichtigung, *Z. physik. Chem.*, vol. 65, p. 744, 1909; Studien zur Chemischen Affinitätix: die allotrope Zinnumwandlung, *Z. physik. Chem.*, vol. 88, pp. 479–489, 1914.

[47] F. Seitz, "The Modern Theory of Solids," p. 483, McGraw-Hill Book Company, Inc., New York, 1940.

[48] H. Enz, diplomarbeit (thesis), Eidgenossische Technische Hochschule, Zurich, 1951 (unpublished).

[49] L. S. Darken and R. W. Gurry, "Physical Chemistry of Metals," McGraw-Hill Book Company, Inc., New York, 1953.

[49a] F. Birch, The Alpha-Gamma Transformation of Iron at High Pressures, *Am. J. Sci.*, vol. 238, pp. 192–211, 1940, measured $(dT/dP) \approx -8.5$°C/kilobar at pressures up to 4 kilobars.

[50] C. H. Johansson, Thermodynamisch begrundete Deutung der Vorgänge bei der Austenit-Martensit-Umwandlung, *Arch. Eisenhüttenw.*, vol. 11, p. 241, 1937.

[51] C. Zener, Equilibrium Relations in Medium-alloy Steels, *Trans. AIME*, vol. 167, pp. 513–534, 1946.

[52] J. C. Fisher, The Free Energy Change Accompanying the Martensite Transformation in Steels, *Trans. AIME*, vol. 185, pp. 688–690, 1949.

[53] R. J. Weiss and K. J. Tauer, Components of the Thermodynamic Functions of Iron, *Phys. Rev.*, vol. 102, pp. 1490–1495, 1956.

ent.[20] This behavior arises from the complex electronic and magnetic properties of the α and γ forms.[53] Consequently it must be presumed that the slope of the T-P curve for the $\alpha \rightarrow \gamma$ reaction in iron will deviate from the calculated initial slope of -9.8°K/kilobar as the pressure is increased. In order to obtain a better estimate of the expected behavior, it is convenient to use an equation similar to Eq. (11-3) and calculate $\Delta F^{\alpha\rightarrow\gamma}{}_{\mathrm{Fe}}(T, P)$. Since the compressibilities of both phases are unknown the assumption is made that the compressibilities are equal, yielding[54–56]

$$\Delta F^{\alpha\rightarrow\gamma}{}_{\mathrm{Fe}}(T, P) \approx \Delta F^{\alpha\rightarrow\gamma}{}_{\mathrm{Fe}}(T) + 23.9P\,\Delta V^{\alpha\rightarrow\gamma}{}_{\mathrm{Fe}}(T) \qquad \text{cal/mole} \qquad (11\text{-}8)$$

The free-energy change at 1 atm $\Delta F^{\alpha\rightarrow\gamma}{}_{\mathrm{Fe}}(T)$ can be evaluated as a function of temperature,[54–56] while the volume change is determined from the work of Basinski et al.[31] For temperatures below 1200°K,[54]

$$\Delta V^{\alpha\rightarrow\gamma}{}_{\mathrm{Fe}} \approx -0.312 + 2 \times 10^{-4}T \qquad \text{cm}^3\text{/mole} \qquad (11\text{-}9)$$

Combination of Eqs. (11-8) and (11-9) yields

$$\Delta F^{\alpha\rightarrow\gamma}{}_{\mathrm{Fe}}(T, P) \approx 1{,}202 - 2.63 \times 10^{-3}T^2 + 1.54 \times 10^{-6}T^3 - 23.9P(0.312 - 2 \times 10^{-4}T) \qquad \text{cal/mole} \qquad (11\text{-}10)$$

for temperatures below 950°K.

The T_0-versus-P curve for pure iron can now be calculated by setting $\Delta F^{\alpha\rightarrow\gamma}{}_{\mathrm{Fe}}(T_0, P) = 0$.

The result of this calculation is shown in Fig. 11-5. Recent determinations of the T_0-P curve over a wide range of temperature have been carried out by Claussen[57] using a method of differential thermal analysis in the belt apparatus. These data have been corrected[10,55,56] with regard to the pressure in accordance with the work of Kennedy and LaMori,[58] who showed that the pressure calibration used in the belt apparatus was too high at pressures above 25 kilobars. Metallographic determinations of the T_0-P curve for pure iron by Kaufman et al.[54] and Hilliard[59] are in good agreement with the determination by Claussen

[54] L. Kaufman, A. Leyenaar, and J. S. Harvey, The Effect of Hydrostatic Pressure on the F.C.C. ⇆ B.C.C. Reactions in Iron-base Alloys, pp. 90–108 in F. P. Bundy, W. R. Hibbard, and H. M. Strong (eds.), "Progress in Very High Pressure Research," John Wiley & Sons, Inc., New York, 1961.

[55] L. Kaufman, discussion to reference 18.

[56] L. Kaufman, discussion to paper by C. M. Fowler et al., in "Response of Metals to High-velocity Deformation," Interscience Publishers, Inc., New York, 1961.

[57] W. Claussen, discussion to reference 18.

[58] G. C. Kennedy and P. N. LaMori, Some Fixed Points on the High Pressure Scale, pp. 304–313 in F. P. Bundy, W. R. Hibbard, and H. M. Strong, (eds.), "Progress in Very High Pressure Research," John Wiley & Sons, Inc., New York, 1961.

[59] J. E. Hilliard, private communication, presented at the AIME Fall Meeting, Philadelphia, Pa., October, 1960 (to be published in the *Trans. AIME*, 1962–3).

and are shown in Fig. 11-5 along with the calculated curve. In addition, Fig. 11-5 shows the recent measurements of the $\alpha \rightarrow \gamma$ transition carried out by Kennedy and Newton at pressures up to 47 kilobars.[25] In general, the agreement between the calculated *T-P* curve and the experimental *T-P* curve for the $\alpha \rightarrow \gamma$ reaction is good in the pressure range up to 80 kilobars.

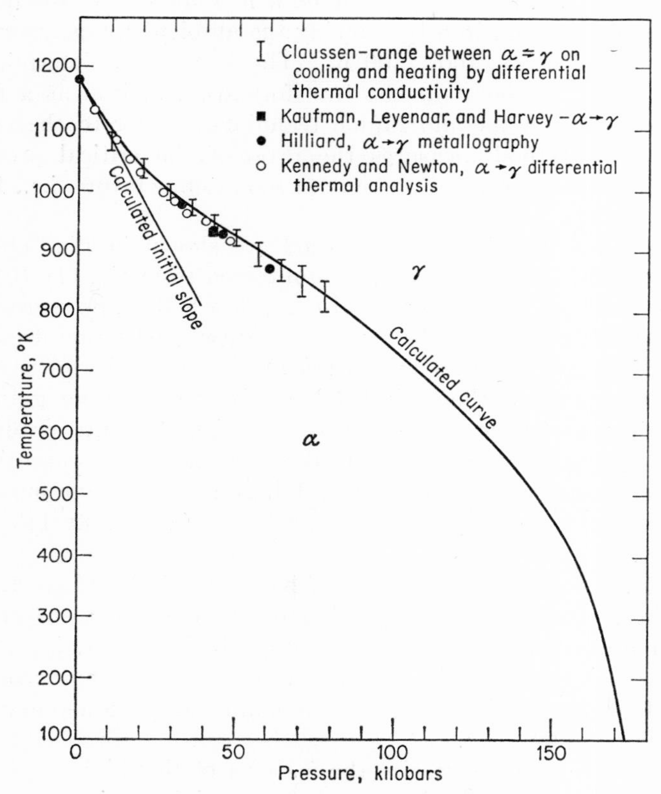

Fig. 11-5 Effect of hydrostatic pressure on the α-γ transformation in iron.

The effect of dynamic pressure produced by intense shock waves on the pressure-volume relations in iron was first studied by Bancroft, Peterson, and Minshall.[60] These investigators showed evidence for a transition in the vicinity of 130 kilobars at room temperature. The nature of the high-pressure phase which exists in the high-velocity shock front and hence must form and revert in the order of 10^{-6} sec has not been established. However, a metallographic study of the shock-wave

[60] D. Bancroft, E. L. Peterson, and S. Minshall, Polymorphism of Iron at High Pressure, *J. Appl. Phys.*, vol. 27, pp. 291–298, 1956.

transition carried out by Smith[61] showed that the transformation resulted in profuse twinning when the critical pressure was exceeded.

Fowler[62] carried out several experiments over a limited temperature range (245 to 365°K) and found virtually no change in the transition pressure with temperature. Extension of the pressure range to 2 megabars produces no additional transformations at room temperature.[5] Johnson, Stein, and Davis[7] have added a new dimension to the shock-wave measurements on iron by varying the ambient temperature of the specimen between 77 and 1300°K. These workers determined the dynamic critical pressure for the transformation in iron as a function of temperature by a metallographic technique similar to that used by Smith.[61] The method measures the ratio of the critical pressure at temperature T to the critical pressure at room temperature, i.e., 130 kilobars determined by Bancroft et al.[60]

The results obtained by this method are shown in Fig. 11-6 along with the calculated T_0-versus-P curve obtained from Eq. (11-10) for the $\alpha \rightarrow \gamma$ transformation. At temperatures below 800°K, pressures exceeding the critical pressure produce a profusely twinned structure as found by Smith.[61] However, at temperatures above 800°K the microstructure produced by exceeding the critical pressure is extremely fine grained and entirely different in appearance from the microstructure produced by the low-temperature transition. On the basis of these observations and the general shape of the P-T curve, Johnson et al.[7] have suggested a triple point between α, γ, and an additional phase X at 110 kilobars and 800°K.

Recently, Balchan and Drickamer[63] have reported a phase transition in iron in a static-pressure experiment at room temperature. The transition pressure was found to be about 130 kilobars, in agreement with the shock-wave result, and the transformation was accompanied by a fourfold increase in resistance in going from the low-pressure form to the high-pressure form.

It is instructive to summarize the features of this high-pressure form of iron which have been obtained from static and dynamic measurements. The volume change $\Delta V^{\alpha \rightarrow X}{}_{\mathrm{Fe}}$ reported by Bancroft et al.[60] of -0.25 cm³/mole at room temperature is very close to $\Delta V^{\alpha \rightarrow \gamma}{}_{\mathrm{Fe}}$ at room temperature calculated from Eq. (11-9). In addition, the fourfold increase in resistivity reported by Balchan and Drickamer is comparable to the eight-

[61] C. S. Smith, Metallographic Studies of Metals after Explosive Shock, *Trans. AIME*, vol. 212, pp. 574–589, 1958.

[62] C. M. Fowler, discussion to paper by Fowler et al., in V. F. Zackay and P. Shewmon (eds.), "Response of Metals to High-velocity Deformation," Interscience Publishers, Inc., New York, 1961, p. 306.

[63] A. Balchan and H. G. Drickamer, High Pressure Electrical Resistance Cell, and Calibration Points above 100 Kilobars, *Rev. Sci. Instr.*, vol. 32, pp. 308–313, 1961.

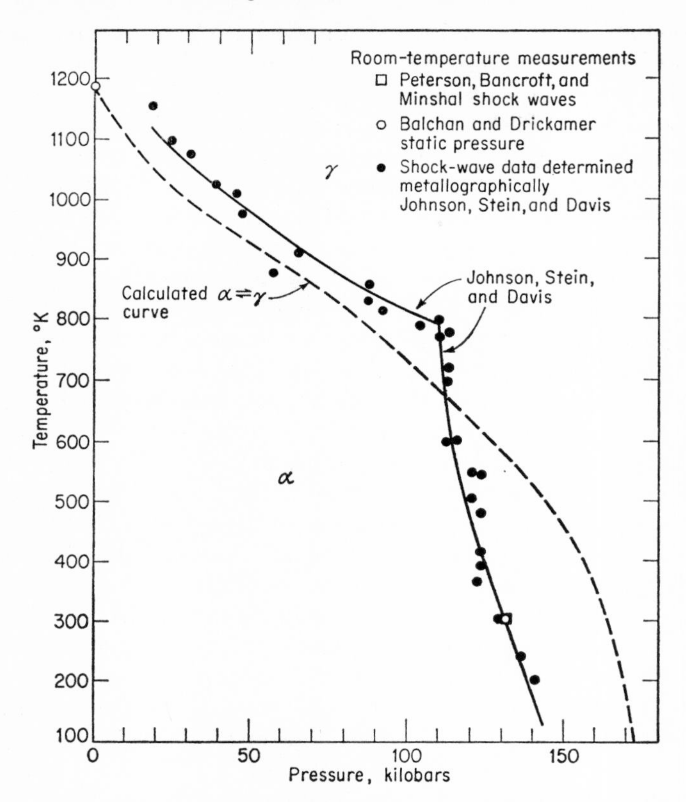

Fig. 11-6 Effect of dynamic pressure on phase transformation in iron.

fold increase anticipated for an $\alpha \rightarrow \gamma$ reaction at 300°K. Weiss and Marotta[64] have analyzed the electrical resistivity of iron. At 300°K the resistivity of α-iron is 11 μohm-cm; at the same temperature the extrapolated resistivity of γ-iron is 85 μohm-cm.‡ Moreover, the energy

‡ Measurements of the electrical resistance of α- and γ-iron at pressures up to 80 kilobars have been carried out recently in our laboratory.[64a,64b] The $\alpha \rightarrow \gamma$ temperatures determined in these experiments are in good agreement with Claussen's data and the calculated $T_0(\alpha \rightarrow \gamma)$-$P$ curve. At 80 kilobars and 800°K, the resistance of γ-iron is about 1.5 times that of α-iron. This is roughly equivalent to extrapolating the Marotta-Weiss curve for γ-iron to low temperatures.

[64] R. J. Weiss and A. Marotta, Spin-dependence of the Resistivity of Magnetic Metals, *J. Phys. Chem. Solids*, vol. 9, pp. 302–308, 1959.

[64a] E. V. Clougherty and L. Kaufman, The Electrical Resistivity of Iron from 20 to 1250°C at Static Pressures from 25 to 95 Kilobars, *ASME Paper* 62-WA-258, New York, November, 1962.

[64b] L. Kaufman, E. V. Clougherty, and R. J. Weiss, The Lattice Stability of Metals III-Iron, to be published in *Acta Met.*, 1963.

difference between the γ and X forms appears to be less than 300 cal/mole over the temperature-pressure range shown. Although the exact nature of this low-temperature high-pressure form remains unknown, its properties seem quite similar to those of γ-iron.[64b] Another possible structure for X is merely a denser bcc form with a magnetic structure different from ordinary α-iron at low temperatures.[7]

(*d*) *Case B: Cobalt.* Cobalt exhibits polymorphism at 1 atm with a transition at 720°K[22] in which the low-temperature ϵ hcp phase transforms into the α fcc form. The enthalpy change attending the transformation is very small,[22] i.e., $\Delta H^{\epsilon \to \alpha}{}_{Co} = 60$ cal/mole. Thus, $\Delta S^{\epsilon \to \alpha}{}_{Co} \approx 0.083$ cal/mole °K. Taylor and Floyd[65] have determined the lattice parameters of both phases in the vicinity of the transition temperature[65,39] from which the molar volumes can be computed. With these data it is found that $V^{\epsilon}{}_{Co} = 6.675$ cm³/mole, $V^{\alpha}{}_{Co} = 6.706$ cm³/mole, and

$$\Delta V^{\epsilon \to \alpha}{}_{Co} = +0.083 \text{ cal/mole °K}$$

Thus, the hcp (ϵ) form which is nearly ideal (i.e., $c/a = 1.623$) is more dense than the high-temperature α form. The calculated initial slope of the transition temperature is found to be

$$\left(\frac{dT}{dP}\right)_{Co}^{\epsilon \to \alpha} = +8.9\text{°K/kilobar}$$

Kennedy[25] has determined the effect of pressure on the $\epsilon \to \alpha$ reaction in cobalt to 45 kilobars. The initial slope of his curve is about +6.0°K/kilobar. Thus agreement between the calculated and observed initial slopes is comparable with that obtained for melting data.

(*e*) *Case C.* We now turn our attention to case C, in which high-pressure polymorphism occurs in a metal which exhibits no solid-state transformations at 1 atm. In view of the arguments advanced previously, i.e., the small energy differences between various structures, the present experimental difficulties in establishing the crystal structure of the high-pressure phase, and the pressure-temperature hysteresis associated with solid-phase transformations, a discussion of this class of transformations is obviously quite difficult. However, because of the large number of cases in which such transformations are observed (and this number will undoubtedly increase as high-pressure capabilities expand), it seems worthwhile (to the author at least) to explore the possible correlation of case-C transitions with 1-atm thermodynamic data. Cottrell[66] has suggested that, except for the intervention of the

[65] A. Taylor and R. W. Floyd, Precision Measurements of Lattice Parameters of Non-cubic Crystals, *Acta Cryst.*, vol. 3, pp. 285–289, 1950.

[66] A. Cottrell, "Theoretical Structural Metallurgy," p. 115, St. Martin's Press, Inc., New York, 1955.

liquid phase (i.e., melting), polymorphism would be the rule for all metals because the phase which is stable at 0°K should have a smaller entropy and become less stable at higher temperatures than a phase which by virtue of its low-temperature instability has a high entropy. Although there are undoubtedly exceptions to this rule (i.e., the stable phase has the lowest entropy), this concept appears to be correct in general.

Thus, elevation of the melting point by the application of hydrostatic pressure should increase the observations of polymorphism in metals, at least in those cases in which the differences in volume between the solid phases are small and the molar volume of the liquid is greater than that of the solid phases.

The most realistic approach to our discussion of high-pressure polymorphism is a consideration of the following problem: Given a metal A which is stable as β-A for $0°K \leq T \leq \bar{T}_A{}^\beta$, what are the temperature-pressure conditions for conversion of the β structure into a denser fcc α configuration? The statement of this question in itself contains the assumption that the α form is denser than other configurations and the corollary that fcc metals should not exhibit polymorphism. While the latter statement is known to be incorrect, i.e., polymorphism at high pressure is exhibited by fcc calcium, strontium (see Table 11-1), and cerium (to a denser fcc structure), the former statement is generally accepted. In any case, a solution to the problem posed above would in itself provide a useful guide for future experimentation, as well as an aid in interpreting available high-pressure information.

(*f*) *Thallium.* An approach to this problem may be illustrated by considering the metal thallium. At 1 atm the hcp form of thallium, ϵ-thallium, is stable over the range $0 \leq T \leq 505°K$. This structure has a c/a ratio equal to 1.598 at room temperature, where[39] $V^\epsilon{}_{Tl} = 17.221$ cm³/mole. At 505°K[14] thallium undergoes a hcp → bcc reaction, $\epsilon \rightarrow \beta$, with $\Delta H^{\epsilon\rightarrow\beta}{}_{Tl} = 74$ cal/mole.[14] Thus we may approximate

$$\Delta F^{\epsilon\rightarrow\beta}{}_{Tl} = 74 - 0.15T \qquad \text{cal/mole} \tag{11-11}$$

Body-centered-cubic thallium melts at $\bar{T}^\beta{}_{Tl} = 576°K$, where the latent heat of fusion is 1,025 cal/mole.[14] Hence,

$$\Delta F^{\beta\rightarrow L}{}_{Tl} \approx 1{,}025 - 1.78T \qquad \text{cal/mole} \tag{11-12}$$

Figure 11-7 shows the lead-thallium system and a portion of the thallium-bismuth system.[11] It can be seen that the α or fcc solid solution exists in the lead-thallium system between 0 and 88 percent thallium, i.e., $0 \leq x \leq 0.88$. Similarly, an α solid solution exists in the thallium-bismuth system at room temperature between $0.63 \leq x \leq 0.96$. The lattice parameters of the α-lead-thallium solution have been measured by Tang

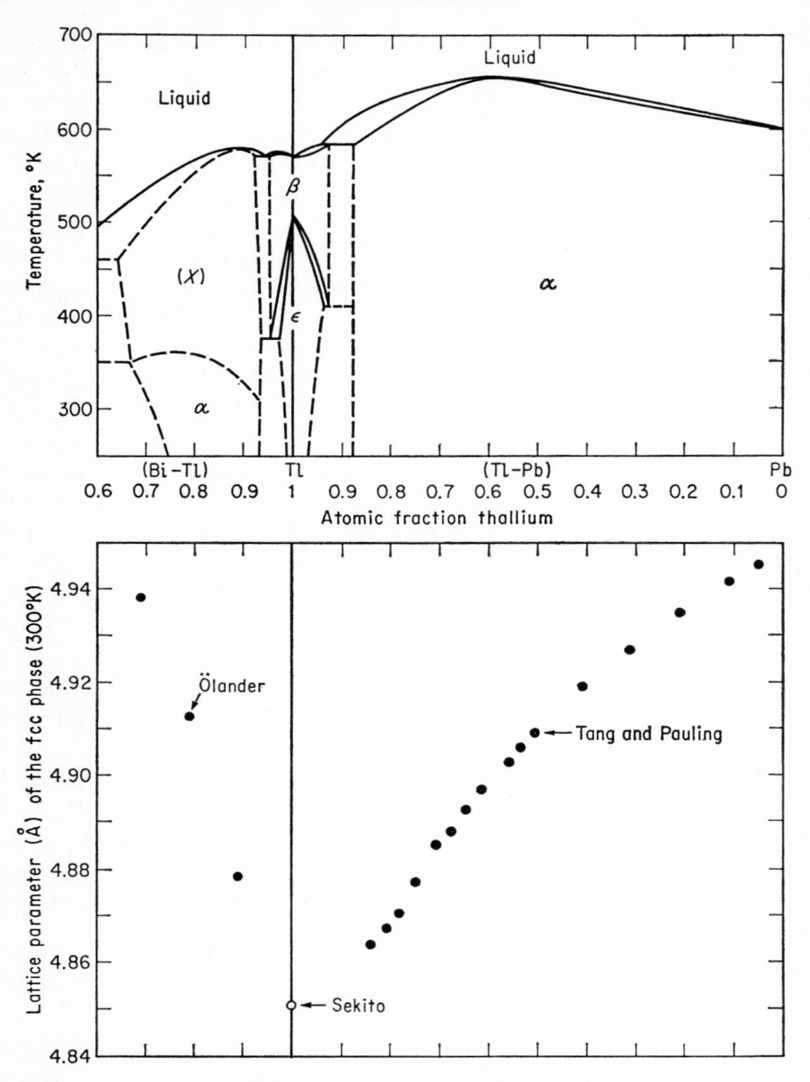

Fig. 11-7 Lattice parameter and compositional range of stability of the fcc (α) phase in bismuth-thallium and thallium-lead alloys.

and Pauling[67,39] for $0 \leq x \leq 0.88$, and these are shown in Fig. 11-7 along with the lattice parameters of α-thallium-bismuth solutions measured for $0.63 \leq x \leq 0.96$ by Olander.[68,39] Pearson,[39] in his review of the

[67] Y. C. Tang and L. Pauling, The Structure of Alloys of Lead and Thallium, *Acta Cryst.*, vol. 5, pp. 39–44, 1952.

[68] A. Olander, Kristall Struktur der Thallium-Wismut-Legierungen, *Z. Krist.*, vol. A89, pp. 89–92, 1934.

crystal structure of thallium, cites the work of Sekito,[69] who measured the lattice parameter of ϵ-thallium. Sekito quenched thallium from the liquid phase and obtained metastable fcc α-thallium at room temperature. He determined the lattice parameter of α-thallium and found it equal to 4.851Å.[69,39] Schneider and Heymer[70,39] did high-temperature X-ray diffraction of thallium and observed α-thallium at 517°K and 557°K with lattice parameters of 4.889Å and 4.897Å, respectively. These values are in good agreement with the result of Sekito, which is shown in Fig. 11-7 for comparison with the lead-thallium and thallium-bismuth data. The experiments of Sekito, and Schneider and Heymer, in which a metastable or unstable phase is observed on quenching from the melt, are not unusual. This is especially true in the case of thallium, for which the free-energy differences between the α, ϵ, and β forms (as we shall see) are small. Moreover, it has been shown[71] that it is possible to nucleate an unstable crystalline form from the melt if the interfacial energy between the liquid and the unstable form is less than the corresponding interfacial energy between the liquid and the stable form. Thus, Cech[71] was able to nucleate small particles of iron-nickel alloys in the bcc modification at about 1700°K and cool them rapidly to room temperature, even though the fcc phase is most stable over the entire temperature range.

With the lattice parameter of α-thallium at room temperature equal to 4.851Å as found by Sekito, $V^{\alpha}{}_{\mathrm{Tl}} = 17.195$ cm³/mole at room temperature, or $\Delta V^{\alpha\to\epsilon}{}_{\mathrm{Tl}} = 0.026$ cm³/mole at 300°K.

Olander[72] measured the chemical activity of thallium in α-PbTl solid solutions over a wide variation of composition, $0 \leq x \leq 0.90$, in a temperature range near 523°K. Lumsden[14] has analyzed these data to estimate $\Delta F^{\alpha\to\epsilon}{}_{\mathrm{Tl}}$ in the following manner: According to Eq. (11-A10) in the Appendix, the activity of thallium in α-lead-thallium relative to β-thallium can be represented by

$$RT \ln a^{\alpha}{}_{\mathrm{Tl}}\Big|_{\mathrm{Tl}^{\beta}} = F_E{}^{\beta} + (1 - x)\frac{\partial}{\partial x}F_E{}^{\beta} + \Delta F^{\beta\to\alpha}{}_{\mathrm{Tl}} + RT \ln x \quad (11\text{-}13)$$

or

$$RT \ln f^{\alpha}{}_{\mathrm{Tl}}\Big|_{\mathrm{Tl}^{\beta}} = \Delta F^{\beta\to\alpha}{}_{\mathrm{Tl}} + (1 - x)^2[g(x, T) + xg'(x, T)] \quad (11\text{-}14)$$

Thus if data for $RT \ln f^{\alpha}{}_{\mathrm{Tl}}\Big|_{\mathrm{Tl}^{\beta}}$ are available[72] at a given temperature for $0 \leq x \leq 0.9$ they can be plotted versus $(1 - x)^2$ over the range $1 \leq (1 -$

[69] S. Sekito, On the Crystal Structure of Thallium, *Z. Krist.*, vol. A74, pp. 189–201, 1930.

[70] A. Schneider and G. Heymer, Die Temperaturabhängigkeit der Molvolumina der Phasen NaTl und LiCd, *Z. anorg. Chem.*, vol. 286, p. 118, 1956.

[71] R. E. Cech, Evidence for Solidification of a Metastable Phase in Fe-Ni Alloys, *Trans. AIME*, vol. 206, pp. 585–589, 1956; also in *J. Metals*, vol. 8, 1956.

[72] A. Olander, Eine elektrochemische und Röntgenographische Untersuchung von fester Thallium-Blei-Legierungen, *Z. physik. Chem.*, vol. 168A, pp. 274–282, 1934.

$x)^2 \leq 0.01$ in order to separate $\Delta F^{\beta\to\alpha}{}_{\mathrm{Tl}}$ from the compositional-dependent component of the activity coefficient. By carrying out such an analysis, Lumsden[14] found

$$\Delta F^{\alpha\to\beta}{}_{\mathrm{Tl}} \sim 65 - 0.20T \quad \text{cal/mole} \tag{11-15}$$

hence

$$\Delta F^{\alpha\to\epsilon}{}_{\mathrm{Tl}} \sim -9 - 0.05T \quad \text{cal/mole} \tag{11-16}$$

These results indicate the extremely small energy differences (i.e., 4×10^{-4} to 3×10^{-3} ev/atom at 0°K) between the various forms of thallium. It is interesting to combine Eqs. (11-12) and (11-15) and calculate

$$\Delta F^{\alpha\to L}{}_{\mathrm{Tl}} = 1090 - 1.98T \quad \text{cal/mole} \tag{11-17}$$

which yields $\bar{T}^{\alpha}{}_{\mathrm{Tl}} = 550°\mathrm{K}$ and $\Delta S^{\alpha\to L}{}_{\mathrm{Tl}} = 1.98$ cal/mole °K.

Lumsden has compared the entropy of fusion of the crystal structures of various metals. He suggests that the magnitude of the entropy-of-fusion data can be classified for metals within certain limits. This comparison indicates that the entropy of fusion for metals which the fcc at 1 atm $\Delta S^{\alpha\to L}$ lies within the range 2.20 ± 0.40 cal/mole. $\Delta S^{\alpha\to L}{}_{\mathrm{Tl}}$ is in this range even though α-thallium is not stable at atmospheric pressure. It should be pointed out that the analysis of thallium carried out by Lumsden could be checked independently if measurements of the chemical activity of thallium could be made in the α solid solution of the thallium-bismuth system, $0.63 \leq x \leq 0.96$, relative to ϵ-thallium. The data so obtained for $\Delta F^{\alpha\to\epsilon}{}_{\mathrm{Tl}}$ should be directly comparable with the results obtained from the lead-thallium system and thus provide an independent check on Eqs. (11-16) through (11-18).

The thermodynamic and volumetric data may now be combined in order to estimate the transition pressure for the $\epsilon \to \alpha$ reaction in thallium at 300°K, assuming that the compressibilities are equal. Thus,

$$\Delta F^{\alpha\to\epsilon}{}_{\mathrm{Tl}}(T, P) \approx -9 - 0.05T + 23.9P\,\Delta V^{\alpha\to\epsilon}{}_{\mathrm{Tl}} \tag{11-18}$$

Setting $\Delta V^{\alpha\to\epsilon}{}_{\mathrm{Tl}} = 0.026$ cm³/mole, we find $\Delta F^{\alpha\to\epsilon}{}_{\mathrm{Tl}}(T, P) = 0$ at 300°K and 38 kilobars.

Bridgman[73] reported the transition in thallium as occurring in the vicinity of 40 kilobars at room temperature with a volume change of about 0.00046 cm³/gm or 0.094 cm³/mole. The latter figure is slightly smaller than that quoted by Lawson[8] in his review of Bridgman's work. Recently, Kennedy and LaMori[58] redetermined the transition pressure as 36.7 kilobars but did not report the volume change. The degree of

[73] P. W. Bridgman, Polymorphism, Principally of the Elements, up to 50,000 kg/cm², *Phys. Rev.*, vol. 48, pp. 893–906, 1935.

agreement between the calculated and observed transition is undoubtedly fortuitous, and the measured volume change of 0.094 cm^3/mole is about four times the calculated change (0.026 cm^3/mole). However, the calculation does suggest that the high-pressure form of thallium is fcc, a suggestion which must await X-ray investigation for verification.‡ The thermodynamic calculations do indicate that the stacking-fault energy of thallium, which should be qualitatively related to $\Delta F^{\alpha \to \epsilon}{}_{Tl}$, is probably quite low. This is another point worthy of investigation.

(*g*) *Tin.* We shall now return to a consideration of tin, which was discussed earlier with respect to the grey → white ($\delta \to \tau$) transformation. In the earlier consideration the entropy change $\Delta S^{\delta \to \tau}{}_{Sn}$ was found to be 1.88 cal/mole °K. The τ structure is stable at 1 atm between 286°K and $\bar{T}^{\tau}{}_{Sn} = 505$°K, where the heat of fusion is[22] 1,720 cal/mole; thus

$$\Delta S^{\tau \to L}{}_{Sn} = 3.41 \text{ cal/mole °K} \tag{11-19}$$

We now estimate the entropy of melting of grey tin (δ) as

$$\Delta S^{\delta \to L}{}_{Sn} = \Delta S^{\delta \to \tau}{}_{Sn} + \Delta S^{\tau \to L}{}_{Sn} \approx 5.29 \text{ cal/mole °K} \tag{11-20}$$

This value is comparable in magnitude with the entropy of fusion of the diamond-cubic (δ) forms of silicon and germanium which are[22] $\Delta S^{\delta \to L}{}_{Si} = 6.60$ cal/mole °K and $\Delta S^{\delta \to L}{}_{Ge} = 6.28$ cal/mole °K. Reasoning by analogy (which may be dangerous), we might expect that fcc α-tin would have an entropy of melting of the order of 2.20 cal/mole °K, or that

$$\Delta S^{\tau \to \alpha}{}_{Sn} = \Delta S^{\tau \to L}{}_{Sn} + \Delta S^{L \to \alpha}{}_{Sn} \approx 1.21 \text{ cal/mole °K} \tag{11-21}$$

If this line of reasoning is correct, we might expect that the free-energy–temperature relationships between the α and τ crystal forms of tin are of the form shown schematically in Fig. 11-3. The enthalpy difference between the α and τ forms may be estimated in a similar manner; i.e.,

$$\Delta H^{\tau \to \alpha}{}_{Sn} \approx 1720 - 2.20\bar{T}^{\alpha}{}_{Sn} \qquad \text{cal/mole} \tag{11-22}$$

Geguzin and Pines[74] have estimated $\bar{T}^{\alpha}{}_{Sn} = 350$°K from a study of the fcc-liquid equilibria in the lead-tin system (see Appendix); hence $\Delta H^{\tau \to \alpha}{}_{Sn} \approx 950$ cal/mole, $\Delta H^{\alpha \to L}{}_{Sn} \approx 770$ cal/mole, and $T_0{}^{\tau \to \alpha} \approx 785$°K.

‡ The calculations were first published in 1961.[73a] About one year later Piermarini and Weir[31b] showed that the high-pressure form of thallium was fcc in an X-ray experiment

[73a] L. Kaufman, Calculation of the Effect of Pressure on the Phase Transformations in Thallium, *Acta Met.*, vol. 9, p. 861, 1961.

[74] Ya. E. Geguzin and B. Ya. Pines, Energy of Mixing of Binary Metallic Systems, *Doklady Akad. Nauk S. S. S. R.*, vol. 75, pp. 535–538, 1950; *Chem. Abstrs.*, vol. 46, p. 1341d, 1952.

On the basis of these estimates we conclude that tetragonal tin would transform into fcc tin at 785°K at 1 atm were it not for the intervention of the liquid phase (i.e., Cottrell's argument[66]). Reference to Table 11-2 shows that $V^{\tau}{}_{\text{Sn}} \approx 16.5$ cm³/mole at 1 atm and 505°K, and that $\Delta V^{\tau\to L}{}_{\text{Sn}} \approx 0.462$ cm³/mole at this temperature. In order to compute the phase relationships, which must qualitatively resemble Fig. 11-3, it is necessary to approximate $\Delta V^{\alpha\to L}{}_{\text{Sn}}$ or $\Delta V^{\alpha\to\tau}{}_{\text{Sn}}$. This can be accomplished with the help of Eq. (11-6), which, when applied to tin, yields

$$\frac{V^{\alpha}{}_{\text{Sn}}\,\Delta S^{\alpha\to L}{}_{\text{Sn}}}{\Delta V^{\alpha\to L}{}_{\text{Sn}}} \approx 60 \text{ cal/mole°K} \qquad (11\text{-}23)$$

Setting $\Delta S^{\alpha\to L}{}_{\text{Sn}} \approx 2.20$ and $V^{\alpha}{}_{\text{Sn}} \approx V^{\tau}{}_{\text{Sn}} \approx 16.5$ cm³/mole, we find $\Delta V^{\alpha\to L}{}_{\text{Sn}} = 0.605$ cm³/mole and $\Delta V^{\tau\to\alpha}{}_{\text{Sn}} = -0.143$ cm³/mole.

Ignoring the pressure and temperature dependences of the volume changes as a first approximation, we obtain

$$\Delta F^{\tau\to L}{}_{\text{Sn}} = 1720 - 3.41T + 23.9P(0.462) \quad \text{cal/mole} \qquad (11\text{-}24)$$
$$\Delta F^{\tau\to\alpha}{}_{\text{Sn}} = 950 - 1.21T - 23.9P(0.143) \quad \text{cal/mole} \qquad (11\text{-}25)$$
$$\Delta F^{\alpha\to L}{}_{\text{Sn}} = 770 - 2.20T + 23.9P(0.605) \quad \text{cal/mole} \qquad (11\text{-}26)$$

The *T-P* relationships resulting from Eqs. (11-24) to (11-26) are shown in Fig. 11-8 along with the calculated *T-P* relation for the $\delta \to \tau$ reaction discussed earlier. Dudley and Hall[19] and Kennedy[25] have studied the effects of pressure on the phase relations in tin. In both cases a triple point between liquid tin, Sn I (i.e., τ-Sn), and a high-pressure phase Sn II was reported at about 31 kilobars and 580°K. Dudley and Hall,[19] however, were not able to follow the *P-T* curve for the solid phase transformation. Kennedy's results are shown in Fig. 11-8 along with the calculations. Although the identity of the high-pressure phase of tin awaits development of suitable X-ray techniques, the features of the calculated *P-T* relationships for α, τ, and liquid tin do resemble the Sn II, Sn I (τ-Sn), and liquid curves. Table 11-3 summarizes the theoretical results and experimental data.

(*h*) *Zinc.* Another possible metal in which a case-*C* transition *may* occur is zinc. At 1 atm η-zinc is hcp with a c/a ratio[39] of 1.856, which is considerably larger than the ratio for ideally close-packed-hexagonal structures (i.e., 1.633). The enthalpy of fusion $\Delta H^{\eta\to L}{}_{\text{Zn}}$ of η-zinc is 1,765 cal/mole, and $\bar{T}^{\eta}{}_{\text{Zn}}$ is 693°K ($\Delta S^{\eta\to L}{}_{\text{Zn}} = 2.55$ cm³/mole). The melting point and entropy of fusion of fcc α-Zinc have been calculated as $\bar{T}^{\alpha}{}_{\text{Zn}} \approx 615$°K and $\Delta S^{\alpha\to L}{}_{\text{Zn}} \approx 2.12$ cal/mole, respectively, by considering the α/L equilibria in the aluminum-zinc, copper-zinc, and silver-zinc systems.[75] These results indicate $T_0{}^{\eta\to\alpha} \approx 1080$°K at 1 atm. In prin-

[75] L. Kaufman, Lattice Stability of Metals. II. Zinc, Copper, and Silver, *Bull. Am. Phys. Soc.*, vol. 4, p. 181, 1959.

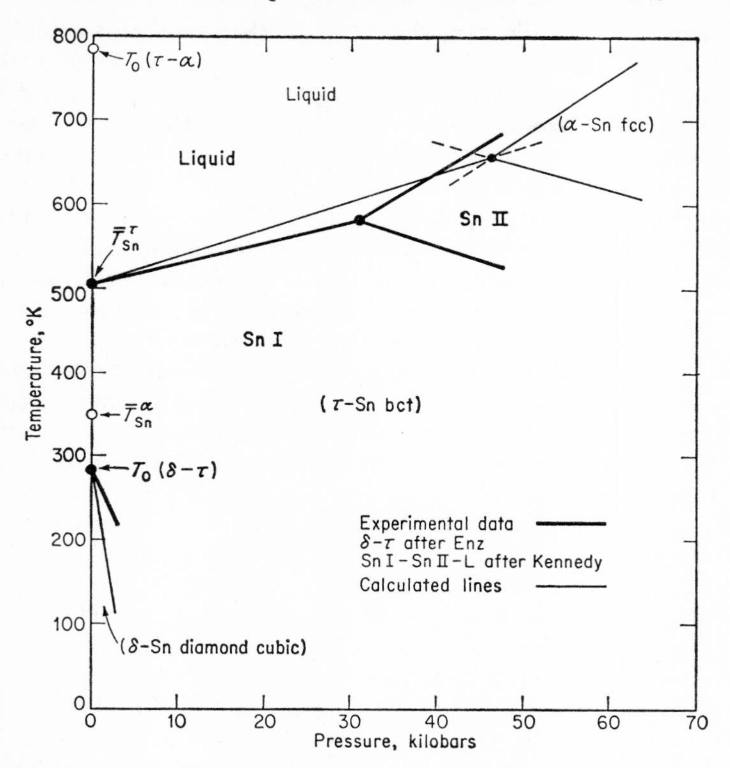

Fig. 11-8 Experimental and theoretical phase relations in tin as a function of temperature and pressure.

Table 11-3 Comparison of Theoretical and Experimental T-P Relations between the Solid and Liquid Phases of Tin

Quantity	Calculated, °K/kilobar	Observed,[25] °K/kilobar
$\delta \rightarrow \tau$		
dT/dP	−56	−20
$\tau \rightarrow L$		
dT/dP	3.3	2.7
$\alpha \rightarrow L$		
dT/dP	6.6	6.0
$\tau \rightarrow \alpha$		
dT/dP	−2.8	−3.0
T_c, °K	655	580
P_c, kilobars	46	31

ciple, then, the P-T diagram should be of the same type exhibited by the $\tau \rightarrow \alpha$ relations in tin (i.e., Fig. 11-3). Unfortunately, it is difficult to estimate the volume changes for the $\alpha \rightarrow L$ reaction as was done for tin because both α- and η-zinc are close-packed. However, if fcc α-zinc is as dense or denser than η-zinc, the triple point should occur below 1080°K and 100 kilobars.

The foregoing discussion of case-C transitions was not presented for the purpose of illustrating how a priori thermodynamic calculations can be used to predict high-pressure transformations. Indeed, the calculations for thallium and tin were performed *after* the high-pressure transitions had been established by experiment; moreover the identity of the high-pressure forms, which are presumed to be fcc in the calculations, *has not been conclusively established.*‡ Under these circumstances it is natural to question the value of such considerations.

At the outset of this discussion it was pointed out that little is known concerning the relative stability of atomic configurations in metals. The difficulty of establishing the lattice stability arises from the small energy differences between various modifications. Nevertheless, the availability of quantitative data on the lattice stability of metals would have widespread applicability in many areas of metal physics.[21] The usefulness of such data in a priori prediction of high-pressure transitions has been illustrated[54–56] for the case of the $\alpha \rightarrow \gamma$ transition in iron and iron alloys. Since expansion of the temperature-pressure field will probably result in the discovery of many new phase transitions, future progress in determining the lattice stability of metals may stem directly from investigations of metals under pressure.

11-3 Two-component Systems

Discussion of the effects of pressure on equilibria in binary metallic systems requires consideration of several additional factors which were absent in the discussion of one-component systems. In addition to dealing with phases of variable composition, it is necessary to concern oneself with the approach to equilibrium and the kinetic aspects of phase transformations. This is particularly true in the case of diffusion-controlled phase separation. In view of the recent coverage of the kinetic aspects of the problem by Hilliard[10] and Hilliard and Cahn,[76] this paper will be concerned primarily with equilibrium situations and, except for specific instances, the kinetic effects of pressure will not be considered.

In some respects the simplest type of phase transformation in a binary

‡ The high-pressure form of thallium has now been conclusively established as fcc.[31b]

[76] J. E. Hilliard and J. Cahn, The Effect of High Pressures on Transformation Rates, pp. 109–125 in F. P. Bundy, W. R. Hibbard, and H. M. Strong (eds.), "Progress in Very High Pressure Research," John Wiley & Sons, Inc., New York, 1961.

system is the diffusionless martensitic transformation.[20] This type reaction, which is the binary-system analogue of polymorphism, occurs at 1 atm when an alloy is cooled (or heated) through a critical range of temperature at a rate which is rapid relative to the rate of diffusion required for diffusion-controlled phase separation. Since the cooling/heating rate is relative, it can be a slow rate versus substitutional diffusion or a rapid rate versus interstitial diffusion. Interestingly enough, the reaction nearly always exhibits some degree of temperature hysteresis. Thus if the high-temperature β form is cooled below T_0, it will not transform to the low-temperature α form until some temperature M_s is reached. Cooling below M_s produces the low-temperature α form which will require heating above T_0 to a temperature A_s before the $\alpha \rightarrow \beta$ reaction proceeds. This hysteresis, $A_s - M_s$, is found to vary from several degrees to several hundred degrees (or several calories per mole to several hundred calories per mole) depending on the particular alloy system.[20] It has been found that shearing stresses and plastic deformation can be used to enhance nucleation of the more stable configuration and to lead to a reduction in the observed hysteresis.[20] In this respect the temperature hysteresis observed for martensitic transformations is similar to the pressure hysteresis exhibited by many high-pressure transitions. Bridgman[1] points out that the range of hysteresis about a critical pressure can often be reduced by superposition of shearing stresses; the function of these stresses is undoubtedly to provide nucleation sites for the growth of a stable phase.

The effect of pressure on the temperature range of martensitic transformations (on cooling) and reversals (on heating) can be calculated by using the same approach as was applied to one-component systems. Thus the Clausius-Clapeyron equation can be applied to calculate the change in T_0 with pressure. Calculation of the effect of pressure on M_s and A_s should take into account the change in driving force required to initiate the transformation with temperature and pressure, particularly if the degree of supercooling ($T_0 - M_s$) and superheating ($A_s - T_0$) is large.

Order-disorder transformations in binary systems have been studied under hydrostatic pressure by Wilson,[77] who measured the change in ordering temperature with pressure in several binary systems. In principle the shift in the ordering temperature can be calculated on the basis of the Ehrenfest relation by using 1-atm thermodynamic information. Lawson[8] has discussed Wilson's results for the change in the ordering temperature in CuZn with pressure on the basis of the Ehrenfest relation. Although the magnitude of the observed pressure shift is in

[77] T. C. Wilson, The Effect of High Pressure on the Order Disorder Transformation in Alloys, *Phys. Rev.*, vol. 56, pp. 598–611, 1939.

accordance with atmospheric-pressure specific-heat, compressibility, and thermal-expansion data, there are difficulties in making a precise calculation of the shift. The difficulties arise from the fact that the Ehrenfest relation applies to an ideal second-order transition exhibiting discontinuities in the specific heat, compressibility, and expansion coefficient, while the real system shows continuous variations of these properties. However, Lawson has shown that the relation can be applied by treating the thermodynamic properties above and below the ordering temperature uniformly and minimizing the errors involved in estimating the discrete changes in thermodynamic properties.

We now turn to a brief discussion of the vast, and experimentally unexplored, area of two- and three-phase equilibrium in metallic systems. In principle free-energy expressions for binary alloys, analogous to Eqs. (11-1) and (11-3), can be written as functions of temperature, composition, and pressure. The chemical potentials for each component as defined by such equations can then be equated to determine equilibrium lines on phase diagrams. This type of formulation has been carried out in the Appendix [Eqs. (11-A1) to (11-A19)] and will be applied to specific systems. The mathematical formulation, albeit correct, does not yield a clear understanding of the system properties which play a dominant role in controlling high-pressure phase equilibria.

In line with the earlier discussion of one-component equilibria, it is instructive to consider several hypothetical examples of free-energy volumetric relationships in binary systems for the purpose of illustrating the pressure effects. These examples are illustrated in Figs. 11-9 to 11-11. The free-energy volumetric relations shown in these figures have been overexaggerated and may be unrealistic (i.e., solid solutions showing large positive deviations from Vegard's rule generally do not exhibit homogeneous solid solubility at all temperatures, etc.).[78,79] However, they serve to illustrate the factors controlling high-pressure equilibria.

Figure 11-9 illustrates a simple system in which there is complete solubility in the low-temperature α and high-temperature β phases (β might also be a liquid phase). In Fig. 11-9*a* the molar volumes of both phases are linear with composition, and the α phase is denser than the β phase across the system. The free-energy curves shown in Fig. 11-9*a* have been sketched on the assumption that the volumetric relations are independent of temperature and pressure. The simple case of Fig. 11-9*a* results in an expanded temperature range of stability for the α phase with no qualitative change in the shape of the two phase fields.

[78] J. H. Hildebrand and R. L. Scott, "The Solubility of Nonelectrolytes," Reinhold Publishing Corporation, New York, 1950.

[79] C. Wagner, "Thermodynamics of Alloys," Addison-Wesley Publishing Company, Inc., Reading, Mass., 1952.

The examples shown in Fig. 11-9*b* and *c* illustrate how positive values of the mixing volume V_M affect high-pressure equilibria. The molar volume of the α phase of the A-B system is defined as

$$V^{\alpha} = (1 - x)V_A{}^{\alpha} + xV_B{}^{\alpha} + V_M{}^{\alpha} \qquad \text{cm}^3/\text{mole} \qquad (11\text{-}27)$$

The case illustrated in Fig. 11-9*b* shows how positive values of $V_M{}^{\alpha}$ result in a miscibility gap in the low-temperature phase and eutectoid

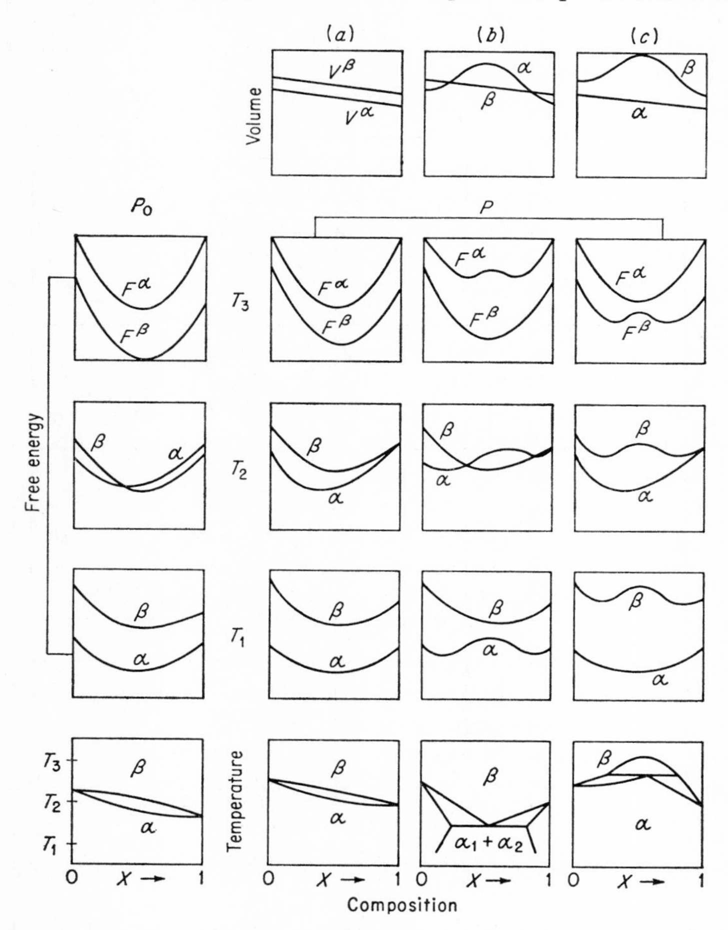

Fig. 11-9 Schematic representation of the effects of pressure on two-phase equilibria.

formation, while Fig. 11-9*c* illustrates monotectoid reactions caused by a solubility gap in the high-temperature phase (i.e., $V_M{}^{\beta} > 0$).

A second type of high-pressure behavior is illustrated in Fig. 11-10. In this situation, element A exhibits polymorphism at 1 atm which is similar to that of iron, i.e., case B. The simple linear relation for V^α and V^β as a function of composition (Fig. 11-10a) results in depression of the two-phase field. However, if $V_M{}^\alpha$ is positive (Fig. 11-10b), a miscibility gap in the high-temperature phase can be formed, resulting

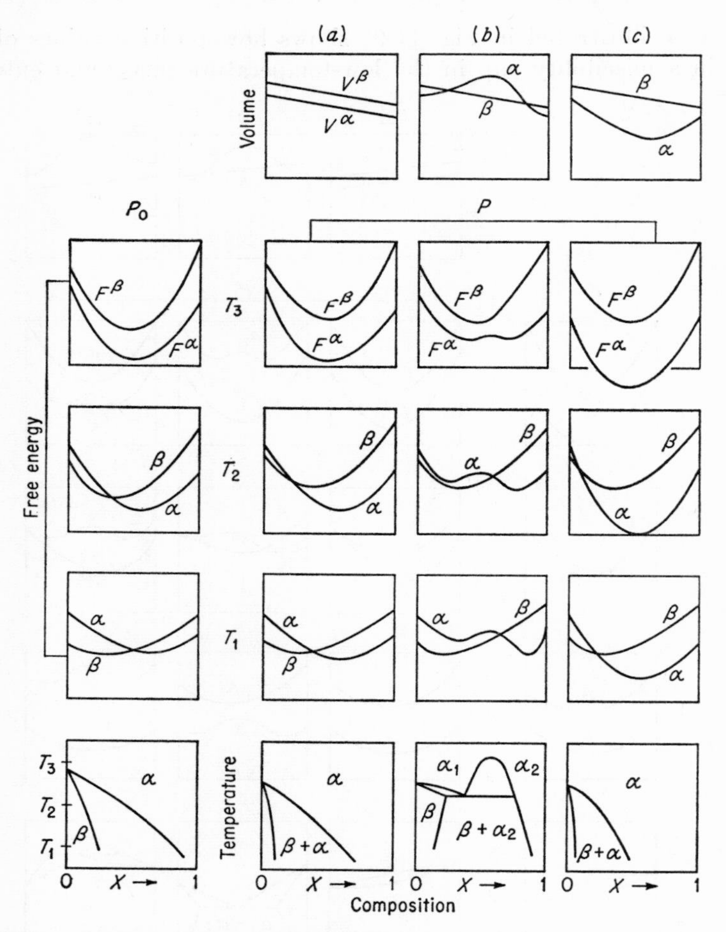

Fig. 11-10 Schematic representation of the effects of pressure on two-phase equilibria.

in a eutectoid decomposition. On the other hand, negative values of $V_M{}^\alpha$ cause further contraction of the two-phase field and enhanced stability for the α phase.

Three-phase equilibria present even more possibilities for the effects of pressure on the shape of phase diagrams. Figure 11-11 illustrates some of the alternatives for a eutectoid system in which all the molar-volume curves are linear but arranged in different order of densities. In general the eutectoid temperature and composition shift so as to expand the phase field of the densest phase. Solubilities and transition points move in the same direction. The quantitative prediction of the

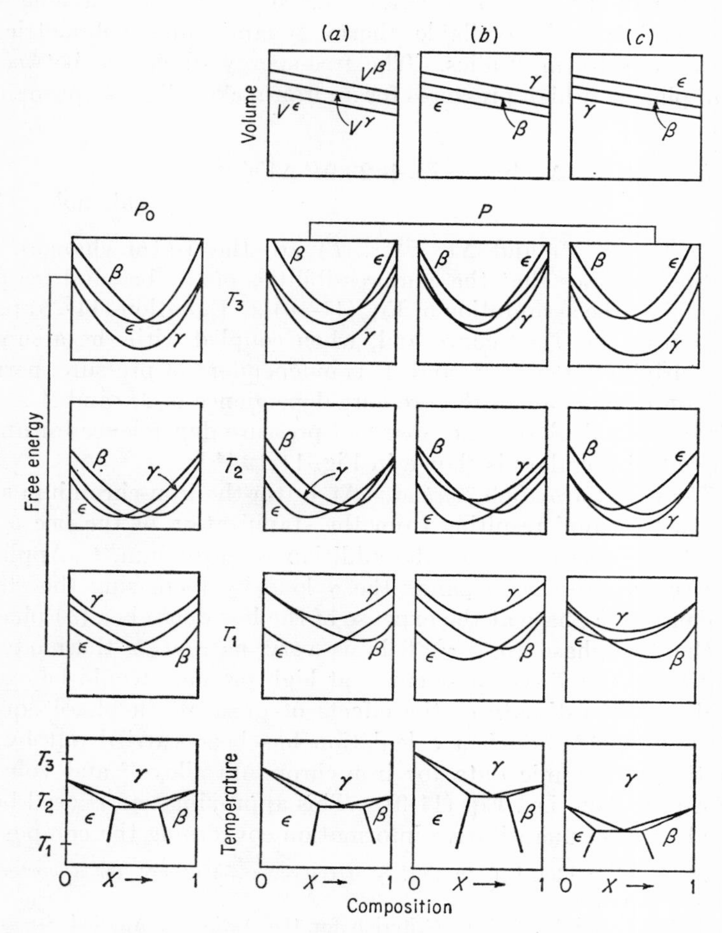

Fig. 11-11 Schematic representation of the effects of pressure on two-phase equilibria.

compositional and temperature displacements at high pressure depend on the thermodynamic and volumetric properties of the system and will be discussed in some detail in following sections.

11-3a Transformation in binary metallic systems under pressure. (*a*) *The Iron-Nickel System.* Studies of the effects of pressure on the martensitic fcc (γ) $\rightleftarrows$ bcc (α') reactions in iron-nickel alloys have been performed for a number of alloys[54,80,81] over a range of pressure up to 50 kilobars.[54] The experimental results indicate an increase in the temperature range of stability of the denser, high-temperature austenite (γ) at the expense of the bcc martensite (α'). Calculations of the depression of M_s and A_s have been performed[54] by using the analogue of Eq. (11-3) together with available thermodynamic and volumetric data obtained from 1-atm studies. The free-energy difference between the γ and α' phases at high pressures for an iron-nickel alloy is approximated by

$$\Delta F^{\alpha' \to \gamma}(x, T, P) \approx \Delta F^{\alpha' \to \gamma}(x, T) + 23.9P\,\Delta V^{\alpha' \to \gamma}(x, T) \quad \text{cal/mole} \qquad (11\text{-}28)$$

where $\Delta F^{\alpha' \to \gamma}(x, T)$ and $\Delta V^{\alpha' \to \gamma}(x, T)$ are the 1-atm changes. This calculation assumes that the compressibilities of the bcc and fcc phases are equal [i.e., the assumption of Eq. (11-10)]. Equation (11-28) permits calculation of the T_0-P curve and, when coupled with the assumption that the driving force at M_s and A_s is independent of pressure, permits a calculation to be made of the pressure dependence of M_s and A_s. Comparison of the calculated and observed pressure dependence for an iron–9.5 percent nickel alloy is shown in Fig. 11-12.[54,‡]

(*b*) *The Iron-Chromium System.* At 1 atm the iron-chromium system exhibits a "γ loop" resulting from the stabilization of the bcc α phase at high temperatures due to the addition of chromium.[82] Application of hydrostatic pressure expands the γ loop by increasing the stability of the denser fcc phase at the expense of the less dense bcc (α) phase.[54,83] Since the two-phase ($\alpha \to \gamma$) field is very narrow, a thermodynamic calculation of the T_0-versus-x curve at high pressure would be expected to yield a good estimate of the effects of pressure on phase equilibria in this system.[82,54] Such a calculation has been carried out by using 1-atm thermodynamic data for iron-chromium alloys[82] and volumetric data for pure iron, i.e., Eq. (11-9). This approximation is used because of the absence of quantitative information concerning the compositional

‡ Figure 11-12 is identical to Fig. 8 of reference 54 except for a correction in the pressure scale.[58]

[80] J. R. Patel and M. Cohen, Criterion for the Action of Applied Stress in the Martensitic Transformation, *Acta Met.*, vol. 1, pp. 531–538, 1953.

[81] E. Scheil and W. Normann, Untersuchung thermodynamischer grossen der Martensitischen $\gamma \leftrightarrows \alpha$-Umwandlung von Eisen-Nickel-Legierungen, *Arch. Eisenhüttenw.*, vol. 30, pp. 751–754, 1959.

[82] L. Kaufman, The Free Energy Changes Attending the Martensitic Transformation in the Iron-Chromium and Iron-Chromium-Nickel Systems, *Trans. AIME*, vol. 215, pp. 218–231, 1959.

[83] E. W. Goliber and K. H. McKee, Research and Development on the Effects of High Pressure and Temperature on Various Elements and Binary Alloys, pp. 126–151 in F. P. Bundy, W. R. Hibbard, and H. M. Strong (eds.), "Progress in Very High Pressure Research," John Wiley & Sons, Inc., New York, 1961.

dependence of $\Delta V^{\alpha \to \gamma}$ for iron-chromium alloys. On this basis, an equation similar to Eq. (11-28) is written for $\Delta F^{\alpha \to \gamma}(x, T, P)$, and the T_0-versus-x curve is calculated for various pressures. The calculated and experimental T_0-versus-x curve determined at 42 kilobars[54] is shown

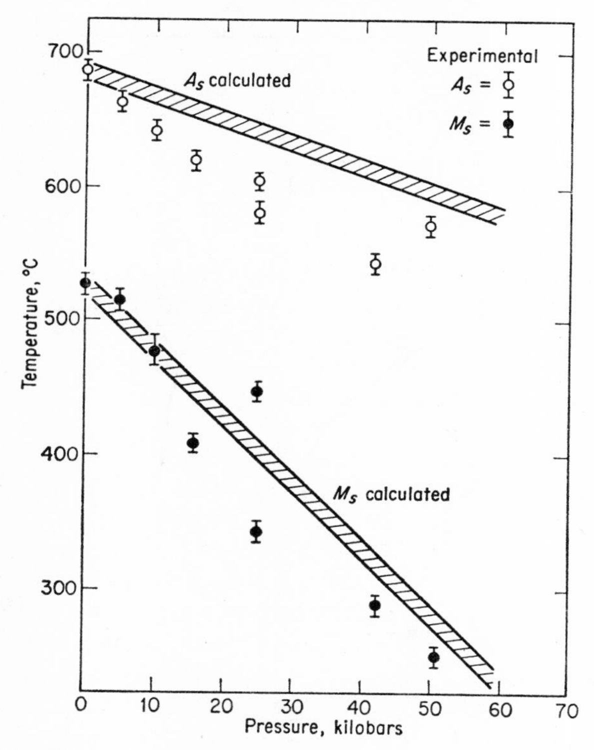

Fig. 11-12 The effect of pressure on A_s and M_s in an iron–9.5 percent nickel alloy. (*Kaufman, Leyenaar, and Harvey.*[54])

in Fig. 11-13. Agreement between the calculation and experiment is good at low chromium levels, with a disparity which increases as the chromium level is increased.‡ The probable cause of this discrepancy is the approximation of $\Delta V^{\alpha \to \gamma} = \Delta V^{\alpha \to \gamma}{}_{\mathrm{Fe}}$. Dilatometric measurements on iron-chromium alloys[84] indicate that addition of chromium does

‡ The iron-silicon measurements were performed using a chromel-alumel thermocouple to measure temperature, while the iron-chromium measurements and the measurements on iron[54] were performed in the same apparatus with platinum–13 percent rhodium couples. In both instances the indicated transition temperature for iron at 42 kilobars agrees with the calculated value.

[84] J. B. Austin and R. H. H. Pierce, Linear Thermal Expansion and Transformation Phenomena of Some Low-carbon Iron-Chromium Alloys, *Trans. AIME*, vol. 116, pp. 289–308, 1935.

indeed decrease $\Delta V^{\alpha\to\gamma}$. This effect would explain the increasing disparity between the calculated and observed T_0-x curves as the chromium content is increased. X-ray measurements of the lattice parameters of α- and γ-iron-chromium alloys could be used to evaluate

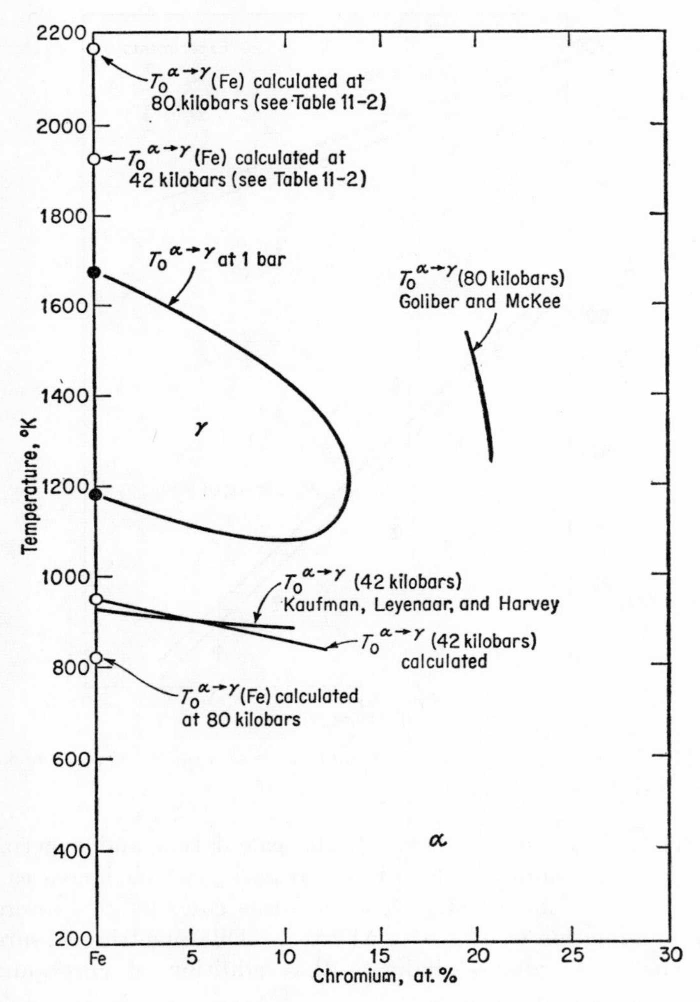

Fig. 11-13 The effect of pressure on the $\alpha \rightleftharpoons \gamma$ reactions in the iron-chromium system.

quantitatively the effect of chromium on $\Delta V^{\alpha\to\gamma}$. Goliber and McKee[83] have established the extent of the γ loop at about 80 kilobars as about 20 percent chromium in the vicinity of 1400°K. Their results have been included in Fig. 11-13.

(*c*) *The Iron-Silicon System.* Tanner and Kulin[85] investigated the effects of pressure on the γ loop of the iron-silicon system at 42 kilobars. They found an expansion which is compared with the calculated T_0-x curve in Fig. 11-14. Calculation of the T_0-x curve is accomplished by

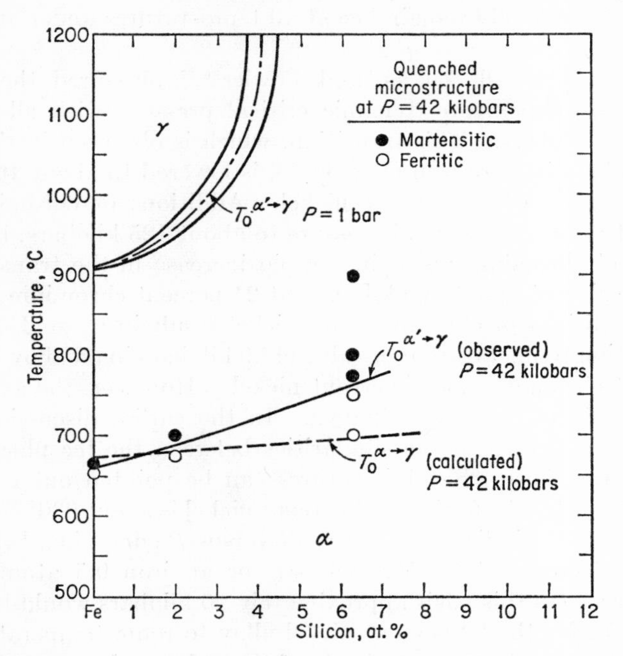

Fig. 11-14 The effect of hydrostatic pressure on the γ loop of the iron-silicon system. (*Tanner and Kulin.*[85])

approximating $\Delta V^{\alpha\to\gamma} \sim \Delta V^{\alpha\to\gamma}{}_{\text{Fe}}$. The approximation used is given, for iron-silicon alloys, by

$$\Delta F^{\alpha'\to\gamma}(x, T, P) \approx (1 - x)\Delta F^{\alpha\to\gamma}{}_{\text{Fe}} + 450x - 23.9P(0.312 - 2 \times 10^{-4}T) \qquad \text{cal/mole} \quad (11\text{-}29)$$

The disparity between the calculated and experimental T_0-x curves at 42 kilobars is seen to increase with increasing silicon. As in the case of the iron-chromium system, the discrepancy probably is due to the decrease in $\Delta V^{\alpha\to\gamma}$ with increasing silicon.‡

(*d*) *The Iron-Aluminum System.* Goliber and McKee[83] have expanded the γ loop in the iron-aluminum system to aluminum compositions above

‡ This inference has been substantiated by G. H. Cockett and C. D. Davis, The Effect of Volume Changes on the High-pressure $\alpha \rightleftarrows \gamma$ Transformation in Fe-Si Alloys, *Acta Met.*, vol. 10, p. 974, 1962.

[85] L. Tanner and S. A. Kulin, The Effect of Pressure on the $\alpha \rightleftarrows \gamma$ Transformation in the Iron-Silicon System, *Acta Met.*, vol. 9, pp. 1038–1040, 1961.

3 percent by application of about 80 kilobars. At 1 atm the maximum extent of the loop is about 2 percent.

Thus it is seen that the application of hydrostatic pressure to γ-loop systems expands the range of stability of the γ phase to compositions which would normally remain bcc at all temperatures under atmospheric conditions.

Recently, Minshall, Zukas, and Fowler[86,87] measured the variation of the room-temperature dynamic critical pressure with alloy content in iron-nickel alloys. This transition, which is observed in the vicinity of 130 kilobars in pure iron (Fig. 11-6), is lowered to about 100 kilobars by the addition of 22 percent nickel. Additions of chromium up to 10 percent reduce the critical pressure to about 125 kilobars, but further additions of chromium result in a rapid increase in the transition pressure to a value of about 180 kilobars at 21 percent chromium.[87] Simultaneous additions of chromium and nickel result in a rapid decrease of the transition temperature to a value of 30 kilobars in an alloy containing 18 percent chromium and 8 percent nickel. However, the exact nature of the transition remains unknown. In the earlier discussion of iron, attention was drawn to the similarities between the fcc phase and the high-pressure phase. Similar features can be pointed out for the iron alloys. At 1 atm, T_0 for iron–22 percent nickel is about 630°K.[20] Reference to Fig. 11-12 indicates that the T_0-versus-P curve, i.e., $\frac{1}{2}(M_s + A_s)$ versus P, decreases by 3.5°K/kilobar for an iron–9.5 atomic percent nickel alloy. On this basis approximately 90 kilobars would be required to reduce T_0 for the 22 percent nickel alloy to room temperature. The apparent decrease in the magnitude of the volume change attending the $\alpha \rightarrow \gamma$ transition in iron with increasing chromium content makes it difficult to estimate the pressure required to convert bcc iron–21 percent chromium into the fcc form at room temperature. However, the decrease in the volume change can explain the rapid increase in the transition pressure observed with increasing chromium content. In this connection, measurements of the volume change attending the dynamic pressure transitions as a function of alloy content would be highly desirable. In view of the importance of determining the similarities and differences between the behavior of metals under static and dynamic pressures, the nature of the transition in iron should be fully investigated.

11-3b Equilibrium in binary metallic systems under pressure. (*a*) *General.* The boundaries and critical points for two- and three-

[86] C. M. Fowler, F. S. Minshall, and E. G. Zukas, "The Response of Metals to High-velocity Deformation," Interscience Publishers, Inc., New York, 1960.

[87] F. S. Minshall, E. G. Zukas, and C. M. Fowler, Additional Data on the Shock-induced Transition in Iron-base Binary and Ternary Alloys of Chromium and/or Nickel (Philadelphia Meeting, AIME, 1960), *J. Metals*, vol. 12, p. 733, 1960.

phase equilibria in binary systems can be described mathematically by relationships equating the chemical potentials or partial molar free energies of both components at the phase boundaries. The development of these equations is presented in the Appendix. The equations can be differentiated with respect to pressure in order to formulate the change in equilibrium composition or invariant temperature with pressure. The shift in equilibrium composition x_β at the boundary of a two-phase $\alpha + \beta$ field at a temperature T by the application of pressure is given by

$$\frac{dx_\beta}{dP} = -\frac{1 - x_\beta}{x_\beta - x_\alpha} \Delta V\Big|_{x_\alpha} \left(\frac{\partial \bar{F}_B{}^\beta}{\partial x}\Big|_{x_\beta}\right)^{-1} \tag{11-30}$$

where‡

$$\Delta V\Big|_{x_\alpha} = V^\alpha\Big|_{x_\alpha} - (1 - x_\alpha)\bar{V}_A{}^\beta\Big|_{x_\beta} - x_\alpha \bar{V}_B{}^\beta\Big|_{x_\beta} \tag{11-31}$$

$V^\alpha\Big|_{x_\alpha}$ = molar volume of α phase at α-boundary composition x_α

$\bar{V}_A{}^\beta\Big|_{x_\beta}, \bar{V}_B{}^\beta\Big|_{x_\beta}$ = partial molar volumes of A, B in β phase at x_β

$\bar{F}_B{}^\beta$ = chemical potential of B in β phase

If suitable thermodynamic and volumetric data are available, Eq. (11-30) can be integrated to obtain $x_\beta(T, P)$. Hilliard and Cahn[76] have devised a simple graphical method for evaluating the first term of the product in Eq. (11-30). This construction is useful in determining how the volumetric term tends to shift x_β with pressure.

Equation (11-30) may be rewritten in a slightly different form in order to illustrate the pressure dependence of the solubility in a terminal solid solution as follows:

$$\frac{dx_\beta}{dP} = -(1 - x_\beta)\left(\frac{\partial V^\beta}{\partial x}\Big|_{x_\beta} - \frac{V^\beta - V^\alpha}{x_\beta - x_\alpha}\right)\left(\frac{\partial \bar{F}^\beta}{\partial x}\Big|_{x_\beta}\right)^{-1} \tag{11-32}$$

In Eq. (11-32), V^β and V^α refer to the molar volumes of the β and α phases at x_β and x_α, respectively. If x_β is nearly unity, i.e., β is a terminal solid solution with little solubility of A in β-B, then the thermodynamic term is approximately $(RT)^{-1}$. Under these circumstances the following volumetric conditions would lead to an expansion of the β field under hydrostatic pressure, i.e., $dx_\beta/dP < 0$:

1. Solution of A in β-B decreases the molar volume, i.e., $dV^\beta/dx > 0$.
2. The molar volume of the β phase at x_β is less than the volume of the x phase at x_α, i.e., $V^\beta < V^\alpha$.

If the reverse is true, the β field will contract, i.e., the solubility of A in β-B will decrease. Hilliard and Cahn[76] have investigated the kinetics of precipitation from terminal solid solutions in a number of substitutional solid solutions. However, the change in solubility with pressure

‡ In this paper x is the atomic fraction of element B.

in these systems was too small to compare observed changes in solubility with estimates afforded by Eqs. (11-30) to (11-32).

(*b*) *The Iron-Carbon System.* The only binary metallic system which, to the author's knowledge, has been studied extensively at high temperature and pressure is the iron-carbon system. Hilliard and Cahn,[76] Hilliard,[10] and Radcliffe, Schatz, and Kulin[88] have investigated the equilibria between austenite (γ), ferrite (α), and cementite (Cm) over a fairly wide range of temperature and pressure. Sufficient thermodynamic and volumetric data concerning these phases are available to permit a calculation of the two-phase equilibria between γ and orthorhombic cementite (Fe_3C) at high pressure. Combination of these calculations yields a calculation of the effect of pressure on the eutectoid decomposition in this system. The partial molar free energy of iron in fcc iron-carbon alloys has been derived from activity measurements, carried out by R. P. Smith,[89] and a consideration of the thermodynamic properties of interstitial solid solutions.[90] On this basis it is found that the partial molar free energy of iron in austenite relative to pure fcc iron is given by

$$\bar{F}^{\gamma}{}_{\mathrm{Fe}} - F^{\gamma}{}_{\mathrm{Fe}} = \frac{RT}{5} \ln \frac{1 - 6x}{1 - x} \qquad \text{cal/mole} \tag{11-33}$$

where x is the atom fraction of carbon.

The numerical factors in Eq. (11-33) arise from the interstitial carbon-carbon interaction which excludes some of the possible interstitial sites in the vicinity of a carbon atom from occupancy by other carbon atoms.[90] The partial molar free energy of iron in ferrite relative to pure bcc iron is[90]

$$\bar{F}^{\alpha}{}_{\mathrm{Fe}} - F^{\alpha}{}_{\mathrm{Fe}} = \frac{3RT}{z} \ln \frac{3 - x(3 + z)}{3(1 - x)} \qquad \text{cal/mole} \tag{11-34}$$

Although the factor z in Eq. (11-34) is presently unknown, consideration of very dilute solutions of ferrite permits the approximation

$$\bar{F}^{\alpha}{}_{\mathrm{Fe}} \approx F^{\alpha}{}_{\mathrm{Fe}} \qquad x \rightarrow 0 \tag{11-35}$$

Equations (11-33) and (11-35) can be used to compute the equilibrium boundary of the $(\alpha + \gamma)/\gamma$ field $x_{\gamma\text{-}\alpha}$, on the assumption that $x_{\alpha\text{-}\gamma}$, the carbon content at the boundary of the $\alpha/(\alpha + \gamma)$ field, is very small.

[88] S. V. Radcliffe, M. Schatz, and S. A. Kulin, Effects of High Pressure on Phase Transformations in the Iron-Carbon System *J. Metals*, vol. 12, p. 731, 1960.

[89] R. P. Smith, Equilibrium of Iron-Carbon Alloys with Mixtures of CO—CO_2 and CH_4—H_2, *J. Am. Chem. Soc.*, vol. 68, pp. 1163–1175, 1946.

[90] L. Kaufman, S. V. Radcliffe, and M. Cohen, Thermodynamics of the Bainite Reaction, pp. 313–352 in V. F. Zackay and H. I. Aarinson (eds.), "Decomposition of Austenite by Diffusional Processes," Interscience Publishers, Inc., New York, 1962.

Thus at 1 atm,[90]

$$\Delta F_{\mathrm{Fe}}{}^{\alpha\to\gamma}(T) = \frac{RT}{5} \ln \frac{1 - x_{\gamma\text{-}\alpha}}{1 - 6x_{\gamma\text{-}\alpha}} \tag{11-36}$$

At high pressure, $\Delta F^{\alpha\to\gamma}{}_{\mathrm{Fe}}(T)$ is replaced by $\Delta F^{\alpha\to\gamma}{}_{\mathrm{Fe}}(T, P)$ [Eq. (11-10)], and $x_{\gamma\text{-}\alpha}(T, P)$ can be calculated explicitly. Figure 11-15 shows the result of this calculation, which indicates the expected expansion of the γ field at the expense of the ferrite (Fig. 11-10*a*), which is less dense.

In the iron-carbon system, the cementite is denser than the austenite, so that an expansion of the γ + Cm field at the expense of the austenite

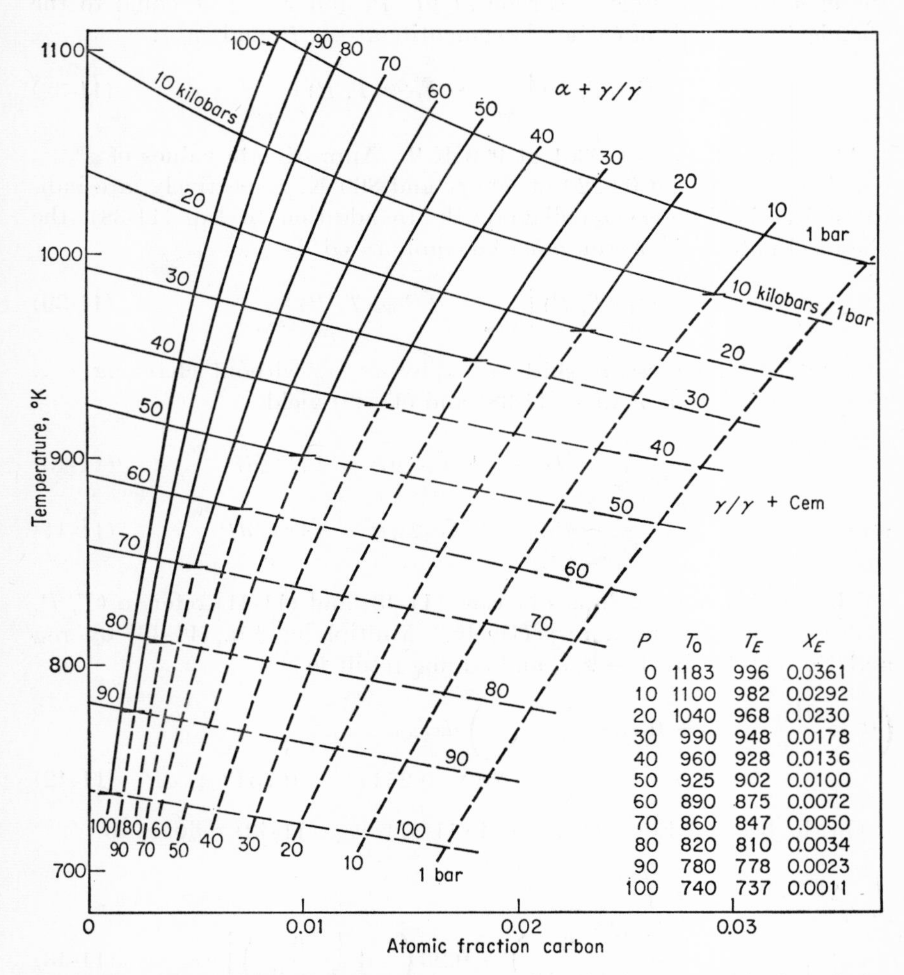

P	T_0	T_E	X_E
0	1183	996	0.0361
10	1100	982	0.0292
20	1040	968	0.0230
30	990	948	0.0178
40	960	928	0.0136
50	925	902	0.0100
60	890	875	0.0072
70	860	847	0.0050
80	820	810	0.0034
90	780	778	0.0023
100	740	737	0.0011

Fig. 11-15 Theoretical calculation of the $\alpha + \gamma/\gamma$ and γ/γ + cementite boundaries and the eutectoid temperature in the iron-carbon system as a function of pressure.

field is to be anticipated at high pressure. A calculation of the $x_{\gamma\text{-Cm}}$-versus-T curve at high pressure can be made (on the assumption that x_{Cm} in Fe_3C remains fixed at 0.25) as follows: The chemical potential of carbon in austenite relative to graphite has been derived[90] from the measurements of Smith[89] as being equal to

$$\bar{F}_{\text{C}}{}^{\gamma} - F_{\text{C}}{}^{G} = RT \ln \frac{x}{1 - 6x} + 10{,}580 - 4.01T \qquad \text{cal/mole} \qquad (11\text{-}37)$$

One condition for equilibrium along the $\gamma/(\gamma + \text{Cm})$ boundary is that the chemical potentials of carbon at (T, P, and $x_{\gamma\text{-Cm}}$) be equal to the chemical potentials of carbon in cementite at (T, P, and x_{Cm}):

$$\bar{F}_{\text{C}}{}^{\gamma}(T, P)\Big|_{x_{\gamma\text{-Cm}}} = \bar{F}_{\text{C}}{}^{\text{Cm}}(T, P)\Big|_{x_{\text{Cm}}} \qquad (11\text{-}38)$$

At 1 atm, $x^0{}_{\gamma\text{-Cm}} = 0.0361$ at 996°K.[11] Approximate values of $x^0{}_{\gamma\text{-Cm}}$ equal to 0.0286 and 0.0220 at 900°K and 800°K, respectively, are indicated by the iron-carbon diagram.[11] In addition to Eq. (11-38), the chemical potentials of iron must be equilibrated; i.e.,

$$\bar{F}^{\gamma}{}_{\text{Fe}}(T, P)\Big|_{x_{\gamma\text{-Cm}}} = \bar{F}^{\text{Cm}}{}_{\text{Fe}}(T, P)\Big|_{x_{\text{Cm}}} \qquad (11\text{-}39)$$

If hydrostatic pressure shifts $x_{\gamma\text{-Cm}}$ by $dx_{\gamma\text{-Cm}}$ without changing x_{Cm}, then differentiation of Eqs. (11-38) and (11-39) yields

$$\frac{\partial \bar{F}_{\text{C}}{}^{\gamma}}{\partial x}\Big|_{x_{\gamma\text{-Cm}}} dx_{\gamma\text{-Cm}} + \bar{V}_{\text{C}}{}^{\gamma}\, dP = \bar{V}_{\text{C}}{}^{\text{Cm}}\, dP \qquad (11\text{-}40)$$

and

$$\frac{\partial \bar{F}^{\gamma}{}_{\text{Fe}}}{\partial x}\Big|_{x_{\gamma\text{-Cm}}} dx_{\gamma\text{-Cm}} + \bar{V}^{\gamma}{}_{\text{Fe}}\, dP = \bar{V}^{\text{Cm}}{}_{\text{Fe}}\, dP \qquad (11\text{-}41)$$

The partial molar volumes in Eqs. (11-40) and (11-41) refer to (T, P, $x_{\gamma\text{-Cm}}$) and (T, P, x_{Cm}), respectively. Multiplying Eq. (11-40) by x_{Cm} and Eq. (11-41) by $1 - x_{\text{Cm}}$ and adding result in

$$\left(0.25 \frac{\partial \bar{F}_{\text{C}}{}^{\gamma}}{\partial x}\Big|_{x_{\gamma\text{-Cm}}} + 0.75 \frac{\partial \bar{F}^{\gamma}{}_{\text{Fe}}}{\partial x}\Big|_{x_{\gamma\text{-Cm}}}\right) dx_{\gamma\text{-Cm}} = (V^{\text{Cm}} - 0.25\bar{V}_{\text{C}}{}^{\gamma} - 0.75\bar{V}^{\gamma}{}_{\text{Fe}})\, dP \qquad (11\text{-}42)$$

On the basis of Eqs. (11-33) and (11-37), Eq. (11-42) reduces to

$$\int_{P_0}^{P} \Delta V''\, dP = RT \int_{x^0{}_{\gamma\text{-Cm}}}^{x_{\gamma\text{-Cm}}} \left[0.15\left(\frac{1}{1 - x} - \frac{6}{1 - 6x}\right) + 0.25\left(\frac{1}{x} + \frac{6}{1 - 6x}\right)\right] dx_{\gamma\text{-Cm}} \qquad (11\text{-}43)$$

where

$$\Delta V'' = V^{\text{Cm}} - 0.25\bar{V}_{\text{C}}{}^{\gamma} - 0.75\bar{V}^{\gamma}{}_{\text{Fe}} \qquad (11\text{-}44)$$

The volume change $\Delta V''$ may be directly calculated at 1 atm and 996°K in the following manner: Mehl and Wells[91] have measured the volume change for the decomposition of austenite via the pearlite reaction at 996°K. The fractional change in volume when austenite ($x = 0.0361$) transforms to ferrite ($x = 0.00095$) and cementite ($x = 0.25$) at 996°K is +0.6 percent. Since the molar volume of ferrite may be safely approximated by the molar volume of pure bcc iron at this temperature,

$$1.006(0.9639\bar{V}^{\gamma}_{Fe} + 0.0361\bar{V}_C^{\gamma}) = 0.8585V^{\alpha}_{Fe} + 0.1415V^{Cm} \quad (11\text{-}45)$$

or

$$6.853\bar{V}^{\gamma}_{Fe} - 6.067V^{\alpha}_{Fe} = V^{Cm} - 0.2565\bar{V}_C^{\gamma} \quad (11\text{-}46)$$

Hence $\Delta V''(P_0, 996°K) = 6.103\bar{V}^{\gamma}_{Fe} - 6.067V^{\alpha}_{Fe} + 0.0065\bar{V}_C^{\gamma}$ (11-47)

The measurements of Basinski et al.[31] indicate that

$$V^{\alpha}_{Fe} = 6.991 + 3.27 \times 10^{-4}T \quad \text{cm}^3/\text{mole} \quad (11\text{-}48)$$

and

$$V^{\gamma}_{Fe} = 6.679 + 5.27 \times 10^{-4}T \quad \text{cm}^3/\text{mole} \quad (11\text{-}49)$$

for $T \leq 1200°K$.

Since the concentration of carbon in austenite is small (i.e., $x = 0.0361$), the partial molar volume of iron at $x = 0.0361$ can be approximated by V^{γ}_{Fe}. Thus at 1 atm and 996°K,

$$\Delta V'' \approx -0.451 + 0.0065\bar{V}_C^{\gamma} \quad \text{cm}^3/\text{mole} \quad (11\text{-}50)$$

Esser and Müller[92] and Roberts[93] have measured the carbon dependence of the lattice parameter of austenite as a function of carbon content. These measurements indicate that $\bar{V}_C^{\gamma} \approx 5.0 \pm 0.5$ cm³/mole. Thus

$$\Delta V''(P_0, 996°K) \approx -0.42 \text{ cm}^3/\text{mole} \quad (11\text{-}51)$$

In the absence of compressibility data and reliable thermal-expansion information concerning cementite, $\Delta V''$ is considered constant for temperatures near 996°K. On this basis, Eq. (11-43) is integrated to obtain

$$\frac{23.9\,\Delta V''\,P}{RT} = 0.25 \ln \frac{x_{\gamma\text{-Cm}}}{x^0_{\gamma\text{-Cm}}} - 0.15 \ln \frac{1 - x_{\gamma\text{-Cm}}}{1 - x^0_{\gamma\text{-Cm}}} - 0.10 \ln \frac{1 - 6x_{\gamma\text{-Cm}}}{1 - 6x^0_{\gamma\text{-Cm}}} \quad (11\text{-}52)$$

Calculation of $x_{\gamma\text{-Cm}}(T, P)$ from Eq. (11-5) is2 shown in Fig. 11-15. The intersections of the $x_{\gamma\text{-Cm}}(T, P)$ curves with the $x_{\gamma\text{-}\alpha}(T, P)$ curves

[91] R. F. Mehl and C. Wells, Constitution of High-purity Iron-Carbon Alloys, *Trans. AIME*, vol. 125, pp. 429–472, 1937.

[92] H. Esser and G. Müller, Die Gitterkonstanten von reinen Eisen und Eisen-Kohlenstoff-Legierungen bei Temperaturen bis 1100°, *Arch. Eisenhüttenw.*, vol. 7, pp. 265–268, 1933.

[93] C. S. Roberts, Effect of Carbon on the Volume Fractions and Lattice Parameters of Retained Austenite and Martensite, *Trans. AIME*, vol. 197, pp. 203–204, 1953.

define the eutectoid temperature T_E and composition x_E as functions of pressure.

The experimental and calculated values of $T_E(P)$ are compared in Fig. 11-16. The agreement is satisfactory. Figure 11-16 also shows the initial slope calculated on the basis of the Clausius-Clapeyron equation

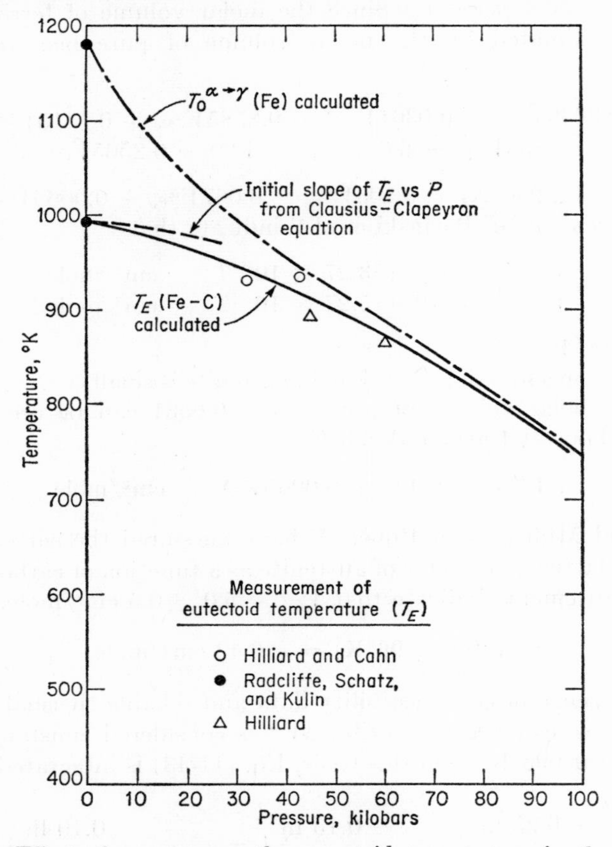

Fig. 11-16 Effect of pressure on the eutectoid temperature in the iron-carbon system.

as applied to an invariant reaction in a binary system [see Eq. (11-A18)]:

$$\frac{dT_E}{dP} = 23.9 \frac{\Delta V}{\Delta H} T_E \tag{11-53}$$

The value of ΔH for the eutectoid decomposition of austenite is about 1,000 cal/mole,[94] while Eq. (11-45) indicates that $\Delta V \approx -0.043$ cm³/mole, leading to an initial slope of dT_E/dP equal to -1.0°K/kilobar.

[94] J. J. Kramer, G. M. Pound, and R. F. Mehl, The Free Energy of Formation and the Interfacial Enthalpy in Pearlite, *Acta Met.*, vol. 6, p. 763, 1958.

Figure 11-17 compares the calculated and experimental phase diagrams at 42 kilobars, while Fig. 11-18 shows the experimentally determined phase diagrams at 32[10] and 42[88] kilobars, respectively. The general level of agreement between calculation and observation appears to be quite good.

(*c*) *The Iron-Nickel System.* Although the effect of pressure on equilibria in the iron-nickel system has not been investigated experimentally, it is interesting to discuss this system from a theoretical viewpoint. It has been studied by geophysicists and metallurgists interested

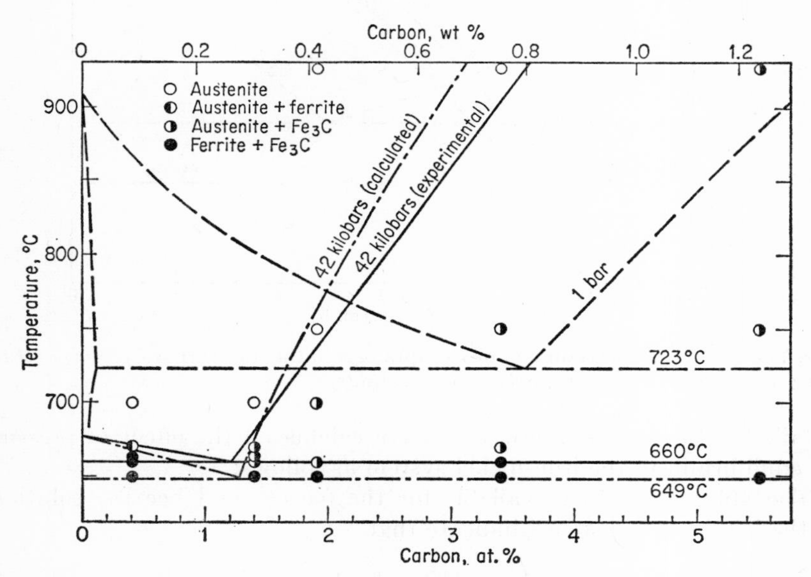

Fig. 11-17 Phase diagram for the iron-carbon system at 42 kilobars pressure. (*Radcliffe, Schatz, and Kulin.*[88])

in the interpretation of the microstructure of meteorites. One of the first metallographic studies of metallic meteorites was performed by Osmond and Cartaud[95] in 1904. The plessitic structure shown in Fig. 2 of reference 97, consisting of alternate layers of bcc ferrite and fcc austenite, observed by Osmond and Cartaud, led them to suggest the existence of a eutectoid-decomposition reaction in the iron-nickel system. Subsequent investigations of this system showed that no such reactions were observed at 1 atm.[11]

On the basis of recent studies, Uhlig[96] has suggested that some of the

[95] F. Osmond and G. Cartaud, *Rev. met.*, vol. 1, p. 69, 1904.

[96] H. H. Uhlig, Contribution of Metallurgy to the Origin of Meteorites: Part I., *Geochim. et Cosmochim. Acta*, vol. 6, pp. 282–301, 1954.

meteorite microstructures indicate exposure to high pressures at some time in their history. In order to explore this suggestion in greater

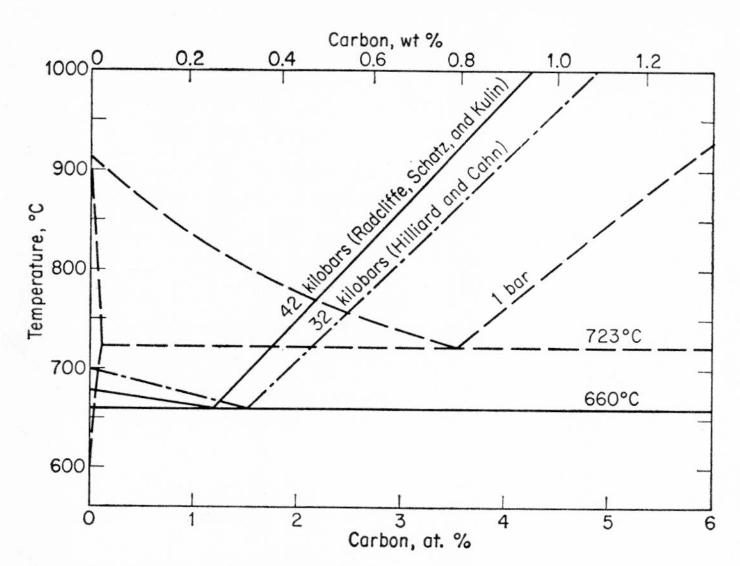

Fig. 11-18 Effect of pressure on phase equilibria in the iron-carbon system. *(Hilliard and Cahn*[76] *and Radcliffe, Schatz, and Kulin.*[88]*)*

detail, Kaufman and Ringwood[97] have calculated the effect of pressure on equilibrium in the iron-nickel system as follows:

The volumetric data available for the fcc (γ) and bcc (α) solutions in the iron-nickel system[39] indicate that

$$V^{\gamma} = (1 - x)V^{\gamma}{}_{\text{Fe}} + xV^{\gamma}{}_{\text{Ni}} + V_{\text{M}}{}^{\gamma}$$

where $V^{\gamma}{}_{\text{Ni}} \approx 6.475 + 3.55 \times 10^{-4}T \quad \text{cm}^3/\text{mole} \qquad (11\text{-}54)$

and $V_{\text{M}}{}^{\gamma} \approx (1.67 - 1.09 \times 10^{-3}T)x(1 - x)^2(0.3 + 2x) \quad \text{cm}^3/\text{mole} \qquad (11\text{-}55)$

for $300°\text{K} \leq T \leq 900°\text{K}$. The molar volume of γ-iron is given by Eq. (11-48). Equation (11-55) indicates a positive mixing volume which should lead to a miscibility gap at high pressure (Fig. 11-10*b*).

The limited data on the α phase[39] may be represented as

$$V^{\alpha} = V^{\alpha}{}_{\text{Fe}} + 0.4x \qquad \text{cm}^3/\text{mole} \qquad (11\text{-}56)$$

From Eqs. (11-54) through (11-56), together with the 1-atm thermodynamic information for the iron-nickel system,[98] a calculation can be

[97] L. Kaufman and A. E. Ringwood, High Pressure Equilibrium in the Iron-Nickel System and the Structure of Metallic Meteorites, *Acta Met.*, vol. 9, pp. 941–944, 1961.

made of the phase relations at high pressure. Figure 11-19 shows the atmospheric-pressure diagram[11,98] and the calculated diagrams at 50 and 100 kilobars, respectively.[97] The calculations indicate incipient

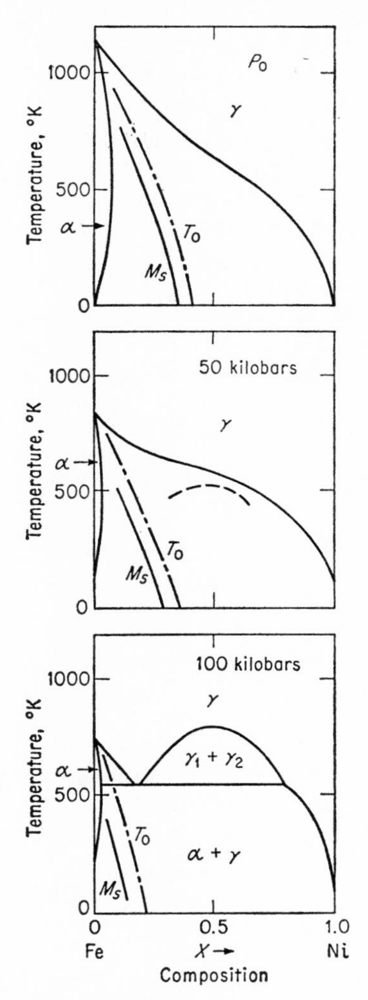

Fig. 11-19 Calculation of the effect of pressure on α-γ equilibria in the iron-nickel system. (*After Kaufman and Ringwood.*[97])

miscibility-gap formation at 50 kilobars, with gap formation and eutectoid decomposition above 60 kilobars.

It must be pointed out that the extensive approximations inherent in

[98] L. Kaufman and M. Cohen, Martensitic Transformation in the Iron-Nickel System, *Trans. AIME*, vol. 206, pp. 1393–1401, 1956.

these calculations limit the quantitative application of the results. However, the qualitative features of the calculated high-pressure diagrams should resemble reality. The calculations ignore the effects of the temperature and compositional dependences of the compressibilities of the fcc and bcc phases and the existence of ordering reactions in fcc Ni_3Fe. This latter factor would tend to displace the computed high-nickel phase boundary to lower nickel compositions.

There are a number of other interesting cases in which single-phase solid solutions exist over a wide range of temperature at 1 atm[11] with positive deviations from Vegard's rule indicated[39] (i.e., $V_M > 0$). Table 11-4 lists some of these systems which exhibit complete solid solubility,

Table 11-4 Binary Metallic Systems Exhibiting Positive Deviations from Vegard's Law in an Extended Solid Solution[11,39]

System	Structure	Solution type at 1 atm
Cu-Au	fcc	Ordering
Cu-Mn	fcc	Solid solution
Cu-Pd	fcc	Ordering
Cu-Pt	fcc	Ordering
Ni-Au	fcc	Miscibility gap
Ni-Fe	fcc	Solid solution
Ni-Pd	fcc	Solid solution
Ni-Pt	fcc	Ordering
Pd-Fe	fcc	Ordering
Pt-Co	fcc	Ordering
Pb-In	fcc	Solid solution
Fe-Co	bcc	Ordering

miscibility-gap formation, or ordering reactions at 1 atm.[11] Since positive values of V_M should, in principle, lead to gap formation, a systematic study of such systems would be extremely illuminating. This would be particularly true in the case of the ordering systems, wherein the effect of pressure should act to cause segregation of A and B atoms in opposition to the attractive forces between these atoms evidenced by ordering at 1 atm.

11-4 Summary

Consideration of high-pressure effects on phase equilibria and transformations from a thermodynamic point of view leads to the following conclusions:

1. In most cases quantitative thermodynamic predictions at a level of accuracy and reliability comparable to current high-pressure observations cannot be carried out. This is true even in cases in which the exact nature of the high-pressure phase is known. Thus the use of

thermodynamic data for making quantitative predictions of high-pressure effects is limited.

2. In cases in which the nature of the high-pressure phase can be directly determined or inferred with some assurance, qualitative predictions of high-pressure effects can be made by the proper utilization of 1-atm thermodynamic data.

3. The present considerations indicate that a reiterative combination of 1-atm thermodynamic data and high-pressure observations could lead to a greater understanding of phase transformations and equilibria in metals at 1 atm and high pressure.

11-5 Acknowledgments

Studies of the "Lattice Stability of Metals," sponsored by the Metallurgy Branch of the Office of Naval Research, Washington, and the "Effects of High Pressures and High Temperatures on Metals and Alloys," sponsored by the Materials Central of Wright Air Development Division, Dayton, Ohio, are the basis of this paper. The support of these organizations via contract NONR2600(00) and contract AF33(616)-6837 is herewith acknowledged.

The author is indebted to Drs. G. C. Kennedy of UCLA, J. E. Hilliard of the General Electric Company, H. G. Drickamer of the University of Illinois, R. S. Davis of Arthur D. Little, Inc., and to Dr. S. V. Radcliffe, Dr. S. A. Kulin, and Mr. L. Tanner of Man Labs, Inc., for making the results of their research available prior to publication.

Finally, the author is grateful to his colleagues, Drs. S. A. Kulin, S. V. Radcliffe, E. V. Clougherty, and Mr. J. S. Harvey at Man Labs, Inc., and to Dr. A. E. Ringwood of the Australian National University for many stimulating discussions of phase transformations under pressure.

11-6 Appendix

The thermodynamic representation of equilibrium in binary systems can be illustrated by reviewing the formulation suggested at the turn of the century by J. J. Van Laar.[99] In recent years Pines[100] and Meijering[101] have applied similar considerations in theoretical studies of equilibria in metallic systems.

[99] J. J. Van Laar, Die Schmelz, oder Erstarrungskurven bei binären Systemen, wenn die feste Phase ein Gemisch (amorphe feste Lösung oder Mischkristallen) den beiden Komponenten ist, *Z. physik. Chem.*, vol. 63A, p. 216, 1908, and vol. 64A, p. 257, 1908.

[100] B. Ya. Pines, О расчете простейших диаграмм равновесия бинарных сплавов, *Zhur. Fiz. Khim.*, vol. 23, p. 625, 1949.

[101] J. L. Meijering, "The Physical Chemistry of Metallic Solutions and Intermetallic Compounds," H.M. Stationery Office, London, 1959.

In this formulation the free energy of the liquid phase F^L, in a binary substitutional solution, is represented by

$$F^L = (1 - x)F_A{}^L + xF_B{}^L + F_E{}^L + RT[x \ln x + (1 - x) \ln (1 - x)] \quad (11\text{-A1})$$

where $F_E{}^L$, which is equal to zero for $x = 0$ and $x = 1$, is the excess free energy of mixing. In general $F_E{}^L = F_E{}^L(x,T)$ at 1 atm. Similar

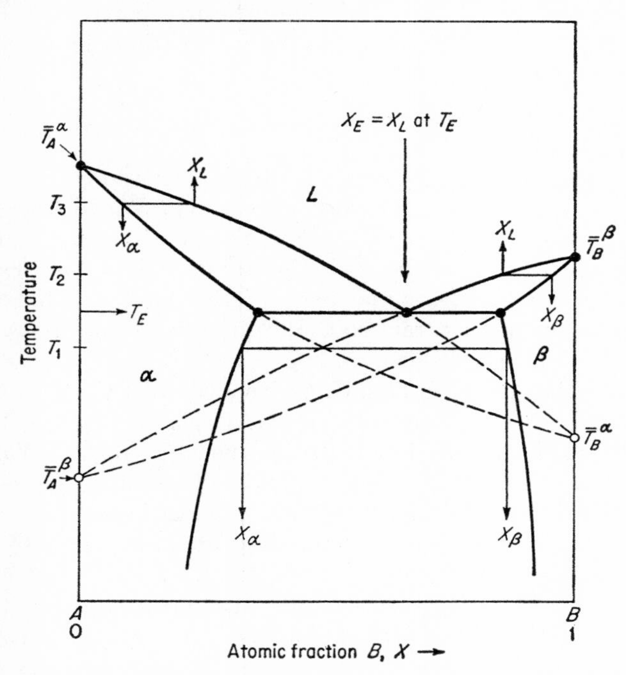

Fig. 11-20 Schematic representation of α-β-L equilibria in the A-B (eutectic) system.

equations can be written for the α and β phases of the A-B system (Fig. 11-20). The partial molar free energies of A and B in the binary system are defined by

$$\bar{F}_A = F - x\frac{\partial F}{\partial x} \quad (11\text{-A2})$$

$$\bar{F}_B = F + (1 - x)\frac{\partial F}{\partial x} \quad (11\text{-A3})$$

Equilibrium between the α and liquid phases at T_3 requires that

$$\bar{F}_A{}^\alpha \Big|_{x_\alpha} = \bar{F}_A{}^L \Big|_{x_L} \quad (11\text{-A4})$$

and

$$\bar{F}_B{}^\alpha \Big|_{x_\alpha} = \bar{F}_B{}^L \Big|_{x_L} \quad (11\text{-A5})$$

Combination of Eqs. (11-A1) to (11-A5) yields the conditions for α/L equilibrium at T_3:

$$\Delta F_{\mathrm{A}}{}^{\alpha\to L} + RT \ln \frac{1 - x_L}{1 - x_\alpha} = \left(F_E{}^\alpha - x \frac{\partial F_E{}^\alpha}{\partial x}\right)_{x_\alpha} - \left(F_E{}^L - x \frac{\partial F_E{}^L}{\partial x}\right)_{x_L} \tag{11-A6}$$

$$\Delta F_{\mathrm{B}}{}^{\alpha\to L} + RT \ln \frac{x_L}{x_\alpha} = \left[F_E{}^\alpha + (1 - x) \frac{\partial F_E{}^\alpha}{\partial x}\right]_{x_\alpha} - \left[F_E{}^L + (1 - x) \frac{\partial F_E{}^L}{\partial x}\right]_{x_L} \tag{11-A7}$$

Similar sets of equations can be written for α-β equilibrium at T_1 and β-L equilibrium at T_2. At the eutectic temperature, all six equations apply simultaneously, and $x_L \to x_E$. When $\bar{T}_{\mathrm{A}}{}^\alpha > \bar{T}_{\mathrm{A}}{}^\beta > \bar{T}_{\mathrm{B}}{}^\beta > \bar{T}_{\mathrm{B}}{}^\alpha$, a peritectic, rather than eutectic, reaction occurs.

If the activity of element B is measured in the β field at T_1 relative to pure β-B between $x_\beta \leq x \leq 1$, then[21]

$$\bar{F}_{\mathrm{B}}{}^\beta - F_{\mathrm{B}}{}^\beta = RT \ln a_{\mathrm{B}}{}^\beta \Big|_{\mathrm{B}^\beta} = RT \ln x + F_E{}^\beta + (1 - x) \frac{\partial F_E{}^\beta}{\partial x} \tag{11-A8}$$

The activity coefficient $f_{\mathrm{B}}{}^\beta$ is defined as

$$RT \ln f_{\mathrm{B}}{}^\beta \Big|_{\mathrm{B}^\beta} = RT \ln \frac{a_{\mathrm{B}}{}^\beta}{x} \Big|_{\mathrm{B}^\beta} = F_E{}^\beta + (1 - x) \frac{\partial F_E{}^\beta}{\partial x} \tag{11-A9}$$

If, on the other hand, the activity of B in the α phase is measured at T_1 for $0 \leq x \leq x_\alpha$, then

$$\bar{F}_{\mathrm{B}}{}^\alpha - F_{\mathrm{B}}{}^\beta = RT \ln a_{\mathrm{B}}{}^\alpha \Big|_{\mathrm{B}^\beta} = RT \ln x + F_E{}^\alpha + (1 - x) \frac{\partial F_E{}^\alpha}{\partial x} + \Delta F_{\mathrm{B}}{}^{\beta\to\alpha} \tag{11-A10}$$

or

$$RT \ln f_{\mathrm{B}}{}^\alpha \Big|_{\mathrm{B}^\beta} = \Delta F_{\mathrm{B}}{}^{\beta\to\alpha} + F_E{}^\alpha + (1 - x) \frac{\partial F_E{}^\alpha}{\partial x} \tag{11-A11}$$

Equations (11-A10) and (11-A11) are the basis of Eqs. (11-14) and (11-15) of the text. Since $F_E = 0$ for $x = 0$ and $x = 1$, the excess free energy of mixing may be represented as a power-series expansion in the form

$$F_E = x(1 - x)g(x, T) \tag{11-A12}$$

where $g(x, T)$ is a function of temperature and composition. Application of Eq. (11-A11) to Eq. (11-A12) yields Eq. (11-15), used by Lumsden[14] in the analysis of thallium.

Geguzin and Pines[74,102] have analyzed the solid-liquid equilibria of a

[102] Ya. E. Geguzin and B. Ya. Pines, Calculated and Experimental Equilibrium Diagrams for Simple Binary Systems, *Doklady Akad. Nauk S. S. S. R.*, vol. 75, pp. 387–390, 1950; *Chem. Abstrs.*, vol. 45, p. 9351i, 1951.

number of systems quite successfully by using Eqs. (11-A6) and (11-A7) and the approximation that

$$F_E{}^L = U^L x(1 - x) \tag{11-A13}$$

and

$$F_E{}^\alpha = U^\alpha x(1 - x) \tag{11-A14}$$

where U^L and U^α are constants. They have carried out calorimetric measurements on the α and liquid phases of the lead-tin system in order to evaluate the constants in their approximation.[74] With these constants and the approximation that $\Delta S^{\alpha \to L}{}_{\text{Sn}}$ is about the same as the entropy of melting of other fcc structures, they find that $\bar{T}^\alpha{}_{\text{Sn}} = 350°\text{K}$ gives agreement with the published α-L equilibrium in the lead-tin system.[74]

The shift in equilibrium concentration with pressure [Eq. (11-30)] is derived by differentiating Eqs. (11-A4) and (11-A5) with respect to pressure at a fixed temperature. This operation yields

$$\left.\frac{\partial \bar{F}_{\text{A}}{}^\alpha}{\partial x}\right|_{x_\alpha} \frac{dx_\alpha}{dP} + \left.\bar{V}_{\text{A}}{}^\alpha\right|_{x_\alpha} = \left.\frac{\partial \bar{F}_{\text{A}}{}^L}{\partial x}\right|_{x_L} \frac{dx_L}{dP} + \left.\bar{V}_{\text{A}}{}^L\right|_{x_L} \tag{11-A15}$$

and

$$\left.\frac{\partial \bar{F}_{\text{B}}{}^\alpha}{\partial x}\right|_{x_\alpha} \frac{dx_\alpha}{dP} + \left.\bar{V}_{\text{B}}{}^\alpha\right|_{x_\alpha} = \left.\frac{\partial \bar{F}_{\text{B}}{}^L}{\partial x}\right|_{x_L} \frac{dx_L}{dP} + \left.\bar{V}_{\text{B}}{}^L\right|_{x_L} \tag{11-A16}$$

Equation (11-A15) is then multiplied by $1 - x_\alpha$, and Eq. (11-A16) multiplied by x_α. The products are added and the Gibbs-Duhem equation,

$$(1 - x)\frac{\partial \bar{F}_{\text{A}}}{\partial x} + x\frac{\partial \bar{F}_{\text{B}}}{\partial x} = 0 \tag{11-A17}$$

is used to eliminate dx_α/dP and the partial free energy of the α phase from the sum-of-products equation. The result is Eq. (11-30) with superscript L interchanged with superscript β.

To derive the change in eutectic temperature with pressure, the same sort of procedure can be used, although the algebraic manipulations are more tedious. Briefly, the procedure is as follows: Equations (11-A4) and (11-A5), applied at T_E, are differentiated with respect to changes in temperature, composition, and pressure. The entropy terms are then eliminated by noting that $\bar{F} = \bar{H} - T_E\bar{S}$. Next the compositional derivatives of the partial free energies of the α phase are eliminated by multiplying the differential of Eq. (11-A4) by $(1 - x_\alpha)$ and the differential of Eq. (11-A5) by x_α and summing. A similar procedure is carried out, starting with the analogues of Eqs. (11-A4) and (11-A5), for β-L equilibrium. The equation derived from the α-L equilibrium is multiplied by $x_\beta - x_L$, and the equation derived from the β-L equilibrium is multiplied by $(x_L - x_\alpha)$. Addition eliminates the compositional derivatives of the partial free energies of the liquid phase, yielding

$$\frac{dT_E}{dP} = \frac{(x_\beta - x_L)V^\alpha + (x_L - x_\alpha)V^\beta - (x_\beta - x_\alpha)V^L}{(x_\beta - x_L)H^\alpha + (x_L - x_\alpha)H^\beta - (x_\beta - x_\alpha)H^L} T_E \quad (11\text{-A}18)$$

The enthalpies and volumes in Eq. (11-A18) refer to the equilibrium compositions at the eutectic temperature. Since the compositional differences are identical to the lever-rule ratios, Eq. (11-A18) is equivalent to

$$\frac{dT_E}{dP} = \frac{\Delta V}{\Delta H} T_E \quad (11\text{-A}19)$$

where ΔV and ΔH are the overall enthalpy and volume changes at the eutectic.

11-7 Table A-1 Table of Symbols

Symbol	Meaning
$\bar{T}_A^\alpha$	Melting temperature of the α modification of metal A
$F_A^\alpha(T)$	Free energy of the α modification of metal A at 1 atm and temperature T
P	Pressure
P_0	Atmospheric pressure
$F_A^\alpha(T, P)$	Free energy of α modification of metal A at pressure P and temperature T
V_A^α	Molar volume of α forms pure A
$\Delta V_A^{\alpha\to L}$	Difference in volume of α form of pure A
$\Delta F_A^{\alpha\to L}(T, P)$	Free-energy difference between α and liquid forms of A at temperature T and pressure P
$T_A^\alpha(P)$	Pressure-temperature curve along which the α form of element A melts
T_0	Temperature at which the difference in free energy between two different crystal forms of a metal (or alloy) is zero
$\Delta S_A^{\alpha\to L}$	Entropy difference between α and liquid forms of metal A
$\Delta S_A^{\alpha\to\beta}$	Entropy difference between α and β forms of metal A
$\Delta V_A^{\alpha\to\beta}$	Difference in volume between α and β forms of metal A
$\Delta H_A^{\alpha\to\beta}$	Difference in enthalpy between α and β forms of metal A
$\Delta F_A^{\alpha\to\beta}$	Difference in free energy between α and β forms of metal A
x	Atomic fraction of element B in the A-B system
$a_B^\alpha \Big\|_{B^\beta}$	Activity of B in the α phase of the A-B system relative to pure β-B
F_E^β	Excess free energy of mixing of the β phase of the A-B system
$f_B^\alpha \Big\|_{B^\beta}$	Activity coefficient of B in the α phase of the A-B system relative to pure β-B
$g(x, T)$	Temperature- and composition-dependent function
$g'(x, T)$	Derivative of $g(x, T)$ with respect to x
R	Gas constant (1.987 cal/mole °K)
T_c	Temperature at triple point
P_c	Pressure at triple point
M_s	Temperature at which a martensitic transformation starts on cooling
A_s	Temperature at which a martensitic transformation reverses on heating

$V_M{}^\alpha$	Molar volume of mixing of α phase
$\Delta F^{\alpha\to\beta}(x, T)$	Free-energy difference between α and β structures in the A-B system at 1 atm and temperature T when the composition of both phases is x
$\Delta F^{\alpha\to\beta}(x, T, P)$	Free-energy difference $\Delta F^{\alpha\to\beta}(x, T)$ at pressure P
$\Delta V^{\alpha\to\beta}(x, T)$	Difference in volume between α and β forms of the same composition at temperature T
x_β	Atomic fraction of B at the boundary of the single-phase β field
$\bar{F}_B{}^\beta$	Partial molar free energy or chemical potential of B in the β phase of the A-B system
$\bar{V}_B{}^\beta$	Partial molar volume of B in the β phase of the A-B system
z	Interstitial-solution exclusion parameter
$x_{\gamma\text{-}\alpha}$	Atomic fraction of carbon in the γ phase at the boundary of the two-phase $\alpha + \gamma$ field
$x_{\alpha\text{-}\gamma}$	Atomic fraction of carbon in the α phase at the boundary of the two-phase $\alpha + \gamma$ field
$x_{\gamma\text{-Cm}}$	Atomic fraction of carbon in the γ phase at the boundary of the two-phase γ + Cm field
T_E	Eutectic (toid) temperature
x_E	Eutectic (toid) composition

12

The Electronic Structure of Solids under Pressure

H. G. DRICKAMER

Department of Chemistry and Chemical Engineering
University of Illinois
Urbana, Illinois

12-1 Introduction

This paper constitutes a review of some observations in our laboratory concerning the effects of pressure on electronic structure and interaction in solids.

The measurements are primarily of optical absorption spectra and, to a lesser extent, of electrical resistance. The techniques and the pressure calibrations are described in detail elsewhere.[1–4] There appear to be no large nonhydrostatic effects in the optical measurements. The absolute electrical resistivities are undoubtedly affected by lack of hydrostaticity, but not the transitions discussed in this work. The first type of phenomenon discussed is the essentially internal *d-d* transition

[1] R. A. Fitch, T. E. Slykhouse, and H. G. Drickamer, Apparatus for Optical Studies to Very High Pressures, *J. Opt. Soc. Am.*, vol. 47, pp. 1015–1017, 1957.

[2] A. S. Balchan and H. G. Drickamer, High Pressure–High Temperature Optical Device, *Rev. Sci. Instr.*, vol. 31, pp. 511–513, 1960.

[3] A. S. Balchan and H. G. Drickamer, A High Pressure Electrical Resistance Cell, and Calibration Points above 100 Kilobars, *Rev. Sci. Instr.*, vol. 32, p. 308, 1961.

[4] H. G. Drickamer and A. S. Balchan, High Pressure Optical and Electrical Measurements, pp. 25–50 in R. H. Wentorf (ed.) "Modern Very High Pressure Techniques," Butterworth & Co. (Publishers), Ltd., London, 1962.

observed in transition-metal complexes. Then we take up charge transfer, both intramolecular and intermolecular. The ultimate in delocalization of charge transfer leads to interband transitions which cause the absorption edge in elements and ionic and molecular crystals, and then to the approach to the metallic state as observed by optical and electrical resistance measurements. Finally, we discuss the mixing of *d* and *s* levels of metals at high pressures.

Certain phenomena, including the effect of pressure on transition probability and on the spectra of point imperfections, are not discussed at any length because they have been reviewed in detail elsewhere.[5] Valence semiconductors are discussed in Chap. 8 of this book.

12-2 Crystal-field Effects

Transition-metal ions are characterized by their partially filled *d* shells. This discussion will be restricted to the first transition-metal series, in which the partially filled shell is 3*d*. In the free ion, the five *d* states are degenerate, and the electronic energy levels are characterized by "term symbols" classifying them according to the quantum numbers l and s. The separation in energy between these levels can be calculated, in principle, from the interelectronic repulsion and described in terms of Slater-Condon parameters F_0, F_2, and F_4 or Racah parameters A, B, and C. These two sets of parameters are simply related, but in crystal-field work it is more usual to employ the Racah coefficients. In a field of less than spherical symmetry the degenerate states corresponding to any term ^{2s+1}L are split by the field. Optical absorption peaks observed in solids containing transition-metal ions can be related to the strength and symmetry of the crystal field and to the Racah parameters.

The status of crystal-field theory and the available literature have recently been reviewed in detail by McClure,[6] so that we shall introduce only relevant results of the theory as it becomes necessary to do so.

One can approach crystal field theory from the "weak-field" viewpoint, treating the field of the ligands as a perturbation on the free-ion levels which shifts them and partially removes the degeneracy. On the other hand, in the "strong-field" approach, the primary effect is the electrostatic interaction of the crystalline field with the orbitals. The interelectronic repulsion is added as a perturbation. In strong-field terms, in octahedral or tetrahedral fields the d_{xy}, d_{yz}, and d_{xz} orbitals are known as t orbitals, while the d_{z^2} and $d_{x^2-y^2}$ orbitals are called e orbitals (using

[5] H. G. Drickamer and J. C. Zahner, The Effect of Pressure on Electronic Structure, pp. 161–200. in "Advances in Chemical Physics IV," Interscience Publishers, Inc., New York, 1962.

[6] D. S. McClure, Electronic Spectra of Molecules and Ions in Crystals, II, pp. 399–525 in F. Seitz and D. Turnbull (eds.), "Solid State Physics," vol. 9, Academic Press, Inc., New York, 1959.

group-theoretical nomenclature). Ultimately both the strong- and weak-field approaches must yield the same splittings at the same field intensity. Tanabe and Sugano[7] have made extensive calculations describing the entire crystalline field in strong-field nomenclature, and extensive use of their results is made in this discussion.

In an octahedral field, the crystal-field strength is defined in terms of the equation

$$10Dq = \int d_e^* |V| d_e \, d\tau - \int d_t^* |V| d_t \, d\tau$$

where V is the electrostatic potential. Dq (tetrahedron) is equal to $-4/9\ Dq$ (octahedron). Tanabe and Sugano describe the energy levels in terms of $10Dq$ and the Racah parameters B and C. It can be shown[6] that for either an octahedral or a tetrahedral field, the crystal-field strength should vary as R^{-5}, where R is the ion-ligand distance for point-charge ligands. (The field strength varies as R^{-6} for point dipoles.) One can thus see that the intensity of the crystal field and the splitting of the levels should definitely be pressure dependent.

Pure crystal-field theory in its simplest form, involving only electrostatic interaction of point charges with the d electrons, implies that the free-ion values of B and C should be valid in the crystal. One finds however that there is almost always a significant amount of covalency between the ligands and the metal ion. This tends to spread out the metal-ion charge cloud and decrease interelectronic repulsion. A measurement of the Racah parameters as a function of pressure (especially B; it is usually necessary to assume a constant ratio C/B) gives a first-order approximation of the effect of pressure on covalency.

Spin-orbital coupling is usually not large in ions of the first transition-metal series. Measurable splittings have been observed in a number of crystal-field peaks, however. Pressure effects on spin-orbital coupling can be related to pressure-covalency effects as discussed below.

Most of the d-d transitions discussed in this paper are spin-allowed but LaPorte-forbidden. They have oscillator strengths of the order of 10^{-3} or less. The intensity arises from coupling of the $3d$ and $4p$ levels by odd terms in crystal potential. For tetrahedral complexes the odd terms are nonzero because there is no center of symmetry. For octahedral complexes all odd terms appear from vibrational-electronic interaction. The effect of pressure on the intensity of LaPorte-forbidden transitions has been discussed in detail elsewhere[5,6,8,9] and will not be included here in any detail. The most general effect is a small increase

[7] Y. Tanabe and S. Sugano, On the Absorption Spectra of Complex Ions, I, II, *J. Phys. Soc. Japan*, vol. 9, pp. 753–779, 1954.

[8] K. B. Keating and H. G. Drickamer, Effect of Pressure on Crystalline UF_4 and UF_3, *J. Chem. Phys.*, vol. 34, pp. 140–143, 1961.

[9] K. B. Keating and H. G. Drickamer, Effect of Pressure on the Spectra of Rare Earth Ions in Crystals, *J. Chem. Phys.*, vol. 34, pp. 143–152, 1961.

in intensity with increasing pressure. A few unusual effects due to distortion of the symmetry will be included below. The effects of pressure on crystal-field absorption peaks have been discussed in a number of papers.[10–14] For peaks which depend strongly on *Dq*, the most general result is an increase in the energy of the transition, as might be expected. Since the transitions can be described in terms of 10 *Dq* and the Racah parameters, one can use the free-ion values of the Racah parameters and calculate the change in *Dq* with pressure.

If simple crystal-field theory applies, one should get the same change in field strength with pressure for all transitions in a given crystal. Figures 12-1 through 12-3 show the change in *Dq* with pressure for Cr^{3+} in Al_2O_3, for Ni^{++} in NiO, and for Ni^{++} in MgO. In each case there is

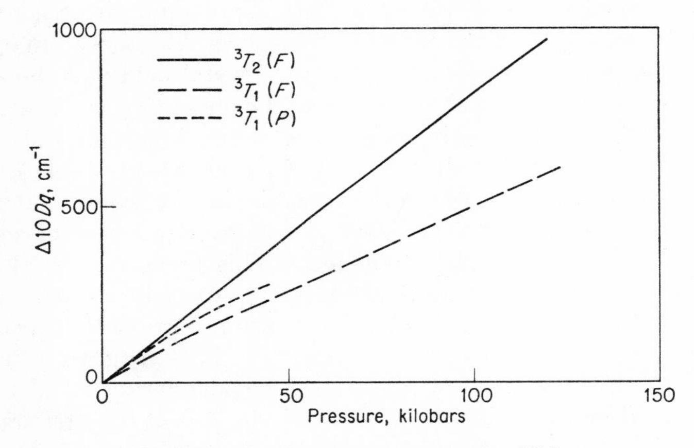

Fig. 12-1 10*Dq* versus pressure for NiO.

qualitative agreement for the increase of *Dq* calculated from different transitions, but the quantitative discrepancies are larger than experimental error. Evidently the covalency is a distinct function of pressure, and the shifts from two or more peaks must be solved simultaneously to give changes in *Dq* and *B*. Figure 12-4 shows the change in *Dq* with pressure for Co^{++} in a series of tetrahedral environments. While the

[10] R. W. Parsons and H. G. Drickamer, Effect of Pressure on the Spectra of Certain Transition Metal Ion Complexes, *J. Chem. Phys.*, vol. 29, pp. 930–937, 1958.

[11] D. R. Stephens and H. G. Drickamer, The Effect of Pressure on the Spectra of Five Nickel Complexes, *J. Chem. Phys.*, vol. 34, p. 937, 1961.

[12] D. R. Stephens and H. G. Drickamer, The Effect of Pressure on the Spectrum of Ruby, *J. Chem. Phys.*, vol. 35, p. 427, 1961.

[13] D. R. Stephens and H. G. Drickamer, The Effect of Pressure on the Spectra of Tetrahedral Ni^{2+} and Co^{2+} Complexes, *J. Chem. Phys.*, vol. 35, p. 429, 1961.

[14] S. Minomura and H. G. Drickamer, The Effect of Pressure on the Spectra of Transition Metal Ions in MgO and Al_2O_3, *J. Chem. Phys.*, vol. 35, p. 903, 1961.

compressibility certainly varies somewhat with environment, the variation in Dq is much larger and correlates rather well with the ligand polarizability.

As mentioned earlier, the crystal-field intensity should vary with ligand-metal distance as R^{-5}. For isotropic compressibility, and local compressibility equal to bulk compressibility, Dq/Dq_0 should vary as $(\rho/\rho_0)^{5/3}$. Figure 12-5 shows this relationship for a series of ions in Al_2O_3 using Bridgman's compressibility data to 30 kilobars.[15] The agreement is excellent. Figures 12-6 and 12-7 show similar plots for ions in ZnS and MgO, again using Bridgman's[16] P-V data. For these cases, the shifts are always larger than predicted. They are roughly, but not exactly, in the order one might estimate from ionic radii. Probably the largest single cause of this discrepancy is local relaxation in the neighborhood of the foreign ion, which would be less important in the rigid corundum lattice.

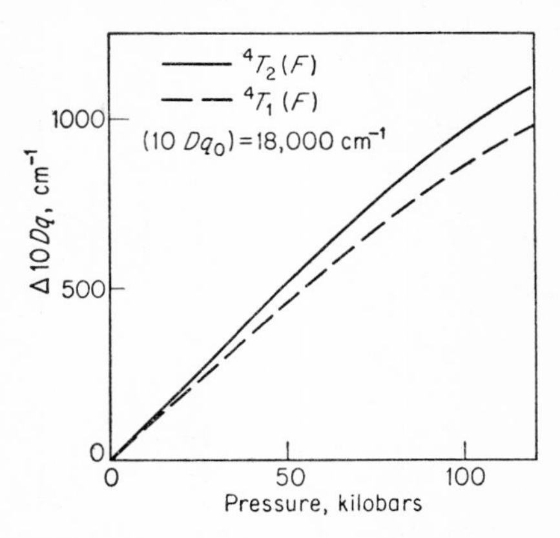

Fig. 12-2 10 Dq versus pressure for $Al_2O_3:Cr^{3+}$.

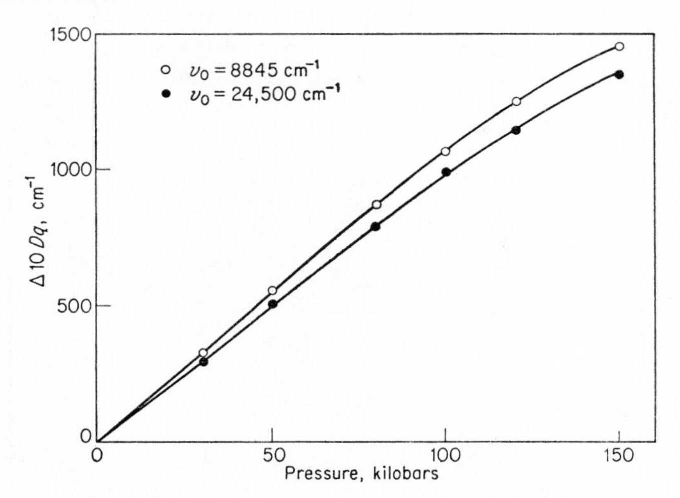

Fig. 12-3 10 Dq versus pressure for $MgO:Ni^{++}$.

[15] P. W. Bridgman, Linear Compressions to 30,000 kg/cm², including Relatively Incompressible Substances, *Proc. Am. Acad. Arts Sci.*, vol. 77, pp. 187–234, 1949.

[16] P. W. Bridgman, Compression of 39 Substances to 100,000 kg/cm², *Proc. Am. Acad. Arts Sci.*, vol. 76, pp. 55–70, 1948.

As indicated, it is clear that both the crystal-field parameter Dq and the interelectronic-repulsion parameter B vary with pressure. Figures 12-8 and 12-9 show the variation of B for Ni^{++} in NiO and for Cr^{3+} in Al_2O_3. For these, and for all other complexes studied, there is a decrease of B with increasing pressure, indicating that the covalency increases and the metal-ion charge cloud spreads out as the pressure increases. Where three or more peaks are present, more than one value of B could be obtained. The discrepancies shown are probably not significant, as B is very sensitive to the measured shift. Figure 12-10 shows the change of B with pressure for Co^{++} in various environments. The decrease in B (increase in covalency) depends very strongly on the polarizability of the ligand, as one might expect.

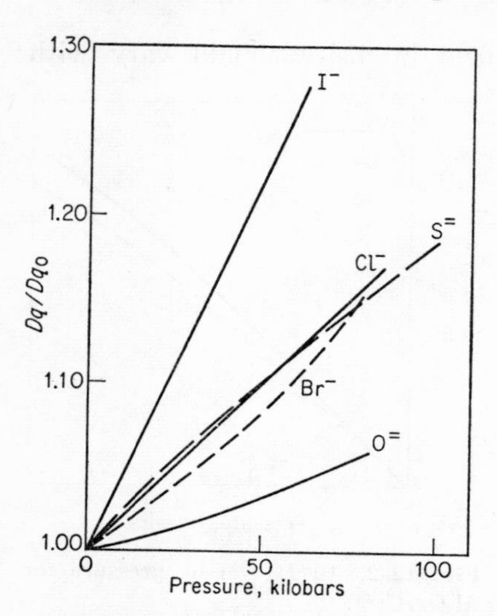

Fig. 12-4 Dq/Dq_0 versus pressure for tetrahedral Co^{++}.

The low-energy peak in tetrahedral Co^{++} complexes, representing the ${}^4A_2(F) \rightarrow {}^4T_1(F)$ transition, is split by spin-orbital coupling. Figure 12-11 shows the change in the splitting with pressure. With increase of covalency, the metal-ion electron has an increased probability of

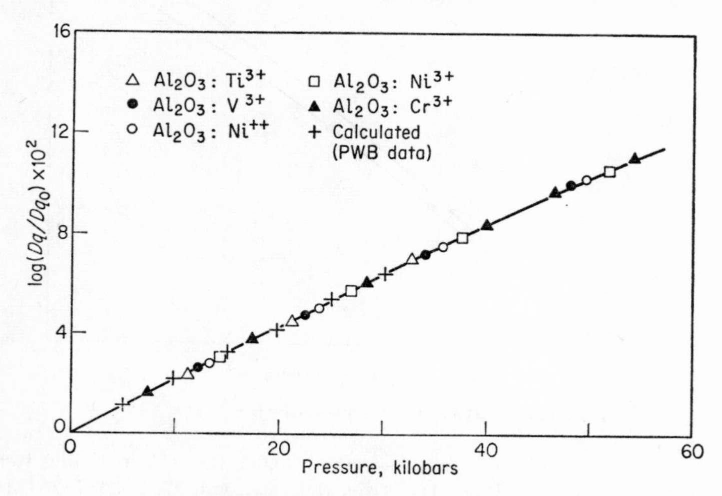

Fig. 12-5 Test of R^{-5} law for Al_2O_3.

coupling either with metal or ligand nuclei. The increased splitting correlates very well with increased mass of the ligand nucleus.

In addition to the effects of essentially isotropic compression, certain effects due to distortion of the symmetry are observable. In ruby, the

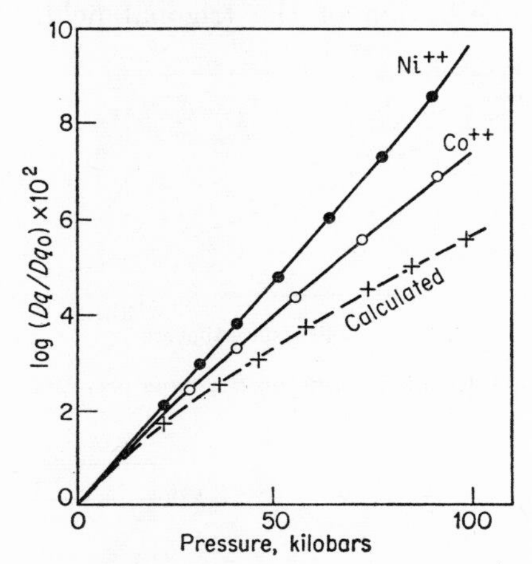

Fig. 12-6 Test of R^{-5} law for ZnS.

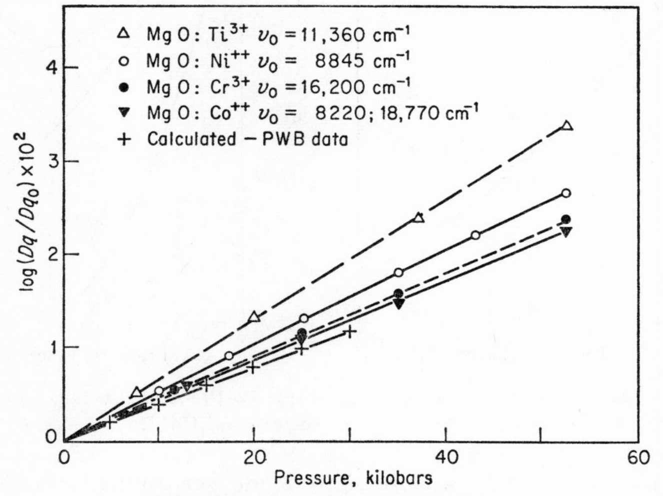

Fig. 12-7 Test of R^{-5} law for MgO.

Cr^{3+} ion substitutes for Al^{3+} in the corundum lattice. The site is essentially octahedral but has a measurable trigonal component, as shown by Sugano, Tanabe, and Tsujikawa.[17] This results in a splitting of the

[17] S. Sugano, Y. Tanabe, and I. Tsujikawa, Absorption Spectra of Cr^{3+} in Al_2O_3, *J. Phys. Soc. Japan*, vol. 13, pp. 880–899, 1958.

levels, as shown in Fig. 12-12. The ${}^4A_2 \rightarrow {}^4E(T_2)$ and ${}^4A_2 \rightarrow {}^4E(T_1)$ transitions are observed with perpendicularly polarized light, while the ${}^4A_2 \rightarrow {}^4A_1(T_1)$ and ${}^4A_2 \rightarrow {}^4A_2(T_1)$ transitions are observed in parallel-polarized light. The splitting is described in terms of a parameter $-\frac{3}{2}K$ representing the contribution of the trigonal field. The splitting can

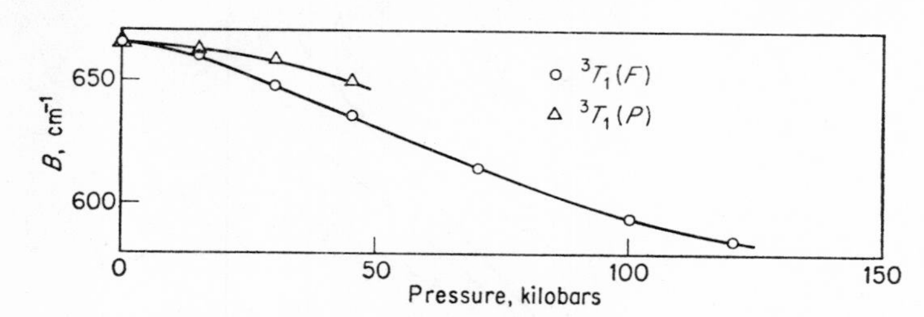

Fig. 12-8 Racah parameter B versus pressure for NiO.

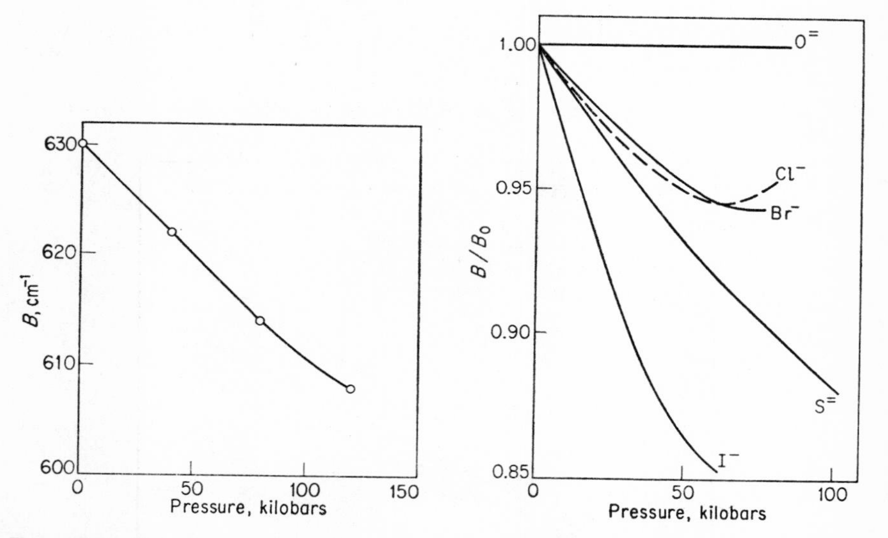

Fig. 12-9 Racah parameter B versus pressure for $Al_2O_3:Cr^{3+}$.

Fig. 12-10 B/B_0 versus pressure for tetrahedral Co^{++}.

also be calculated from measurements made perpendicular and parallel to the C axis.[12] Figure 12-13 shows the change of splitting with pressure. Below about 60 kilobars the compression is evidently essentially isotropic, but above this pressure there is a rapid increase in the trigonal distortion with pressure.

A rather spectacular effect of distortion can be observed in Cs_2CoCl_4 and the bromo and iodo analogues. As indicated earlier, there usually

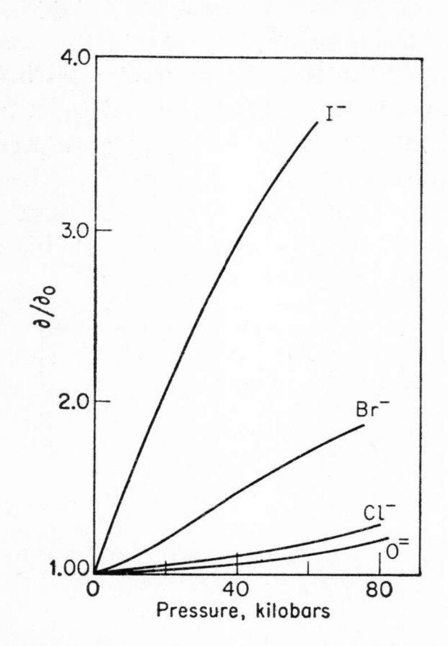

Fig. 12-11 ∂/∂_0 versus pressure for tetrahedral Co^{++}.

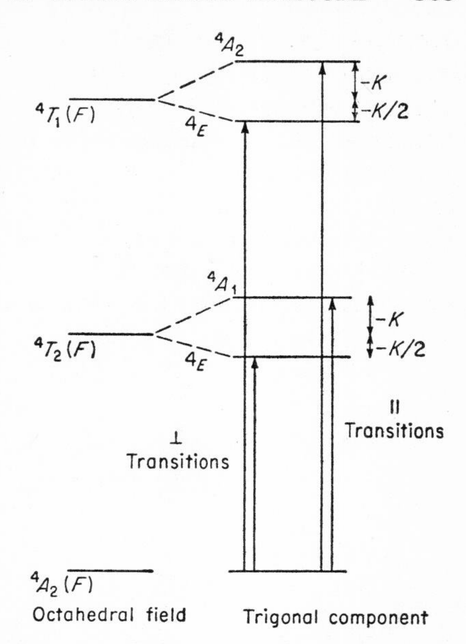

Fig. 12-12 Energy-level diagram for $Al_2O_3:Cr^{3+}$.

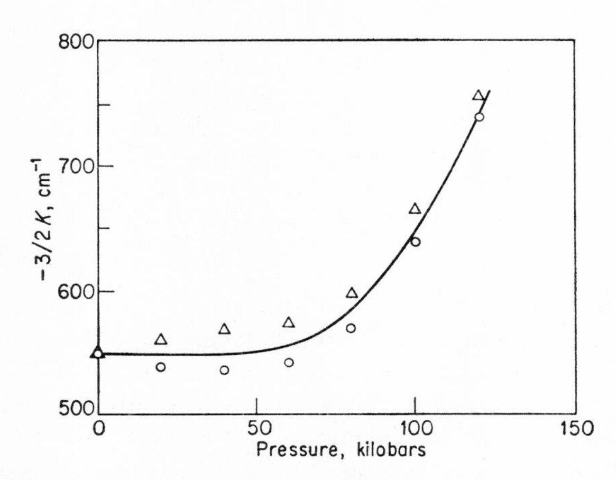

Fig. 12-13 Trigonal field component $(-\frac{3}{2}K)$ versus pressure for $Al_2O_3:Cr^{3+}$.

is a modest increase of intensity with pressure. In Fig. 12-14 the relative transition probability is shown as a function of pressure for the $^4T_1(F)$ peak in Cs_2CoCl_4. The usual increase was observed up to about 80 kilobars. Above this pressure there was a rapid decrease in intensity. At the same time a new peak appeared to be growing at 9,000 cm^{-1}, although the resolution was poor. Similarly, a new peak seemed to grow on the high-energy side of the $^4T_1(P)$ peak at about 16,000 cm^{-1}, as shown in Fig. 12-15.

There was none of the usual cutoff of light ordinarily associated with a first-order phase transition. In any case such a transition would only rearrange the Cs^+ and $CoCl_4^-$ ions and not affect the internal symmetry of the $CoCl_4^-$ ion. From crystal-field theory one would predict that Co^{++} in octahedral symmetry would show peaks at 7,000 to 8,000 cm^{-1} [$^4T_2(F)$] and at 15,000 to 16,000 cm^{-1}[$^4A_2(F)$]. Apparently at high pressures the symmetry is distorted to become nearly octahedral.

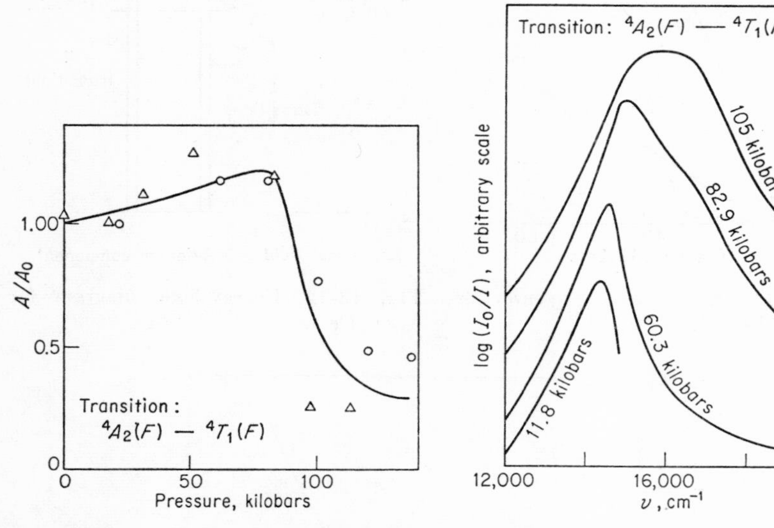

Fig. 12-14 A/A_0 versus pressure for Cs_2CoCl_4.

Fig. 12-15 Log I_0/I versus pressure for Cs_2CoCl_4.

12-3 Charge Transfer

In the previous section we discussed transitions which occur largely within the *d* shell of a transition-metal ion. We now consider situations in which the electronic energy levels are increasingly less isolated. The classical discussion of these phenomena has been given by Mulliken.[18,19]

The first example involves the permanganate and chromate ions.[20] These are "molecular ions" which constitute highly stable configurations which retain their identity in solution as well as in the solid state. The

[18] R. S. Mulliken, Molecular Compounds and Their Spectra, II, *J. Am. Chem. Soc.*, vol. 74, pp. 811–824, 1952.

[19] R. S. Mulliken, Molecular Compounds and Their Spectra, III, *J. Phys. Chem.*, vol. 56, pp. 801–831, 1952.

[20] W. H. Bentley and H. G. Drickamer, The Effect of Pressure on the Spectra of MnO_4^- and CrO_4^-, *J Chem. Phys.*, vol. 34, p. 2200, 1961.

ions are strongly colored, owing to an allowed transition which can be described, in the language of Ballhausen and Liehr,[21] as a transition from the $\pi(t_1)$ level on the oxygen to the $e(\pi)$ molecular orbital which is an antibonding mixture of metal ion $3d(e)$ and oxygen $\pi(e)$, as can be seen from the energy-level diagram of Fig. 12-16.

Figure 12-17 shows the shift of the energy peak with pressure. The blue shift measures the increase in energy of the antibonding level with

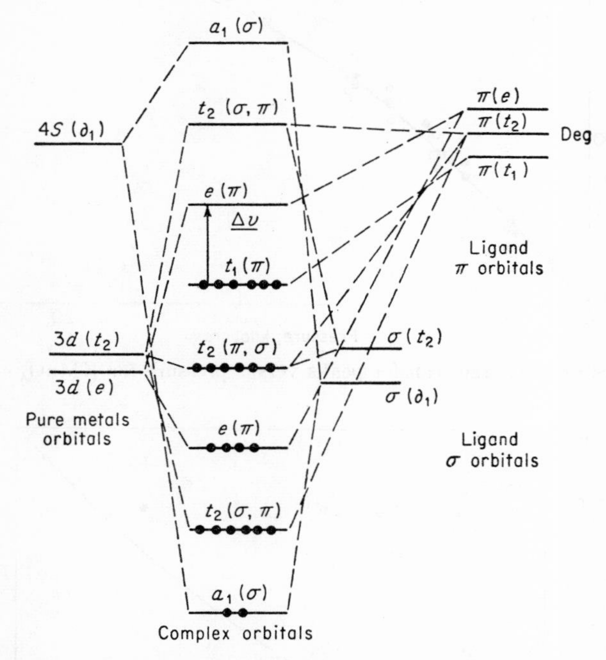

Fig. 12-16 Schematic energy-level diagram for MnO_4^- and CrO_4^{--}.

increasing compression of the ion and mirrors the decrease in energy of the corresponding bonding level $e(\pi)$, and thus the increase in binding energy with increased pressure.

The second charge-transfer situation[22] involves three complexes: $Co[(NH_3)_5I]I_2$, K_2ReCl_6, and K_2ReBr_6. The bonding is much weaker than that for permanganate and chromate, so that the energy levels can be definitely identified with metal ion or ligand. These compounds have intense peaks in the ultraviolet generally assigned to an allowed electron

[21] C. J. Ballhausen and A. D. Liehr, Intensities in Inorganic Complexes, II, Tetrahedral Complexes, *Mol. Spectroscopy*, vol. 2, pp. 342–360, 1958.

[22] D. R. Stephens and H. G. Drickamer, Effect of Pressure on Some Charge Transfer Spectra, *J. Chem. Phys.*, vol. 30, pp. 1518–1520, 1959.

transfer from ligand to metal. The shifts of these peaks with pressure are shown in Figs. 12-18 and 12-19. ν_{max} for $Co[(NH_3)_5I]I_2$ shifts blue by about 900 cm^{-1} in 67 kilobars (500 cm^{-1} in 45 kilobars). In K_2ReCl_6

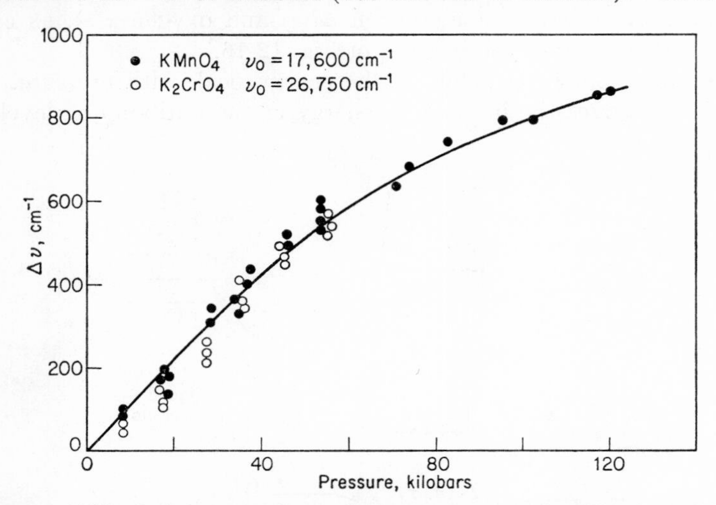

Fig. 12-17 Shift of charge-transfer peaks versus pressure for $KMnO_4$ and K_2CrO_4.

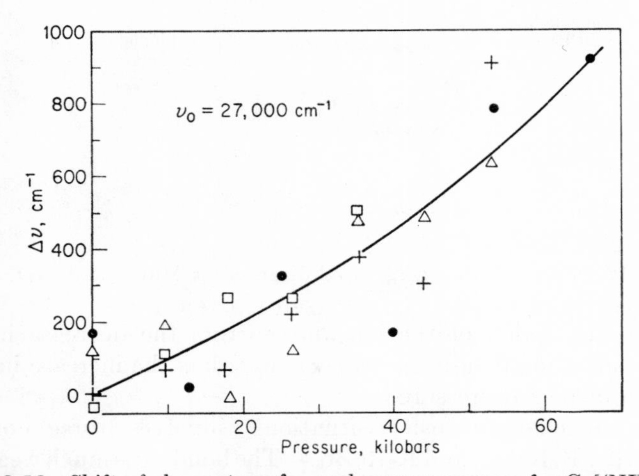

Fig. 12-18 Shift of charge-transfer peak versus pressure for $Co[(NH_3)_5I]I_2$.

and K_2ReBr_6, ν_{max} shifts red by 700 to 750 cm^{-1} in 45 kilobars. A reasonable explanation of these shifts can be given in terms of the levels probably involved. Orgel[23] assigns the 27,000-cm^{-1} transition in

[23] L. E. Orgel, Some Applications of Crystal Field Theory Problems in Transition Metal Chemistry, "Proceedings of the Tenth Solvay Conference," pp. 289–338, J. Stoop, Brussels, 1956.

$Co[(NH_3)_5I]I_2$ to an electron transfer from a ligand π level to a metal-ion level. Since the lower (T_{2g}) levels are all filled, the acceptor level must be an upper (E_g) level. The donor levels for the ReIV complexes are undoubtedly ligand σ or π levels, but the acceptor levels may now be either the metal T_{2g} or E_g levels, as the T_{2g} levels are only partially filled. In Sec. 12-2 and in the references given therein, it is shown that for a number of complexes the T_{2g} and E_g levels spread by an additional 600 to 1,200 cm^{-1} in 45 kilobars. The T_{2g} levels thus may well move red with respect to the ligand levels by an amount consistent with the shifts for the ReIV complexes. The pressure data thus enable one to assign the acceptor levels in K_2ReCl_6 and K_2ReBr_6 as the T_{2g} levels.

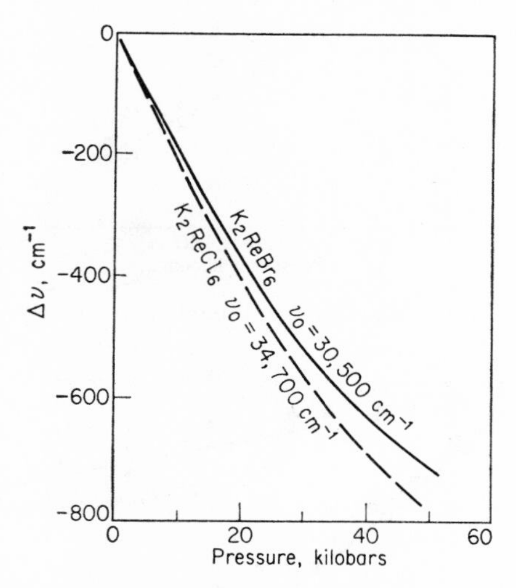

Fig. 12-19 Shift of charge-transfer peak versus pressure for K_2ReX_6.

The hexahalides of other heavy transition-metal ions offer a further opportunity to use high-pressure optical experiments to test theory. Jorgensen[24] has identified the first two peaks (really groups of peaks) in the complexes of hexahalides containing ions of d^4 and d^5 configuration as $\pi \rightarrow T_{2g}$ transitions split by spin-orbital coupling. He has given diagrams showing the increased splitting with increased spin-orbital coupling. As discussed in Sec. 12-2, one would expect increasing covalency with increasing pressure, and therefore increased spin-orbital splitting, as the electron couples with the metal ion and halide nuclei. Figures 12-20 and 12-21 illustrate that this increased splitting does indeed occur and helps to confirm the theory.

[24] C. K. Jorgensen, Electron Transfer Spectra of Hexahalide Complexes, *Mol. Phys.*, vol. 2, pp. 309–332, 1959.

The next stage in our consideration of charge transfer involves the transfer of electrons among neighboring molecules[22] bound only by the van der Waals forces of the molecular crystal. Typical examples include quinhydrone and chloranil-hexamethylbenzene. In both cases

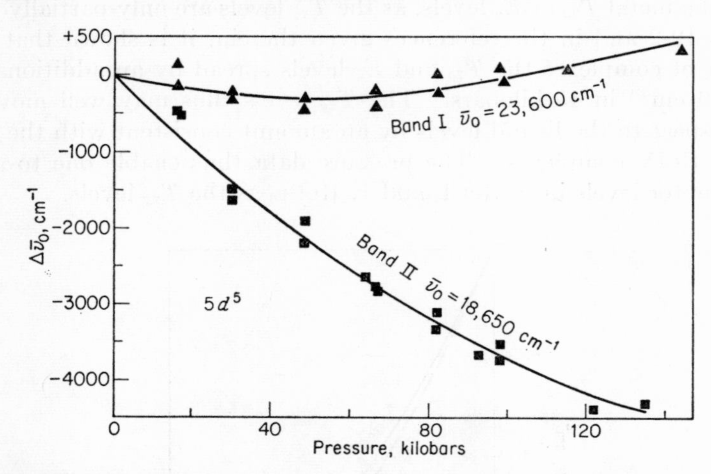

Fig. 12-20 Shift of charge-transfer-band maxima versus pressure for Na_2IrCl_6.

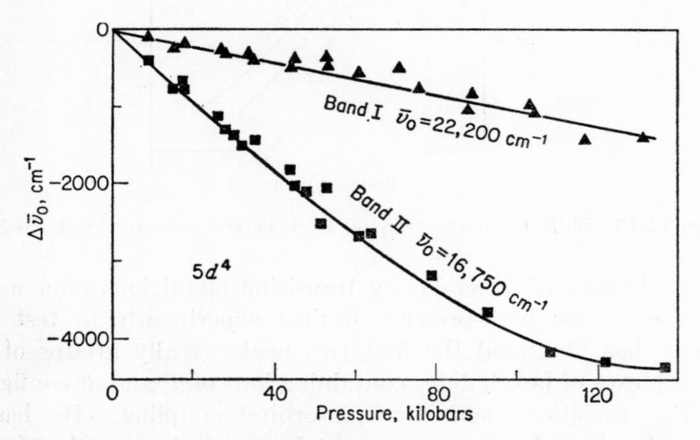

Fig. 12-21 Shift of charge-transfer-band maxima versus pressure for K_2OsBr_6.

the crystal consists essentially of alternating layers of the two types of planar molecule containing more or less delocalized π electrons.[25] Although crystals of the pure components are colorless, the mixed crystals contain intense absorption bands in the visible, owing to electron

[25] K. J. Nakamota, Peculiar Dichroism of Aromatic Molecular Compounds I, *J. Am. Chem. Soc.*, vol. 74, pp. 1739–1742, 1952.

transfer from the less electronegative (donor) molecule to the more electronegative (acceptor) species. Figure 12-22 shows the shift of these peaks with pressure. The large red shift is analogous to the red shift of the absorption edge of molecular crystals to be discussed later. This effect was predicted by Mulliken.[18,19] The increase in transition moment with decreasing intermolecular distance is quite reasonable for charge transfer between loosely packed molecules.

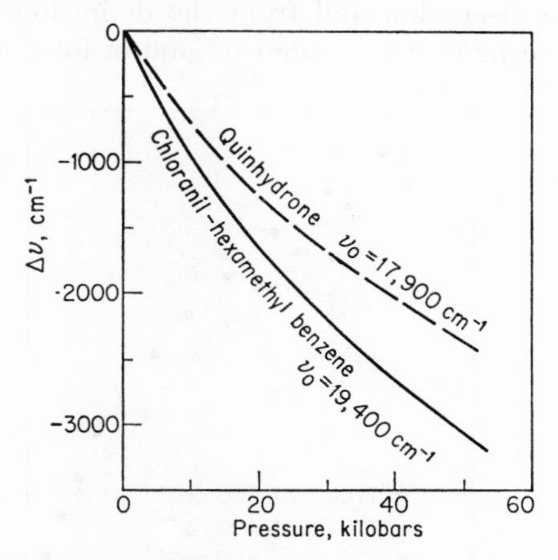

Fig. 12-22 Shift of charge-transfer peaks versus pressure for organic crystals.

12-4 Band Structure in Insulators

The next step in the delocalization of charge transfer involves consideration of fundamental absorption in insulating crystals. This again involves donor and acceptor levels arising from atoms, ions, or molecules of different electronegativity. In many cases, however, the energy states are so delocalized that they can best be described in terms of Bloch theory. One then deals with bands of allowed energy levels separated by forbidden zones. The highest filled band is known as the valence band, while the next empty band is called the conduction band. The process of exciting an electron from the valence band to the conduction band may involve photoconductivity, or the excitation may propagate through the lattice without complete separation of electron and hole (the exciton process). In either case, there is very intense absorption of light of the appropriate energy. In most crystals of thickness greater than a few hundred angstroms, one observes the tail only of the peak. This gives a very steep cutoff of light, known as the absorption edge. In this section we shall discuss the effect of pressure on the absorption edges of ionic crystals, molecular crystals, and several elements, and the approach to the metallic state will be illustrated.

Two considerations are important in setting up wave functions to describe the valence band and conduction band of an insulator; one is the type of corresponding electronic state on the free atom or ion, and the other is the symmetry of the lattice. As the electronic states become more delocalized (as in metals), the relationship to original atomic functions becomes more remote, and states can be described in terms of nearly free electrons and lattice symmetry.

From the above discussion and from the definition of a purely ionic crystal it would appear that the valence band of ionic crystals should be

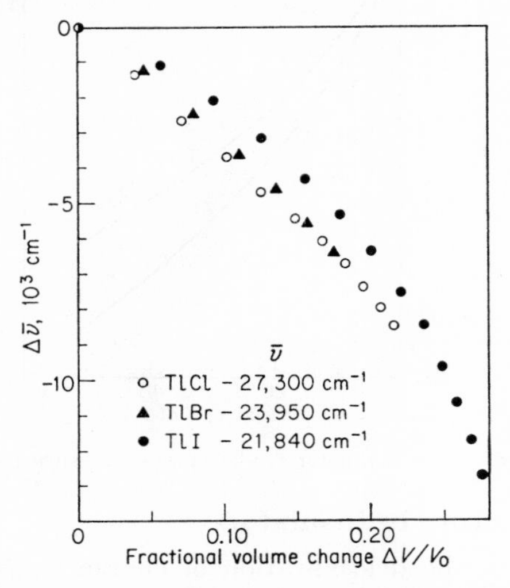

Fig. 12-23 Shift of absorption edge versus fractional volume change for TlX (CsCl structure).

constructed from pure anion wave functions of the proper symmetry, and the conduction band from pure cation wave functions. One might then expect that the conduction band is more sensitive to compression than is the valence band. Figure 12-23 shows the shift of the absorption edge of three thallous halides[26] plotted as a function of density, using Bridgman's[27] density data. All three crystallize in the simple cubic (CsCl) lattice. We see that indeed the shifts seem to be quite independent of the anion, as predicted above. Figure 12-24 is a plot of shift of edge versus pressure for $PbCl_2$ and $PbBr_2$, both of which have $V_h{}^{16}$ symmetry. Again the shift is quite independent of anion.

[26] J. C. Zahner and H. G. Drickamer, The Effect of Pressure on the Absorption Edge in Heavy Metal Halides, *J. Phys. Chem. Solids*, vol. 11, pp. 92–96, 1959.

[27] P. W. Bridgman, Compression of Twenty-one Halogen Compounds and Eleven Other Simple Substances to 100,000 kg/cm², *Proc. Am. Acad. Arts Sci.*, vol. 76, pp. 1–24, 1945.

In general, one might expect that a first-order phase transition induced by pressure would result in more compact packing, probably giving rise to a decrease in the gap between conduction and valence band and thus to a red shift of the absorption edge. Figure 12-25, for $HgCl_2$, is a typical example.

HgI_2 presents an interesting exception. At 1 atm and room temperature the symmetry is $D^{15}{}_{4h}$. There is a phase transition at 13 kilobars and room temperature. Bridgman[28] showed that this high-pressure phase is the same $C^{12}{}_{2v}$ as one obtains at 1 atm above 127°C. Figure 12-26 shows that at this transition one obtains a blue shift of the edge, as one would expect going from "red" to "yellow" HgI_2.

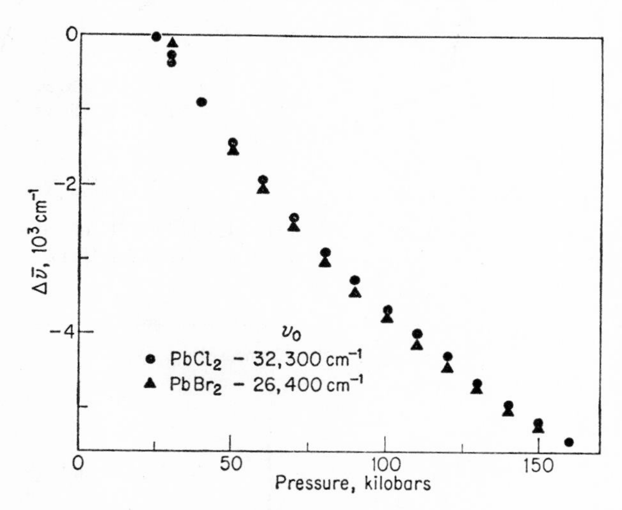

Fig. 12-24 Shift of absorption edge versus pressure for V_h^{16} structure.

The silver halides present a more complex problem in ionic band structure. The chloride and bromide behave almost exactly alike.[29,30] Figure 12-27 shows the absorption edge as a function of pressure and temperature for AgCl. There are a number of significant features:

1. In the low-pressure (NaCl) phase the shift of the edge with pressure is much smaller than for most ionic crystals. This seems consistent

[28] P. W. Bridgman, Polymorphic Transitions of Some Solids under Pressure, *Proc. Am. Acad. Arts Sci.*, vol. 51, pp. 55–124, 1915.

[29] T. E. Slykhouse and H. G. Drickamer, The Effect of Pressure on the Absorption Edges of Silver Halides, *J. Phys. Chem. Solids*, vol. 7, pp. 207–209, 1958.

[30] A. S. Balchan and H. G. Drickamer, The Effect of Pressure and Temperature on the Absorption Edges of Three Silver Halides, *J. Phys. Chem. Solids*, vol. 19, p. 261, 1961.

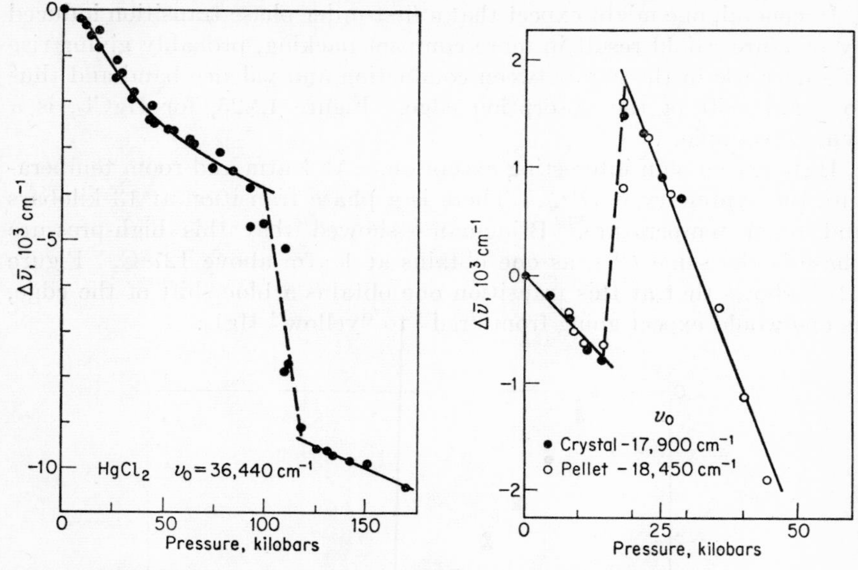

Fig. 12-25 Shift of absorption edge versus pressure for $HgCl_2$.

Fig. 12-26 Shift of absorption edge versus pressure for HgI_2.

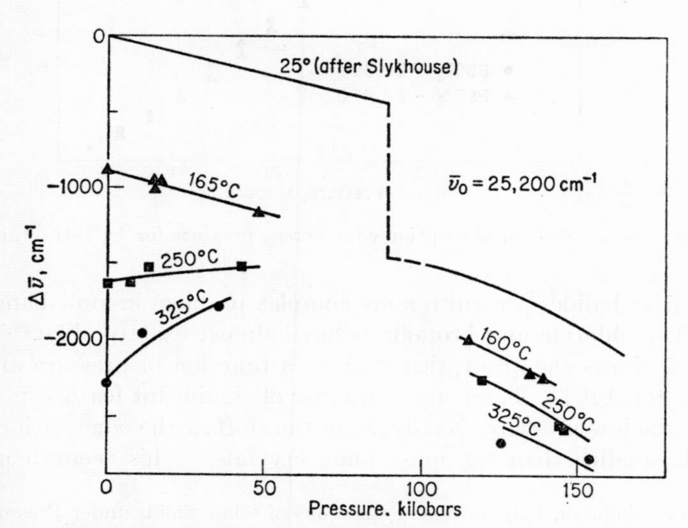

Fig. 12-27 Shift of absorption edge versus pressure and temperature for AgCl.

with Seitz's[31] argument that the tail on the absorption edge of AgCl and AgBr is due to an indirect transition.

2. At about 83 kilobars there is a transition (first noted by Bridgman in his *P-V* studies)[27] presumably to the simple cubic (CsCl) structure. This is accompanied by a large red shift of the edge.

3. The high-pressure phase shows a small red shift accelerating at the higher pressures.

4. At atmospheric pressure there is a very large red shift of the edge with temperature. This is presumably associated with a large concentration of defects in the lattice at high temperature, probably largely Frenkel defects.[31]

5. At temperatures above 165°C the absorption edge of the low-pressure phase shifts blue with increasing pressure. It is reasonable to associate this blue shift with the inhibiting effect of pressure on the formation of Frenkel defects.

6. The absorption edge of the high-pressure phase shifts red with increasing pressure at all temperatures, with a slope relatively independent of temperature. Evidently in this close-packed phase at high pressure the formation of Frenkel defects is inhibited at any temperature reached in this work.

Figure 12-28 shows the absorption edge of AgI as a function of pressure and temperature. AgI evidently has a considerably different band structure from AgCl or AgBr. At 1 atm and room temperature it has the zincblende structure. At 5 kilobars it transforms to the NaCl structure. The shift in the edge with pressure is very rapid, as it is with most ionic crystals. One may well be dealing with the direct transition here. At about 110 kilobars there is a transition accompanied by a blue shift of the edge. The high-pressure phase behaves much like the high-pressure phases of AgCl and AgBr. In the fcc phase the edge shifts slightly blue with increasing temperature. Irreversible effects made it impossible to get to high temperature, but evidently at sufficiently high temperature the shift of the edge at the fcc-sc transition will be to red.

Suchan and Drickamer[32] have studied the absorption edges of a number of molecular crystals as a function of pressure. Figure 12-29 shows the shifts for a series of mercurous halides. The pressure shift varies by a factor of 2 from chloride to iodide, which is much larger than any reasonable variation in compressibility. Figure 12-30 is a similar comparison for SnI_4, CI_4, and Hg_2I_2. All mercurous halides have the tetragonal $D^{17}{}_{4h}$ structure. SnI_4 and CI_4 crystallize in the cubic $T_h{}^6$ structure.

[31] F. Seitz, Speculations on the Properties of the Silver Halides, *Rev. Mod. Phys.*, vol. 23, pp. 328–352, 1951.

[32] H. L. Suchan and H. G. Drickamer, The Effect of Pressure on the Absorption Edges of Certain Molecular Crystals, *J. Phys. Chem. Solids*, vol. 11, pp. 111–114, 1959.

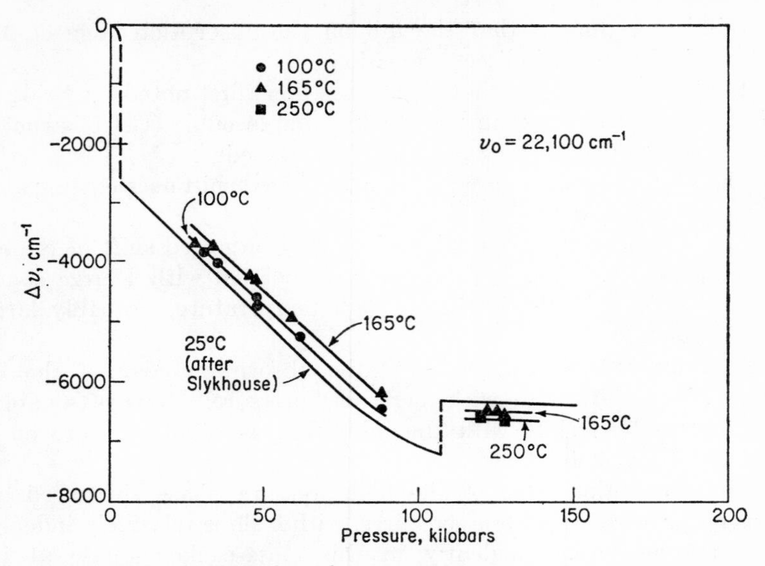

Fig. 12-28 Shift of absorption edge versus pressure and temperature for AgI.

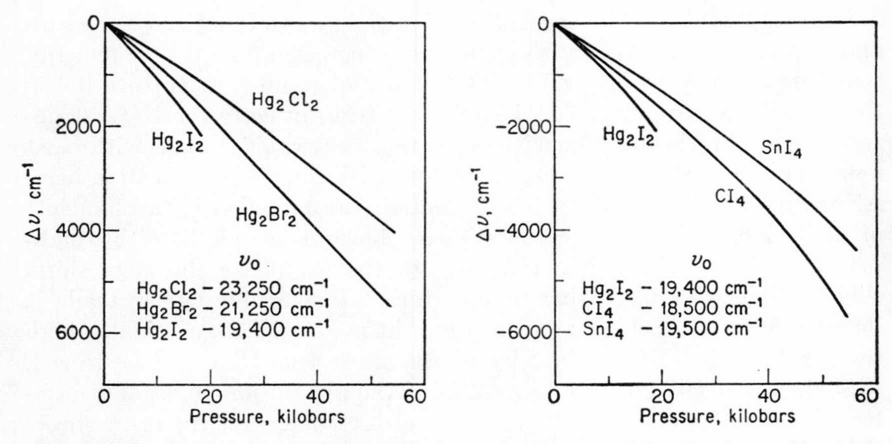

Fig. 12-29 Shift of absorption edge versus pressure for mercurous halides.

Fig. 12-30 Shift of absorption edge versus pressure for molecular iodides.

Molecular crystals are characterized by covalently bound molecular units held together by weak van der Waals forces. The Bloch functions which describe these crystals are distinctly of the "tight-binding" type, made from the wave functions of the individual molecules. The molecular orbitals contain contributions from all the atoms in the molecule, even though there is some difference in electronegativity among the atoms. Thus, the conduction-band Bloch function is constructed from wave functions from all the atoms present. It would appear from these results that the picture of molecular crystals outlined above is a realistic one.

The ultimate effect of compression of any insulating crystal[3,4] would be the overlap of the conduction and valence bands, with resulting metallic conductivity. The transformation to a metal could be accompanied by a first-order phase transition or could take place continuously. Since most good metals have relatively simple crystal structures, one would expect that insulating crystals with relatively complex crystal

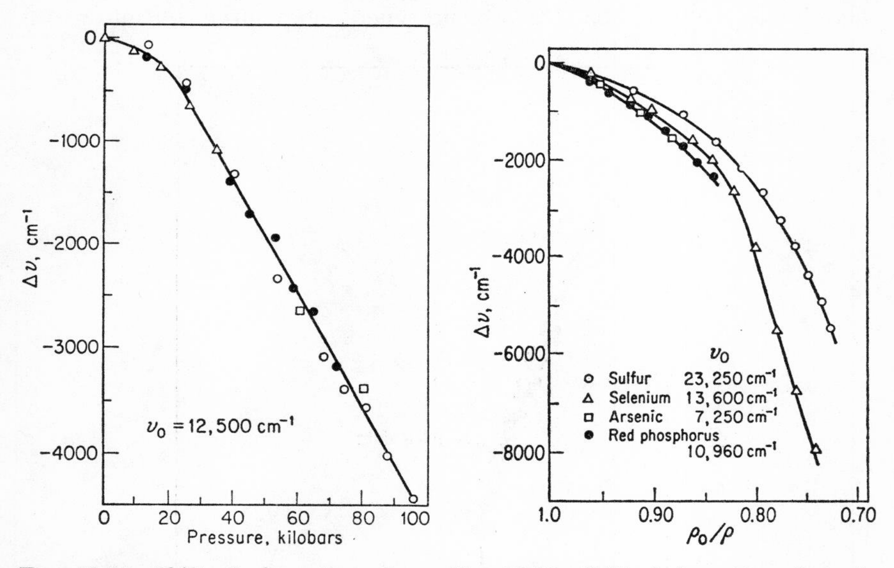

Fig. 12-31 Shift of absorption edge versus pressure for iodine.

Fig. 12-32 Shift of absorption edges of some elements versus relative density.

structures would undergo a phase transition, either on becoming a metal or ultimately in the metallic state. It is of particular interest to consider the approach to the metallic state for nonconducting solid elements. Figure 12-31 shows the shift of the absorption edge of iodine versus pressure.[33] The low-pressure data are not reliable owing to problems in handling iodine, but the slope at high pressure was quite reproducible. Figure 12-32 shows the shifts of the absorption edges of several elements[33] as a function of density, using Bridgman's[34] density data.

[33] H. L. Suchan, S. Wiederhorn, and H. G. Drickamer, The Effect of Pressure on the Absorption Edges of Certain Elements, *J. Chem. Phys.*, vol. 31, pp. 355–358, 1959.

[34] P. W. Bridgman, Pressure-Volume Relations for Seventeen Elements to 100,000 kg/cm^2, *Proc. Am. Acad. Arts Sci.*, vol. 74, pp. 425–440, 1942.

Table 12-1 Pressure for Which the Optical Energy Gap Disappears

Element	*P, kilobars*
Sulfur	400
Phosphorus (white)	30–35
Phosphorus (red)	90
Selenium	130
Iodine	240
Arsenic	160

Table 12-1 shows the pressure at which the energy gap extrapolates to zero for several elements. Such extrapolation is, of course, risky, as there is no guarantee that the pressure–energy-gap curve continues with

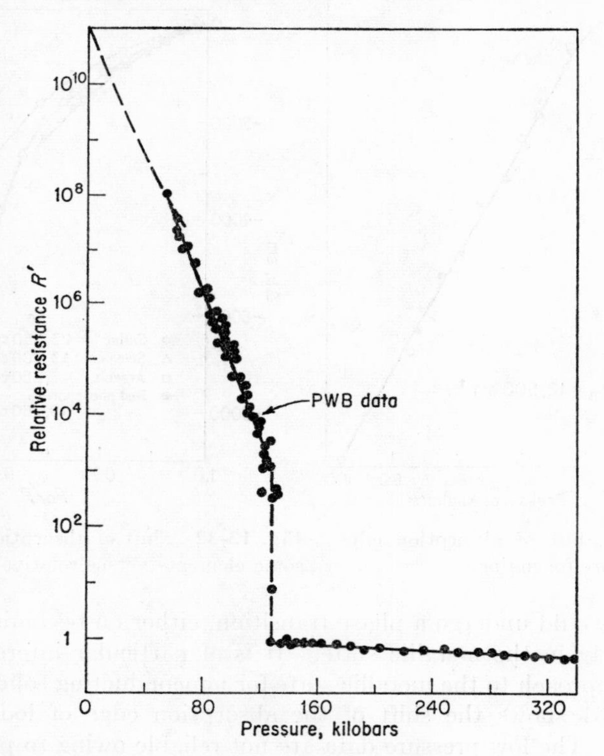

Fig. 12-33 Relative resistance versus pressure for selenium.

the same form. With our recently developed technique[3] for electrical measurements it has been possible to study the conductivity of selenium and iodine to high pressure.[35] Figure 12-33 shows the resistance of

[35] A. S. Balchan and H. G. Drickamer, The Effect of Pressure on the Resistance of Iodine and Selenium, *J. Chem. Phys.*, vol. 34, p. 1948, 1961.

selenium. The drop of resistance is very rapid to 128 kilobars, where there is a discontinuous drop of about three orders of magnitude. Above this transition the resistance drops much more slowly, but continuously, as shown in Fig. 12-34. The resistivity just after the transition is estimated as 50×10^{-6} to 100×10^{-6} ohm-cm. It would seem to be definitely metallic. It is interesting to note the excellent agreement between the extrapolated disappearance of the optical energy gap and the metallic transition. While there are a number of reasons why the

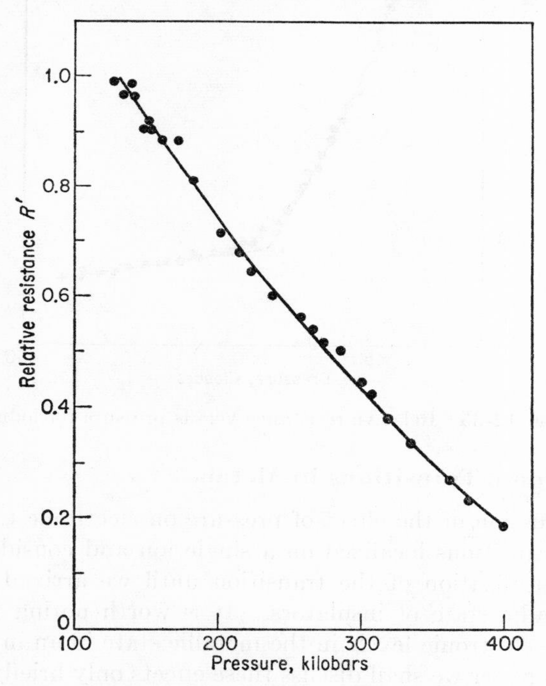

Fig. 12-34 Relative resistance versus pressure for selenium (metallic phase).

agreement might not be expected to be so good, it cannot be entirely fortuitous.

The resistance of iodine as a function of pressure is shown in Fig. 12-35. It can be seen that there are two relatively straight curves of radically differing slopes. The intersection lies at 235 kilobars, which corresponds closely to the pressure at which the optical absorption edge extrapolates to zero. The resistivity just beyond this point is estimated as 60×10^{-5} to 120×10^{-5} ohm-cm, which is definitely in the metallic range. Ultimately one would expect a first-order transition in iodine, although the large atoms may inhibit a diffusion-controlled rearrangement at high pressure and room temperature.

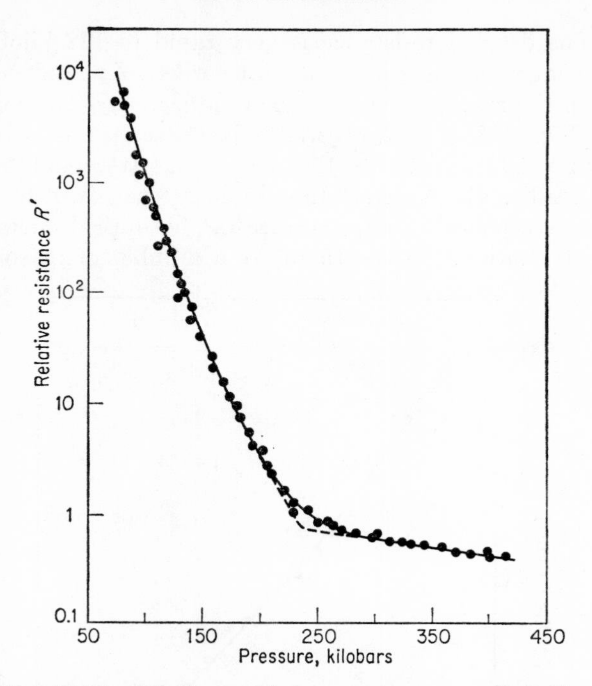

Fig. 12-35 Relative resistance versus pressure for iodine.

12-5 Electronic Transitions in Metals

In our discussion of the effect of pressure on electronic transitions, we began with transitions localized on a single ion and considered, step by step, the delocalization of the transition until we arrived at the high-pressure metallic state of insulators. It is worth noting that pressure can affect the electronic levels in the metallic state in an interesting way also. In this paper we shall discuss these effects only briefly, as only one or two electronic transitions are well established.

Cerium has a phase transition at about 7 kilobars at room temperature[36–39] between two states having the same crystal structure. The transition is accompanied by sharp decreases in volume and electrical

[36] P. W. Bridgman, The Electrical Resistance to 30,000 kg/cm² of Twenty-nine Metals and Intermetallic Compounds, *Proc. Am. Acad. Arts Sci.*, vol. 79, pp. 149–179, 1951.

[37] A. W. Lawson and T. Y. Tang, Concerning the High Pressure Allotropic Modification of Cerium, *Phys. Rev.*, vol. 76, pp. 301–302, 1949.

[38] I. Likhter, N. Riabinin, and L. F. Vereschaguin, The Phase Diagram for Cerium, *Soviet Phys. JETP*, vol. 6, pp. 469–471, 1958.

[39] R. Herman and C. A. Swenson, Temperature Dependence of the Phase Transition in Cerium, *J. Chem. Phys.*, vol. 29, pp. 398–400, 1958.

resistance.[40] It is generally agreed that the transition involves the promotion of a $4f$ electron to the $5d$ band.

Cesium has a transition at 41 kilobars involving a discontinuous decrease in volume and a sharp cusp in the resistance.[40] Sternheimer[41] has discussed this transition as an electronic one in which a $5d$ band is sufficiently lowered in energy so that a $6s$ valence electron assumes $5d$ character at 41 kilobars. His calculations are open to criticism, as one should consider, not the $6s$ and $5d$ states, but states of appropriate symmetry in the face-centered-cubic lattice; e.g., the d shell splits into one

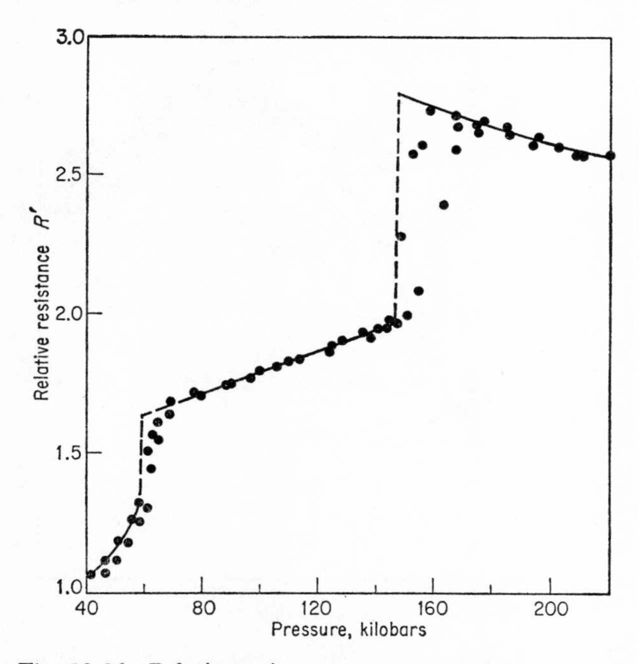

Fig. 12-36 Relative resistance versus pressure for barium.

triply degenerate and one doubly degenerate configuration in the crystal field. Nevertheless, there is considerable reason to believe in the qualitative soundness of his theory. Lawson[42] explains maxima in the resistance of ytterbium and strontium as due to gradual overlap of the same type

[40] P. W. Bridgman, The Resistance of 72 Elements, Alloys and Compounds to 100,000 kg/cm², *Proc. Am. Acad. Arts Sci.*, vol. 81, pp. 165–251, 1952.

[41] R. Sternheimer, On the Compressibility of Metallic Cesium, *Phys. Rev.*, vol. 78, pp. 235–243, 1950.

[42] A. W. Lawson, The Effect of Pressure on Electrical Resistivity of Metals, p.1062 in B. Chalmers and R. King (eds.), "Progress in Metal Physics," vol. 6, Pergamon Press, New York, 1956.

as the discontinuous events in cerium and cesium, with consequent interband scattering. It would seem desirable to explore the effect of pressure on resistance for a number of metals whose free atoms have vacant d shells with partially filled or filled s shells of higher principal quantum number (or with partially filled f shells as in the rare earths) to see if these transitions are general, and perhaps to get a generalized picture of band shifts in metals with pressure.

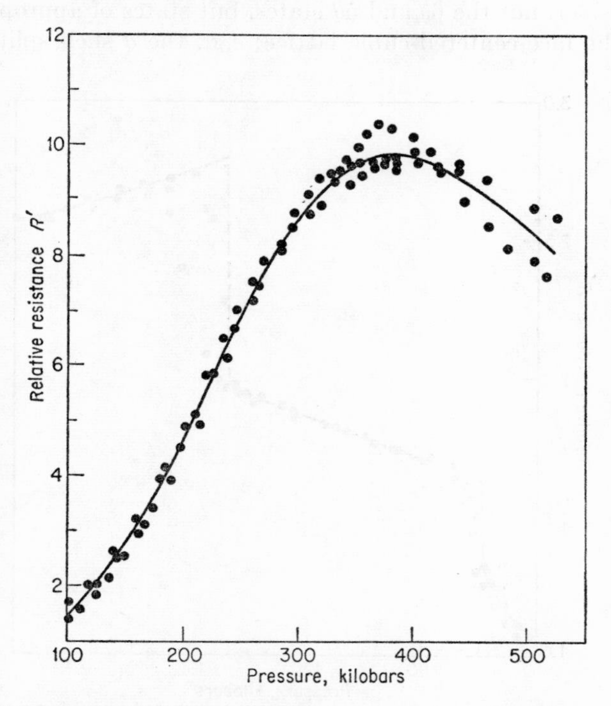

Fig. 12-37 Relative resistance versus pressure for calcium.

Figures 12-36 through 12-38 show the relative resistance of barium, calcium, and rubidium in the high-pressure region.[34] Barium and rubidium have the bcc structure at 1 atm, but both have first-order transitions, barium at about 58.5 kilobars[34] and rubidium apparently at about 70 kilobars,[43] almost certainly to the fcc close-packed phase. Calcium already has a close-packed structure at 1 atm. One would not then expect, in any of these metals, transitions involving more efficient arrangement of the atoms. The normal behavior which one would expect is a continuous decrease in resistance with pressure due to a stiffening of the

[43] F. P. Bundy, Phase Diagram of Rubidium to 150,000 Atmospheres and 400°C, *Phys. Rev.*, vol. 115, pp. 274–277, 1959.

lattice. For each of these metals the resistance increases with increasing pressure in the lower-pressure part of the region of interest. At 144 kilobars there is a discontinuous sharp rise in the resistance of barium, above which pressure the resistance drops off continuously. Calcium exhibits a maximum of resistance at about 365 kilobars. Rubidium has a discontinuous rise in resistance at 193 kilobars and a maximum at about 425 kilobars. A conclusive explanation of these phenomena is still

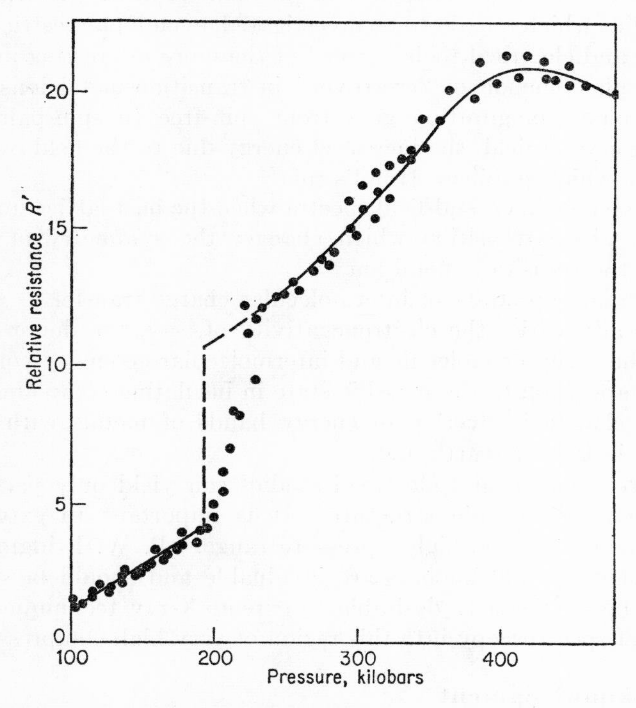

Fig. 12-38 Relative resistance versus pressure for rubidium.

lacking. It would seem most probable that the phenomena are analogous to those observed by Bridgman in cesium and strontium and are concerned with the motion of empty levels arising from the *d* shell relative to the highest occupied levels. The phenomena would appear to be rather general for metals constructed of atoms with empty *d* levels and filled levels of higher principal quantum numbers.

The behavior of calcium and rubidium near the maximum is particularly interesting. When pressure is first applied, the resistance surges upward before it drops to an equilibrium value, just as it does in the initial stages of a phase transition. Upon a lowering of the pressure through the maximum, the resistance shows metastability and overshooting (see figures in the original paper), just as in a first-order phase transition. There is apparently an activation energy involved in the process, although it is difficult to see that it could be diffusion controlled in the usual sense of the phrase.

12-6 Conclusions

There are a tremendous variety of phenomena in the electronic structure of solids which remain to be investigated, even if one restricts himself to optical and electrical tools. Some of the more interesting include:

1. The phenomenon of "crossover" in transition-metal ions, wherein the electronic configuration goes from spin-free to spin-paired in an increasing crystal field, the increased energy due to the field overcoming the energy which stabilizes Hund's rule
2. The change in crystal-field spectra when the host lattice undergoes a first-order phase transition which changes the symmetry of the local field near the transition-metal ion
3. An organized study of intermolecular charge transfer in which one systematically varies the electronegativity of, say, the donor molecule, keeping the acceptor molecule and intermolecular geometry constant
4. The approach to the metallic state in insulating compounds
5. The change in overlap of energy bands of metals with pressure, especially in the rare-earth metals

Of course, optical and electrical studies can yield only partial information about electronic structure. It is important to extend other measurements into the higher pressure range. P. W. Bridgman's *P-V* measurements to 100 kilobars are invaluable and should be expanded. It would be particularly desirable to extend X-ray techniques and the methods of spectroscopy into this region of very high compression.

12-7 Acknowledgment

It is a pleasure to acknowledge the financial support of the United States Atomic Energy Commission for much of this work.

13

Physics Experiments with Strong Pressure Pulses

Berni J. Alder

Lawrence Radiation Laboratory
University of California
Livermore, California

13-1 Introduction

It is particularly appropriate to write a chapter about shock-wave experiments in solids and liquids in this book dedicated to Professor Bridgman, because this field is, I imagine, in very much the same state as the field of static high-pressure research was when Professor Bridgman began his pioneering work. The shock method of reaching high pressure is relatively new[1] (less than 15 years old), and its potential contribution to the understanding of the state of matter at high pressure is largely unrealized. The analogy carries further in that the effort of a superb experimentalist will be required before the most interesting physical information can be extracted. Although the details of experimental techniques will not be emphasized, their need for improvement and the necessity for developing new ones will be constantly evident.

13-2 Experimental Limitations

13-2a Duration of experiment and attainment of equilibrium. Experimentation is difficult in the shock method, because the materials are under pressure for very short times. For quantitative purposes the shock must have a reasonably sharp front (small compared to the dimension of the material under study) with a constant pressure behind it. It is hard to maintain a uniform pressure profile for times much longer than a few microseconds before the pressure degrades. Hence the observation time of a few microseconds is restrictive, but, on the other hand, the advent of fast electronics and fast optics which helped open this field makes experiments at these speeds quite routine now. The other development which enabled the shock method to become a quantitative scientific tool was the manufacture of high-quality explosives and an explosive lens to produce very plane shocks. The art consists in either combining various explosives or so shaping the explosive chain that detonation at a point is converted to the desired shock shape a short distance away from the initiation point.

Unfortunately the whole operation is cumbersome and expensive and hence not well suited to university work. One requires an underground bunker containing extensive electronic and optical equipment, away from populated areas so that up to 100 lb of explosive can be set off or, alternatively, a facility to contain the charge. The operating expense is large because each experiment destroys accurately machined equipment which, in some of the more complicated experiments, takes weeks to build up.

The short times for which the high pressure is maintained raise the problem of whether equilibrium is attained behind the shock front. This appears at first as a great limitation to the method. High pressure slows down almost all transformations, since the more repulsive interactions of a more compressed state increase activation energies. Static measurements have shown that even with considerably more time available and even in their lower pressure region, metastable states occur.

[1] R. W. Goranson, D. Bancroft, B. L. Burton, T. Blechar, E. E. Houston, E. F. Gittings, and S. A. Landeen, Dynamic Determination of the Compressibility of Metals, *J. Appl. Phys.*, vol. 26, p. 1472, December, 1955.

The shock method, however, necessarily has a temperature rise associated with it which easily may overcome a factor of 10^9 in time, since in a typical activation-type process the rate is a sensitive function of temperature. In addition, under the large shearing stresses within a shock front, a different and faster transformation mechanism seems to occur, at least in some instances. This is concluded from experiments in which transformations under shock conditions have been observed at lower pressures and temperatures than under static conditions. Thus, the shock method can be used to investigate, in a limited way, transformation mechanisms and rates in solids. Rate processes in gases have been studied as well, but will not be considered here. Only a few experiments have been carried out in this area, and they will be described in some detail. In this, as well as in other instances, some of our own unpublished and preliminary results will be discussed. They are quoted mainly as illustrations of what can be learned and they should be considered tentative, subject to later revisions.

13-2b Shock-wave pressures. On the positive side of the ledger is the fact that this method reaches considerably higher pressures than have been obtained statically and that the pressure and density can be measured with high precision. In a reasonably careful experiment the directly measured quantities are known to 1 percent. The method is not limited by the strength of materials or uncertainties in the forces dissipated in friction, but only by the accuracy with which a constant-pressure profile behind the shock front can be maintained and by the precision with which the shock and free-surface velocities can be measured. The shock and free-surface velocities are involved in the material, momentum, and energy balances across the shock front.[2] Since these conservation laws involve the pressure, density, and internal energy as well, these quantities can be determined from the two velocity measurements. More precisely, the conservation laws involve the shock and particle velocities, but the particle velocity can be simply derived in most cases from the measured velocity with which a free surface moves. The point is that the physics is extremely simple and involves only two assumptions, namely, that a steady state is eventually reached behind the shock front (however thick) and that the material under pressure acts as a fluid. The last requirement is not very confining, since it restricts shock experiments to those which are several times greater in pressure than the dynamic yield strength of the material,[3] although by observation of the elastic and plastic waves, pressure data can be obtained

[2] R. Courant and K. O. Friedricks, "Supersonic Flow and Shock Waves," Interscience Publishers, Inc., New York, 1948.

[3] M. H. Rice, R. G. McQueen, and J. M. Walsh, Compression of Solids by Strong Shock Waves, p. 10 in F. Seitz and D. Turnbull (eds.), "Solid State Physics," vol. 6, Academic Press, Inc., New York, 1958.

down to the yield point.[4] For example, the yield strength of steel is about 15 kilobars, so that shock experiments can be carried out in a pressure region which overlaps the statically accessible region. In fact, one useful suggestion would be to calibrate the static pressures against the dynamic ones in the regime above 30 kilobars, where the lack of hydrostatic pressure-transmitting media makes static data subject to errors. The shock data can serve as a primary standard.

The pressures that can be reached in a material depend on the pressure generated in the explosive. Most chemical explosives do not vary greatly in this pressure; it is around 250 kilobars.[5] The more powerful explosives might generate pressures up to 400 kilobars, while the weaker explosives may go as low as 50 kilobars. At pressures much below that, the common explosives do not detonate; hence a different technique has to be used to study that region dynamically.

The pressure generated in the substance placed in contact with the explosive depends on its "shock impedance."[6] This means that the condition reached in the sample will depend on the product of the shock velocity and the initial density. This relation is arrived at by considering that at any interface the particle velocity and pressure must be continuous, and by applying the conservation laws again in the new material. The shock velocity at low pressures behaves as the speed of sound, that is, it is inversely proportional to the square root of the compressibility, so that higher pressures can be reached in dense and stiff materials. Thus pressures close to 1 megabar can be achieved in such substances as tungsten[7] by placing the sample directly in contact with the explosive.

To reach still higher (and lower) pressures by single shocks, the flying-plate technique is used. In this method a flying-plate projectile impacts on a target. In this case, the particle velocity can be directly deduced from the velocity of the free-running projectile, since if the projectile and target are of the same material the particle velocity is just half the projectile velocity, and if not, the same impedance-matching conditions can be applied. Equivalently, the free-surface velocity of the target can be measured, as before. At lower pressures, various types of guns can be reliably used to propel the projectile.[8] To obtain higher pressures,

[4] G. R. Fowles, "Shock Wave Compression of Hardened and Annealed 2024 Aluminum," Poulter Laboratory Tech. Rept. 011, October, 1960.

[5] W. E. Deal, Measurement of Chapman-Jouguet Pressure for Explosives, *J. Chem. Phys.*, vol. 27, p. 796, September, 1957.

[6] D. C. Pack, The Reflection and Transmission of Shock Waves, *Phil. Mag.*, vol. 2, p. 182, February, 1957.

[7] R. G. McQueen and S. P. Marsh, Equation of State for Nineteen Metallic Elements from Shock-wave Measurements to Two Megabars, *J. Appl. Phys.*, vol. 31, p. 1253, July, 1960.

[8] F. Genevese (ed.), "Third Symposium on Hypervelocity," Armour Research Foundation, Chicago, 1959.

the plate is driven by an explosive-lens system which allows the expanding gases from the explosion a longer time to act on the projectile. Thus more of the energy released in the explosion is transferred to the flying plate. By use of these or similar means, pressures as high as 5 megabars in iron[9] have been reported.

This pressure is by no means the upper limit of the dynamic method. Higher pressures can be reached in single shocks if higher-energy sources are used. Nuclear explosives seem at the moment the best candidate for these. If a flying plate were accelerated with the same efficiency as with 100 lb of chemical explosives, pressures of several hundred megabars instead of a few megabars could be reached using a 5-ton nuclear device. This 5-ton nuclear explosive power could be part of the energy released by a bigger device. There is little doubt that the technical problems can be overcome and that these pressures can be achieved. The ultimate limitation of the shock method from the practical point of view is that the materials (like the projectile) become so hot that a strong single shock melts and eventually vaporizes them. Thus the projectile disintegrates if too much internal energy is imparted to it as its velocity is increased to larger and larger values.

Although these higher-pressure experiments are interesting technically, they are less interesting from the point of view of the physics involved. At the higher pressures molecules disintegrate, their atoms become close-packed, and even the electrons are pressure and temperature ionized, so that the Thomas-Fermi description of the system or its various modifications should be quite adequate. The several-hundred-megabar pressure experiments would allow an investigation of deviations of the system from the Thomas-Fermi model, since the pressure at which the discrepancy becomes appreciable is hard to estimate theoretically.

13-2c Multiple shocks. A disadvantage of single-shock high-pressure experiments is that as the shock strength is increased, an increasingly larger fraction of the pressure is contributed by the kinetic energy of the particles, because the compressibility of materials decreases with pressure. Thus, the total work done by the shock on the system raises the temperature rather than decreases the volume by P-V work. For example, in iron[9] the first $2\frac{1}{2}$ megabars changes the density by 60 percent, while another $2\frac{1}{2}$ megabars changes the density by only 10 percent more. Although an increase in pressure by a factor of 100 will further increase the density by an amount estimated to be another factor of 2, these high shock pressures are misleading in terms of static isothermal experiments because of the high temperature produced.

The disadvantage of the high temperature accompanying high pressure

[9] L. V. Al'tshuler, K. K. Krupnikov, B. N. Ledenev, V. I. Zhuchikhin, and M. I. Brazhnik, Dynamic Compressibility and Equation of State of Iron under High Pressure, *Soviet Phys. JETP*, vol. 34, p. 606, October, 1958.

can be overcome in a limited way. The smallest temperature rise is achieved dynamically at a given pressure by a series of infinitesimally small shocks (so that the process is reversible). This thermodynamically adiabatic process can be approached by a double-shock technique.[10] In this method the first shock in the material is reflected back from what otherwise would be a free surface by a material which has a higher shock impedance, that is, a dense and stiff anvil material. From the shock and free-surface velocity measurements on the anvil, combined with the impedance-matching conditions, the state of the sample after shock reflection can be deduced with somewhat decreased accuracy. This method is particularly useful for low-density and easily compressible materials, not only to lower the temperature at a given density, but also to reach higher pressures. For dense material it is hard to find an anvil material which will do much good; however, one might think of using a spherically converging system with multiple shocks both to reach higher pressures and to achieve more adiabatic conditions. In a spherically convergent system with the sample at the center, the shock is reflected from the center of the sample, and indeed the aim can be achieved; however, taking reliable data is a very complicated matter.

13-2d Deductions from the Hugoniot equation of state. The reflected-shock technique is important as well in connection with the question of what region of the phase diagram can be explored with shocks. At the moment, it appears that only singly reflected plane shocks can be handled experimentally in a quantitative way; however even here very little work has been done. Almost exclusively, only a single Hugoniot has been explored experimentally. The Hugoniot is defined as the series of pressure, volume, and energy points generated by a series of single shocks applied to a material always in a specified initial state. The Hugoniot equation of state is obtained from several Hugoniots, starting from several initial states. Since Hugoniot data have been almost always confined to the material initially in its state at room temperature, it has been necessary to resort to rather crude theories[11] of unknown accuracy to evaluate the remaining thermodynamic quantities along the Hugoniot (for example, to evaluate the temperature or deduce the isotherms). To obtain a complete description of the thermodynamics in the region covered by static experiments, a number of isotherms are necessary if theoretical approximations are to be avoided. Similarly, a

[10] J. M. Walsh and M. H. Rice, Dynamic Compression of Liquids from Measurements on Strong Shock Waves, *J. Chem. Phys.*, vol. 26, p. 815, April, 1957.

[11] M. H. Rice, R. G. McQueen, and J. M. Walsh, Compression of Solids by Strong Shock Waves, p. 40 in F. Seitz and D. Turnbull (eds.), "Solid State Physics," vol. 6, Academic Press, Inc., New York, 1958.

series of Hugoniots is required to accomplish the same task dynamically. Of course, statically the option exists to perform experiments other than pressure-volume experiments to get the remaining thermodynamic quantities along a given isotherm. This is not so easily done dynamically.

Several Hugoniots can be obtained for a given material by changing either the initial temperature or density or both. Also, reflected shocks can be used to get additional Hugoniots. A given initial shock can be reflected by a series of anvil materials, resulting in a Hugoniot starting from the conditions behind the shock front due to the first shock. In these ways a region of the phase diagram surrounding the Hugoniot starting with the material under the initial condition can be covered. Some of our preliminary attempts in this direction will be discussed, although more accurate experimental techniques remain to be developed. In the region covered it will then be possible to evaluate, from the series of pressure, volume, and internal-energy points defined by the various Hugoniots, other thermodynamic functions; in particular the Grüneisen $\gamma = V(\partial P/\partial E)_V$ can be obtained very directly. γ appears in the Mie-Grüneisen[12] theory, which has been used to calculate other thermodynamic functions from a single Hugoniot. Solid-state theories[11] predict γ to be independent of temperature and insensitive to volume. The volume dependence has been predicted from crude theoretical models of the solid state and can now be checked over a wide region experimetally. The region of the phase diagram for a condensed system that can be covered by shock techniques will then be a band around an increasing pressure-and-temperature curve. The low-temperature high-pressure region will have to be reached by other means.

The importance of γ derives from the fact that knowing it is equivalent to knowing the division of the internal energy of a given Hugoniot into potential ($P\,dV$) and kinetic ($C_V\,dT$) energy. Once this is known, the isotherms and the temperature can be evaluated. The thermodynamic way to obtain temperature, as described, is somewhat cumbersome, and it would be desirable to have available something equivalent to a thermometer. To measure temperatures of microseconds duration requires the use of either optical or electronic methods. The deduction of shock temperatures in transparent solids from the radiation observed near the surface of the high-pressure region suffers from uncertainties in the corrections to be made due to rarefaction waves generated at the free surfaces. In fact, by this measurement it seems possible to get accurate temperatures only after the pressure has been released to atmospheric

[12] E. Grüneisen, Zustand des festen Körpers, p. 22 in H. Geiger and K. Scheel (eds.), "Handbuch der Physik," vol. 10, Springer-Verlag, Berlin, 1926.

pressure. Care must also be taken, in surrounding the sample by vacuum, to avoid absorption of the radiation by gases (usually air). These difficulties are avoided when electrical conductivity is used, since it is a measure of the charge density of the bulk sample while subjected to the shock pressure. It is in the semiconducting state that the electrical conductivity is most sensitive to temperature and can best serve as a thermometer.

13-2e Measurements of physical properties. Experimental techniques have been developed which measure the electrical resistance of solid insulators under shock conditions.[13] The results will be described. If static data were available for the resistance and the energy gap at the same pressure, the temperature could be deduced. Without that, the gap and the mobility of the charge carriers can be deduced from shock experiments by measuring the temperature variation of the resistance under shock conditions. Again reflected shocks can be used here, or the initial temperature can be changed. This technique is limited at the moment by the inability to measure by simple means very high conductivities in very short times, but some preliminary temperature estimates have been made.

The mobilities and energy gaps as a function of density are of interest in themselves. They allow observation of how an insulator is changed into a metal with the application of high pressure. Although a great amount of development work is required before the sophisticated experiments in solid-state physics now performed under atmospheric conditions can be performed under shock pressure, considerably more could be done than has been done. Outside of electrical conductivity in a limited resistance region, no quantitative physical measurements have been attempted under shock conditions. Future experimentation ought to include at least the simpler kinds of such measurements, since even these can provide insight into solid-state theories by checking predictions under conditions far removed from the area in which these theories have been normalized.

Magnetic-susceptibility measurements do not seem very difficult to perform and have interesting applications. They could provide data on how the Curie point changes with pressure, now hard to measure because, over the limited static pressure range, the variation is quite small. Magnetic susceptibility could also help to clarify the nature of the transition in iron found at 130 kilobars,[14] although that controversial

[13] B. J. Alder and R. H. Christian, Pressure-induced Metallic Transitions in Insulators, *Discussions Faraday Soc.*, vol. 22, p. 44, 1956.

[14] D. Bancroft, E. L. Peterson, and S. Minshall, Polymorphism of Iron at High Pressure, *J. Appl. Phys.*, vol. 27, p. 291, March, 1956.

issue seems to have been settled already.[15] Perhaps most importantly the magnetic susceptibility of iron as it exists at the center of the earth could be measured. The approximate pressure and temperature conditions there (4 megabars and a few thousand degrees) have already been reached in shock experiments,[9] and a measurement of magnetic susceptibility and possibly electrical conductivity would have important bearing on the theory of the magnetic field of the earth.

The next more complex but still quite feasible experiment might be to carry out Hall measurements. They could, for example, settle at least the current problem[16] of whether the charge carriers in an ionic salt under shock conditions are electrons or ions.

These are just a few illustrations of a host of problems in which existing physical techniques carried out at shock pressure, and hence, most importantly, in short times, can aid in understanding the highly compressed condensed state.

13-3 Repulsive Potential

Equation-of-state data at high pressures allow the nature of the repulsive forces between atoms to be explored at much closer distances than heretofore. Pressures of a megabar compress condensed systems by about a factor of 2, and hence the atoms are about 30 percent nearer to each other than under normal atmospheric conditions. The question arises as to whether the potential of interactions determined experimentally at lower densities still holds over this much wider range. Furthermore, these experiments will eventually be able to answer the question of when the pairwise-additivity assumption of the total potential for insulators breaks down seriously enough to cause perceptible deviation between theory and experiment.

13-3a Ionic systems. For this purpose, some preliminary work has been done on both ionic and molecular systems. A number of alkali halides were investigated, and the Hugoniot compared to various empirical and semitheoretical predictions.[17] Figure 13-1 illustrates such a comparison for NaCl in its face-centered-cubic form, and Fig. 13-2 for CsI in its body-centered-cubic modification. The 0°K isotherm is cal-

[15] A. W. Lawson, comment on p. 193 of F. P. Bundy, W. R. Hibbard, and H. M. Strong (eds.), "Progress in Very High Pressure Research," John Wiley & Sons, Inc., New York, 1960.

[16] L. V. Al'tshuler, L. V. Kuleshova, and M. N. Pavlowskii, The Dynamic Compressibility, Equation of State, and Electrical Conductivity of NaCl at High Pressures, *Soviet Phys. JETP*, vol. 12, p. 10, January, 1960.

[17] R. H. Christian, "The Equation of State of the Alkali Halides at High Pressure," University of California Radiation Laboratory Report 4900, May, 1957.

culated from the experimental Hugoniot by assuming that the heat capacity and $(\partial P/\partial T)_V$ are constants. Since these experiments are carried out above the Debye temperature of the alkali halide under atmospheric conditions, the assumption of constant heat capacity is probably satisfactory, since the Debye temperature would have to increase rapidly with increasing density to affect the result. Furthermore, static data of Bridgman[18] up to 50 kilobars roughly support the constancy of $(\partial P/\partial T)_V$, and crude measurements of Grüneisen γ to be

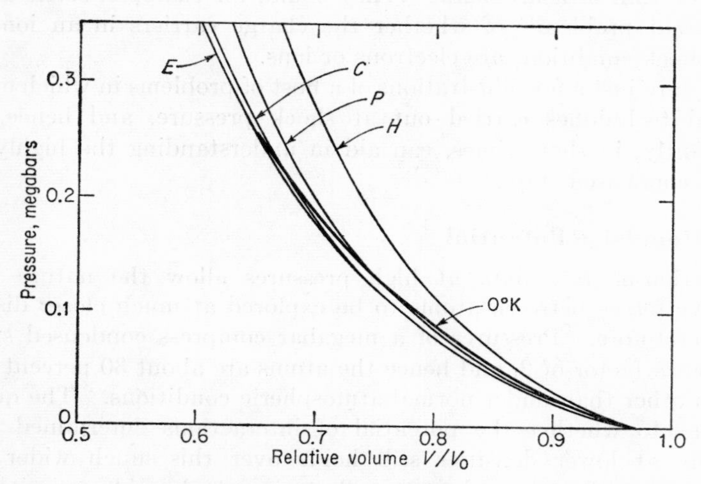

Fig. 13-1 The 0°K isotherm for NaCl derived from the experimental Hugoniot compared to various calculated isotherms: (*E*) assuming an exponential form for the repulsive potential; (*P*) assuming a power-law repulsive potential; (*C*) assuming the Born-Mayer interaction potential; (*H*) using the theoretical results of Howland.

reported in Sec. 13-6 also show that the above assumptions are not grossly in error. Besides, the difference between the Hugoniot and the low-temperature isotherm is not very large up to these pressures.

The theoretical curves assume various pair potentials of interaction. The attractive part always includes the Madelung sum of the point-charge centers. The van der Waals attractive energy has also been added in curves E and P, although its effect is small. Curve P[19] uses a power-law repulsive force with an exponent of 7.89 for NaCl and 11.83

[18] P. W. Bridgman, The Compression of 46 Substances to 50,000 kg/cm², *Proc. Am. Acad. Arts Sci.*, vol. 74, p. 1, 1940; The Compression of 21 Halogen Compounds and 11 Other Simple Substances to 100,000 kg/cm², *Proc. Am. Acad. Arts Sci.*, vol. 76, p. 1, 1945.

[19] M. Born and K. Huang, "Dynamical Theory of Crystal Lattices," p. 54, Oxford University Press, New York, 1954.

for CsI. The exponent and the additional constant in the repulsive law were obtained from the measured density and compressibility at 0°K and 1 atm. Curve E, on the other hand, uses an exponential repulsive power law, as does curve C. C[20] uses the Born-Mayer model and includes the contribution of next-nearest neighbors, while E[21] uses an exponential form which empirically represents the results of a quantum-mechanical calculation. The reciprocal distance (in angstroms) which enters the exponential law is 3.08 for NaCl and 2.80 for CsI. The least satisfactory curve is H,[22] due to Howland, which is based on a more extensive quantum-mechanical calculation. The result has been cast in the form on which curve C is based, with a different set of ionic radii.

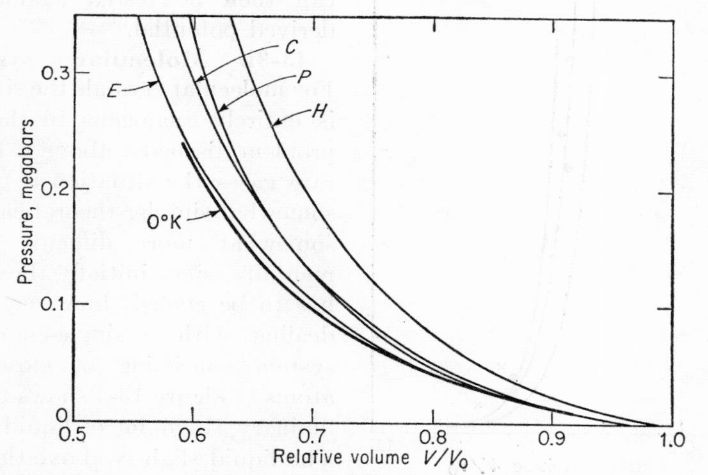

Fig. 13-2 The 0°K isotherm for CsI derived from the experimental Hugoniot compared to various calculated isotherms: (E) assuming an exponential form for the repulsive potential; (P) assuming a power-law repulsive potential; (C) assuming the Born-Mayer interaction potential; (H) using the theoretical results of Howland.

The two examples given are fairly representative of all the alkali halides investigated. On the whole it is remarkable how well the empirical laws are able to extend the experimental agreement from the limited region over which they were forced to represent the data. At high enough pressure these laws will eventually fail as the nature of the forces between

[20] M. L. Huggins, Lattice Energies, Equilibrium Distances, Compressibilities and Characteristic Frequencies of Alkali Halide Crystals, *J. Chem. Phys.*, vol. 5, p. 143, 1937.

[21] P. O. Löwdin, Quantum Theory of Cohesive Properties of Solids, p. 1 in N. F. Mott (ed.), "Advances in Physics," vol. 5, Taylor and Francis, Ltd., London, 1956.

[22] L. P. Howland, Quarterly Progress Report No. 21, p. 29, Solid State and Molecular Theory Group, MIT, July, 1956.

the ions changes from pairwise additivity to that giving rise to metallic behavior. The conductivity to be discussed in Sec. 13-5 will be an important clue to the onset of this phenomenon.

The job that remains to be done for the alkali halides is to extend the data to higher pressures so that the laws can be tested over a still wider region (see Sec. 13-4 for data on NaCl). Furthermore, it will be necessary to get data on the temperature along the Hugoniot so that the 0°K isotherm can be more reliably estimated (see Sec. 13-6). It will then be possible to fit the experimental isotherm by means of an empirical potential, and the approximations in the quantum-mechanical theory can then be tested against this derived potential.

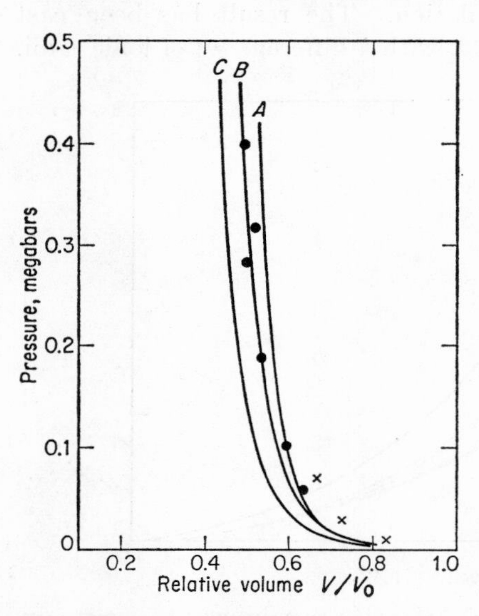

Fig. 13-3 The Hugoniot for argon initially a liquid 2°C above the melting point. The crosses represent earlier experimental results, and the dots present results. The curves represent theoretical Hugoniots for three different pair potentials: (A) from virial data; (B) from virial and crystal data; (C) from molecular-beam data.

13-3b Molecular systems. For molecular crystals the situation is entirely analogous to the ionic problem discussed above. For the rare gases the situation is perhaps somewhat simpler theoretically but somewhat more difficult experimentally, since initially the system has to be cooled; however, one is dealing with a single-component system consisting of closed-shell atoms. Figure 13-3 shows the preliminary Hugoniot of liquid argon. The liquid slightly above the melting point, rather than the solid, was chosen as the initial state for experimental convenience. The circles represent the new data, while the crosses show earlier data.[23] The size of a circle is a rough indication of the estimated experimental uncertainties before refinement of the data analysis. The experimental agreement at the lower pressures has yet to be improved, but if the earlier data are correct, the shock velocity extrapolated to low pressures results in a sound velocity characteristic of solid argon. This indicates the entirely possible occurrence of the Hugoniot starting with liquid argon and skirting the solid-phase boundary before reentering the liquid phase.

[23] J. Dapoigny, J. Kieffer, and B. Vodar, Compression de l'argon aux très hautes pressions, *J. Rech. Centre Natl. Rech. Sci., Lab. Bellevue (Paris)*, vol. 31, p. 260, 1955.

Curves A, B, and C are calculated Hugoniots based on three different pair potentials.[24] Curve A is obtained from low-density second-virial data, while curve B includes crystal data as well, and curve C represents a fit to molecular-beam scattering-cross-section data.[25] Again the agreement at higher pressures is gratifying, while the data at lower pressures need checking before the serious disagreement between theory and experiment can be clarified.

Since many substances eventually melt along the Hugoniot due to increasing temperatures, one is faced, as in the liquid-argon case, with the statistical-mechanical problem of deriving the Hugoniot from the pair potential for a fluid. In the case of chemically saturated short-range forces this problem can be solved to any desired degree of accuracy by the Monte Carlo method[26] under the assumption of pairwise additivity of the potential. This is how, in essence at least, the theoretical curves in Fig. 13-3 were obtained. The pair potentials used in the calculation were experimentally derived from situations in which the pairwise additivity strictly holds, so that any deviations between the theoretical and experimental Hugoniot must in principle be due to the invalidity of this assumption. The difficulty is that the pair potential is not yet accurately enough determined to make any reliable statement about the deviations. Molecular-beam data are difficult to obtain; however, interestingly enough, they cover about the same range of intermolecular distances as the shock work. The low-density data are rather insensitive to the repulsive potential and hence not very useful for predicting high-density Hugoniot data.

For argon, however, it will also be possible to obtain Hugoniot data which emphasize larger intermolecular distances, so that the potential obtained from low-density data may prove useful there. This is done by starting with an initial state near the critical point. The density is about three times less than under ordinary liquid conditions and is achieved by raising the temperature and applying a small initial static pressure. A few experiments of this type have been carried out; they show the feasibility of obtaining such a Hugoniot. This, and possibly additional Hugoniots starting at intermediate densities between the normal liquid and critical point, will enable one to calculate experimentally the entire thermodynamic behavior over a wide region for argon.

[24] W. Fickett and W. W. Wood, Shock Hugoniots for Liquid Argon, *Phys. Fluids*, vol. 3, p. 204, March, 1960.

[25] I. Amdur and E. A. Mason, Properties of Gases at Very High Temperatures, *Phys. Fluids*, vol. 1, p. 370, September, 1958.

[26] W. W. Wood and F. R. Parker, Monte Carlo Equation of State of Molecules Interacting with the Lennard-Jones Potential, *J. Chem. Phys.*, vol. 27, p. 720, September, 1957.

This region can be and has been extended by reflected shock experiments. Furthermore, when such experiments have also been carried out on xenon, it will be possible to check the validity of the theory of corresponding states over a much wider region than heretofore.

The theory of corresponding states will certainly break down seriously in the highly compressed state, since a two-parameter pairwise additive potential is no longer adequate. For xenon, with its more loosely bound outer electrons, the electrons will be promoted into a conduction band at a pressure lower than that for argon. In this connection it was already found that argon conducted appreciably (with resistivity less than 100 ohm-cm) at the highest pressure so far investigated. The effect of this lack of additivity on the thermodynamic functions can be investigated once the molecular-beam and shock experiments are precise enough.

13-4 Phase Transitions

13-4a Static and shock conditions. A question most important to the shock method is whether phase transitions can take place in the approximately one microsecond during which the high-pressure pulse is applied. It is connected with the larger problem of whether this method is equivalent to a hydrostatic pressure measurement performed in a reversible way at the same pressure and temperature. The shock method reaches the pressure and temperature conditions behind the shock front irreversibly. Although one can somewhat lengthen the time during which the sample is under high pressure after the irreversible step by lengthening the sample and the pressure pulse, an extrapolation to very long times or to the true equilibrium state is clearly dangerous. In other words, unless the transition can be made to take place in about a microsecond, no phase change will be observed, and the system will appear to be in a metastable state. Of course, the same is true statically except that the time scale is larger by a factor of about 10^8.

Analogously to the static case, a phase transition will take place dynamically if the metastable system is so much overdriven that 1 μsec suffices for the transformation. As stated in Sec. 13-1, the pleasant fact is that little or no overdriving is necessary. Not only is the temperature much higher in dynamic experiments, but the mechanism of transformation is in many cases different from that in the static situation. This dynamic mechanism is not well understood, and many more detailed experiments will have to be performed. What seems to be indicated to date by the experiments is that the temperature behind the shock front is not as significant as the forces within the shock front. There violent agitation occurs, to which can be ascribed a much higher "temperature" than the ambient temperature behind the shock front. If the pressure gradient were large enough, the shock front could be likened to a mill which atomizes the low-density material ahead of it and deposits the atoms at the high-density side in whatever state is stable under these conditions. From energetic considerations, the shocks used do not create pressure gradients so great that there is no correlation of information about the order of particles across the shock front; however, it is not necessary to disrupt the system totally in order to transform it. It suffices to agitate the atoms into a high vibrational state so that they can overcome the potential barrier to their new equilibrium positions. Although the atoms still have to be rearranged to form crystalline material, the agitation enormously reduces the nucleation times which frequently limit crystal growth under static conditions.

13-4b Experiments on alkali halides. In order to verify that hydrostatic conditions, that is, conditions equivalent to three-dimensional uniform compression, are achieved by applying a one-dimensional shock, NaCl single crystals were studied with their crystal axes in different orientations relative to the plane shock. Regardless of whether the (111) axis or the (100) axis was lined up perpendicularly to the shock, the same results were obtained at 120 kilobars (within the accuracy of the experiment). Also a crystalline powder initially compacted to the crystal density of NaCl behaved identically. These results confirm that the stress which shortens interatomic distances in one direction is partially relieved by a redistribution in which the atoms in other directions respond quickly (compared to fractions of a microsecond) to the forces generated by the changed position of a neighbor. If this were not the case, different results would have been obtained along different crystal axes. Of course, the fact that the connection between static and dynamic data is smooth within the estimated accuracy of both methods is another good indication that hydrostatic conditions are reproduced by shocks.[27] Figure 13-4

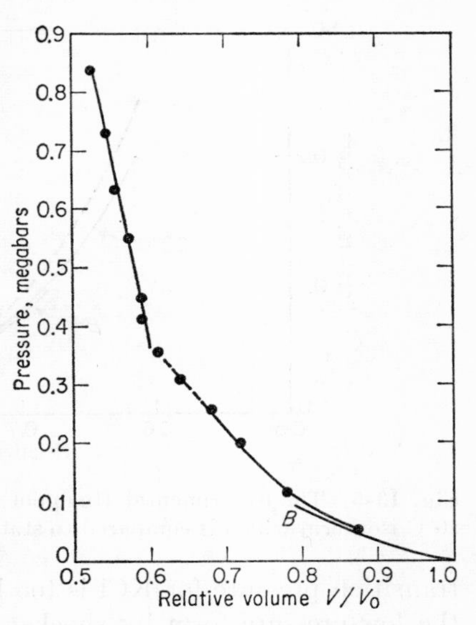

Fig. 13-4 The Hugoniot for NaCl compared to static data (*B*). The dashed line indicates the extent of the phase-transition region.

[27] M. H. Rice, R. G. McQueen, and J. M. Walsh, Compression of Solids by Strong Shock Waves, p. 33 in F. Seitz and D. Turnbull (eds.), "Solid State Physics," vol. 6, Academic Press, Inc., New York, 1958.

illustrates this for NaCl; the difference between the static and dynamic data is actually less since the Hugoniot has not been corrected to the isothermal conditions of the static experiments.

For KCl (in Fig. 13-5) this correction is indicated, and the difference between the two different kinds of experiments is indeed small. KCl is, however, also interesting in that the Hugoniot follows the static curve of the high-pressure form of the material.[18] This means that during the shock-transit time, KCl was able to change from its initial low-pressure, face-centered-cubic form to its high-pressure, body-centered form. The

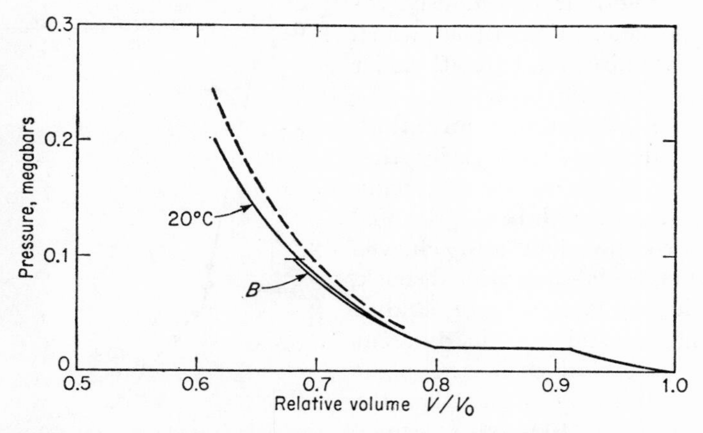

Fig. 13-5 The experimental Hugoniot for KCl (dashed line) is used to derive the 20°C isotherm which is compared to static data (*B*).

transition pressure for KCl is too low for us to conveniently investigate the low-pressure form by shocks. It was thus not possible to observe the resulting break in the Hugoniot and to make a comparison between the two ways of measuring the transition pressure. However, for NaCl, as Fig. 13-4 shows, the break in the Hugoniot is clearly observable. The pressure of the transition is not yet precisely located but is approximately 300 kilobars. Incidentally, below the transition this curve agrees very well with the data of Al'tshuler et al.;[16] however, at the highest pressures the particle velocities at a given shock velocity differ by about 3 percent. In any case, not enough observations were reported by Al'tshuler et al. to establish the existence of a transition.

The face-centered–to–body-centered transformation is a simple displacement type, equivalent to compression of the unit cell of a face-centered crystal along the (111) axis. It is therefore interesting to report that a single crystal oriented with the (111) axis perpendicular to the shock front transforms at a lower pressure to the body-centered form than one that has the (100) axis so orientated. At the volume corresponding to 270 kilobars it was found in three separate experiments that the difference in pressure between the two differently arranged single crystals was three times the probable error and that pressed powder gave intermediate results. In view of the previously mentioned perfect agreement at lower pressures (120 kilobars), there appears to be a time requirement somewhat greater than 1 μsec at 270 kilobars in transferring the energy from the (100) to the (111) direction, since the process is accompanied by a relative displacement of the atoms and not just a uniform shortening of distances. The likely explanation of this result is that a shock which initially excites atoms to vibrate preferentially in the (111) direction gives the atoms enough energy to be displaced over a barrier in that direction before that energy is randomized, while if the shock is applied in another direction the vibrational energy that eventually gets into the mode leading to the transformation is not quite sufficient to overcome the barrier in 1 μsec. However, this effect is small, since a little overdriving will also transform the (100)-orientated material, although an accurate quantitative measure of this has yet to be made.

It was found that when the shock reverses at the free surface of an alkali halide in which a phase transition has occurred, the system returns to the initial phase when the pressure returns to normal. The pressure is rapidly released by an adiabatic decompression,[28] and thus these alkali-halide transitions are reversible within 1 μsec. The final atmospheric state of these alkali halides is naturally much hotter than the initial room-temperature state because of the large irreversible work done during the shock. In fact, with strong pressure pulses the alkali halides are molten upon rarefaction, and with still higher pressure pulses they might melt along the Hugoniot. Thus, for example, a 200-kilobar shock in KCl leaves the rarefied material about one-half melted, while a 300 kilobar shock in CsI leaves this salt a hot liquid. Melting along the Hugoniot might occur because the material becomes stiffer at higher pressures and the temperature rises very rapidly. In NaCl, for example, the temperature at 250 kilobars is about 1200°K behind the shock front, while at 800 kilobars it is 6000°K. A long extrapolation of static melting data by means of the Simon equation[29] indicates that the melting point at 250 kilobars is 3000°K, while at 1 megabar it is 5000°K. The temperatures cross each other if the Simon equation can be trusted over an extrapolation by a factor of 40 and across a phase change. However, the melting transition has not been observed as a break in the Hugoniot. Clearly the transition found near 250 kilobars is not melting to the liquid

[28] J. O. Hirschfelder, C. F. Curtiss, and R. B. Bird, "Molecular Theory of Gases and Liquids," p. 789, John Wiley & Sons, Inc., New York, 1954.

[29] S. P. Clark, Effect of Pressure on the Melting Points of Eight Alkali Halides, *J. Chem. Phys.*, vol. 31, p. 1526, December, 1959.

state. In any case the rarefaction data on alkali halides show that melting can occur within 1 μsec. This is not so surprising, since the energy is distributed uniformly throughout the body.

The information about the rarefied state is rather indirect, since it comes from a measurement of the free-surface velocity of the alkali halide which is compared with its particle velocity, derived from an impedance-matching solution with a standard material for which the particle velocity is known. If the shock and rarefaction followed identical paths, the free-surface velocity would be twice the particle velocity, since the surface would get a kick identical to the initial one as the momentum associated with the shock wave was reversed. However, as just pointed out, the rarefaction follows an adiabatic path, so the factor of 2 has to be corrected.[30] The correction is small for most systems up to a megabar, since the adiabat and Hugoniot do not differ very much. In any case, the correction can be calculated accurately if sufficient data are available. However, if a phase change, such as an irreversible transition along the Hugoniot or the melting of the alkali halides upon rarefaction, occurs along one path but not the other, the factor of 2 does not hold at all. The rarefaction velocity can then be calculated as the difference between the free-surface velocity and the particle velocity and can be used to estimate the final density at atmospheric conditions from the conservation laws. This density is sufficiently accurate to note the occurrence of a nonreversed first-order phase transition.

Phase transitions can also be detected in some cases, such as in endothermic systems, by the occurrence of a two-shock-front structure, since a single shock is unstable under such conditions.[31] The reason for the instability is that the Hugoniot intercepts an isotherm with a horizontal section twice if the pressure is greater than the transition pressure and less than the pressure of the transformed material which lies on the extension of the line passing through the initial P-V point and the P-V point signifying the onset of the transition. At higher pressures the Hugoniot bypasses the transition, which means the second shock has caught up with the first and a single-shock structure is stable again. The first shock, according to the above picture, travels with a constant speed, independent of the applied pressure between the two pressure limits quoted, and it is this which frequently calls attention to a phase transition. Depending upon the slopes of the Hugoniots of the two phases, the two-shock-front structure can extend over a pressure region several times larger than the transition pressure (especially when the volume

[30] J. M. Walsh and R. H. Christian, Equation of State of Metals from Shock Wave Measurements, *Phys. Rev.*, vol. 97, p. 1544, March, 1955.

[31] H. A. Bethe, "The Theory of Shock Waves for an Arbitrary Equation of State," Office of Scientific Research and Development, No. 545, Serial No. 237, 1942.

change of the transition is large and the new phase is very soft). For NaCl (see Fig. 13-4) the transition region (dashed) starts at about 270 kilobars and ends at about 350 kilobars, and the corresponding volume change is about 10 percent and hence of the same order as found for KCl by static means (see Fig. 13-5).

13-4c Experiments on phosphorus. The phase transitions one can expect to find at increasing pressures are the ones that lead to more efficient packing of the atoms. For molecular crystals this means the eventual breakdown of the directional character of the chemical bonds. These crystals are converted by a first-order transition into metals by a redistribution of the electrons. Judging by the experience gained so far, many of these transitions will be found in the pressure range of a few megabars available now by means of shock, although some have been predicted to be as high as 20 megabars.[32] The other phase transitions that can be expected to occur are electronic ones for the heavier elements, in which an unoccupied band of lower principal- but higher angular-momentum quantum number suddenly becomes stabilized at higher pressures relative to one of higher principal- and lower angular-momentum number. These first-order phase transitions are rapidly reversible and are not expected to be very temperature dependent. They might thus make very good reference points between static and dynamic experiments. Our own data on cesium and rubidium are as yet too incomplete to locate the transition pressure very precisely.

A study of phosphorus was undertaken because it represents an irreversible transition which has been studied statically.[33] Unfortunately, the red form of phosphorus is not well defined since it is a polymer, probably of various degrees of polymerization depending on its preparation. When these short-chain polymers crystallize into long chains, black phosphorus forms. Black phosphorus has the crystal structure of graphite except that the rings are puckered; that is, alternate phosphorus atoms are above and below the basal plane of the six-atom ring. The third form of phosphorus, yellow or white, on the other hand, is a van der Waals–bound crystal consisting of tetrahedral P_4 molecules incorporated into a complex unit cell.

Both yellow and red phosphorus have been converted to black statically. For red phosphorus 80 kilobars was necessary if no shear was applied,[34] while the transition was accomplished at 45 kilobars in the

[32] B. J. Alder, State of Matter at High Pressure, p. 152 in F. P. Bundy, W. R. Hibbard, and H. M. Strong (eds.), "Progress in Very High Pressure Research," John Wiley & Sons, Inc., New York, 1960.

[33] R. Grover, R. H. Christian, and B. J. Alder, Shock-induced Phase Transitions in Nonmetallic Elements, *Bull. Am. Phys. Soc.*, vol. 3, p. 230, 1958.

[34] P. W. Bridgman, The Compression of 39 Substances to 100,000 kg/cm^2, *Proc. Am. Acad. Arts Sci.*, vol. 76, p. 55, 1948.

presence of shear[35] at room temperature. The shock data indicate that the transition takes place between 25 and 35 kilobars. The single shock heats the phosphorus to about 500°K. However, starting the experiments initially at liquid-nitrogen temperature lowers the heating to room temperature, and yet the transition pressure is still between 25 and 35 kilobars. The establishment of long-range order is apparently helped by shear as the static data show; the shock certainly provides still larger shear, so this might be the explanation of the lower dynamic transition pressure. On the other hand, the conversion of yellow phosphorus to black requires rearrangements of bonds and atoms between all neighbors, and it was found that dynamically the system has to be overdriven. Statically the requirements were 500°K and 12 kilobars, while dynamically a pressure of about 70 kilobars was required, which heated the material to about 700°K. However, changing the initial temperature from room temperature to liquid-nitrogen temperature, and hence materially changing the temperature behind the shock front in yellow phosphorus to approximately 500°K, again did not affect the transition pressure of 70 kilobars within the presently rather large uncertainties. Thus, to a first approximation at least, the steepness of the shock front determines the rapidity of the transition in this case.

The transition pressure in phosphorus is low enough so that the material can be recovered by enclosing it in a heavy aluminum container. X-ray patterns showed black phosphorus to be present in recovered samples. Furthermore, this reaction can be followed by conductivity measurements, since both yellow and red phosphorus are insulators, while black is a semiconductor which, under small additional pressure, turns into a metal.[36] Rapid resistance changes across the transition have been observed.

13-4d Experiments on carbon. The carbon system behaves similarly to yellow phosphorus, since rearrangements of bonds and atoms are necessary in order to go from the graphite structure to the diamond structure.[37] The system has to be overdriven to about 200 kilobars before partial conversion can be noted. Partial conversion is established since the measured quantities depended on the size of the sample. The conversion is not complete until graphite has been compressed at 400 kilobars to diamond density. Thermodynamically the diamond phase is

[35] P. W. Bridgman, Shearing Phenomena at High Pressures, Particularly in Inorganic Compounds, *Proc. Am. Acad. Arts Sci.*, vol. 71, p. 424, 1937.

[36] R. E. Harris, R. J. Vaisnys, H. Stromberg, and G. Jura, Resistance and Thermal Gap Measurements to 400,000 Atmospheres, p. 165 in F. P. Bundy, W. R. Hibbard, and H. M. Strong (eds.), "Progress in Very High Pressure Research," John Wiley & Sons, Inc., New York, 1960.

[37] B. J. Alder and R. H. Christian, Behavior of Strongly Shocked Carbon, *Phys. Rev. Letters*, vol. 7, p. 367, November, 1961.

stable at pressures above 30 kilobars; however, the static experiments, even in the presence of a catalyst, indicate that a considerable amount of overdriving is necessary.[38] The dynamic conversion at about 500°K and 200 kilobars without a catalyst seems impossible to duplicate statically, so that the shock front induces the transformation by a different mechanism. The adiabatic release of the pressure, however, does not convert the diamond, metastable at low pressure, back to graphite.

For the graphite system it was also possible to demonstrate the loss of directional character of chemical bonds with pressure. At about 600 kilobars diamonds convert to a metallic close-packed system, as noted from the independence of the shock velocity on pressure. Although the diamond bonds are among the strongest known chemically, the diamond structure is so inefficiently packed that the volume change which accompanies the transition is large (about 15 percent). This might explain the relatively low pressure that induces the transition. In fact the same transition has been observed in isomorphous germanium[39] on mere heating of the material. The transition is thus very temperature sensitive; this has been observed dynamically by starting initially with low-density graphite. Shocking low-density material produces additional irreversible heating (see Sec. 13-6), and it was possible to observe the conversion of diamonds to the metallic phase at considerably lower pressures. In a study of germanium the transition has been observed dynamically, and by comparison with accurate static data on the melting-point dependence with pressure, a temperature could be established along the Hugoniot from the transition pressure. This will be useful in checking some of the theoretical estimates of temperature. For silicon, on the other hand, the transition pressure is probably too high to observe statically with any accuracy, so our plans are to measure the transition pressure as a function of temperature by starting with various initial densities.

13-4e Experiments on iodine. In iodine, too, the collapse of the chemical bond has been observed.[40] Iodine was chosen as the simplest system in which to observe the conversion of the diatomic bond into a metallic bond, although the whole series of diatomic halogens should be studied eventually. It is, however, necessary to start with a phase of liquid or solid density in order to achieve high pressures by shocks, since

[38] F. P. Bundy, H. P. Bovenkirk, H. M. Strong, and R. H. Wentorf, Diamond-Graphite Equilibrium Line from Growth and Graphitization of Diamond, *J. Chem. Phys.*, vol. 35, p. 383. August, 1961.

[39] H. T. Hall, The Melting Point of Germanium as a Function of Pressure to 180,000 Atmospheres, *J. Phys. Chem.*, vol. 59, p. 1144, 1955.

[40] B. J. Alder and R. H. Christian, Destruction of Diatomic Bonds by Pressure, *Phys. Rev. Letters*, vol. 4, p. 450, May, 1960.

for gases most of the shock energy goes into heating the gas and not into P-V work. However, for hydrogen, even in its liquid phase, the density is so low and the compressibility so high that the strongest single shock from a chemical explosive probably does not compress it beyond 100 kilobars. The density thus will likely be no greater than that already achieved statically by compression to 20 kilobars. The point, then, of studying the other diatomic systems is to obtain more empirical evidence for these transition pressures, so that the hydrogen transition can be predicted with fair confidence. The importance of hydrogen lies in the possibility of being able to calculate the transition pressure, which, from the empirical evidence on iodine, was estimated to be about 20 megabars.[32]

The transition in iodine was observed at about 700 kilobars. Because the material is very compressible, the temperature is very high at that pressure, namely, about 10^4 °K. The adiabatic heating to that pressure would have been only to about 10^3 °K, so that it is worthwhile to try reflected experiments to study the temperature dependence of this transition. This is particularly important in view of static experiments up to 400 kilobars which failed to show the transition,[36] even though, from the dynamic data, the estimated pressure of the transition at room temperature is only about 300 kilobars. From one experiment using the reflected technique, the highly tentative conclusion can be drawn that the reaction rate would not be observable statically at room temperature even if the mechanism were the same. In that experiment, a short sample did not have time to transform while a longer one did, so that a microsecond reaction rate could be roughly determined at the estimated temperature of the experiment. The room-temperature reaction rate could then be deduced if a typical activation-type process is assumed. The reflected experiment also showed that the density at which the transition occurred was little changed with temperature. This means that as soon as the critical density or critical distance of approach of the iodine atoms is reached, the atoms will rearrange themselves into the more stable monatomic crystal, as long as the reaction rate is not limiting. At low temperatures at which the reaction rate is slow, the system will have to be overdriven to higher densities.

Although iodine is certainly metallic in the monatomic crystal form, it could be metallic in the molecular form if the filled molecular valence band overlapped the empty conduction band. This latter transition is hard to observe by dynamic means. Very likely such a transition is not first order and thus would not be noticed as a break in the Hugoniot. Conductivity measurements, on the other hand, are difficult to make in the metallic range, and the high temperature in the shock experiments smears out such a transition. However, experiments on how the valence and conduction bands approach each other can be made dynamically as long as the gap is several kT in energy. These will be described in Sec. 13-5.

13-4f Other experiments. Several other phase transitions have been investigated by shock. For example, the most accurate comparison with static data to date has been made in bismuth.[41] The comparison is fair (21.5 kilobars statically to 25 kilobars dynamically) and shows that a rather complex rearrangement in a metal can take place in less than 1 μsec. Further shock work is required before such low-pressure transition points can be used for pressure comparisons; then the effects due to yield strength can be quantitatively evaluated. Similar transitions in arsenic and antimony seem to require longer times, perhaps 10 μsec. The transition in iron[14] at 130 kilobars, first found by shock, now seems to have been identified as the α-γ transition by extrapolation of static data, once these data were corrected for an error in the pressure scale. However, it is possible that the transition is to a new phase of hexagonal iron. In any case, enough work on phase transitions has already been done to show that the microsecond time limitation is not nearly as restrictive as once thought and that, in addition, useful information about rates of solid rearrangements can be obtained. More detailed data must be taken on one system to elucidate mechanisms of transformation.

13-5 Conductivity Experiments

A measurement of the conductivity gives more detailed information about the band structure in a solid than an equation-of-state measurement. By measuring resistances of the material behind the shock front at various pressures, one may study the relative shifts of the conduction and valence bands as functions of density. It can then be learned how an insulating material becomes metallic under pressure by the rate at which the energy gap decreases. In this crude analysis, and at the present stage of experimentation, all the complications in the interpretation of the data due to impurity and F-center conduction, changes in effective masses, and contact effects at a probe, for example, have been ignored. These features, hopefully, do not invalidate the gross picture presented here, but only modify it in detail; however, impurity conduction has already been observed to limit the interpretation of the data.

Unfortunately, due to experimental difficulties, it has not been possible to develop simple techniques to measure resistances when the energy gap is very small. This is basically due to the fact that the resistance measurement in shock times is a high-frequency experiment. Stray

[41] R. E. Duff and F. S. Minshall, Investigation of a Shock-induced Transition in Bismuth, *Phys. Rev.*, vol. 108, p. 1207, December, 1957.

inductances of circuit components make the measurement of low resistances difficult with the high voltages employed so far. It is thus presently possible only to follow the system as it is converted from an insulating to a semiconducting state. Nevertheless these results will still be theoretically challenging. Resistance data might also indicate when the Thomas-Fermi theory of the atom becomes valid. Certainly, before that theory becomes applicable, all the outer electrons of an atom must be parts of a band, so that a statistical distribution of electrons about the nucleus is not too poor an approximation.

Resistance measurements in the semiconducting region are also useful in determining the temperature of the material behind the shock. In the region in which the energy gap is considerably greater than kT, the resistance depends exponentially on temperature:

$$R = R_\infty e^{-E_g/2kT}$$

If no static data are available, the three unknowns in this equation, the temperature T, the energy gap E_g, and the high-temperature resistance R_∞ must be experimentally determined. This is done, for example, by starting with a material at three different initial temperatures and shocking it to the same final volume. If it is assumed that the energy gap and R_∞ are insensitive to temperature at a given volume, the temperature can be experimentally evaluated and compared to theory.

If static data were available on the energy gap and R_∞, one measurement would suffice to determine the temperature. With the exception of the alkali halides, the effort so far has been to make comparisons only with static data so that the shock method of measuring conductivity could be established as a quantitatively accurate tool. This was partly necessitated by earlier divergent data and by theoretical studies which showed that the gap could not change nearly as much with pressure as the data indicated it did. Early efforts centered on finding a substance which actually turned very conducting at pressures below 100 kilobars, so that comparison to static data could be made. Shocked $LiAlH_4$[13] repeatedly had shown this property, but static data[42] on the same material failed to confirm it. The disagreement has not been resolved, but likely involves a decomposition and/or phase transition in $LiAlH_4$ under shock. The Hugoniot of this material was not subsequently investigated because the material was not readily available in pure form; however, it is known to decompose thermally.

13-5a Experiments on phosphorus. Subsequent measurements on the rather irreproducible red-phosphorus system initially at liquid-

[42] D. T. Griggs, W. G. McMillan, E. D. Michael, and C. P. Nash, Lack of Metallic Transitions in LiH and $LiAlH_4$ under Static Pressure, *Phys. Rev.*, vol. 109, p. 1858, March, 1958.

nitrogen, dry-ice, and room temperatures showed qualitative agreement with static data. The gap, which initially is about 1.5 ev at 1 bar, reduces to 0.88 ev at 34 kilobars, as determined from the temperature variation of the resistance behind the shock front. From the absolute resistance value from only one shock experiment together with a static measurement of the mobility (R_∞) and a theoretical estimate of the temperature along the Hugoniot, the gap is estimated to be 0.81 $\pm$0.07 ev at 34 kilobars. Static data yield energy gaps in the range of 0.75 to 0.80 at this pressure.[36] The agreement is perhaps surprising in view of the fact that impurity conduction could play a large role and the static measurements were made with more, though not highly, purified phosphorus. Possibly the impurity levels are squeezed close to the conduction band under pressure. The work was not pursued further because of the complicating features of the variety of forms of red phosphorus and the phase transition at low pressures. Sulfur, too, has been turned metallic,[43] but again it has some of the disadvantages of the phosphorus system and, in addition, seems to melt along the Hugoniot.[44]

13-5b Experiments on iodine. Iodine does not have the above-mentioned disadvantages, but its high reactivity and vapor pressure present some experimental problems. On the other hand, it is an interesting system, since its Hugoniot has given evidence of conversion to a monatomic metal. For this system a number of experiments were carried out which confirmed the ohmic nature of the shock resistance; that is, the resistance varied properly with applied voltage in different geometric arrangements and was independent of the electrode material. A semilog plot of the resistance at a pressure of 45 kilobars versus the reciprocal of the absolute temperature behind the shock front is given in Fig. 13-6. The temperatures behind the shock front were assumed to be lowered by the same amount as the initial temperature was lowered, although a small correction for initial density contraction can and ought to be made. For purposes of comparison with static data, furthermore, an approximate estimate of the absolute temperature for the shocked iodine initially at room temperature has been made by the Mie-Grüneisen theory under the assumption of constant heat capacity. The static measurements on highly purified iodine[36] were interpolated to the same density as the shocked iodine experiments and are shown in Fig. 13-6 by the straight line.

The graph shows the consistency of the static and dynamic resistivity data at high temperatures; at lower temperatures and higher resistances

[43] H. G. David and S. D. Hamann, Sulfur, a Possible Metallic Form, *J. Chem. Phys.*, vol. 28, p. 1006, May, 1958.

[44] J. Berger, S. Joigneau, and G. Battet, Comportement du soufre sous l'action d'une onde de choc, *Compt. rend.*, vol. 250, p. 4331, June, 1960.

some kind of impurity conductivity is likely dominant in the shock data, since no precautions were taken to purify the sample and to keep it pure when the iodine powder was prepressed to almost theoretical crystal density. The impurity situation seems to be similar to that in germanium, which, as in iodine at 45 kilobars, has a gap near 0.85 ev. The conductivity of germanium is also extraordinarily affected by a small amount of impurity. These experiments are being repeated with

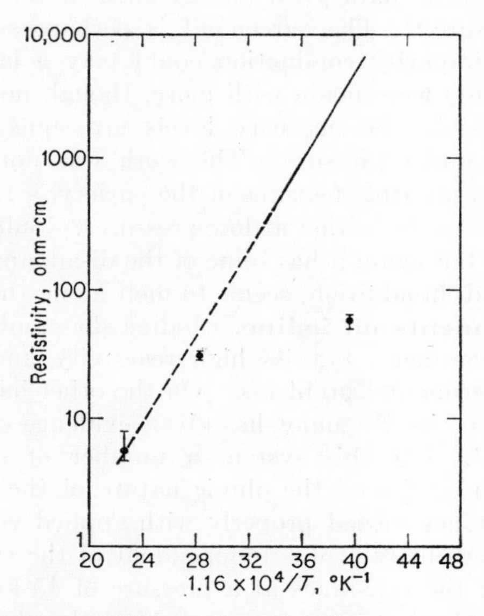

Fig. 13-6 A plot of the logarithm of the resistivity as a function of the reciprocal of the absolute temperature for iodine at 45 kilobars from shock data (points) compared to static data (solid line) and extrapolated to higher temperature (dashed line).

resublimed iodine at a somewhat higher pressure so that impurity conduction is less likely to limit the usefulness of the results. Then a more critical test of the temperature calculation will be possible.

In any case these results show that reproducible and interpretable measurements of the electrical resistivity can be made at high shock pressures and that the shock temperature can be determined from the rate of change of resistance with temperature. Furthermore, the gap changes rapidly with density. The iodine gap at normal pressures is about 1.5 ev, both optically and thermally. When iodine is compressed to 80 per cent of its initial volume, the gap changes to 0.85 ev. The disagreement of optical static data[45] at high density with static or dynamic

[45] H. L. Suchan, S. Wiederhorn, and H. G. Drickamer, Effect of Pressure on the Absorption Edges of Certain Elements, *J. Chem. Phys.*, vol. 31, p. 355, August, 1959.

resistance measurements can likely be traced in this case to a difficulty in the interpretation of the absorption edge in optical data. Although the pressure of the transition of iodine to a monatomic metal is very much higher than the pressure of the present gap measurements, the density change is only approximately again as much (to 53 percent of initial density) as already investigated. In the extrapolation of the energy gap linearly with density to higher pressures, the possibility can not be excluded that, at the density at which the molecular valence and conduction band overlap, the atoms of iodine also rearrange themselves into the monatomic phase, though these two phenomena do not, off hand, necessarily coincide.

13-5c Experiments on alkali halides. With confidence in the results established, the original alkali-halide data were reexamined. For the alkali halides only single resistance measurements are available, so

Table 13-1 Conductivity Data on Alkali Halides

Alkali halide	P, kilobars	V/V_0	T, °K	R, ohm-cm	E_g, ev	E_{g0}, ev
NaCl.	220	0.71	1000	1.000 ±200	>2.1	8.4 ±0.7
KI.	160	0.64	2250	50–150	4.1	
CsI.	260	0.61	3900	≤0.2	≤3.4	6.3
	190	0.65	2500	50–200	4.7	6.3
CsBr.	270	0.64	2700	20 ±10	4.3	7.0 ±0.3
CsCl.	270	0.66	2300	50–100	4.3	7.7 ±0.1

that a theoretical estimate of the temperature and the mobility had to be made to arrive at an energy gap at a given pressure. Fortunately, the result is insensitive to the approximations in the mobility estimate. The temperature estimates previously stated, based on constant heat capacity and $(\partial P/\partial T)_V$, were used. The room-temperature mobility was calculated by assuming a constant-charge mean free path of 5 Å, characteristic of optical-mode lattice scattering in ionic crystals, and an equal current contribution from charges of both signs. The mobility then varies as the reciprocal of the square root of the temperature. The temperature variation of R_∞ also involves that of the charge density, namely, the three-halves power of the temperature. Then R_∞ is $T_0/55T$, where T_0 is room temperature and R_∞ is in ohm-centimeters. The results are given in Table 13-1. The measurements did not depend on whether single crystals or powder were used and did not show any frequency dependence. However, the data on NaCl are in such a high-resistance range that impurity conduction could be the conduction mechanism. Hence the gap is given as greater than the value estimated from the data. However, the value given agrees roughly with the measurements[16] of Al'tshuler et al., which fluctuated by a factor up to 3, attributed to impurities.

If the impurities do not decrease the NaCl resistance by more than a factor of 3 (although the factor could be much larger), an energy gap of about 2.5 ev results. This is a much larger change than that shown for the heavier alkali halides. The optical energy gap at atmospheric pressure is indicated in the last column of Table 13-1. Because of possible slow relaxation processes in an ionic crystal, the optical gap is an upper limit to the thermal gap.[46] It thus should not be presumed that the gap in CsI, for example, changes from 6.3 to 4.7 ev as the relative volume changes from 1 to 0.65. The thermal gap under atmospheric conditions could be considerably less than 6.3 ev. However, the gap does change rapidly near a V/V_0 of 0.60 for CsI, as Table 13-1 indicates. Although most calculations so far are in disagreement with this fact,[47] those of Howland[22] on KCl agree more or less. The data on the cesium halides show that the nature of the halides is not very important to the gap value at a given compression. The gap value for KI is not strictly comparable to the others, owing to a phase change in that material. This may also be the cause of the lower NaCl gap, since it is the only substance in Table 13-1 in the face-centered crystal form. Also, the larger halide atom, compared to the alkali atom, may influence the result. Ionic conductivity cannot be the cause of this result, since the Hugoniot is still well in the solid phase. Ionic conductivities in the solid phase near the melting point are too small to contribute appreciably to the resistivity, and it is improbable that their magnitudes near the melting point at high pressures will change radically.[48] Possibly at the highest pressures investigated by Al'tshuler et al., ionic conduction could contribute; however, as pointed out before (see Sec. 13-4b), the large phase change associated with melting was not seen. A Hall measurement could distinguish between the two conduction mechanisms, should it be impossible to settle the problem otherwise. However, in some cases such as water,[49] it has been shown that the conductivity is likely ionic, because of a large displacement of the ionization equilibrium with temperature and pressure. For the alkali halides the next job should be a careful study similar to the one on iodine, to gain empirical experience on the mechanism of energy-gap collapse.

[46] T. S. Moss, "Photoconductivity in the Elements," Academic Press, Inc., New York, 1952.

[47] M. Flower and N. H. March, Transitions to Metallic States in Ionic Crystals, with Particular Reference to Cesium Iodide, *Phys. Rev.*, to be published.

[48] F. Seitz, "The Modern Theory of Solids," p. 55, McGraw-Hill Book Company, Inc., New York, 1940.

[49] H. G. David and S. D. Hamann, The Chemical Effects of Pressure—The Electrical Conductivity of Water at High Shock Pressures, *Trans. Faraday Soc.*, vol. 56, p. 72, July, 1960.

13-6 Thermodynamic Deductions

13-6a Linear relations between shock and particle velocities. The most striking fact that has emerged from the single Hugoniot measurements so far is that a plot of the shock velocity u_s versus particle velocity u_p is a straight line for almost all the substances investigated. These substances include ionic, molecular, and metallic crystals. They include liquids as well as solids and alloys, although water[10] seems to be an exception. This linear relation seems to hold only within a given phase; that is, if a material undergoes a phase change, the slope changes across the transition. This fact can be used in turn to discover and to locate more precisely where phase transitions occur.

The reason for this linear relation

$$u_s = a + bu_p \tag{13-1}$$

is not well understood at present.[50] It presents a challenging theoretical problem. In this section only the consequences of such a relation are explored. However, it should be strongly emphasized at the beginning of such a discussion that this linear relation has been experimentally established only as the average behavior of the large number of substances investigated, because the Hugoniot pressure-volume points are spaced very far apart. In this respect, experimenters with the shock method are even more guilty of covering the accessible region of the phase diagram coarsely than experimenters with static apparatus. Usually shock experiments are 50 or even 100 kilobars apart, so that much detail is lost. However, an explosive-wedge system has been developed which can record the pressure continuously over a limited pressure interval.[51] It is interesting to note that for the one substance for which most data have been accumulated because it has been used as a standard (unfortunately an aluminum alloy), the straight-line behavior is pretty well obeyed but the deviations are statistically significant. It is thus possible to discuss only the gross thermodynamic behavior along a Hugoniot.

If the linear relation is considered as an expansion of the shock velocity in terms of the particle velocity, it is indeed surprising that higher terms do not contribute, since the dimensionless expansion parameter u_p/a is not small. From experimental data for various substances at the highest pressure, where u_p is largest, u_p/a is found to be in the range of $\frac{1}{2}$ to $\frac{3}{2}$.

[50] J. Berger and S. Joigneau, Au sujet de la relation linéaire existant entre la vitesse matérielle et la vitesse de l'onde de choc se propageant dans un metal, *Compt. rend.*, vol. 249, p. 2506, December, 1959.

[51] S. Katz, D. G. Doran, and D. R. Curran, Hugoniot Equation of State of Aluminum and Steel from Oblique Shock Measurements, *J. Appl. Phys.*, vol. 30, p. 568, April, 1959.

On the other hand, the slope b is experimentally found to vary between 1 and 2, so that the second term in the linear relation is comparable to the first. Moreover, it is impossible, for example, to neglect the thermal energy along a Hugoniot compared to the total potential energy, since the ratio of those two energies at the highest available pressure is of the order of 2 or 3. The quantity that does appear to become small along a Hugoniot path is the attractive energy compared to thermal energy kT. Thus the repulsive energy predominates, not only because compression forces the electrons to overlap more, but also because the temperature rises rapidly. Hence the explanation of the linear relation probably lies in the similar character of the repulsive potentials of all atoms, molecules, and ions. It has already been shown in Sec. 13-3 that a similar repulsive potential for NaCl and argon (whether in either case an exponential form or an inverse-power-law form was used) can reproduce the Hugoniot, and hence the roughly linear relation. The distance scale in an exponential repulsive-potential law, for example, should then be correlated with the slope b. In this connection it is interesting to note that for NaCl this slope does not appreciably change across the transition, presumably because the nature of the interaction between neighbors does not change.

If the linear relation is presumed to hold all the way down to low pressures at which the particle velocity is zero, the shock velocity, and hence a, should become identical to the "hydrodynamic" sound velocity. This is experimentally found to be valid within a few percent,[7] where the sound velocity for comparison purposes must be obtained from hydrostatic P-V data corrected to constant entropy or calculated from longitudinal and transverse sound velocities of the crystal. Furthermore, the slope b should be related to the linear pressure dependence of the sound velocity or, more precisely,

$$b = -\tfrac{1}{4} \frac{V^2(\partial^2 P/\partial V^2)_s}{V(\partial P/\partial V)_s} \tag{13-2}$$

where P = pressure
V = volume
s = entropy, held constant

In other words, if the linear relation would hold exactly, one would not have to carry out any shock experiments except for the observations on phase transitions, since the intercept and slope could be determined from low-pressure static experiments on sound velocities. Equation (13-1) with its known constants could then be substituted in the conservation laws to give the pressure along the Hugoniot:

$$P = \frac{-a^2(V/V_0 - 1)}{V_0(b - 1 - bV/V_0)^2} \tag{13-3}$$

The energy is, of course, then also determined. This observation is similar to one of Birch's[52] for isothermal data.

The first two columns of Table 13-2 compare the slopes derived from shock and ultrasonic data. The comparison is fair if it is remembered that neither set of data can be considered to be more accurate than 5 percent. With that criterion, however, the discrepancy for the noble metals is outside the range of experimental error. It is preferable to use the pressure dependence of ultrasonic data to get the slope rather than to use P-V data. The latter data are rarely accurate enough to allow a second derivative to be determined with any accuracy. From the sound data it suffices to take first derivatives.

The next three columns in Table 13-2 refer to the predictions of three simple theories of the solid state about the slope. The Slater[53] theory

Table 13-2 Comparison of the Slopes of the Shock Velocity versus Particle Velocity for Various Substances

	Sound	Shock	Dugdale-MacDonald	Slater	Thomas-Fermi
NaCl	1.35 ±.05	1.43 ±.02	1.29	1.12	
Aluminum	1.54 ±.05	1.2–1.6*	1.55	1.38	1.21
Copper	1.64	1.50	1.50	1.33	1.24
Silver	1.79	1.59	1.75	1.58	1.29
Gold	1.85	1.56	2.02	1.85	1.32
Sodium	1.15	1.2	1.07–1.18	0.90–1.01	1.25

* The corrections for impurities in the 2024 aluminum alloy cause the uncertainty in the results.

uses an elastic-continuum approximation together with an ad hoc assumption about the volume dependence of the elastic constants, while the Dugdale-MacDonald[54] relation involves a similar ad hoc assumption about the volume dependence of the harmonic force constants of a crystal. At low pressures the Dugdale-MacDonald relation predicts the slope to be $\gamma/2 + \frac{1}{2}$, while Slater predicts $\gamma/2 + \frac{1}{3}$. Substitution of the experimental values for the Grüneisen value of γ from thermodynamic data in these expressions (Table 13-2) shows that the Dugdale-MacDonald formula is reasonably successful in predicting the slopes, in spite of the crudeness of the theory.

[52] F. Birch, Elasticity and Constitution of the Earth's Interior, *J. Geophys. Research*, vol. 57, p. 227, 1952.

[53] J. C. Slater, "Introduction to Chemical Physics," chap. 14, McGraw-Hill Book Company, Inc., New York, 1939.

[54] J. S. Dugdale and D. K. C. MacDonald, The Thermal Expansion of Solids, *Phys. Rev.*, vol. 89, p. 832, February, 1953.

The last column in Table 13-2 refers to a calculation using a semi-empirical correction to the Thomas-Fermi model of the atom.[55] The Thomas-Fermi model is altered in a way suggested by the Dirac modification of the model such that the pressure vanishes at the normal volume. It has already been shown that such a modified model can predict the compressibility, and hence the sound speed a, quite well, on the average, for a large number of metals. The mean deviation of the sound speed for all metals from the average is within 25 percent. The last column in Table 13-2 shows how well such a crude theory can predict the second derivative of the pressure, the slope b. The order-of-magnitude agreement is remarkable considering that there is no adjustable constant. For all the metals investigated the mean fractional deviation of b from the theory is less than 50 percent. In spite of the neglect of chemical binding in the Thomas-Fermi model, partially corrected for by the Dirac modification, the model does well on the average for all metallic elements, the slope ranging from 1.1 for the lightest element to 1.5 for the heaviest. This suggests further theoretical study using this model as the first approximation and, in addition, using the temperature-dependent Thomas-Fermi theory, normalized as above, or better yet, the temperature-dependent Thomas-Fermi-Dirac theory itself, to calculate the experimental Hugoniot. This might throw light on the linear u_s-u_p relation, particularly for metals.

At high pressures, Eq. (13-3) shows that if the linear relation continues to infinite pressures, the minimum value of the relative volume, or the maximum compression, that can be reached by a single shock in solids is $V/V_0 = (b - 1)/b$. Since b for most substances is around $3/2$, the minimum value of V/V_0 is about $1/3$. For comparison, a perfect monatomic gas can be compressed fourfold.[56] The limiting compression for solids is reflected in the data which show that at twofold compression most of the experimental Hugoniots become rather steep. In fact, with infinite pressure shocks, since the thermal energy predominates, any solid will become a perfect gas, and the correct limiting value of V/V_0 is $1/4$ and of b is $4/3$. Thus the value of b does not differ greatly at high and low pressures. The Thomas-Fermi theory also shows that b cannot continue to be strictly constant at higher pressures. In fact, this theory predicts that b will decrease below the perfect gas value of $4/3$ before returning to it at very high pressures and that compressions larger than fourfold (about sixfold for the heavier elements) can then be achieved.

13-6b Behavior of Grüneisen γ. At maximum compression, mate-

[55] W. G. McMillan, Approximate Compressibilities of Elements on the Statistical Model, *Phys. Rev.*, vol. 111, p. 479, July, 1958.

[56] S. D. Hamann, The Use of Explosions in High Pressure Research, *Rev. Pure and Appl. Chem. Australia*, vol. 10, p. 139, 1960.

rials behave as classical perfect gases of electrons and nuclei, since the temperature is infinite, and thus Grüneisen's constant γ becomes $\frac{2}{3}$; $PV = \frac{2}{3}E$. Even at smaller compressions, at which the substances behave as Thomas-Fermi gases (entailing pressures estimated to be 10 to 100 times larger than pressures reached by shocks so far), the virial theorem can be used to show that γ is also $\frac{2}{3}$. Since most substances under normal conditions have γ's of about 2, it can be seen that, on the average, γ decreases proportionally to the volume; that is, a change of V/V_0 from 1 to $\frac{1}{3}$ decreases γ from 2 to $\frac{2}{3}$ along a typical Hugoniot. Since $\gamma = V(\partial P/\partial E)_V = VC_V^{-1}(\partial P/\partial T)_V$, this means that $(1/C_V)(\partial P/\partial T)_V$ is, on the average, a constant. Here also only a gross statement about γ has been made, since the experimental situation is not clear, although for most substances γ has been found to decrease with increasing pressure as predicted above. For the previously mentioned modified Thomas-Fermi model, γ decreases from about 1.3 to $\frac{2}{3}$ at high pressures.

From the thermodynamic identity

$$\left(\frac{\partial C_V}{\partial V}\right)_T = T\left(\frac{\partial^2 P}{\partial T^2}\right)_V$$

it can be seen that for a solid at any density above the Debye temperature, $(\partial P/\partial T)_V$ is a function of volume only, since C_V is a constant. For most substances investigated, the initial room-temperature conditions are above the Debye temperature. Hence it can be seen that under these circumstances γ is a function of volume only, but a general statement about the variation of $(\partial P/\partial T)_V$ with volume is hard to make, let alone the statement that it should be a constant on the average. However, γ is clearly a function of temperature also as soon as the above conditions are violated. For example, as the temperature is raised indefinitely holding the density constant, γ must again decrease from about 2 to its classical perfect-gas value of $\frac{2}{3}$. However, C_V, and hence γ, might be nearly independent of temperature up to a few electron volts in temperature (when electron effects become important), provided the substance does not melt or, even more consequential, vaporize.

Even though γ does decrease on the average with increasing density along the Hugoniot, it will be found experimentally that γ will increase with decreasing volume over certain density regions for some substances. On the other hand, in other density regions (depending on the steepness of the repulsive potential), γ will decrease faster with decreasing volume than indicated by the average falloff. If the repulsive potential behaves like that of a hard sphere over a certain density region, it can be seen, since $\gamma = \frac{2}{3}PV/NkT$, that γ increases with density, since PV/NkT

does. This argument holds even if an attractive potential is present, as long as the attractive part can be treated as small compared to kT.[57] This is also shown by the van der Waals equation of state, for which $\gamma = \frac{2}{3}V/(V - V_c)$, where V_c is the volume occupied by the particles, approximately the volume of the solid at absolute-zero temperature. Again γ increases as V decreases along the Hugoniot. On the other hand, if the repulsive potential is very soft, γ decreases more rapidly with increasing density.

Also the Dugdale-MacDonald formula, combined with the experimental Hugoniots, predicts a decrease of γ with decreasing volume. The volume dependence of γ is arrived at by using the consistency relation which states that the γ at a given density calculated by means of the Dugdale-MacDonald formula from an assumed 0°K isotherm must be consistent with the thermodynamic γ calculated from the difference in pressure and energy between the Hugoniot and the assumed 0°K isotherm (see definition of γ). Although the 0°K isotherm and the values of γ arrived at in this way behave reasonably, the crudeness of the theory makes it preferable to actually measure γ as a function of volume and temperature and compare to it with the predictions of the theory.

There are several ways to measure γ experimentally and hence to deduce temperature and the remaining thermodynamic properties along a Hugoniot. From the definition of γ it can be seen that it is necessary to reach a given density with a different internal energy which will result in a pressure different at that density from the pressure resulting from shocking the normal-density material. The reflected method has already been mentioned as one means to achieve this end. The experimental difficulty is that usually the differences in internal energy and pressure are small compared to the total energy and pressure. This necessitates taking differences between large quantities, with a resulting loss in accuracy. The practicality of the method has been demonstrated for the experimentally favorable case of water.[10] Since water is rather soft, a large energy change is caused upon reflection. The accuracy of the results for γ was, however, still only of the order of 15 percent. Unfortunately, a possible phase transition in water[58] at the pressures investigated puts the quantitative values for γ in doubt.

Another way to measure γ is subject to similar difficulties. Changing the initial temperature to either lower or higher values for solids causes a

[57] E. B. Smith and B. J. Alder, Perturbation Calculations in Equilibrium Statistical Mechanics, *J. Chem. Phys.*, vol. 30, p. 1190, 1959.

[58] L. V. Al'tshuler, A. A. Bakanova, and R. F. Trunin, Phase Transformation of Water Compressed by Strong Shock Waves, *Doklady Akad. Nauk, Phys.*, vol. 121, p. 67, 1958.

small initial change in volume and energy. However, for a liquid, particularly when a small static pressure is initially applied, a large change in initial density can be brought about, as was already demonstrated for liquid argon. This large change in volume vastly changes the energy content at a given density, as can be seen from the conservation-law expression for the energy,

$$E_1 - E_0 = \frac{P_1 + P_0}{2}(V_0 - V_1)$$

where the subscripts 0 and 1 refer to the initial and final Hugoniot conditions. For solids the equivalent effect can be achieved by using porous samples of uniform density made up of very small particles. The particles must be small enough so that the width of the shock front is still small compared to the size of the sample. In this case the energy changes can be so large that it is necessary to restrict the porosity so that the material does not melt at a given density. Also the low initial densities restrict the maximum Hugoniot pressure and density that can be reached.

Another interesting indirect technique has been used to obtain γ. This involves measuring the sound speed behind the shock front by measuring the velocity of a weak disturbance behind the strong shock.[59] This difficult technique allows the adiabat to be calculated; then γ can be deduced. It was found that for aluminum, copper, and lead, γ decreased with increasing density. For iron,[9] γ was found, by means of the porous-sample technique, to decrease from a value of 1.95 at $V/V_0 = 0.82$ to 1.6 at $V/V_0 = 0.73$.

Our own preliminary data on aluminum seem to contradict the decrease of γ with density, as Tables 13-3 and 13-4 show. Both the reflected and porous-sample techniques show that γ increases from its initial value of 2.09 to about 4, although the two kinds of experiments are not strictly

Table 13-3 Aluminum Reflected-shock Data at $V/V_0 = 0.74$

*Anvil**	γ
Gold	3.1
Brass	4.4
Copper	3.7
Nickel	4.0
Average	3.8 ±0.5†

* The first shock was at a pressure of 285 kilobars.

† The error of 0.5 represents the statistical deviation of the results from the mean without taking into account any consistent errors in the experimental method.

[59] L. V. Al'tshuler, S. B. Kormer, M. D. Brazhnik, L. A. Vladimirov, M. P. Speranskaya, and A. I. Funtikov, The Isentropic Compressibility of Aluminum, Copper, Lead, and Iron at High Pressures, *Soviet Phys. JETP*, vol. 38, p. 1061, 1960.

comparable, since the porous samples are at a lower final density and considerably hotter. The NaCl results, on the other hand, collected in Table 13-5, show that γ decreases with increasing density. These results also show the possibility of measuring γ as a function of temperature at a given density by using two different initial densities. The observed decrease of γ with increasing temperature at $V/V_0 = 0.78$ might just be barely significant within the accuracy of the results.

Table 13-4 Porous Aluminum Results

V_i/V_0*	V/V_0	γ
1.073	0.86	3.7 ±0.4
1.205	0.91	4.2 ±0.4

* The initial volume relative to the single-crystal volume.

Table 13-5 Porous Sodium Chloride Results

V_i/V_0*	V/V_0	γ†
1.15	0.78	1.45
1.15	0.75	1.49
1.15	0.72	1.15
1.27	0.81	1.35
1.27	0.78	1.27

* Initial volume relative to the single-crystal volume.

† The estimated accuracy of γ is 10 percent. The value of γ under normal conditions ($V/V_0 = 1$) is 1.56.

Nevertheless, with some extensive experimentation in the future it is clear that γ, and hence further thermodynamic functions, can be measured at high pressure in a region surrounding a given Hugoniot.

13-7 Acknowledgments

The unpublished work quoted in this report has been obtained with the help of a number of co-workers, to whom I am deeply indebted. Russ Christian obtained the results on the alkali halides, Richard Grover on the conductivity, Matt van Thiel on argon, and Leroy Hord on reflected and porous samples. Much of the success of the projects depended on the great skill of the technicians, particularly Matt D'Addario.

The work was performed under the auspices of the Atomic Energy Commission.

14

Review and Prospect

HARVEY BROOKS
Division of Engineering and Applied Physics
Harvard University
Cambridge, Massachusetts

The field of high-pressure physics is coming of age in the sense that there exists an increasing range of pressures in which pressure measurements have become a tool of solid-state research rather than a field of research in themselves. High-pressure research is thus in the same kind of transition that took place in low-temperature physics with the advent of a commercial helium liquifier. However, just as low-temperature research below 2°K is still a specialized field of research, so the range of pressures above about 40 kilobars still represents a field for high-pressure specialists. The natural dividing line between "conventional" high pressures and "very" high pressures is the maximum which strictly hydrostatic pressures can achieve: a pressure of about 30 kilobars in a range of temperatures near room temperature. Thus, within limits it is possible to measure practically all the physical properties of solids that can be studied in the laboratory in the absence of pressure: electrical resistivity, Hall effect, optical transmission and reflectivity, electron spin and nuclear resonance, magnetization, tracer diffusion, thermal conductivity, and thermoelectric power. The detailed quantitative study of many physical properties simultaneously on simple, well-characterized materials is a relatively new aspect of high-pressure research whose advantages are emphasized in the paper by Lawson. This type of research is well illustrated also in the papers by Paul and Warschauer and by Benedek, and to a slightly lesser degree in the papers by Lazarus, Keyes, and Kouvel. The worker in high pressures finds himself continually torn between the temptation to explore for new phenomena on a "quick-and-dirty" basis and the desire to investigate quantitatively in detail some of the phenomena already observed in an exploratory way. Experience shows that it is only when theory catches up with experiment that there is sufficient incentive to carry out this latter type of research.

Thus it is no accident that by far the most detailed high-pressure measurements have been made on the simplest semiconductors, for which theory was already in an advanced state of development as a result of intensive experimentation at atmospheric pressure.

Beyond the range of purely hydrostatic pressures the research emphasis is on rather rougher physical measurements of an exploratory character, on a wide variety of not too well-characterized materials. Reasons for this lie not only in the fact that technique limits us at present to only the simplest physical measurements but also in the fact that above 30 kilobars, pressure techniques necessarily introduce complex shearing stresses superposed on the purely hydrostatic stress which is of interest. The shearing stresses introduce two types of complications. On the one hand, by producing plastic flow, they generate crystal imperfections which preclude the quantitative study of any physical properties that are strongly structure sensitive. On the other, they may produce effects, such as piezoresistance, which arise from purely elastic shear strains but which in some instances are an order of magnitude larger than the changes in properties arising from purely hydrostatic strains. This type of problem is especially troublesome in connection with electrical measurements on many-valley semiconductors, for example. Bridgman, in his introductory paper, has emphasized the importance of knowing the complete stress system acting on the sample before interpreting results in the very-high-pressure range. In practice, studies in the pressure and temperature ranges outside the "conventional" limits have been confined to measurement of pressure-volume relations, the location of the fundamental optical absorption edge in insulators and semiconductors, and some fairly rough electrical-resistivity measurements. Fortunately, *P-V* relations and optical gaps are quite insensitive to shearing effects and crystal imperfections. The study of phase transformations under pressure by looking for thermal arrests as the material is cycled up and down in temperature at constant pressure represents a technique, exploited by Kennedy, which permits one to locate the exact transformation point more reliably. Electrical resistivity is quite structure sensitive, especially in semiconductors, but the results are still of interest when the changes observed cover orders of magnitude in resistivity, as in some of the measurements reported by Drickamer, rather than merely percentage changes. The effects of crystal imperfections can sometimes be discounted because of their irreversibility.

The pressure range beyond the conventional is attractive because it is a range in which there are still new phenomena to be discovered—for example, the conversion of an insulator into a semimetal, the existence of a maximum melting point, and the production of a wealth of new allotropic modifications. One of the most interesting phenomena is the purely electronic phase transition found in cerium and cesium and probably also occurring in rubidium. We may expect to find this phenomenon increasingly common as we continue to explore higher pressure ranges.

It is quite striking that there is now a substantial overlap between the pressure range accessible in "static" experiments and that accessible through shock waves. Thus we are rapidly approaching the situation in which the pressure range from 0 to 5 megabars is accessible, though essentially only for the study of phase transformations and P-V relations. The shock-wave experiments have produced an unexpected dividend. Despite the fact that the peak pressures last only for microseconds, the violent plastic deformation occurring in the shock front apparently catalyzes many phase transformations which do not involve extensive atomic diffusion. Some transformations are more readily observed in dynamic than in static experiments, despite a factor of 10^7 or more in the time scales involved. This is an intriguing phenomenon by itself and merits further theoretical and experimental study. It may have considerable technological importance in connection with the irreversible production of new metastable phases. However, the shock-wave technique suffers from even more severe limitations than the ultra-high-pressure static techniques. It is extremely costly and so far suitable only for national laboratories. It suffers from all the problems of uncontrolled shearing stresses involved in static experiments, and unquestionably the shock front generates even more crystal imperfections than the shearing stresses in static experiments; but on the other hand, the imperfections may also be partly annealed due to the high temperatures reached in the shock. Thus, for example, electrical-resistivity measurements are of very uncertain value in dynamic experiments. In the case of metals and semimetals the resistivity is so low that inductance effects in the measuring system have so far precluded reliable results in the microsecond time intervals involved. On the other hand, in semiconductors and insulators, plastic flow in the shock front probably excites carriers into the conduction band and places the crystal in a nonequilibrium state whose life may be longer than the duration of the pressure pulse. Measurements of the optical gap in dynamic experiments would be of particular interest because they should be insensitive both to crystal imperfections and to transient excitation of carriers. However, the problems involved in making such measurements without destroying the optical equipment are formidable, though probably not insurmountable.

As pointed out in the article by Birch, the study of pressure-volume relations, phase changes, and elastic wave velocities in natural minerals at high pressures is central to the problem of understanding the structure and composition of the earth's mantle and core. With the advent of dynamic techniques it is now possible to reproduce the whole range of pressures and most of the range of temperatures believed to occur in the earth's interior. Down to the boundary between core and mantle the pressure reaches only 10 kilobars, well within the "conventional" range. Pressures accessible only through shock-wave techniques are required to study conditions in the core and in the lower part of the mantle. Already it seems fairly well established that the core is molten iron, probably alloyed with some silicon. Experiments on the correct alloy and experiments to locate the exact temperature of the melting point of this alloy remain to be performed, although they are probably feasible. Unfortunately, also, dynamic experiments on the material of the mantle have still not proved very reproducible. Enough work has been done to demonstrate the unreliability of the Simon equation as a method for extrapolating melting curves much beyond the range of actual observation. Better theoretical understanding, as well as further experiment, is required in this connection. A relatively unexplored field is that of the electrical properties of the mantle material at high pressures; this could yield new evidence on the mantle phases and their distribution.

Several authors have pointed to the need for a reliable and easily applied technique for determining crystal structure at high pressures. This has been successfully done in the "conventional" range, but its application has until recently been severely limited. As this volume goes to press, a paper by Jamieson and Lawson has appeared in which new apparatus is described permitting extension of X-ray-structure work to 150 kilobars at room temperature, and probably adaptable to structural studies at low temperature and moderately high temperature as well. This promises a substantial advance in the precision and reliability of information concerning new allotropic modifications which can be obtained in the ultrahigh-pressure region. The possibility of making precision lattice-parameter determinations also affords the opportunity for determination of the compressibility of high-pressure phases and for obtaining better estimates of the stress distribution and the true average pressure under the nonhydrostatic conditions obtaining in most ultrahigh-pressure experiments. Some estimate of the degree of crystal imperfection introduced should also be possible.

The rapid accumulation of new experimental knowledge on the effects of high pressure has pointed up the inadequacy of existing theory, even in the case of the three simplest solid types: solid noble gases, alkali metals, and alkali halides. The theory is inadequate to give a really quantitative explanation from first principles of the P-V relations over the whole range of accessible pressures. In the case of the noble gases and the alkali halides, the deficiency appears to be in the theory of the repulsion of closed shells, an aspect of solid-state theory that has received relatively little attention in recent years. In the case of alkali halides it is striking that the conceptually most rigorous theory, the band calculation of Howland, gives the poorest agreement with experiment, overestimating by a considerable factor the rigidity of the closed shells at the highest pressures. This is, perhaps, not too surprising when it is considered that we are here dealing with a band-type theory which tends to underestimate correlation effects. These effects will certainly tend to reduce repulsive interactions by contracting the shells and by permitting overlapping of shells to occur with less "promotion" energy than would be suggested by an independent electron picture. Theoretical interest in closed-shell repulsions is being stimulated from a number of different areas of physics. Knowledge of these repulsions is important for the understanding of radiation damage and sputtering in solids. It is of increasing importance for predicting the transport properties of gases at very high temperatures. Direct experimental studies are now being made of collisions between atomic beams. Correlation of the P-V relations of noble gases in the crystalline state with their transport properties at high temperature would be of interest.

There is, of course, no good theory for predicting or understanding the allotropic modifications of solids at atmospheric pressure, let alone estimating the effects of high pressure. In general the energy differences involved in these modifications are an order of magnitude smaller than the present accuracy of the theory. However, there may be some hope of progress by treating the effect of crystal structure as a small perturbation on a relatively inaccurately specified standard state, although nothing of this kind has yet really been attempted. The most hopeful area for theory seems to lie in trying to understand the electronic transformations, especially in alkali metals. Here the volume and energy changes are much larger, and the crystal structure does not change, so that the conventional techniques of cohesive energy calculations are applicable. The transformation in cesium has been qualitatively explained by Sternheimer, but his theory was based on a spherical approximation which can be shown to give rise to too low a d band; hence it is not certain whether Sternheimer's picture, if treated accurately, would predict a transformation at as low a pressure as is observed.

There are other areas in which theoretical understanding may be good enough to permit quantitative comparison with experiment. As discussed by Drickamer, the energy levels of transition-metal and rare-earth ions in ionic crystals can be studied by optical techniques as a function of pressure. In the simplest cases the crystal-field splittings can be computed from purely electrostatic considerations, but in most cases the splittings are complicated by covalency or overlap effects. These effects may be amenable to theoretical treatment, though no detailed quantitative calculations have been carried out for pressure effects. This may be of special interest because it represents an area in which experiments can be extended into the ultrahigh-pressure range.

Recent advances in theoretical understanding of the optical properties of the simpler semiconductors give promise that high-pressure experiments would throw light on the rearrangements of energies at symmetry points high up in the conduction bands of these semiconductors. Similarly, such experiments, if they could be carried out, would be very interesting in the alkali halides, for which theory should permit useful predictions. Unfortunately, the most interesting effects often occur in the vacuum ultraviolet, where the difficulties of carrying out pressure experiments are very formidable.

In the field of magnetism, theory is in too primitive a state to permit predictions a priori. The work described by Kouvel shows that it is possible to correlate some of the pressure data in transition metals and alloys with the rather simple idea of an interatomic exchange integral whose variation with interatomic distance is arrived at empirically, but the fundamental theoretical basis of the underlying model has been progressively eroded in recent years. Nevertheless, the lattice parameter is an important new independent variable for studying exchange interactions, and the Curie point is one of the few physical parameters which is insensitive to shear effects and can hence be studied in the ultrahigh-pressure range. Thus pressure experiments may be especially valuable in throwing some light on the theory of exchange interactions. The difficulty is to obtain a large enough range of lattice parameters to be significant, since most of the ferromagnetic materials are relatively incompressible; this is why extending the measurements to ultrahigh pressures is of special importance.

What is especially called for in the field of magnetism is a series of systematic experiments on a simple material, whose properties can be elaborated in detail, analogous to that achieved for germanium and silicon in the semiconductor field. Such a material should (1) possess a high compressibility, so that a wide range of lattice constants can be obtained at relatively modest pressures, (2) preferably be an insulator, so that complications due to conduction electrons and nonintegral Bohr magneton numbers can be avoided, (3) have a Curie temperature near or somewhat below room temperature so that behavior in the vicinity of the Curie point can be explored in detail, (4) possess a simple type of exchange interaction, in which one particular mechanism overwhelmingly predominates, and preferably one in which only nearest-neighbor interactions are important, and (5) be of a nuclear species having a nuclear resonance which facilitates study of the hyperfine field arising from the local electronic moment. At present we do not know of a single material which satisfies all these requirements. The rare-earth metals have a single predominant exchange mechanism, the "indirect" exchange via the conduction electrons which should be calculable from first principles, but it probably extends over several neighbors. The ferrimagnetic materials have rather complicated superexchange interactions with a directional dependence on the anion positions. Some of the simple antiferromagnetic salts such as manganous fluoride look fairly promising, but the superexchange interaction is still only hazily understood and is not calculable from first principles as yet. True ferromagnetic insulators such as gadolinium halides or certain rare-earth oxides may be quite interesting in that the exchange interactions are possibly of the classical Heisenberg type, or very close to it.

Comparison of pressure and temperature coefficients of many physical properties has led to the recognition of large explicit effects of temperature. In many cases the temperature effects arising from interaction between electrons and lattice vibrations are greater in magnitude than the effects which would be expected from thermal expansion. This discovery has proved especially surprising in connection with the nuclear and electron spin-resonance effects. Although there is some qualitative understanding of the effect of temperature on the Knight shift in metals and on relative positions of band edges in semiconductors, theory in this area is very inadequate, and there are unexplained effects such as the apparent increase of the energy gap in lead telluride with temperature and the relatively large shift with temperature of the hyperfine field in ferromagnetic metals.

Probably if there is any one need of the high-pressure field which should be singled out in this summary, it is the need for more attention by solid-state theorists to the field and closer collaboration between theorists and experimentalists. Despite the present inadequacy of theory for many of the properties being studied, the example of the work on semiconductors shows that progress is possible.

15

Bibliography of High-pressure Techniques

15-1 Introduction

To our knowledge, up to 1962 no treatise devoted exclusively to the technique of high pressure existed in English. Pertinent book sections and papers were seldom both sufficiently general and sufficiently exhaustive. Furthermore, the really useful articles were scattered throughout a number of journals and hence were often difficult to discover.

Although several manufacturers have responded admirably to the need for pressure apparatus and components, skill and technique are still demanded of the experimenter, and a resumé of experience could be extremely valuable to the uninitiated.

With this philosophy, we present the bibliography which follows. It may be less convenient than a monograph on the art, but it may be almost as useful for advanced research work.

The compilation which follows is neither exhaustive nor critical; it consists of about 250 references listed alphabetically by author. Preceding this is a set of notes arranged by subject, giving a brief description of the pertinence of each reference to the particular category. Because most of the works described are adequately documented in themselves, the seeker should have no difficulty tracing a given line of inquiry further than set forth here.

The beginning of the list cites a number of general works embodying sections on technique, while at the end are listed in toto the contents of two untranslated Russian treatises which may have sections of particular importance to some workers.

15-2 General Works

15-2a Books and symposia

[51] is a study of large plastic flow and fracture under conditions of high stress.

[54] is a summary of work by Professor Bridgman originally extending over a period of twenty-five years, first published in 1931, and reprinted in 1949 with minor revisions and a supplement containing work done after 1931. The first four chapters are an introduction to, and recapitulation of, technique. An appendix lists 136 papers by Bridgman.

[60] is a compilation of papers presented at a high-pressure conference held in June, 1960. Equipment and technique, particularly in the "ultrahigh" range, receive great emphasis in these papers. The problem of absolute pressure calibration is discussed, and discrepancies unrecognized prior to the conference are dealt with. A brief review of some Russian work is included.

[68] emphasizes applications to chemical engineering. Included are extensive chapters on safety, design of equipment, and experimental technique. Appendixes treat units, properties of gases, liquids, and solids and give a list of steels and alloys, among other things.

[106] is a short Russian treatise on high pressure in chemistry.

[117] attempts to bridge the gap between the high-pressure treatises dealing with physics under pressure and those covering the uses of pressure in the chemical industry by providing a wide survey of the effects of pressure in the field of physical chemistry. The first chapter summarizes technique, appendixes give tables of liquid compressibility and freezing temperature, and a bibliography of 582 entries is provided.

[125] is a symposium of articles, primarily on processing at high pressure, but covering such subjects as design of vessels, closures, barricades, selection of alloys for components, pump design, and the effect of hydrogen on metals.

[126] is a high-pressure symposium containing articles on pump, vessel, and apparatus design, safety, gauge calibration, sealing problems, and properties of materials under pressure.

[144] is a Russian text on high-pressure technique applied to chemical problems.

[168] is a book covering the properties of materials, the design of apparatus, cylinders in particular, the stresses in cylinders, measurement of pressure, P-V-T relations, equations of state, compressibility, and other properties of substances under pressure.

[219] deals primarily with the design of equipment useful for chemical processing. Such subjects as safety codes, pressure measurement, vessel and closure design and fabrication, pumps, and materials for specific environments are covered. A chapter describing the pipe, valves, and fittings supplied by major manufacturers of pressure equipment is useful.

[220] is a revised version of a Russian text on technique published earlier. Because the book was not available in 1961 in translation to any other language, a table of contents is given in this chapter.

[243*a*] is a collection of papers primarily on apparatus and technique useful above 20 kilobars. Among the subjects covered are apparatus design, optical and electrical measurements, optical squeeze apparatus, X-ray techniques, high-temperature high-pressure measurements, platen (or anvil) apparatus, low-temperature high-pressure measurements, and shock-wave methods for obtaining high-stress conditions.

15-2b Review articles

[42] is a review by Bridgman of work published in accessible form between the writing of his book in 1930 and June, 1945. Progress in technique and pressure measurement is summarized; the rest of the article is devoted to a report of research on the physical properties of single- and multi-component systems, with additional sections on photographic, chemical, and biological effects of pressure. References to 674 papers are included.

[49] is a brief general review of the problems and methods of generating high pressure and its applicability to research on compressibility and polymorphism.

[52] is a brief survey of the problems of high-pressure instrumentation above 30

kilobars. Problems of cascading apparatus and of measuring pressure in this range are discussed.

[132] reviews the generation and measurement of pressure and the measurement of temperature at high pressure. Ways of measuring changes in physical properties as a function of pressure and shock-wave techniques are discussed.

[169] discusses the free-piston gauge, mercury columns, and the bismuth I-II transition and gives viscosity curves for ether and carbon disulfide. Vessel design, autofrettage, and metal properties under pressure are treated.

[193] treats the production of shock-wave pressures ranging from 100 kilobars to above 1,000 kilobars. The experimental approaches to determining the pressure-compression states and the necessary hydrodynamic equations are derived. Experimental data are presented and reviewed for agreement with theory.

[217] is a comprehensive review of the types of measurements, and the methods of making them, used in high-pressure research between 1 and 25 kilobars carried on between June, 1945, the closing date of Bridgman's review article, and 1961. Over half the article is devoted to results in a number of areas of physical interest, although a great deal of attention is paid to technique, particularly at low temperature. There are 421 references.

15-2c Bibliographies

[17] is a 50-page bibliography on high-pressure technology listing title and, occasionally, subject.

[79] claims to be "a summary of all 'known' high-pressure work done on solids since 1947, with selected reference to work on liquids and gases." Two hundred fifty references are cited with brief summaries or paragraphs selected from the works cited. Forty tables and 500 figures from these references are printed. It is to be noted that the original figures have been redrawn, not directly reproduced.

[148] is an alphabetized listing of articles on pressure technique, vessel construction, internal heating, and some materials, often with brief comment.

15-3 Deformation and Rupture

15-3a Theory and design

[51] is devoted to the study of plastic flow and fracture under conditions of interest in high-pressure work.

[65] derives equations for apparatus which uses multiring support. A three-ring apparatus capable of withstanding 160 kilobars for over two weeks is described.

[68] has chapters on the mechanical properties of metals and thick-walled cylinders written from the high-pressure engineer's viewpoint.

[93] gives design formulas, tables, and curves for designing and calculating shrink fits.

[94] discusses residual stress resulting from autofrettage as related to the structure and hardness of the steel concerned.

[95] uses data from nearly 100 static cylinder tests to propose design formulas.

[96] treats residual stress tests on Cr-Ni-Mo-V and SAE 3320, 4340, and 1045 steel cylinders and gives methods for approximate prediction of overstrain and twisting and heavy-wall pressure-strain curves.

[97] deals with circular and elliptic side holes in thick cylinders.

[160] discusses the design of thick-walled pressure-vessel shells.

[162] gives design methods for problems of fatigue and creep imposed by high temperature and fluctuating loads.

[169] discusses vessel design, autofrettage, changes of metal properties, and Manning's theory.
[189] gives curves and tables of stresses and strains in elastic thick-walled cylinders resulting from axially symmetric loading.
[246] contains calculations based on plasticity theory for the design of autofrettaged and built-up vessels to 10 kilobars.

15-3b Observations and practice

[41] discusses the principle of external support and the application of coned rings.
[43] discusses the two-stage apparatus concept.
[54] mentions on page 33 that pinch-off and bursting occur at about the order of the tensile strength, although in general the pinch-off limit is always somewhat lower than the bursting limit. On page 46, "glass-hard" steel is said to withstand 750,000 psi compressive stress. The pinch-off paradox is discussed, starting on page 91.
[112] discusses piston and binding-ring design and such materials as pyrophyllite and tungsten carbide.
[168] discusses autofrettage, the use of bands or binding rings, and allied topics in chap. 3.
[217] mentions an unsupported Carboloy cylinder used for over 100 cycles to 21 kilobars before failure.
[243*a*] reviews practical designs developed over the past decade.

15-4 Pressure Seals

15-4a Bridgman cone-and-ring seal

[6] combines the Bridgman seal with an O ring to provide initial sealing.
[54] discusses the Bridgman seal on pages 37 and 38.

15-4b Unsupported-area seal

[54] discusses development of unsupported-area principle and application on pages 30 to 32 and 35. Mushroom head is discussed on pages 39 and 40.
[232] gives observations on unsupported-area seals, particularly on allowable area ratios.
[233] discusses a number of unsupported-area seals and methods of packing tubing in a leakfree fashion.

15-4c O-ring seal

[6] combines O ring with cone-and-ring seal to give initial packing.
[75] uses O rings combined with antiextrusion rings to obviate pinch-off up to 16 kilobars.
[110] discusses static O-ring seals in an application.
[124] uses O rings plus Teflon and brass to seal an optical apparatus for use to 6 kilobars.
[151] describes a method of sealing a piston to 10 kilobars using O rings. (Note that [75] discusses extrusion past the piston and the possibility of jamming with such a configuration.)

15-4d Antiextrusion rings

[24] uses beryllium-copper rings combined with a loaded Teflon gasket for a low-friction seal useful to 10 kilobars.
[29] illustrates the technique of tapering metal washers to a knife edge.
[54] discusses antiextrusion rings on pages 34 and 39.
[75] uses rings differently from [54] to obtain long life and simple removal to 10 kilobars.

[104] describes uses of rings with Teflon gasket for temperatures above 327°C, at which temperature Teflon transforms from a semicrystalline to a soft amorphous state.

15-4e Electrical and microwave techniques

[20] illustrates application of pipestone cones for electrical leads.
[23] uses a sapphire or quartz bushing in conjunction with an O ring to 11 kilobars for a lead having over 1 kilomegohm leakage resistance. Use of lithographic limestone is also mentioned.
[38] describes pipestone-cone insulation for pressures to 30 kilobars.
[43] describes pipestone cones for insulation to 30 kilobars.
[70] used eight or more electrical leads in a ½-in.-diameter chamber to pressures above 30 kilobars by using metal-sheathed thermocouple wire.
[85] used electrical leads to 3 kilobars which were brought out through small-diameter tubing plugged with silicone oil frozen at the temperature of liquid nitrogen.
[100] describes an electrical conductance cell for use to 800°C at 4 kilobars.
[102] produced an electrical lead good to 4.5 kilobars, having 100 picofarad capacity and 1 kilomegohm leakage resistance, by insulating and sealing a threaded insert with epoxy resin.
[110] found a typical Bridgman cone had 10^7 ohms leakage resistance, but an Araldite seal designed for 5 kilobars and tested briefly to 9.7 kilobars had 10^{11} ohms leakage resistance. O rings were also applied to plug closure in the same device.
[136] found epoxy cement (Dow Novolac) filled with TiO_2 as a thickener could be used as a pipestone substitute for insulation in cone-type electrical leads to 30 kilobars.
[153] tested a microwave window for a 1-cm circular waveguide having tapered sapphire inserts used to 10 kilobars. It was felt that the window may work to 30 kilobars.
[205] saved space where large electrical conductors enter a vessel by employing a cone-within-a-cone technique.
[206] produced electrical leads using commercially available magnesia-insulated thermocouple wire and an O-ring closure. The design was used to 300°C at 4 kilobars.
[221] used a fused-quartz cone for a wide-band 0-to-3,000-Mc window at 1.5 kilobars.
[231] used synthetic mica in a cone seal for a study of paramagnetic resonance under pressure.
[233] discusses a technique applicable to pipestone leads used at low temperature.
[240] used a conical Pyrex sleeve for insulation to 3 kilobars and 200°C.
[243*a*] discusses electrical leads for a number of high-pressure configurations.

15-4f Radiation windows

[8] describes salt windows extruded in a cell for optical studies to 400°C and 200 kilobars.
[67] discusses sealing plate-glass windows to 12 kilobars.
[98] used properly oriented sapphire in the mating optical-flat method.
[124] used an O-ring seal on a 0.4-in. sapphire window to 6 kilobars.
[150] used sapphire windows, sealed by mating flats, to 16 kilobars.
[173] describes the use of NaCl and CaF_2 windows to 4.5 kilobars and short-time application of 11 kilobars to CaF_2.
[183] is the original paper on sealing windows by making optically flat surfaces.
[188] used a ½-in.-thick 38° conical beryllium window for a 2-mC source of Co^{57} enclosed in a BeCu pressure bomb.
[233] reviews optical-window techniques and points out that surfaces do not have to

be optically flat. The use of silicon and germanium for windows transparent in the infrared is also treated.

[243*a*] reviews extruded-window technique on pages 25 to 36, optical-platen technique on pages 51 to 59, and other radiation-transmitting methods on pages 70 to 92.

15-4g Other closures

[5] discusses a vessel for 30 kilobars, designed for Hall-effect measurements, using a reentrant method of sealing the piston reminiscent of the controlled-clearance method of sealing.

[54] discusses the application of hard and soft soldering and a solder-coated tinned-screw arrangement for 2 kilobars on page 35. A quick tubing connector is described on page 36, and a hardened double-cone connection on page 37.

[69] describes valves, similar to those now available commercially, which hold at least 2 kilobars with oil and 1.3 kilobars with gas.

[74] describes the use of a hollow cone for the sealing member of a valve used to 10 kilobars, in order to improve the life of the seat.

[164] describes a 3-kilobar needle valve with hardened needle, removable seat, and self-tightening stem packing.

[167] explains the controlled-clearance principle, in which a hollow bearing is shrunk onto the shaft of a moving part in order to seal it by application of pressure within the bearing.

[170] treats a number of seals, some of which are commercially available types.

[177] gives methods of using capillary tubing for pressure transmission.

[195] gives a valve design in which packing friction and seat wear are reduced by using a ball and seat for high-pressure, and a diaphragm for low-pressure, sealing.

[233] describes methods of sealing capillary tubing into vessels.

15-4h Seal failures

[54] discusses pinch-off on page 33 and the difficulties with plumber's threads on page 35.

[75] mentions the troubles that can be experienced with O rings.

[233] discusses the tearing of tubing at threads.

15-4i Gasket materials

[23] discusses sapphire, quartz, and lithographic limestone for electrically insulating gaskets.

[24] describes the application of molybdenum sulfide–loaded Teflon for unsupported-area seals.

[42] points out on page 20 that to 12 kilobars rubber behaves much like a liquid in volume compressibility.

[75] discusses application of a dense low-friction alloy to mating parts to avoid galling.

[112] discusses gasketing and high-friction materials for the 100-kilobar range.

[115] lists the coefficient of friction of selected materials at 24 kilobars.

[134] discusses a system using a 0.010-in.-thick brass disk as a means of seating a gasket and as an initial seal until punched through by the piston head.

[211] and [212] describe the use of a potassium gasket for a low-temperature seal.

15-4j Leak detection

[176] describes a means of detecting and locating small or inaccessible leaks in pressure systems.

[182] used a mixture of 100 gm 1 percent alcoholic phenolphthalein solution and 20 gm triethanolamine to detect leakage of CO_2, HCl, and SO_2 gases. For NH_3, 100 gm of 1 percent alcoholic phenolphthalein solution and 20 gm triethyleneglycol were used.

15-5 Pressure Generation

15-5a Pump design and generation technique

[41] discusses the principles and application of external support.

[42] points out that 30 kilobars hydrostatic pressure on structural elements used to generate pressures of more than 50 kilobars gives more than a linear gain in strength.

[54] discusses stretching of cylinders for final fit on pages 44 and 45; the fact that the mercury attacks steel above 5 kilobars is mentioned on page 94.

[75] describes a trouble-free reentrant-pump piston seal with O rings, usually used to 1.5 kilobars, but which can be used up to 3 kilobars.

[112] discusses use of binding rings and recommends insertion of thin steel between piston components to adjust for alignment error. Quasi-hydrostatic pressure calibration is analyzed.

[115] describes a compact high-tonnage ram using multiple pistons concentrically. Functions of gaskets and of pressure-transmitting materials under quasi-hydrostatic conditions are also treated.

[119] gives details on quasi-hydrostatic apparatus construction and explains sources of pressure error and a radiographic method of correcting for it.

[125] and [126] show much commercial equipment.

[167] discusses the design of pressure intensifiers.

[175] mentions the method of estimating piston friction from half the width of a pressure-displacement hysteresis loop.

[217] discusses Bridgman's principle of massive support on pages 25 and 26.

[233] gives an example of a simple separator useful to 2 kilobars and discusses other apparatus and tools for pressure work.

[243*a*] reviews generation techniques for pressures above 20 kilobars.

[244] shows how to modify a commercial air-driven diaphragm pump so that it can deliver 10 kilobars.

15-5b Gas systems

[32] describes a gas apparatus capable of sustaining 7 kilobars at liquid-oxygen temperature.

[128] contains a description of an early gas apparatus for an X-ray camera which generated 5 kilobars using helium.

[150] illustrates a system capable of reaching 18 kilobars at room temperature, 14 kilobars at liquid-nitrogen temperature, and pressure limited at lower temperatures by the freezing of helium. A cryostatic optical vessel is also described.

[196] describes a multistage cryogenic apparatus for 10 kilobars in which melting and freezing in a tube are detected by the motion of a steel pellet in the fluid.

[247] contains a description of a gas system.

15-5c Fluid systems

[1] claims to have achieved 10 kilobars using Poulter's inverted rubber stopper.

[20] discusses apparatus capable of reaching 27 kilobars and 1400°C hydrostatically.

[42] reviews a number of methods of generation.

[54] illustrates a 20-kilobar system on page 42.

[62] produced pressures of 34 kilobars in liquids up to 600°C and in gases to 1500°C.

[89] used a nonmagnetic beryllium-copper vessel to 3 kilobars.

[124] describes an optical system useful to 10 kilobars.

[175] specifically treats nonmagnetic systems.

[234] discusses an apparatus for the generation of 10 kilobars and describes its use to study volume change.

15-5d Nonhydrostatic and quasi-hydrostatic systems

[42] describes a number of systems, in particular one in which a pressure of 425 kilobars was achieved by using massive support in conjunction with 30 kilobars confining pressure.

[43] used 30-kilobar immersion to reach 100 kilobars in a two-stage apparatus.

[50] describes an ultrahigh-pressure system employing platens.

[108] used a modified Bridgman flat-anvil apparatus to 80 kilobars and 500°C; the temperature was obtained by external heating.

[112] describes the tetrahedral-anvil apparatus, an externally heated carbide cylinder and pistons for 50 kilobars and 300°C, and a stepped-piston design said to have been used for 200 kilobars.

[113] is a semipopular description of the tetrahedral-anvil apparatus, its use, and implications.

[114] is a confined-cylinder apparatus capable of achieving 100 kilobars at temperatures above 2000°C for sustained periods of time.

[115] describes the tetrahedral-anvil apparatus and other techniques.

[119] claims to have reached 400 kilobars without reaching the ultimate limit of the apparatus, a modified Bridgman-anvil arrangement.

[141] describes a supported-piston system using a collar of a salt, which undergoes volumetric transition, for support.

[199] gives a brief description of a compact tetrahedral-anvil press.

[204] describes a high-pressure piston-cylinder combination, a version of the Bridgman-anvil apparatus, the tetrahedral-anvil apparatus, and a "girdle" apparatus similar to the "belt" constrained-cylinder apparatus.

[222] briefly reviews Russian progress to 1960 on ultrahigh-pressure apparatus and research.

[225] contains a description of an apparatus which can compress 2.5 to 3 cm^3 of volume to 70 kilobars at 2000°C.

[243*a*] reviews nonhydrostatic and hydrostatic methods used to obtain pressures above 20 kilobars.

[245] describes the "girdle" apparatus, a platen system with the cylinder confined by binding rings, capable of exceeding 100 kilobars at 2000°C.

15-5e Shock-wave techniques

[165] describes experimental techniques for separating a shock wave into elastic and plastic waves.

[190] and [191] discuss the possibility of achieving high pressure by shooting a projectile into a tightly fitting hole. See comment on page 8 of [42].

[193] reviews technique and results of the shock-wave method.

[230] describes attainment of 150 to 500 kilobars by high explosives. A photographic technique is described and necessary expressions are derived.

[243*a*] reviews shock-wave technique on pages 200 to 228.

15-5f Thermal generation of pressure

[21] used one-way valves and a series of vessels to increase nitrogen gas pressure from 150 bars to 2 kilobars.

[22] discusses a vessel-and-valve system used as a pistonless compressor to 3 kilobars.

[63] used a thermal-generation method starting with CO_2, which solidifies at 9 kilobars at room temperature.

[140] produced 20 kilobars at 150°C using mercury. Also proposed a cycle in three-stage apparatus which could theoretically produce 10 kilobars in ethyl alcohol. Easily produced an expected 3.5 kilobars.

[189] created 6 kilobars by heating gas which had been solidified by cooling to the temperature of liquid nitrogen.

[241] created pressures to 600 bars by condensing or pumping in gas at liquid-air temperature and then allowing the temperature to rise.

15-6 Measurement of Pressure

15-6a Deadweight or free-piston gauge

[10] and [12] claim an accuracy of 1 part in 2,500 using sintered tungsten carbide pistons and cylinders.
[18] calibrated by using a primary mercury standard to 3 kilobars. Contains many references to older work.
[42] compares and discusses free-piston gauge, mercury column, and the like. Eleven references are given.
[54] discusses the free-piston gauge on page 406.
[55] used capacitance measurements to determine the piston-cylinder clearance as a function of pressure.
[68] treats the free-piston gauge on page 82.
[72] used dimensionally identical pistons and cylinders of different materials in constructing a gauge.
[87] discusses the free-piston gauge.
[138] compares the conventional and the controlled-clearance methods of sealing free-piston gauges.
[139] describes the free-piston gauge and details of calibration of the melting pressure of mercury at ice temperature.
[169] discusses the free-piston gauge and the mercury column.
[217] discusses the free-piston gauge on pages 44 to 47.
[249] describes construction of a piston manometer for use to 20 kilobars.

15-6b Resistance gauges

[37] extrapolated the application of the resistance gauge to 30 kilobars. Seasoning is discussed.
[42] discusses and compares the resistance gauge with others. Contains eleven references.
[54] showed that a linear relationship with pressure could be obtained by measuring the resistance of seasoned manganin wire.
[78] describes resistance gauges of various materials and discusses their temperature dependences. Seasoning is discussed.
[88] discusses resistance gauges made of appropriate materials.
[123] treats the temperature dependence of the manganin gauge.
[156] describes construction and seasoning of manganin gauges.
[208] feels manganin pressure scale of 1954 is uncertain to 0.5 percent, whereas Bridgman claimed 0.1 percent accuracy in free-piston-gauge measurements at 13 kilobars.
[217] discusses gauges, giving references.
[233] compares bridges and suggests a circuit for use with the manganin gauge.

15-6c Other gauges

[18] compares mercury column with free-piston gauge and uses former to calibrate latter.
[26] describes a mercury U-tube manometer for measuring small pressure differences at high pressure.
[28] measured pressure at low temperature by vessel elongation as indicated by a mirror arrangement.
[42] discusses mercury column and other gauges. Contains eleven references.

[112] discusses ultrahigh-pressure calibration using a metal wire enclosed in silver chloride.
[143] applied a strain gauge to the circumference of a cylinder for calibration.
[169] treats the free-piston gauge and mercury column.
[178] discusses the application of quartz resonances which stay sharp as pressure is increased.
[192] describes a high-pressure manostat.
[203] describes a manometer for measurement of small pressure differences at high pressure.
[216] describes a quartz gauge.

15-6d Fixed pressure points

[9] discusses calibration of a high-pressure electrical-resistance cell above 100 kilobars relative to shifts in the value of some calibration points.
[37] cites the Bi I–Bi II transition as 25,420 kg/cm^2 (or 24,600 atm).
[42] on page 24 illustrates volume compressions to 100 kilobars, showing breaks due to polymorphic transitions in some cases.
[49] illustrates the P-V isotherms, showing breaks.
[50] gives the bismuth transitions.
[53] determined the freezing pressure of mercury by a discontinuity in its resistance.
[54] cites the freezing pressure of mercury at 0°C as 7,640 kg/cm^2 (or 7,394 atm)., and the Bi I–Bi II transition at 30°C as 25,420 kg/cm^2 (or 24,600 atm).
[56] gives the phase diagram of bismuth to 130 kilobars and 500°C using Bridgman's bismuth and barium values.
[57] gives the phase diagram of rubidium to 150 kilobars and 500°C.
[58] discusses pressure and temperature calibration in ultrahigh-pressure apparatus. The effect of pressure on thermocouples and the values of fixed points are discussed.
[61] discusses the fusion curves of nickel, platinum, rhodium, and iron.
[81] discusses the calibration of a high-pressure optical vessel in terms of changes in the values of fixed points.
[111] determined the fusion curve of germanium to 180 kilobars and treats the thallium transition.
[112] discusses ultrahigh-pressure calibration done by incorporating a metal wire in an AgCl cylinder inside a lava block.
[115] shows in Fig. 5 a shift in apparent pressure with the coefficient of friction of the pressure transmitter; this is instructive regarding certain sources of calibration error.
[134] proposes the zero-field superconducting transition of tin as a secondary pressure-measuring device at low temperature.
[137] says 7,723 ± 2 kg/cm^2 is an English determination of the freezing pressure of mercury at 0°C, found about 1960.
[139] gives the 0°C freezing pressure of mercury as 109,760 psi = 7,719 kg/cm^2. Also notes that the temperature of a bath using good commercial ice can be expected to be 0.00 ± 0.02°C.
[142] is important in dealing with almost all nonhydrostatic-pressure work above 25 kilobars before 1961, since the values for the fixed points cited here suggest that earlier calibrations may have been 30 percent too high. Bismuth, thallium, cobalt, and barium transition values are specified.
[207] discusses the seven modifications of ice. In this connection, Bridgman suggested privately that ice I–ice II, which occurs at 2,150 kg/cm^2 at -30°C, can be a very useful fixed point, since pure water is readily obtainable and since

near the critical point (about $-22°C$) the fractional volume change on freezing is so large ($\Delta V/V = 0.2$ at $-30°C$) that a resistance or volumetric measurement is not really necessary to observe the transition; pumping over the appropriate pressure region readily reveals the discontinuity. Thus, a system in which the piston is inaccessible or which employs a pump with cyclic action may be calibrated. Acetone, to which dry ice is carefully added to hold the temperature constant, makes a satisfactory bath; the water may be enclosed in a flexible container such as a toothpaste tube.

[208] used the freezing pressure of mercury at 0°C and 7,640 kg/cm^2 and the blocking of a capillary with CO_2 at 3,439 kg/cm^2 and 0°C for calibration. Points out that Bridgman's volumetric determination on CO_2 yielded a 1 percent lower value. Following the analysis of an experiment on the velocity of sound in water, concludes that the absolute standards below 10 kilobars are uncertain to ½ percent.

[214] discusses the fusion curve of iron.

[215] gives melting curves of rhodium, platinum, iron, and nickel and phase diagrams of bismuth and rubidium.

[217] gives a number of references to transitions which may be of use as fixed points.

[229] proposes a method of constructing a high-pressure scale by using melting-point-curve intercepts on a pressure-temperature plane. By use of the Simon equation as an analytic expression for the melting-point curve, constructs curves for the interval from 9 to 34 kilobars. Usefulness is determined by the applicability of the Simon equation.

[243*a*] treats calibration by fixed points in Chaps. 1, 2, and 5, and gives in Appendix B a list of transitions which occur between 18 and 425 kilobars.

[248] gives the melting curve of mercury up to 10 kilobars, obtaining 7,710 ± 53 kg/cm^2 at 0°C.

15-7 Specialized Apparatus and Techniques

15-7a Combined pressure and high temperature

[7] is an abstract on thermocouple calibration to 10 kilobars and 400°C by the Bridgman technique.

[19] discusses experiments on thermoelectric power at high temperature and pressure.

[20] describes an apparatus for 27 kilobars and 1400°C using internal heating and gas as the hydraulic medium.

[30] measured thermoelectric emf and Peltier and Thompson heats.

[54] discusses thermoelectric behavior as a function of pressure, beginning on page 295.

[58] discusses pressure and temperature calibration in ultrahigh-pressure apparatus. The effect of pressure on thermocouples and the values of fixed points are discussed.

[59] discusses measurements of thermocouple emf under pressure, obtaining results different from those of Birch.

[76] describes an apparatus for 100 kilobars and temperatures above 3000°C.

[82] describes the fusion curves of indium and tin to 105 kilobars.

[100] describes an electrical-conductance cell for use with aqueous solutions to 800°C and 4 kilobars.

[108] describes a simple "squeezer" for 20 kilobars and 1000°C, using external heating.

[112] discusses internal-heating considerations and methods to achieve high pressures

and temperatures. Obtained 5000°C at 50 kilobars with a carbon heater and carbide cylinder and pistons. Also describes the work of Loring Coes on combined temperature and pressure.

[116] claims to have reached 10,000°C for minutes and 15,000°C for 15-sec periods in condensed phases.

[121] gives diagrams of high-pressure cells used for heating and discusses temperature measurement.

[145] took a conventional fluid system to 8 kilobars and 400°C using silicone fluid and external heating.

[171] is an early work on diamond synthesis.

[172] is an early work on diamond synthesis.

[174] describes an internal furnace for use to 1120°C.

[201] used a CsCl crucible lined with graphite to transmit pressure at high temperature to KCl. Claims CsCl can be formed more easily into a crucible, has a higher melting point, and causes less sample cracking than AgCl. The method is useful to above 1000°C and up to 30 kilobars.

[215] describes melting-point determinations in metals.

[217] discusses high temperature combined with high pressure, pointing out the problem of steel's softening above 300°C.

[218] is an early work on diamond synthesis.

[243] illustrates a high-temperature high-pressure reaction cell.

[243*a*] gives a review of high-temperature high-pressure methods and their applications in Chaps. 5 to 8.

[247] illustrates an internal-heating arrangement.

15-7b Low-temperature apparatus

[2] studied Hall effect and magnetoresistance in bismuth to 2 kilobars and 4°K.

[3] describes superconductivity of cadmium under pressure, the first high-pressure report below 1°K.

[14] tabulates the thermal contraction of materials useful for pressure construction, e.g., brass, german silver, copper, BeCu, Invar, and stainless steel.

[27] claims to have developed a technique for generating uniform pressures of 30 kilobars down to 1.6°K.

[54] describes on page 427 the use of helium gas to attain 7.5 kilobars at 77°K.

[84] used a method of examining solids electrically at low temperature and high pressure which avoids sample deformation and ensures pressure homogeneity.

[85] used helium at low temperature solidified slowly from the bottom. Used BeCu vessel to 3 kilobars.

[134] comments on the accuracy of pressure in the experiments of Lasarew and Kan.

[146] achieved 1 kilobar at 35.7°K in a microwave experiment.

[147] used a mixture of fluids to obtain 10 kilobars at 200°K with good hydrostaticity.

[150] used a gas apparatus capable of attaining 18 kilobars at room temperature, 14 kilobars at liquid-nitrogen temperature, and pressures limited by the solidification of helium at lower temperatures.

[155] describes the "ice-bomb" technique, i.e., generation of pressure by the expansion on freezing of such substances as H_2O, bismuth, antimony, and gallium. Claims pressures up to 10 kilobars may be obtained if bismuth or gallium is used.

[217] reviews low-temperature high-pressure techniques, describes a particular system and a potassium gasket, and gives some points on the helium melting curve.

[233] describes some techniques for pressure work at low temperature.

[243*a*] reviews low-temperature high-pressure techniques in Chap. 10.

15-7c Magnetic techniques

[2] describes measurements of the Hall effect and magnetoresistance in bismuth to 2 kilobars at temperatures down to 4 °K.

[4] discusses construction of a magnet inside a pressure vessel.

[5] discusses an unsupported vessel for Hall-effect measurements to 30 kilobars employing a reentrant piston seal.

[15] describes a nonmagnetic beryllium-copper vessel.

[16] describes a nonmagnetic beryllium-copper vessel.

[89] used a beryllium-copper vessel to 3 kilobars when investigating magnetic permeability.

[147] investigated pure-quadrupole resonance as a function of pressure and temperature.

[175] is a description of nonmagnetic pressure vessels, electrical leads for such vessels, and the like.

[213] describes a high-pressure magnetometer chamber for 30 kilobars with the poles of the magnet screwed into the vessel.

15-7d Microwave techniques

[139a] describes a high-pressure microwave window plug.

[146] studied nuclear resonance to 1 kilobar at 35.7°K.

[147] used a beryllium-copper cylinder and an rf plug to 10 kilobars. It is suggested that since quadrupole resonance is very sensitive to the degree of hydrostaticity, it might be used as an indicator of freezing. A mixture of fluids was used to 10 kilobars at 200°K without loss of fluidity.

[153] describes a high-pressure microwave window.

[158] illustrates a high-pressure dielectric cell in Fig. 26.

[231] describes a high-pressure microwave window plug.

15-7e Optical techniques

[8] describes an optical cell for 200 kilobars at temperatures to 400°C.

[71] describes a cell having a 340-cm path length useful from −195 to +200°C at about 1.2 kilobars.

[80] describes an optical apparatus with salt windows. Is partially a review of earlier work.

[98] treats optical apparatus for 55 and 200 kilobars.

[105] designed a cell for 6 kilobars and used it to 1 kilobar. Contamination is minimized by the design.

[124] used a length of tubing to connect an optical cell with 1-cm-thick windows to a pressure-generating cylinder. Seals were made with O rings, Teflon, and brass.

[127] includes a description of an intensifier optical vessel used to 5 kilobars.

[150] discusses an optical cryostat for use to 16 kilobars from 60 to 370°K.

[173] treats the application of salt windows to 4.5 kilobars and CaF_2 to 11 kilobars.

[180] describes a high-pressure refractometer.

[183] describes the optical-flat method of sealing. The quoted use of glass—or any brittle window—to 30 kilobars has been questioned by later workers.

[184] describes early optical apparatus.

[185] discusses window bulging.

[186] describes diamond windows for 21 kilobars, using water or alcohol for pressure transmission.

[187] used two windows inclined at 30° to one another for a high-pressure prism refractometer.

[194] describes a spectral cell using thermal compression to reduce contamination.

[197] suggests the usefulness of bakelite viewing tubes to 400 bars.

[198] describes a "squeezer" using sapphire pistons.
[202] constructed an infrared microcell used to 12 kilobars with sapphire windows and a plastic bag to contain liquids.
[233] describes sapphire, germanium, and silicon window experience; points out that window seats need not be optically flat, and illustrates an externally controlled sample-raising mechanism.
[241] used a reflection-type absorption cell with quartz and CaF_2 windows and a tantalum mirror. Used thermal pressure generation to 600 bars.
[243*a*] reviews optical techniques in Chaps. 2 and 3.

15-7f Ultrahigh-pressure techniques

[9] discusses the design and calibration of a high-pressure electrical cell used to 500 kilobars
[11] describes an apparatus for 100 kilobars, achieved by cooling a Carboloy vessel with a shrunk-on steel jacket to liquid-air temperature.
[35] is the first publication giving details of the method of external support as applied to conical vessels. Attained 50 kilobars from −80° to +200°C.
[42] describes a shear apparatus for pressures above 50 kilobars and mentions a Carboloy apparatus for 100 kilobars and above.
[48] describes the principle of massive support as applied to platens for pressures above 100 kilobars.
[50] discusses platens.
[65] derives equations for a multiring apparatus and describes a three-ring device for maintaining a pressure of 160 kilobars over long periods.
[76] discusses a 100-kilobar 3000°C apparatus.
[82] contains a description of the tetrahedral-anvil apparatus.
[107] claims achievement of 200 kilobars with 20-kilobar hydrostatic support. Bridgman expresses doubt in [42].
[108] describes a platen apparatus.
[159] describes a compact anvil apparatus.
[243*a*] is a review of ultrahigh-pressure techniques.

15-7g X-ray techniques

[66] used an X-ray camera with two large beryllium windows.
[92] fabricated a conical beryllium container pressed into a steel chamber with a slit for the passage of X-rays. Benzine‡ was used as fluid; pressure to 15 kilobars was achieved.
[101] did X-ray measurements to 1 kilobar using a small Pyrex capillary. Thermal generation was used to obtain pressure.
[109] used monocrystalline-beryllium pressure cylinders.
[119] used radiography to examine the deformation of platen faces under pressure, thus obtaining the relationship between "true" and observed pressure.
[128] gives diagrams of a hydrostatic pressure vessel, camera, beryllium windows, etc., which have the advantage of being able to measure patterns while under pressure without scattering from a second window.
[129] measured compressibility to 4.5 kilobars by X-rays.
[130] gives a description of a diamond X-ray vessel and its use.
[131] discusses diamond containers and diamond platens for use with X-rays.
[133] describes the "squeezer" modified for X-rays.
[152] used coarse-grained cast-beryllium cylinders in two different devices to obtain powder pictures to 15 kilobars.

‡ Note that benzene freezes at about 1 kilobar at 33.4°C and at 5.5°C at atmospheric pressure.

[154] used single-crystal beryllium cylinders to 10 kilobars and diamond to 25 kilobars for powder patterns.
[161] examined ice modifications by pressurizing, cooling, removing the sample, and examining.
[166] used thin-walled containers of steel or beryllium (using powder-metallurgy methods) to transmit X-rays; attained 1.5 kilobars.
[223] applied 30 kilobars to substances confined in a beryllium cone surrounded by a slotted steel cone; pressure was transmitted by lithium.
[226] describes an X-ray study of rubidium halides to 11 kilobars.
[243*a*] has an article (Chap. 4) on high-pressure modifications of the Debye-Scherrer X-ray technique.

15-7h Miscellaneous apparatus and techniques

[42] describes a shear apparatus for pressures above 50 kilobars and use of Carboloy over 100 kilobars; shows a piezometer which takes advantage of the properties of Carboloy when it is subjected to 20 or 30 kilobars of hydrostatic pressure.
[44] describes a lever piezometer used for compressibility to 30 kilobars.
[45] describes the use of a lead capsule for enclosing materials.
[46] describes piezometer compressibility measurements.
[54] describes on pages 397 to 404 the use of a plastic sheath for protecting brittle materials or to reduce wall friction of materials being compressed.
[64] used a fixed clamp or platen method to 50 kilobars at low temperature by locking at room temperature and cooling. See discussion in [217].
[115] describes a compact multiple-piston ram capable of supporting 3,000 tons at 2 kilobars input oil pressure.
[118] discusses the use of Teflon and polyethylene capsules.
[157] gives schematic diagrams of a hydrostatic high-pressure system and apparatus for measuring anelastic relaxation, annealing of quenched vacancies, and ionic conduction.
[176] proposes a method of detecting small leaks in liquid systems.
[177] describes means of sealing and using capillary tubing for pressure transmission in a fluid.
[182] describes methods of detecting leakage of CO_2, HCl, SO_2, and NH_3 from pressure systems.
[188] used a ½-in.-thick conical beryllium window of 28° angle for a 2-millicurie source of Co^{57} diffused in iron which was enclosed in a BeCu pressure vessel.
[193] discusses the achievement of high pressure by shock techniques.
[209] used a sheet of indium 0.002 to 0.005 in. thick to reduce internal wall friction in measuring *P-V* isotherms at low temperature.
[217] describes an 0.850-in-outside-diameter Carboloy cylinder used to 21 kilobars without external support.
[227] avoided the use of packing up to 14 kilobars by using conical, rather than cylindrical, pistons.
[233] describes a hollow extractor ram useful for disassembling apparatus and a means of sealing small-diameter tubing.

15-8 Pressure Transmitters

[28] improved the uniformity of pressures achieved by the method of Lazarev and Kan by using an aqueous solution of ethyl alcohol rather than pure water.
[31] lists properties of eighteen liquids.
[33] gives *P-V-T* relations for some nonvolatile liquids.

[34] gives P-V-T relations for 15 liquids.
[36] is on the P-V-T relation of heavy water.
[39] gives the properties of 21 liquids from 25 to 175°C up to 50 kilobars.
[40] gives freezing data and compressibility of 21 substances to 50 kilobars.
[42] comments on page 20 about rubber's liquidlike behavior to 12 kilobars.
[45] discusses the lead-capsule technique of isolating materials from the pressure fluid; also discusses pressure limitations of fluids.
[47] suggests that isopentane and pentane are useful to 30 kilobars because neither solidifies nor becomes viscous; also indicates that by 40 kilobars all liquids are crystalline or glassy solids, but some may still be used for transmitting hydrostatic pressure.
[54] discusses pressure transmitters and techniques on pages 397 to 404.
[73] measured dielectric constants of CS_2, ethyl ether, n-pentane, chlorobenzene, bromobenzene, hexyl alcohol, ethyl alcohol, glycerin, and eugenol between 0 and 75°C up to 12 kilobars. Only glycerin and i-butyl alcohol showed an effect, and that only at high frequency (247 kc).
[75] used Octoil S to 10 kilobars because of its excellent lubricating qualities and low viscosity.
[77] used Octoil S.
[83] presents the melting curve of helium graphically and a table of Debye and melting temperatures and Grüneisen constants.
[85] gives data on the pressure in solid helium at 2°K and its solidification temperature as a function of initial pressure under certain conditions.
[86] gives the melting curve of helium from 4 to 26°K at pressures up to 3 kilobars. According to Swenson, the large compressibility and small thermal expansion make hydrostaticity and constancy of pressure relatively easy to maintain in solid helium.
[90] deals with the high-pressure low-temperature optical transmission of liquid CO_2.
[91] observes no absorption in argon and methane from 2,130 to 6,780 Å up to 400 bars at low temperature.
[99] describes the use of NaCl to 150 kilobars for optical work.
[103] discusses the compressibility and refractive index of benzene.
[117] gives in Appendix I a list and bibliography of Bridgman's measurements of compressibility of liquids and in Appendix II a compilation of the effect of pressure on the freezing temperatures of a number of liquids.
[118] discusses the use of Teflon and polyethylene capsules for isolation.
[120] discusses the effect of pressure on the refractive index and dispersion of glycerol.
[122] followed the melting curve of helium to about 7.5 kilobars and 50°K and got agreement with Simon, Ruhemann, and Edwards.
[127] used 3-centistoke DC200 fluid, which is transparent in the visible, to 5 kilobars or higher.
[128] claims impurities in helium must be removed if it is to be used in a pressure chamber in which photographic film is to be exposed.
[135] discusses the effect of pressure on the refractive index and dielectric constant of CO_2.
[139] used white gasoline as a pressure transmitter in a determination of the freezing pressure of mercury.
[147] points out that a mixture of equal parts of n-pentane and 2-methyl-butane can be used to 10 kilobars at 200°K without much loss of fluidity. Petroleum ether is satisfactory to 0°C at 10 kilobars, and kerosene is fluid at 100°C and 10 kilobars.

[149] adds data to the melting curve of helium, showing that at 77.3°K a phase change occurs at 14,140 bars, thereby justifying extrapolation of the formula of Simon or of Mills and Grilly.

[156] points out that petroleum ether is mostly hexane with a 60°C boiling point. It does not freeze at room temperature below 10 kilobars but freezes at 6 kilobars when held at 0°C. It should not be used for gauge calibration.

[157] used isopentane from −50 to 0°C, hexane from 0 to 150°C, and Dow Corning DC200 silicone fluid from 150 to 500°C up to 10 kilobars.

[163] details the effect of pressure on the refractive index of CO_2.

[169] presents the viscosity curves for CS_2 and ether.

[175] describes the use of lead and indium in stretching cylinders.

[179] gives the effect of pressure on the refractive index of carbon disulfide.

[181] gives the effect of pressure on the refractive index of aqueous solutions of ethyl alcohol.

[187] gives the effect of pressure on the refractive index of paraffin oil and glycerine.

[196] extends the melting curve to 8.25 kilobars at 234°K for argon and 9 kilobars at 180°K for nitrogen.

[201] used CsCl for pressure transmission at high temperatures in preference to AgCl because it could be formed into crucibles more easily, has a higher melting point, and results in less cracking of crystals. The method is claimed useful to above 1000°C up to 30 kilobars.

[210] studied the solid phases of H_2S, observed two new phases, and plotted the melting curve.

[217] gives melting curves and reviews melting phenomena. The melting curve for He^4 can be represented by $P/P_0 + 1 = (T/T_0)^c$, where $P_0 = 17.30$ and $T_0 = 0.90$°K and c is about 2 for most nonmetals. For hydrogen, $P_0 = 271$ atm and $T_0 = 14$°K, so that helium behaves qualitatively at 1 kilobar and 14°K like hydrogen at 15 kilobars and 196°K. Helium solidifies at 25 atm at 0°K, at 140 atm at liquid-helium temperature (4.2°K), and at 1,800 atm at liquid-hydrogen temperature (20.4°K). Simple crystalline solids such as neon, argon, and oxygen are quite plastic below their triple points, but some may become brittle at liquid-helium temperature, as do argon and oxygen. Gradients of several hundred bars anneal out in solidified hydrogen and become very small within a half hour; thus, hydrogen can be used as an approximately hydrostatic transmitter of pressure at liquid-helium temperature.

[233] used CS_2 as an optically transparent transmitter of pressure since it was nonabsorbing at wavelengths shorter than 5 microns and was liquid to at least 8 kilobars. On the other hand, it has a low flash point, is toxic, and affects rubber gaskets.

[243*a*] discusses a number of transmitting media of value in the ultrahigh-pressure range.

15-9 Pressure Hazards

[42] covers hydrogen embrittlement on page 56 and gives references.

[54] points out on page 33 that the velocity of a pinched-off object can reach that of a rifle bullet. On page 46 the necessity of shielding pistons is discussed, while on page 94 the attack on steel by mercury is described.

[68] discusses hydrogen embrittlement on page 59. A chapter on safety begins on page 63.

[200] is a useful reference covering hazardous properties of many materials, such as BeCu and Teflon, employed in pressure work.

15-10 High-pressure Materials

[13] showed that polymorphic transitions occur in Teflon by pressure measurements to 21 kilobars at temperatures from 75 to 380°K. A Teflon gasket loaded to 3 kilobars at room temperature should maintain a seal at any lower temperature.

[14] gives tables of the low-temperature thermal contraction of such useful pressure materials as brass, german silver, copper, beryllium copper, invar, and stainless steel.

[24] discusses the use of impregnated Teflon as a gasketing material.

[25] discusses high-pressure lubricants such as stearic acid and tungsten and molybdenum disulfides.

[42] comments on page 20 that the behavior of rubber to 12 kilobars is much like that of a liquid; on page 56 hydrogen embrittlement is discussed and references are given. Points out that steels with tensile strengths to 350,000 psi are available and Carboloy has a crushing strength of as much as 75 kilobars with very low elastic deformability, the elastic constants being three times higher than steel. The brittleness of Carboloy disappears at pressures of 20 to 30 kilobars and higher, so it may be used for a vessel as well as a piston. The loss of brittleness and increase of ductility are the prime reasons pressures greater than 100 kilobars can be achieved. The compressibility of iron to 30 kilobars at 24°C is given by $-\Delta V/V_0 = 5.826 \times 10^{-7}P - 0.80 \times 10^{-12}P^2$, where P is in kg/cm².

[68] treats hydrogen embrittlement on page 59.

[112] has comments on a number of materials particularly useful for extremely high-pressure work. For example, silver chloride is an electrically insulating pressure-transmitting solid. Rouge (iron oxide) is a useful friction-inducing material, while molybdenum disulfide is a valuable lubricant. Pyrophyllite is a fine-grained, compact, electrically insulating pressure transmitter, while pipestone is similar but has greater surface and internal friction and is less uniform, more difficult to obtain, and harder to machine. Cemented tungsten carbide with 6 percent cobalt binder is said to have 800,000 psi compressive strength, the highest of any readily obtainable material.

[115] gives a table of coefficients of friction of materials at 24 kilobars and a graph of apparent pressure as a function of coefficient.

[119] used General Electric Carboloy 999 and Kennametal K96 for anvils and found the Kennametal softer and more deformable but possessing a longer life at lower pressure. Acrylic plastic was used for electrical insulation of pistons; silver chloride remained a good insulator at the highest pressures, and MoS_2 was a useful lubricant in shrinking Carboloy anvils into their jackets.

[150] used sapphire windows to 16 kilobars.

[157] used so-called "red-tough" steel for high-temperature vessels and SAE 4340 for vessels used below 200°C.

[169] discusses the effect of pressure on a number of engineering materials.

[175] describes experience in fabricating and using nonmagnetic beryllium copper and stainless steel pressure vessels. Lead and indium are used for pressure transmitters in stretching cylinders.

[211] used potassium for a gasket at low temperature.

[212] discusses potassium as a low-temperature gasket material.

[217] discusses stainless steel and beryllium copper on page 56, also the twinning of sapphire under 50 kilobars compression when immersed in a hydrostatic pressure of 23 kilobars and the effectiveness of work hardening and die drawing under hydrostatic pressure on page 141. Effects of pressure on glass are discussed on page 139.

[224] used lead as a pressure transmitter in a 4:1 intensifier, apparently up to 15 kilobars.

[228] investigated plastic deformation of graphite, pyrophyllite, catlinite, Armco iron, magnesium, and AgCl as potential high-pressure lubricants. Shear stress was measured up to 100 kilobars for all materials except graphite, which was measured to 500 kilobars. Shear stress increased linearly to 100 kilobars, pyrophyllite and graphite having the lowest values and AgCl and magnesium the highest. At 100 kilobars the shear stress of graphite is 8,200 kg/cm^2, increasing sharply to 1.35×10^5 kg/cm^2 at 500 kilobars.

[231] used synthetic mica ($KMgAlSi_3O_{10}F_2$) for an electrical-cone seal.

[233] found Dow Corning DC200 silicone fluid useful for keeping pipestone-insulated electrical leads from leaking at high pressure and low temperature; also investigated germanium, silicon, and sapphire as window materials.

[235] determined the compressibility of certain high polymers.

[236] investigated the transitions which occur in pressurized rubber.

[237] investigated the phases of Teflon under pressure.

[238] determined the temperature dependence of the compression of linear high polymers.

[239] measured the compressibilities of long-chain hydrocarbons.

[242] synthesized cubic boron nitride and found it superior to diamond in scratch hardness.

15-11 List of References by Number and by Author

[1] Adams, L. H.: A Simplified Apparatus for High Hydrostatic Pressures, *Rev. Sci. Instr.*, vol. 7, p. 174, 1936.

[2] Alekseevskiĭ, N. E., and N. B. Brandt: The Effect of a Uniform Compression on the Galvanomagnetic Effects in Bismuth and its Alloys, *Zhur. Eksptl. i Teoret. Fiz.*, vol. 28, pp. 379–383, 1955; *Soviet Phys. JETP*, vol. 1, p. 384, 1955.

[3] Alekseevskiĭ, N. E., and Yu. P. Gaĭdukov: The Effect of Pressure on the Superconductivity of Cadmium, *Zhur. Eksptl. i Teoret. Fiz.*, vol. 29, pp. 898–899, 1955; *Soviet Phys. JETP*, vol. 2, p. 762, 1956.

[4] Averkin, A. A., and V. N. Bogomolov: A Device for Investigating the Magnetoelectric Effects under Hydrostatic Pressure, *Soviet Phys.—Solid State*, vol. 3, p. 460, 1961.

[5] Averkin, A. A., and V. N. Bogomolov: Title not available, *Pribory i Tekh. Eksperimenta*, no. 6, p. 147, 1961.

[6] Babb, S. E., Jr.: Combined Bridgman and O-ring Static Pressure Seal, *Rev. Sci. Instr.*, vol. 31, p. 219, 1960.

[7] Babb, S. E., Jr., and G. J. Scott: Effects of Pressure upon the Thermoelectric Properties of Metals, *Bull. Am. Phys. Soc.*, series II, vol. 7, p. 116, 1962.

[8] Balchan, A. S., and H. G. Drickamer: High Pressure High Temperature Optical Device, *Rev. Sci. Instr.*, vol. 31, p. 511, 1960.

[9] Balchan, A. S., and H. G. Drickamer: High Pressure Electrical Resistance Cell, and Calibration Points above 100 Kilobars, *Rev. Sci. Instr.*, vol. 32, p. 308, 1961.

[10] Basset, J.: Production and Measurement of Very High Pressures, *Chim. & ind. Paris*, vol. 53, p. 303, 1945.

[11] Basset, J.: Réalisation de très hautes pressions comprises entre 50,000 et 100,000 kg/cm^2, *J. phys. radium*, vol. 1, p. 121, 1940.

[12] Basset, J., and J. Basset: Manometer with Free Piston for the Absolute Measurement of High Pressures up to 10^4 kg/cm^2 and Associated Secondary Arrange-

ments for the Electrical Measurement of These Pressures, *J. phys. radium*, vol. 15, p. 57a, 1954.

[13] Beecroft, R. I., and C. A. Swenson: Behavior of Polytetrafluoroethylene (Teflon) under High Pressures, *J. Appl. Phys.*, vol. 30, p. 1793, 1959.

[14] Beenakker, J. J. M., and C. A. Swenson: Total Thermal Contractions of Some Technical Metals to 4.2°K, *Rev. Sci. Instr.*, vol. 26, p. 1204, 1955.

[15] Benedek, G. B., and T. Kushida: The Pressure Dependence of the Knight Shift in the Alkali Metals and Copper, *J. Phys. Chem. Solids*, vol. 5, p. 241, 1958.

[16] Benedek, G. B., and E. M. Purcell: Nuclear Magnetic Resonance in Liquids under Pressure, *J. Chem. Phys.*, vol. 22, p. 2003, 1954.

[17] Borg, L., and H. Herman: Literature Survey on Research and Development on High Pressure Technology, Engineering Supervision Company, New York, 1960, contract AF 33(616)-6729.

[18] Bett, K., P. F. Hayes, and D. M. Newitt: The Construction, Operation, and Performance of a Primary Standard Mercury Column for the Measurement of High Pressures, *Phil. Trans. Roy. Soc. London*, vol. A247, p. 59, 1954.

[19] Birch, F.: Thermoelectric Measurement of High Temperatures in Pressure Apparatus, *Rev. Sci. Instr.*, vol. 10, p. 137, 1939.

[20] Birch, F., E. C. Robertson, and S. P. Clark, Jr.: Apparatus for Pressures of 27,000 Bars and Temperatures of 1400°C, *Ind. Eng. Chem.*, vol. 49, p. 1965, 1957.

[21] Boksha, S. S.: A New Method of Producing Super-high Gas Pressures, *Krystallografiya*, vol. 2, p. 198, 1957; *Soviet Phys. Cryst.*, vol. 2, p. 195, 1958.

[22] Boksha, S. S.: A New Type of Pistonless Compressor for Producing Very High Gas Pressures, pp. 79–81 in "Growth of Crystals," vol. 2, Consultants Bureau, Inc., New York, 1959.

[23] Bowman, H. A.: Insulating Seal for High-pressure Equipment, *Natl. Bur. Standards Tech. News Bull.*, vol. 39, p. 71, 1955.

[24] Bowman, H. A., J. L. Cross, D. P. Johnson, J. D. Hill, and J. S. Ives: Impregnated Teflon as a Packing Material at 150,000 Pounds per Square Inch, *Rev. Sci. Instr.*, vol. 27, p. 550, 1956.

[25] Boyd, J., and B. P. Robertson: The Friction Properties of Various Lubricants at High Pressures, *Trans. ASME*, vol. 67, p. 51, 1945.

[26] Boyd, J. H., Jr.: A Manometer for the Measurement of Small Pressure Differentials at High Pressures, *J. Am. Chem. Soc.*, vol. 52, pp. 5102–5106, 1930.

[27] Brandt, N. V., and N. I. Ginzburg: Investigation of the Crystalline Modifications of Bismuth and Some Problems Arising in the Techniques of High Pressure at Low Temperatures, vol. 3, no. 11, *Soviet Phys.-Solid State* p. 2510, 1961.

[28] Brandt, N. V., and V. A. Venttsel: Effect of Uniform Compression on the Oscillation of the Magnetic Susceptibility of Bismuth at Low Temperatures, *Soviet Phys. JETP*, vol. 35, no. 8, p. 757, 1959.

[29] Bridgman, P. W.: The Technique of High Pressure Experimenting, *Proc. Am. Acad. Arts Sci.*, vol. 49, p. 627, 1914.

[30] Bridgman, P. W.: Thermo-electromotive Force, Peltier Heat, and Thomson Heat under Pressure, *Proc. Am. Acad. Arts Sci.*, vol. 53, p. 269, 1918.

[31] Bridgman, P. W.: The Volume of Eighteen Liquids as a Function of Pressure and Temperature, *Proc. Am. Acad. Arts Sci.*, vol. 66, p. 185, 1931.

[32] Bridgman, P. W.: The Pressure Coefficient of Resistance of Fifteen Metals Down to Liquid Oxygen Temperatures, *Proc. Am. Acad. Arts Sci.*, vol. 67, p. 305, 1932.

[33] Bridgman, P. W.: Volume-Temperature-Pressure Relations for Several Non-volatile Liquids, *Proc. Am. Acad. Arts Sci.*, vol. 67, p. 1, 1932.

[34] Bridgman, P. W.: The Pressure-Volume-Temperature Relations of Fifteen Liquids, *Proc. Am. Acad. Arts Sci.*, vol. 68, p. 1, 1933.

[35] Bridgman, P. W.: Polymorphism, Principally of the Elements up to 50,000 kg/cm^2, *Phys. Rev.*, vol. 48, p. 893, 1935.

[36] Bridgman, P. W.: Pressure-Volume-Temperature Relations of the Liquid, and the Phase Diagram of Heavy Water, *J. Chem. Phys.*, vol. 3, p. 597, 1935.

[37] Bridgman, P. W.: The Measurement of Hydrostatic Pressure to 30,000 kg/cm^2, *Proc. Am. Acad. Arts Sci.*, vol. 74, p. 1, 1940.

[38] Bridgman, P. W.: The Measurement of Hydrostatic Pressure to 30,000 kg/cm^2, *Proc. Am. Acad. Arts Sci.*, vol. 74, p. 11, 1940.

[39] Bridgman, P. W.: Freezing and Compressions to 50,000 kg/cm^2, *J. Chem. Phys.*, vol. 9, p. 794, 1941.

[40] Bridgman, P. W.: Freezing Parameters and Compression of Twenty-one Substances to 50,000 kg/cm^2, *Proc. Am. Acad. Arts Sci.*, vol. 74, p. 399, 1942.

[41] Bridgman, P. W.: The Compression of Sixty-one Solid Substances to 25,000 kg/cm^2, Determined by a New Rapid Method, *Proc. Am. Acad. Arts Sci.*, vol. 76, p. 9, 1945.

[42] Bridgman, P. W.: Recent Work in the Field of High Pressures, *Rev. Mod. Phys.*, vol. 18, p. 1, 1946.

[43] Bridgman, P. W.: Compression of Thirty-nine Substances to 100,000 kg/cm^2, *Proc. Am. Acad. Arts Sci.*, vol. 76, p. 55, 1948.

[44] Bridgman, P. W.: Linear Compression of Various Single Crystals to 30,000 kg/cm^2, *Proc. Am. Acad. Arts Sci.*, vol. 76, p. 89, 1948.

[45] Bridgman, P. W.: Further Rough Compressions to 40,000 kg/cm^2, Especially Certain Liquids, *Proc. Am. Acad. Arts Sci.*, vol. 77, p. 129, 1949.

[46] Bridgman, P. W.: Linear Compression to 30,000 kg/cm^2 Including Relatively Incompressible Substances, *Proc. Am. Acad. Arts Sci.*, vol. 77, p. 187, 1949.

[47] Bridgman, P. W.: Viscosities to 30,000 kg/cm^2, *Proc. Am. Acad. Arts Sci.*, vol. 77, p. 115, 1949.

[48] Bridgman, P. W.: Physics above 20,000 kg/cm^2, *Proc. Roy. Soc. London*, vol. A203, p. 1, 1950.

[49] Bridgman, P. W.: Some Results in the Field of High-pressure Physics, *Endeavour*, vol. 10, p. 63, 1951.

[50] Bridgman, P. W.: The Resistance of Seventy-two Elements, Alloys and Compounds to 100,000 kg/cm^2, *Proc. Am. Acad. Arts Sci.*, vol. 81, p. 165, 1952.

[51] Bridgman, P. W.: "Studies in Large Plastic Flow and Fracture," McGraw-Hill Book Company, Inc., New York, 1952.

[52] Bridgman, P. W.: High-pressure Instrumentation, *Mech. Eng.*, vol. 75, p. 111, 1953.

[53] Bridgman, P. W.: The Use of Electrical Resistance in High Pressure Calibration, *Rev. Sci. Instr.*, vol. 24, p. 400, 1953.

[54] Bridgman, P. W.: "The Physics of High Pressure," G. Bell & Sons, Ltd., London, 1958.

[55] Bultemann, H. J., and M. Schuster: Investigations to Determine the Deformation Corrections for a Piston Manometer by Means of Capacity Measurement of the Gap Width, *Z. angew. Phys.*, vol. 9, p. 29, 1957.

[56] Bundy, F. P.: Phase Diagram of Bismuth to 130,000 kg/cm^2, 500°C, *Phys. Rev.*, vol. 110, p. 314, 1958.

[57] Bundy, F. P.: Phase Diagram of Rubidium to 150,000 kg/cm^2 and 500°C, *Bull. Am. Phys. Soc.*, vol. 4, p. 46, 1959.

[58] Bundy, F. P.: Calibration Techniques in Ultrahigh-pressure Apparatus, *J. Eng. Ind.*, vol. 83, pp. 207–214, 1961; also in *Trans. ASME*, series B, vol. 83, no. 2, pp. 207–214, 1961.

[59] Bundy, F. P.: Effect of Pressure on the EMF of Thermocouples, p. 256 in F. P. Bundy, W. R. Hibbard, Jr., and H. M. Strong (eds.), "Progress in Very High Pressure Research," John Wiley & Sons, Inc., New York, 1961.

[60] Bundy, F. P., W. R. Hibbard, Jr., and H. M. Strong (eds.): "Progress in Very High Pressure Research," John Wiley & Sons, Inc., New York, 1961.

[61] Bundy, F. P., and H. M. Strong: Fusion Curves of Four Group VIII Metals to 100,000 Atmospheres, *Bull. Am. Phys. Soc.*, vol. 4, p. 181, 1959.

[62] Butuzov, V. P.: Study of Phase Transformations at Very High Pressures, *Soviet Phys. Cryst.*, vol. 2, p. 533, 1957.

[63] Butuzov, V. P., and S. S. Boksha: A New Method of Studying Phase Transitions at High Pressures and Temperatures and Its Application to the Polymorphism of Phosphorus, in "Growth of Crystals," vol. I, Consultants Bureau, Inc., New York, 1958.

[64] Chester, P. F., and G. O. Jones: Superconductivity at Very High Pressures, *Phil. Mag.*, vol. 44, p. 1281, 1953.

[65] Christiansen, E. B., S. S. Kistler, and W. B. Gogarty: Design and Construction of Multi-ring Apparatus for Use at High Pressures, *Rev. Sci. Instr.*, vol. 32, p. 775, 1961.

[66] Cohn, W. M.: X-ray Investigations at High Pressures, *Phys. Rev.*, vol. 44, p. 326, 1933.

[67] Collins, J. R.: Effect of High Pressure on Near Infra-red Absorption Spectrum of Certain Liquids, *Phys. Rev.*, vol. 36, p. 305, 1930.

[68] Comings, E. W.: "High Pressure Technology," McGraw-Hill Book Company, Inc., New York, 1956.

[69] Comings, E. W., and H. G. Drickamer: A Simple, Effective High Pressure Valve, *Rev. Sci. Instr.*, vol. 22, p. 1028, 1951.

[70] Cornish, R. H., and A. L. Ruoff: Electrical Leads for Pressure Vessels to 30 Kilobars, *Rev. Sci. Instr.*, vol. 32, p. 639, 1961.

[71] Coulon, R., J. Robin, and B. Vodar: Long Cell for Spectrographic Studies under High Pressures, *J. phys. radium*, vol. 20, p. 570, 1959.

[72] Dadson, R. S.: A New Method for the Absolute Measurement of High Pressures, *Nature*, vol. 176, p. 188, 1955.

[73] Danforth, W. E., Jr.: Dielectric Constants of Liquids under High Pressure, *Phys. Rev.*, vol. 38, p. 1224, 1931.

[74] Daniels, W. B.: Improved High Pressure Valve, *Rev. Sci. Instr.*, vol. 33, p. 131, 1962.

[75] Daniels, W. B., and A. A. Hruschka: Seals for Pressures to 10,000 Atmospheres, *Rev. Sci. Instr.*, vol. 28, p. 1058, 1957.

[76] Daniels, W. B., and M. T. Jones: Simple Apparatus for the Generation of Pressures above 100,000 Atmospheres Simultaneously with Temperatures above 3000°C, *Rev. Sci. Instr.*, vol. 32, p. 885, 1961.

[77] Daniels, W. B., and C. S. Smith: Pressure Derivatives of the Elastic Constants of Cu, Ag, and Au, *Phys. Rev.*, vol. 111, p. 713, 1958.

[78] Darling, H. E., and D. H. Newhall: High-pressure Wire Gage Using Gold-Chrome Wire, *Trans. ASME*, vol. 75, p. 311, 1953.

[79] DeVries, K. L., G. S. Baker, and P. Gibbs: A Survey of High Pressure Effects of Solids, WADC Tech. Rept. 59-341, Contract AF 33(616)-5016, Aeronautical Research Laboratories, Wright-Patterson Air Force Base, Ohio, 1960.

[80] Drickamer, H. G.: Optical Studies at High Pressure, p. 16 in F. P. Bundy,

W. R. Hibbard, Jr., and H. M. Strong (eds.), "Progress in Very High Pressure Research," John Wiley & Sons, New York, 1961.

[81] Drickamer, H. G.: Revised Calibration for High Pressure Optical Bomb, *Rev. Sci. Instr.*, vol. 32, p. 212, 1961.

[82] Dudley, J. Duane, and H. Tracy Hall: Experimental Fusion Curves of Indium and Tin to 105,000 Atmospheres, *Phys. Rev.*, vol. 118, p. 1211, 1960.

[83] Dugdale, J. S.: The Equation of State of Solid Helium, *Nuovo cimento*, vol. 9, supplement, p. 27, 1958.

[84] Dugdale, J. S., and D. Gugan: The Effect of Pressure on the Electrical Resistance of Copper at Low Temperatures, *Proc. Roy. Soc. London*, vol. A241, p. 397, 1957.

[85] Dugdale, J. S., and J. A. Hulbert: Effect of Pressure on the Electrical Resistance of Rubidium, *Can. J. Phys.*, vol. 35, p. 720, 1957.

[86] Dugdale, J. S., and F. E. Simon: Thermodynamic Properties and Melting of Solid Helium, *Proc. Roy. Soc. London*, vol. A218, p. 291, 1953.

[87] Ebert, H.: Establishment of a Pressure Scale and Experimental Realization up to 20,000 Atmospheres, *Z. angew. Phys.*, vol. 1, p. 331, 1949.

[88] Ebert, H., and J. Gielessen: Pressure and Temperature Coefficients of the Electrical Resistance of Some Alloys, *Ann. Phys.*, vol. 6, no. 1, p. 229, 1947.

[89] Ebert, H., and A. Kussman: Änderung der Sättigungsmagnetisierung, *Physik. Z.*, vol. 38, p. 437, 1937.

[90] Eiseman, B. J., Jr., and L. Harris: Absorption Spectra at High Pressures and at Low Temperatures. The Transmission of Liquid Carbon Dioxide, *J. Am. Chem. Soc.*, vol. 54, p. 1782, 1932.

[91] Eiseman, B. J., Jr., and L. Harris: Absorption Spectra at High Pressures and Low Temperatures. The Transparency of Argon and Methane, *J. Am. Chem. Soc.*, vol. 54, p. 1778, 1932.

[92] Evdokimova, V. V., and L. F. Vereshchagin: Determination of Interatomic Distances of Solids under Pressure. I. Compressibility of Barium and Strontium, *Soviet Phys. Solid State*, vol. 2, p. 1539, 1961.

[93] Faupel, J. H.: Designing for Shrink Fits, *Machine Design*, vol. 26, p. 114, 1954.

[94] Faupel, J. H.: Residual Stresses in Heavy-wall Cylinders, *J. Franklin Inst.*, vol. 259, p. 405, 1955.

[95] Faupel, J. H.: Yield and Bursting Characteristics of Heavy-wall Cylinders, *Trans. ASME*, vol. 78, p. 1031, 1956.

[96] Faupel, J. H., and A. R. Furbeck: Influence of Residual Stress on Behavior of Thick-wall Closed-end Cylinders, *Trans. ASME*, vol. 75, p. 345, 1953.

[97] Faupel, J. H., and D. B. Harris: Stress Concentration in Heavy-walled Cylindrical Pressure Vessels, *Ind. Eng. Chem.*, vol. 49, p. 1979, 1957.

[98] Fishman, E., and H. G. Drickamer: Equipment for High Pressure Optical and Spectroscopic Studies, *Anal. Chem.*, vol. 28, p. 804, 1956.

[99] Fitch, R. A., T. E. Slykhouse, and H. G. Drickamer: Apparatus for Optical Studies to Very High Pressures, *J. Opt. Soc. Am.*, vol. 47, p. 1015, 1957.

[100] Franck, E. U., J. E. Savolainen, and W. L. Marshall: Electrical Conductance Cell Assembly for Use with Aqueous Solutions up to 800°C and 4000 Bars, *Rev. Sci. Instr.*, vol. 33, p. 115, 1962.

[101] Frevel, L. K.: Techniques for X-ray Studies of Substances under Pressure, *Rev. Sci. Instr.*, vol. 6, p. 214, 1935.

[102] Gibbs, D. F., and M. Jarman: A High-pressure Electrical Lead-in, *J. Sci. Instr.*, vol. 35, p. 472, 1958.

[103] Gibson, R. E., and J. F. Kincaid: The Influence of Temperature and Pressure

on the Volume and Refractive Index of Benzene, *J. Am. Chem. Soc.*, vol. 60, p. 511, 1938.

[104] Gill, J. S., and W. L. Marshall: High Pressure Vessel Incorporating a Teflon Gasket for Use to 500°C and 1000 Atm., *Rev. Sci. Instr.*, vol. 32, p. 1060, 1961.

[105] Gill, S. J., and W. D. Rummel: Teflon and Sapphire Cell for Optical Absorption Studies under High Pressure, *Rev. Sci. Instr.*, vol. 32, p. 752, 1961.

[106] Gonikberg, M. G.: "Vysokie i Sverkhvysokie Davleniya v Khimii (High and Superhigh Pressures in Chemistry)," Izd-vo AN SSSR, Moscow, 1958.

[107] Goranson, R. W., and E. A. Johnson: The Attainment of High Hydrostatic Pressures, *Phys. Rev.*, vol. 57, p. 845, 1940.

[108] Griggs, D. T., and G. C. Kennedy: A Simple Apparatus for High Pressures and Temperatures, *Am. J. Sci.*, vol. 254, p. 722, 1956.

[109] Guengant, L., and B. Vodar: Contribution à l'étude radiocristallo-graphique des transformations allotropiques induites par la pression, *Compt. rend.*, vol. 239, p. 431, 1954.

[110] Gugan, D.: Simple High-pressure Closures and Electrodes, *J. Sci. Instr.*, vol. 33, p. 160, 1956.

[111] Hall, H. T.: The Melting Point of Germanium as a Function of Pressure to 180,000 Atmospheres, *J. Phys. Chem.*, vol. 59, p. 1144, 1955.

[112] Hall, H. T.: Some High-pressure, High-temperature Apparatus Design Considerations: Equipment for Use at 100,000 Atmospheres and 3000°C, *Rev. Sci. Instr.*, vol. 29, p. 267, 1958.

[113] Hall, H. T.: Ultrahigh Pressure Research, *Science*, vol. 128, p. 445, 1958.

[114] Hall, H. T.: Ultra-high-pressure, High-temperature Apparatus: The "Belt," *Rev. Sci. Instr.*, vol. 31, p. 125, 1960.

[115] Hall, H. T.: High-pressure Apparatus, p. 1 in F. P. Bundy, W. R. Hibbard, Jr., and H. M. Strong (eds.), "Progress in Very High Pressure Research," John Wiley & Sons, Inc., New York, 1961.

[116] Hall, H. T., B. Brown, B. Nelson, and L. A. Compton: I. An Apparatus for Use with Condensed Phases at 10,000°C. II. Some Thermodynamic and Rate Considerations at Very High Temperatures, *J. Phys. Chem.*, vol. 62, p. 346, 1958.

[117] Hamann, S. D.: "Physico-chemical Effects of Pressure," Academic Press, Inc., New York, 1957.

[118] Hamann, S. D., and D. R. Teplitzky: The Kinetics of Some Organic Reactions under Pressure, *Discussions Faraday Soc.*, vol. 22, p. 114, 1956.

[119] Harris, R. E., R. J. Vaisnys, H. Stromberg, and G. Jura: Resistance and Thermal Gap Measurements to 400,000 Atmospheres, in F. P. Bundy, W. R. Hibbard, Jr., and H. M. Strong (eds.), "Progress in Very High Pressure Research," John Wiley & Sons, Inc., New York, 1961.

[120] Hayden, C. K.: The Influence of High Pressure on the Refractive Index and the Dispersive Power of Glycerol, University Microfilms, Ann Arbor, Michigan, No. 173, 1940.

[121] Hilliard, J. E., and J. W. Cahn: The Effect of High Pressures on Transformation Rates, p. 109 in F. P. Bundy, W. R. Hibbard, Jr., and H. M. Strong (eds.), "Progress in Very High Pressure Research," John Wiley & Sons, Inc., New York, 1961.

[122] Holland, F. A., J. A. W. Huggill, and G. O. Jones: The Solid-Fluid Equilibrium of Helium above 5000 Atmosphere Pressure, *Proc. Roy. Soc. London*, vol. A207, p. 268, 1951.

[123] Howe, W. H.: Present Status of High Pressure Measurement and Control, *J. Instr. Soc. Am.*, vol. 2, p. 77 (part 1), p. 109 (part 2), 1955.

[124] Hughes, D. S., and W. W. Robertson: Apparatus for Obtaining Optical Absorption Spectra at Pressures to 6000 Bars, *J. Opt. Soc. Am.*, vol. 46, p. 557, 1956.

[125] *Ind. Eng. Chem.:* Engineering, Design, and Process Development: Processing under Extreme Conditions, vol. 48, pp. 826–921, 1956.

[126] *Ind. Eng. Chem.:* High Pressure, vol. 49, pp. 1945–2050, 1957.

[127] Jacobs, I. S.: Effect of Pressure on F-center Absorption in Alkali Halides, *Phys. Rev.*, vol. 93, p. 993, 1954.

[128] Jacobs, R. B.: X-ray Diffraction of Substances under High Pressures, *Phys. Rev.*, vol. 54, p. 325, 1938.

[129] Jacobs, R. B.: X-ray Measurement of Compressibility, *Phys. Rev.*, vol. 56, p. 211, 1939.

[130] Jamieson, J. C.: Introductory Studies of High Pressure Polymorphism to 24,000 Bars by X-ray Diffraction with Some Comments on Calcite II, *J. Geol.*, vol. 65, p. 334, 1957.

[131] Jamieson, J. C.: Diamond Cells for X-ray Diffraction Studies under High Pressure, p. 10 in F. P. Bundy, W. R. Hibbard, Jr., and H. M. Strong (eds.), "Progress in Very High Pressure Research," John Wiley & Sons, Inc., New York, 1961.

[132] Jamieson, J. C., and A. W. Lawson: Solid State Studies under High Pressure, pp. 407–438 in K. Lark-Horowitz and V. A. Johnson (eds.), "Solid State Physics," vol. 6, part A, Academic Press, Inc., New York, 1959.

[133] Jamieson, J. C., A. W. Lawson, and N. H. Nachtrieb: New Device for Obtaining X-ray Diffraction Patterns from Substances Exposed to High Pressure, *Rev. Sci. Instr.*, vol. 30, p. 1017, 1959.

[134] Jennings, L. D., and C. A. Swenson: Effects of Pressure on the Superconducting Transition Temperatures of Sn, In, Ta, Tl, and Hg, *Phys. Rev.*, vol. 112, p. 31, 1958.

[135] John, P. O.: Refractivity and Dielectric Constant of Carbon Dioxide at High Pressures, *Phil. Mag.*, vol. 22, p. 274, 1936.

[136] Johns, I. B.: private communication.

[137] Johnson, D. P.: private communication.

[138] Johnson, D. P., J. L. Cross, J. D. Hill, and H. A. Bowman: Elastic Distortion Error in the Dead Weight Piston Gauge, *Ind. Eng. Chem.*, vol. 49, p. 2046, 1957.

[139] Johnson, D. P., and D. H. Newhall: The Piston Gauge as a Precise Pressure Measuring Instrument, *Trans. ASME*, vol. 75, p. 301, 1953.

[139a] Kaminow, I. P., and R. V. Jones: Pressure Dependence of the Microwave Resonance Properties of Some Spinel and Garnet Ferrites, *Phys. Rev.*, vol. 123, p. 1122, 1961.

[140] Kan, Ya. S.: The Possibility of Producing Super-high Pressures by Thermal Methods, *Zh. Tekhn. Fiz.*, vol. 18, p. 1156, 1948.

[141] Kaufmann, L., A. Leyenaar, and J. S. Harvey: The Effect of Hydrostatic Pressure on the F.C.C. $\rightleftarrows$ B.C.C. Reactions in Iron-base Alloys, in F. P. Bundy, W. R. Hibbard, Jr., and H. M. Strong (eds.), "Progress in Very High Pressure Research," John Wiley & Sons, Inc., New York, 1961.

[142] Kennedy, G. C., and P. N. LaMori: Some Fixed Points on the High Pressure Scale, p. 304 in F. P. Bundy, W. R. Hibbard, Jr., and H. M. Strong (eds.), "Progress in Very High Pressure Research," John Wiley & Sons, Inc., New York, 1961.

[143] Kondorskii, E. I., and V. L. Sedov: Change of Saturation Magnetization and of Electrical Resistance of Iron-Nickel Alloys under Hydrostatic Compression at Low Temperatures, *Soviet Phys. JETP*, vol. 35, no. 8, p. 586, 1959.

[144] Korndorf, B. A.: "High-pressure Techniques in Chemistry" (in Russian), Gostekhizdat, Moscow, 1952.

[145] Kurnick, S. W.: Effect of Pressure on the Ionic Conductivity of AgBr, *J. Chem. Phys.*, vol. 20, p. 218, 1952.

[146] Kushida, T., and G. B. Benedek: Nuclear Resonance in Antiferromagnetic MnF_2 under Hydrostatic Pressure, *Bull. Am. Phys. Soc.*, vol. 4, p. 183, 1959.

[147] Kushida, T., G. B. Benedek, and N. Bloembergen: Dependence of the Pure Quadrupole Resonance Frequency on Pressure and Temperature, *Phys. Rev.*, vol. 104, p. 1364, 1956.

[148] Lakner, J. F.: "Bibliography on High Pressure Systems and High Pressure–High Temperature Systems: Techniques, Apparatus and Experimental Data," Radiation Laboratory, University of California, Livermore, Calif., Contract No. W-7405-eng-48, 1958.

[149] Langer, D.: Solidification of Helium at 77°K, *J. Phys. Chem. Solids*, vol. 21, p. 122, 1961.

[150] Langer, D., and D. M. Warschauer: Notes on a High Pressure Gas Apparatus, *Rev. Sci. Instr.*, vol. 32, p. 32, 1961.

[151] Lawson, A. W.: A High Pressure "O" Ring Piston Packing, *Rev. Sci. Instr.*, vol. 25, p. 1136, 1954.

[152] Lawson, A. W., and N. A. Riley: X-ray Camera for Obtaining Powder Pictures at High Pressures, *Rev. Sci. Instr.*, vol. 20, p. 763, 1949.

[153] Lawson, A. W., and G. E. Smith: High-pressure Microwave Window, *Rev. Sci. Instr.*, vol. 30, p. 989, 1959.

[154] Lawson, A. W., and T. Y. Tang: Diamond Bomb for Obtaining Powder Pictures at High Pressures, *Rev. Sci. Instr.*, vol. 21, p. 815, 1950.

[155] Lazarev, B., and L. Kan: Measurements at Low Temperatures and High Pressures. I. Method for Obtaining High Pressures at Low Temperatures, *J. Phys. U.S.S.R.*, vol. 8, p. 193, 1944; *Zh. Eksperim. i Teor. Fiz.*, vol. 14, p. 439, 1944.

[156] Lazarus, D.: Variation of the Adiabatic Elastic Constant of KCl, NaCl, CuZn, Cu and Al with Pressure up to 10,000 Bars, *Phys. Rev.*, vol. 76, p. 545, 1949.

[157] Lazarus, D.: Mobility of Vacancies and Interstitials at High Pressure, p. 46 in F. P. Bundy, W. R. Hibbard, Jr., and H. M. Strong (eds.), "Progress in Very High Pressure Research," John Wiley & Sons, Inc., New York, 1961.

[158] Littlefield, E. B., and M. W. Sagal: "High Pressure Cell for Dielectric Measurements on Liquids in the Microwave Region," Progress Report XXVII, Laboratory for Insulation Research, MIT, Cambridge, Mass., July, 1960.

[159] Lloyd, E. C., V. O. Hutton, and D. P. Johnson: Compact Multi-anvil Wedge-type High Pressure Apparatus, *J. Research Natl. Bur. Standards*, vol. 63c, 1959.

[160] Maccary, R. R., and R. F. Fey: Design of Thick-walled Pressure Vessel Shells, *Chem. Eng.*, vol. 56, p. 124, 1949.

[161] McFarlan, R. L.: Apparatus for X-ray Patterns of the High Pressure Modifications of Ice, *Rev. Sci. Instr.*, vol. 7, p. 82, 1936.

[162] Manning, W. R. D.: Strength of Cylinders, *Ind. Eng. Chem.*, vol. 49, p. 1969, 1957.

[163] Michels, A., and J. Hamers: The Effect of Pressure on the Refractive Index of CO_2, *Physica*, vol. 4, p. 995, 1937.

[164] Mills, R. L.: Valve for Gas Service to 50,000 psi, *Rev. Sci. Instr.*, vol. 27, p. 332, 1956.

[165] Minshall, S.: Properties of Elastic and Plastic Waves Determined by Pin Contactors and Crystals, *J. Appl. Phys.*, vol. 26, p. 463, 1955.

[166] Miller, A.: Further Investigations of Solid *n*-paraffins (Repulsion Potential and Compressibility), *Proc. Roy. Soc. London*, vol. 178, p. 227, 1941.

[167] Newhall, D. H.: The Controlled-clearance Principle, *Ind. Eng. Chem.*, vol. 49, p. 1993, 1957.

[168] Newitt, D. M.: "High Pressure Plant and Fluids at High Pressure," Oxford University Press, New York, 1940.

[169] Newitt, D. M.: The Properties of Matter at High Pressure, *Chartered Mech. Engr.*, vol. 3, p. 14, 1956.

[170] Niemier, B. A.: Seals to Minimize Leakage at High Pressures, *Trans. ASME*, vol. 75, p. 369, 1953.

[171] Parsons, Sir Charles: Experiments on Carbon at High Temperatures and under Great Pressures, and in Contact with Other Substances, *Proc. Roy. Soc. London*, vol. 44, p. 320, 1888.

[172] Parsons, Sir Charles: Experiments on the Artificial Production of Diamond, *Trans. Roy. Soc. London*, vol. 220A, p. 67, 1920.

[173] Parsons, R. W., and H. G. Drickamer: Sodium Chloride and Calcium Fluoride Windows for High-pressure Infrared Spectroscopy, *J. Opt. Soc. Am.*, vol. 46, p. 464, 1956.

[174] Patrick, L.: Change of Ferro-magnetic Curie Points with Hydrostatic Pressure, *Phys. Rev.*, vol. 93, p. 384, 1954.

[175] Paul, W., G. B. Benedek, and D. M. Warschauer: Non-magnetic High Pressure Vessels, *Rev. Sci. Instr.*, vol. 30, p. 874, 1959.

[176] Paul, W., and D. M. Warschauer: A High Pressure Leak Detector, *Rev. Sci. Instr.*, vol. 26, p. 731, 1955.

[177] Paul, W., and D. M. Warschauer: High Pressure Tubing, *Rev. Sci. Instr.*, vol. 27, p. 418, 1956.

[178] Perez, J. P., and P. Johannin: Piezoelectric Resonance of Quartz up to 5000 Atm., *J. phys. radium*, vol. 13, p. 428, 1952.

[179] Poindexter, F. E.: The Effect of Pressure on the Refractive Index of Carbon Disulfide, *Phys. Rev.*, vol. 47, p. 202, 1935.

[180] Poindexter, F. E., and L. E. James: A High Pressure Refractometer, *Phys. Rev.*, vol. 42, p. 910, 1932.

[181] Poindexter, F. E., and J. S. Rosen: The Effect of Pressure on the Refractive Index of Aqueous Solutions of Ethyl Alcohol, *Phys. Rev.*, vol. 45, p. 760, 1934.

[182] Pokorný, G.: Leakage Control of Pressure and Vacuum Equipment, *Chem. prumysl*, vol. 8, p. 642, 1958.

[183] Poulter, T. C.: A Glass Window Mounting for Withstanding Pressures of 30,000 Atmos., *Phys. Rev.*, vol. 35, p. 297, 1930.

[184] Poulter, T. C.: Apparatus for Optical Studies at High Pressure, *Phys. Rev.*, vol. 40, p. 860, 1932.

[185] Poulter, T. C., and C. Benz: Lens Effect of Pressure Windows, *Phys. Rev.*, vol. 40, p. 872, 1932.

[186] Poulter, T. C., and F. Buckley: Diamond Windows for Withstanding Very High Pressures, *Phys. Rev.*, vol. 41, p. 364, 1932.

[187] Poulter, T. C., C. Ritchey, and C. A. Benz: Effect of Pressure on the Index of Refraction of Paraffin Oil and Glycerine, *Phys. Rev.*, vol. 41, p. 366, 1932.

[188] Pound, R. V., G. B. Benedek, and R. Drever: Effect of Hydrostatic Compression on the Energy of the 14.4-kev. Gamma Ray from Fe^{57} in Iron, *Phys. Rev. Letters*, vol. 7, p. 405, 1961.

[189] Radkowski, P. P., J. I. Bluhm, and O. L. Bowie: "Thick-walled Cylinder Handbook," O/A Project No. 501-01-006, O. O. Project No. TR3-3027, Watertown Arsenal, Watertown, Mass., 1954.

[190] Ramsauer, C.: Über eine neue Methode zur Enzeungung höchsten Drucke und Temperaturen, *Physik. Z.*, vol. 34, p. 890, 1933.

[191] Ramsauer, C.: Limits of the Technic of High Pressure and Vacuum, *Chem. Fabrik*, p. 391, 1937.

[192] Reamer, H. H., and B. H. Sage: Manostat for High-pressure Operations, *Rev. Sci. Instr.*, vol. 29, p. 709, 1958.

[193] Rice, M. H., R. G. McQueen, and J. M. Walsh: Compression of Solids by Strong Shock Waves, p. 1 in F. Seitz and D. Turnbull (eds.), "Solid State Physics," vol. 6, Academic Press, Inc., New York, 1958.

[194] Robin, J., and B. Vodar: Apparatus for Spectrographic Studies up to 6000 Atmospheres, *J. phys. radium*, vol. 17, p. 500, 1956.

[195] Robinson, D. W.: A High-pressure Gas Valve for Use up to 3000 Atmospheres, *J. Sci. Instr.*, vol. 30, p. 483, 1953.

[196] Robinson, D. W.: An Experimental Determination of the Melting Curves of Argon and Nitrogen into the 10,000 Atmospheres Region, *Proc. Roy. Soc. London*, vol. A225, p. 393, 1954.

[197] Roebuck, J. R., and E. E. Miller: Viewing Tubes for High Pressure, *Rev. Sci. Instr.*, vol. 10, p. 179, 1939.

[198] Runcorn, S. K.: Experiments on the Displacement of the Ultraviolet Absorption Edge of Olivine at High Pressures, *J. Appl. Phys.*, vol. 27, p. 598, 1956.

[199] Saunders, V. T.: The National Physical Laboratory: Solids at Extremely High Pressures, *Contemporary Phys.*, vol. 3, p. 134, 1961.

[200] Sax, N. I.: "Dangerous Properties of Industrial Materials," Reinhold Publishing Corporation, New York, 1957.

[201] Schamp, H. W., Jr.: Use of Cesium Chloride for Transmitting High Pressures at High Temperatures, *Rev. Sci. Instr.*, vol. 30, p. 1051, 1959.

[202] Schamp, H. W., Jr., and W. G. Maisch: Microcell for Infrared Studies on Pure Liquids at High Pressures, *Rev. Sci. Instr.*, vol. 32, p. 414, 1961.

[203] Schmidt, E.: Measurement of Small Pressure Differences at High Pressures, *Z. Ver. deut. Ingr.*, vol. 80, p. 635, 1936.

[204] Schwartz, C. M.: Ultrahigh Pressure Technology, *Chem. Eng. Progress*, vol. 56, p. 71, 1960.

[205] Scott, G. J., and S. E. Babb, Jr.: Multiple Lead High Pressure Plug, *Rev. Sci. Instr.*, vol. 32, p. 868, 1961.

[206] Simon, I.: Electrical Lead for High-pressure Apparatus, *Rev. Sci. Instr.*, vol. 28, p. 963, 1957.

[207] Slater, J. C.: "Introduction to Chemical Physics," McGraw-Hill Book Company, Inc., New York, 1939.

[208] Smith, A. H., and A. W. Lawson: The Velocity of Sound in Water as a Function of Temperature and Pressure, *J. Chem. Phys.*, vol. 22, p. 351, 1954.

[209] Stevenson, R.: Solid Methane—Changes in Phase under Pressure, *J. Chem. Phys.*, vol. 27, p. 656, 1957.

[210] Stevenson, R.: Tentative Phase Diagram for Solid H_2S, *J. Chem. Phys.*, vol. 27, p. 147, 1957.

[211] Stewart, J. W.: Compressibilities of Some Solidified Gases at Low Temperatures, *Phys. Rev.*, vol. 97, p. 578, 1955.

[212] Stewart, J. W., and C. A. Swenson: Compression to 10,000 Atmospheres of Solid Hydrogen and Deuterium at 4.2°K, *Phys. Rev.*, vol. 94, p. 1069, 1954.

[213] Stregulin, A. I., and L. A. Mel'nikov: Transformation of Austenite into Martensite under High Pressure, *Phys. Metals and Metallography*, vol. 8, p. 79, 1959.

[214] Strong, H. M.: Experimental Fusion Curve of Iron to 96,000 Atmospheres: Temperature of Earth's Core, *Bull. Am. Phys. Soc.*, vol. 4, p. 182, 1959.

[215] Strong, H. M.: Melting and Other Phase Transformations at High Pressure, p. 182 of F. P. Bundy, W. R. Hibbard, Jr., and H. M. Strong (eds.), "Progress

in Very High Pressure Research," John Wiley & Sons, Inc., New York, 1961.

[216] Susse, C.: Variation of the Elastic Constants of Quartz as a Function of Pressure up to 1000 Atmospheres, *J. phys. radium*, vol. 16, p. 348, 1955.

[217] Swenson, C. A.: Physics at High Pressure, p. 41 in F. Seitz and D. Turnbull (eds.), "Solid State Physics," vol. 11, Academic Press, Inc., New York, 1960.

[218] Threlfall, R.: Experiments at High Temperatures and Pressures, *Eng.*, vol. 87, p. 425, 1909.

[219] Tongue, H.: "The Design and Construction of High Pressure Chemical Plant," Chapman & Hall, Ltd., London, 1959.

[220] Tsiklis, D. S.: "Техника физико-химических исследований при высоких давлениях (Technology of Physical and Chemical High Pressure Research)," 2d ed., Goskhimizdat, Moscow, 1958.

[221] Vallauri, M. G., and P. W. Forsbergh, Jr.: Wide-band High-pressure Dielectric Cell, *Rev. Sci. Instr.*, vol. 28, p. 198, 1957.

[222] Vereshchagin, L. F.: Investigations (in U.S.S.R.) in the Area of the Physics of High Pressures, in F. P. Bundy, W. R. Hibbard, Jr., and H. M. Strong (eds.), "Progress in Very High Pressure Research," John Wiley & Sons, Inc., New York, 1961.

[223] Vereshchagin, L. F., and N. V. Brandt: X-ray Investigations of the Structure of Matter at Pressures up to 30,000 Atmospheres, *Doklady Akad. Nauk S. S. S. R.*, vol. 108, p. 423, 1956.

[224] Vereshchagin, L. F., A. Ye. Fedorovskiy, V. K. Isaykov, V. N. Slesanev, and A. A. Semerchan: High-plasticity Solids for Pressure Transmission, *Inzhenerno-fizicheskiy Zhur.*, vol. 3, no. 7, pp. 132–134, 1960.

[225] Vereshchagin, L. F., V. A. Galaktionov, A. A. Semerchan, and V. N. Slesanev: Apparatus for High Pressure and High Temperature with a Conical Piston, *Soviet Phys.*, vol. 5, p. 602, 1960.

[226] Vereshchagin, L. F., and S. S. Kabalkina: An Investigation of the Crystal Structure of Rubidium Halides at High Pressure, *Doklady Akad. Nauk S. S. S. R.*, vol. 113, p. 797, 1957.

[227] Vereshchagin, L. F., A. I. Likhter, and V. I. Ivanov: Production of Very High Pressures with a Conical Piston Device, *Zhur. Tekh. Fiz.*, vol. 26, p. 874, 1956.

[228] Vereshchagin, L. F., and Ye. V. Zubova: Shear Stresses of Graphite and Some Other Substances under High Pressure, *Doklady Akad. Nauk S. S. S. R.*, vol. 134, no. 4, pp. 787–788, October, 1960.

[229] Voronel, A. V.: The Thermodynamic Scale of High Pressures, *Fiz. Metal. i Metalloved, Akad. Nauk S. S. S. R. Ural' Filial*, vol. 9, p. 174, 1960.

[230] Walsh, J. M., and R. H. Christian: Equation of State of Metals from Shock Wave Measurements, *Phys. Rev.*, vol. 97, p. 1544, 1955.

[231] Walsh, W. M., Jr., and N. Bloembergen: Paramagnetic Resonance of Nickel Fluorosilicate under High Hydrostatic Pressure, *Phys. Rev.*, vol. 107, p. 904, 1957.

[232] Warschauer, D. M., and W. Paul: The Unsupported Area High Pressure Seal, *Rev. Sci. Instr.*, vol. 28, p. 62, 1957.

[233] Warschauer, D. M., and W. Paul: High Pressure Techniques, *Rev. Sci. Instr.*, vol. 29, p. 675, 1958.

[234] Weir, C. E.: High Pressure Apparatus for Compressibility Studies and Its Application to Measurements on Leather and Collagen, *J. Research Natl. Bur. Standards*, vol. 45, p. 468, 1950.

[235] Weir, C. E.: Compressibility of Natural and Synthetic High Polymers at High Pressures, *J. Research Natl. Bur. Standards*, vol. 46, p. 207, 1951.

[236] Weir, C. E.: Second Order Transitions of Rubber at High Pressures, *J. Research Natl. Bur. Standards*, vol. 50, p. 311, 1953.

[237] Weir, C. E.: Transitions and Phases of Polytetrafluoroethylene (Teflon), *J. Research Natl. Bur. Standards*, vol. 50, p. 95, 1953.

[238] Weir, C. E.: Temperature Dependence of Compression of Linear High Polymers at High Pressures, *J. Research Natl. Bur. Standards*, vol. 53, p. 245, 1954.

[239] Weir, C. E., and J. D. Hoffman: Compressibility of Long Chain Hydrocarbons, *J. Research Natl. Bur. Standards*, vol. 55, p. 307, 1955.

[240] Welbergen, H. J.: New Form of Insulation for the Introduction of Electrical Connections into High Pressure Vessels, *J. Sci. Instr.*, vol. 10, p. 247, 1933.

[241] Welsh, H. L., P. E. Pashler, and A. F. Dunn: Influence of Foreign Gases at High Pressures on the Infrared Absorption Band of Methane at 3.3μ, *J. Chem. Phys.*, vol. 19, p. 340, 1951.

[242] Wentorf, R. H., Jr.: Cubic Form of Boron Nitride, *J. Chem. Phys.*, vol. 26, p. 956, 1957.

[243] Wentorf, R. H., Jr.: The Synthesis of the Cubic Form of Boron Nitride, p. 82 in F. P. Bundy, W. R. Hibbard, Jr., and H. M. Strong (eds.), "Progress in Very High Pressure Research," John Wiley & Sons, Inc., New York, 1961.

[243*a*] Wentorf, R. H., Jr. (ed.): "Modern Very High Pressure Techniques," Butterworth & Co. (Publishers), Ltd., London, 1962.

[244] Whalley, E., and A. Lavergne: Automatic Air-driven Oil Pump for 10 Kilobars, *Rev. Sci. Instr.*, vol. 32, p. 1062, 1961.

[245] Wilson, W. B.: Device for Ultra-high-pressure High-temperature Research, *Rev. Sci. Instr.*, vol. 31, p. 331, 1960.

[246] Wintsch, H. von: The Design of Cold-stretched Thick-walled Cylinders and Tubes for Very High Pressures, *Schweiz. Arch. angew. Wiss. u. Tech.*, vol. 9, p. 81, 1943.

[247] Yoder, H. S.: High-Low Quartz Inversion up to 10,000 Bars, *Trans. Am. Geophys. Union*, vol. 31, p. 827, 1950.

[248] Zhokhovskii, M. K.: Melting Curve of Mercury at Pressures to 10,000 kg/sq. cm., *Izmeritelnaya Tekh.*, no. 5, p. 3, 1955.

[249] Zhokhovskiĭ, Y., S. Konyaev, and V. G. Levchenko: Piston Manometer, *Pribory i Tekh. Eksperimenta*, no. 3, p. 118, 1959.

15-12 Contents of M. G. Gonikberg, "High and Superhigh Pressures in Chemistry," Izd-vo AN SSSR, Moscow, 1958

15-13 Contents of D. S. Tsiklis, "Техника физико-химических исследований при высоких давлениях (Technology of Physical and Chemical High Pressure Research)," 2d ed., Goskhimizdat, Moscow, 1958

Name Index

This index does not include entries from the Bibliography

Subject Index

This index does not include entries from the Bibliography